D1616443

QUATERNARY GEOLOGY FOR SCIENTISTS AND ENGINEERS

ELLIS HORWOOD SERIES IN GEOLOGY

Editors: D. T. DONOVAN, Professor of Geology, University College London, and J. W. MURRAY, Professor of Geology, University of Exeter

A GUIDE TO CLASSIFICATION IN GEOLOGY
J. W. MURRAY, Professor of Geology, University of Exeter
THE CENOZOIC ERA: Tertiary and Quaternary
C. POMEROL, Professor, University of Paris VI
Translated by D. W. HUMPHRIES, Department of Geology, University of Sheffield, and E. E. HUMPHRIES
Edited by Professor D. CURRY and D. T. DONOVAN, University College London
INTRODUCTION TO PALAEOBIOLOGY: GENERAL PALAEONTOLOGY
B. ZIEGLER, Professor of Geology and Palaeontology, University of Stuttgart, and Director of the State Museum for Natural Science, Stuttgart
FAULT AND FOLD TECTONICS
W. JAROSZEWSKI, Faculty of Geology, University of Warsaw
RADIOACTIVITY IN GEOLOGY: Principles and Applications
E. M. DURRANCE, Department of Geology, University of Exeter

ELLIS HORWOOD SERIES IN APPLIED GEOLOGY

Series Editor: J. B. JOSEPH

A GUIDE TO PUMPING TESTS
F. C. BRASSINGTON, Principal Hydrogeologist, North West Water Authority
QUATERNARY GEOLOGY FOR SCIENTISTS AND ENGINEERS
JOHN A. CATT, Rothamsted Experimental Station, Harpenden, UK
TUNNELLING GEOLOGY AND GEOTECHNICS
Editors: M. C. KNIGHTS and T. W. MELLORS, Consulting Engineers, W. S. Atkins & Partners
MODERN STANDARDS FOR AGGREGATES
D. C. PIKE, Consultant in Aggregates, Reading
LASER HOLOGRAPHY IN GEOPHYSICS
S. TAKEMOTO, Disaster Prevention Research Unit, Kyoto University, Japan

BRITISH MICROPALAEONTOLOGICAL SOCIETY SERIES

NANNOFOSSILS AND THEIR APPLICATIONS
Editor: J. A. CRUX, British Petroleum Research Centre, Sunbury-on-Thames
A STRATIGRAPHICAL INDEX OF THE PALAEOZOIC ACRITARCHS AND OTHER MARINE MICROFLORA
Editors: K. J. DORINING, Pallab Research, Sheffield, and S. G. MOLYNEUX, British Geological Survey, Nottingham
STRATIGRAPHICAL ATLAS OF FOSSIL FORAMINIFERA, 2nd Edition
Editors: D. G. JENKINS, The Open University, and J. W. MURRAY, Professor of Geology, University of Exeter
MICROFOSSILS FROM RECENT AND FOSSIL SHELF SEAS
Editors: J. W. NEALE, Professor of Micropalaeontology, University of Hull, and M. D. BRASIER, Lecturer in Geology, University of Hull
FOSSIL AND RECENT OSTRACODS
Editors: R. H. BATE, Stratigraphic Services International, Guildford, E. ROBINSON, Department of Geology, University College London, and L. SHEPPARD, Stratigraphic Services International, Guildford
A STRATIGRAPHICAL INDEX OF CALCAREOUS NANNOFOSSILS
Editor: A. R. LORD, Department of Geology, University College London
A STRATIGRAPHICAL INDEX OF CONODONTS
Editors: A. C. HIGGINS, Geological Survey of Canada, Calgary, and R. L. AUSTIN, Department of Geology, University of Southampton
CONODONTS: Investigative Techniques and Applications
Editor: R. L. AUSTIN, Department of Geology, University of Southampton
PALAEOBIOLOGY OF CONODONTS
Editor: R. J. ALDRIDGE, Department of Geology, University of Nottingham
MICROPALAEONTOLOGY OF CARBONATE ENVIRONMENTS
Editor: M. B. HART, Professor of Micropalaeontology and Head of Department of Geological Studies, Plymouth Polytechnic
OSTRACODA
Editors: R. C. WHATLEY and C. MAYBURY, University College of Wales

689.5
C377q

QUATERNARY GEOLOGY FOR SCIENTISTS AND ENGINEERS

JOHN A. CATT B.Sc., Ph.D., D.Sc., F.I.Geol.,
Principal Scientific Officer
Soils and Plant Nutrition Department
Rothamsted Experimental Station
Harpenden, Herts

Visiting Professor of Geography
Birkbeck College, London

ELLIS HORWOOD LIMITED
Publishers · Chichester

Halsted Press: a division of
JOHN WILEY & SONS
New York · Chichester · Brisbane · Toronto

First published in 1988 by
ELLIS HORWOOD LIMITED
Market Cross House, Cooper Street,
Chichester, West Sussex, PO19 1EB, England
The publisher's colophon is reproduced from James Gillison's drawing of the ancient Market Cross, Chichester.

Distributors:
Australia and New Zealand:
JACARANDA WILEY LIMITED
GPO Box 859, Brisbane, Queensland 4001, Australia
Canada:
JOHN WILEY & SONS CANADA LIMITED
22 Worcester Road, Rexdale, Ontario, Canada
Europe and Africa:
JOHN WILEY & SONS LIMITED
Baffins Lane, Chichester, West Sussex, England
North and South America and the rest of the world:
Halsted Press: a division of
JOHN WILEY & SONS
605 Third Avenue, New York, NY 10158, USA
South-East Asia
JOHN WILEY & SONS (SEA) PTE LIMITED
37 Jalan Pemimpin # 05–04
Block B, Union Industrial Building, Singapore 2057
Indian Subcontinent
WILEY EASTERN LIMITED
4835/24 Ansari Road
Daryaganj, New Delhi 110002, India

© 1988 J.A. Catt/Ellis Horwood Limited

British Library Cataloguing in Publication Data
Catt, John A. (John Alfred), *1939–*
Quaternary geology for scientists and engineers.
1. Quaternary strata. Palaeo-ecology
I. Title
551.7'9

Library of Congress Card No. 88–12271

ISBN 0–85312–915–0 (Ellis Horwood Limited)
ISBN 0–470–21135–0 (Halsted Press)

Typeset in Times by Ellis Horwood Limited
Printed in Great Britain by Hartnolls, Bodmin

LIBRARY

COPYRIGHT NOTICE
All Rights Reserved. No part of this publication may be reproduced, stored in a retrieval system, or transmitted, in any form or by any means, electronic, mechanical, photocopying, recording or otherwise, without the permission of Ellis Horwood Limited, Market Cross House, Cooper Street, Chichester, West Sussex, England.

Contents

Chapter 3. Soil development during the Quaternary

Chapter 4. Quaternary stratigraphic principles and methods

Chapter 5. Dating Quaternary events

Chapter 6. Maps of Quaternary features

Preface

The study of the Quaternary period has expanded over the last twenty years from an insignificant part of geology (the 'Ice Age') to an important multidisciplinary activity. It is now an indispensable part of geomorphology, climatology, archaeology, soil science, plant and animal ecology, oceanography and mineral exploration. In return these and other subjects, such as astronomy, have had significant impacts upon our understanding of events during the last few million years, especially in clarifying the rapid changes of climate, sea level, soil and vegetation characteristics, and the associated animal and human migrations.

In recent years there has also been an increasing awareness of the economic significance of Quaternary studies. A major focus is now the prediction of future climatic and climate-related environmental changes. This has demonstrated very clearly the value of the multidisciplinary approach to Quaternary studies, because changes in the earth's orbit and processes operating in the atmosphere, oceans, glaciers and biosphere (including soils and human activities) all seem to be involved in the working of a very complex natural system determining climate.

Because of its multidisciplinary nature, Quaternary science is hardly ever adequately taught. For example, in Britain there are at present only two MSc/MPhil courses in Quaternary studies, one taught at Cambridge University and the other run jointly by City of London Polytechnic and North-east London Polytechnic, and only one university sub-department (part of the Botany School at Cambridge) conducts multidisciplinary research into Quaternary history. Restricted aspects of the Quaternary are included in many undergraduate courses in archaeology, physical geography, botany and soil science, but the subject is rarely accorded more than a few lectures in geology courses. From an educational viewpoint this is pity, because the Quaternary is useful for relating geological principles to other sciences. In terms of practical training for a geologist it is a disaster, because almost all practising geologists soon encounter Quaternary deposits in the field, and then realize that they are often much more variable in lithology and thickness than pre-Quaternary deposits. Failure to recognize Quaternary features can lead, for example, to misunderstanding of surface outcrops or misinterpretations of borehole information.

The purpose of this book is to explain the effects of Quaternary processes of erosion, deposition and soil development, so that practising geologists can recognize and interpret them correctly. Methods of classifying, correlating, mapping and dating Quaternary deposits are described, and the useful interrelations with other disciplines involved in Quaternary studies are explored. The wide range of analytical laboratory techniques applicable to Quaternary deposits cannot be described in detail, but their uses and limitations are discussed so that the field geologist can decide when it is worth calling upon the services of an expert analyst.

The book was written at the suggestion of colleagues in the Institution of Geologists, the organization representing professional geologists in Britain. It is intended primarily for this readership, but will I hope be read and used by practising scientists and engineers from a much wider range of backgrounds, anyone in fact who feels that a knowledge of the immediate geological past with its climatic vicissitudes might help resolve present or future problems.

I wish to thank Jeremy Joseph for encouraging me in the preparation of the book, Mrs Patricia Ashcroft and Mrs Joyce Munden for drawing many of the figures and Miss Jeanette Gooding for typing the manuscript. Among the many publishers and authors who have readily given permission for reproduction of their figures, I thank especially Professor Hans Jenny, who kindly allowed me to use many graphs from his book *Factors of Soil Formation* (McGraw-Hill, 1941), namely Figs 3.12 to 3.20.

Harpenden John A. Catt
February 1988

1

Nature of the Quaternary period

1.1 INTRODUCTION

For many geologists the Quaternary is the most recent part of geological time, when glaciers deposited chaotically mixed deposits in mid-latitude regions which now have temperate climates. Though broadly true, this is a considerable over-simplification, because in these regions the climate fluctuated between cold and temperate many times, with the result that some areas were glaciated repeatedly.

By both deposition and erosion, glaciations greatly modified land areas and many shallow shelf seas. Also beyond the ice margins land areas were much modified by periglacial processes of aeolian deposition, slope erosion and frost disturbance.

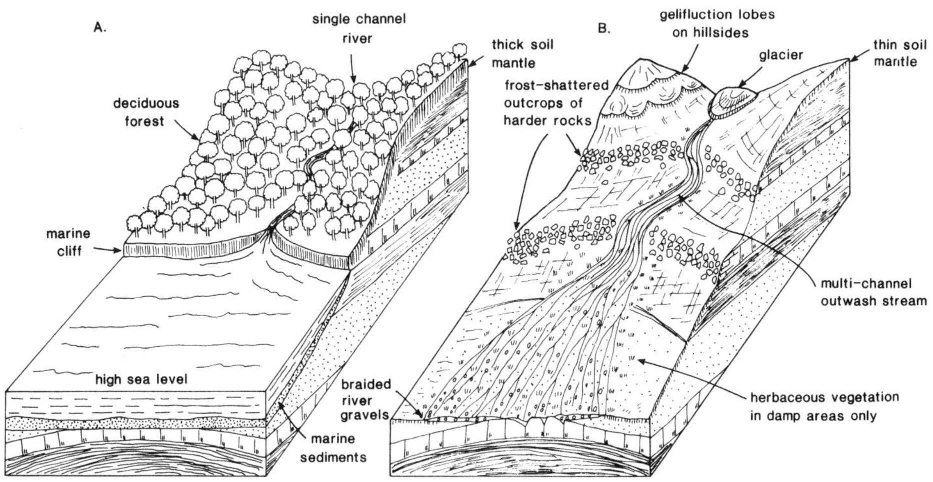

Fig. 1.1 — Typical warm (A) and cold (B) stage landscapes of mid-latitude regions during the Quaternary.

During the cold periods the proportion of land to sea was increased, as the incorporation of large amounts of water into glaciers lowered the sea-level world-wide. In contrast, the intervening warm periods or interglacials were times of high sea level, decreased land areas and greatly diminished deposition and erosion (Fig. 1.1).

Because the interglacial land surfaces were stable, usually under a forest cover, soils developed beneath them, often to depths of several metres. The physiography of the present land surface, the soils beneath it, and modern natural floral and faunal assemblages were all determined by events and processes in later parts of the Quaternary. So, although the climatic fluctuations and their various effects are usually grouped together as "Quaternary geology", this discipline is distinctly multifaceted, and includes aspects of meteorology, zoology, botany, pedology and geomorphology. It also embraces anthropology and archaeology, because the appearance of man as a toolmaker was a Quaternary event in most parts of the world, and stages in his subsequent development are useful to some extent for dating purposes. In addition, applied aspects of Quaternary studies are important in civil engineering, mineral exploration and agriculture.

1.2 THE EVIDENCE OF CLIMATIC CHANGE FROM OCEANIC DEPOSITS

Croll (1864) was the first Quaternary geologist to suggest that sediments on the deep ocean floors would provide the most complete palaeontological record of past climatic changes. However, this potential was not realized until sediment cores could be retrieved with the piston corer, and methods were developed for evaluating and dating climatic changes. In the first oceanic cores to be examined, climatic changes were determined from the relative abundance of individual foraminiferal species indicating warm or cold surface water; the layers containing them were dated by the radiocarbon method (see 5.2), and by extrapolation assuming constant sedimentation rates of 1–3 mm per century for horizons beyond the range of this dating method. Later, multifactorial methods of estimating water temperature from assemblages of foraminifera (Imbrie and Kipp 1971) and other microfossil groups were developed, and some older horizons were dated by the palaeomagnetic method (see 5.10).

The method of determining palaeotemperatures from $^{18}O/^{16}O$ ratios in foraminifera (Emiliani 1955) gave similar results to the multifactorial methods, but usually indicated larger temperature changes; for example, foraminiferal assemblages indicated a fall of 2°C in the temperature of Caribbean surface waters at the beginning of each cold stage, but the isotopic measurements suggested a 6°C drop. Shackleton (1967) showed that the difference results from the concentration of ^{16}O relative to ^{18}O in the ice of glaciers, so that most of the isotopic variation is caused by differences in the total volume of glaciers on the earth's surface, and only a small part results from the local water temperature component. Originally planktonic foraminifera were used for oxygen isotope measurements, because they were thought to show the effects of both these components. However, their isotope ratios are also affected by differences in surface salinity and other factors. More recently benthic species have been used instead, because they avoid these problems, and were thought to provide a purer record of changes in global ice volume, as the deep ocean should be less affected by temperature changes than the surface waters. However, Chappell and Shackleton (1986) showed that even the deep waters of the Pacific Ocean varied by about 1.5°C during the later Quaternary.

During cold periods the glaciers were enlarged quite slowly, but they melted and decreased in size more rapidly at the beginning of warm periods, so the curves for change in the oxygen isotope ratio with time have a typical saw-tooth shape. The alternating cold and warm stages are conventionally given arabic numerals working backwards in time from the present (stage 1), and the steeper parts of the saw-tooth, known as 'terminations', are identified by capital roman numerals, again working backwards in time from Termination I at the Pleistocene/Holocene boundary (Broecker and Van Donk 1970).

Emiliani (1955, 1966) originally recognized 16 oxygen isotope stages in sediment cores from the Caribbean Sea and Atlantic Ocean. Shackleton and Opdyke (1973) analysed another core (V28-238) from the western equatorial Pacific, and recognized 22 stages over the last 800 000 years, the first 16 of which were similar to those of Emiliani. A stratigraphically longer core (V28-239), also from the Pacific, extended the succession continuously back to 2.1 million years ago (Shackleton and Opdyke 1976); this showed that over the last 1.5 million years there have been at least 17 major cold periods separated by warmer episodes (Fig. 1.2). Similar complex successions have been established in other cores from the Atlantic Ocean (e.g. V16-205, Fig. 1.2) and Indian Ocean, so there is no doubt that the numerous changes recorded were worldwide in effect. Cores covering even longer periods of time show that the climatic fluctuations extended well back into the Tertiary. Large glaciers first affected oxygen isotope ratios in the north Atlantic and Pacific about 3.2 million years ago (Shackleton and Opdyke 1977), though it is thought that small mountain glaciers began forming in the northern hemisphere in the late Miocene (10 million years ago). The Antarctic ice cap has also existed for at least as long as this, and even may have begun forming in the early Oligocene about 38 million years ago (Mercer 1983).

As well as the micropalaeontological and oxygen isotope record of Quaternary climatic change, it is also possible to use the calcium carbonate content of deep ocean sediments as a palaeoclimatic indicator. This is because during cold stages lower sea surface temperatures depressed biological productivity of calcareous plankton, and ice-rafted clastic material diluted any carbonate precipitated from the water. Analyses of several Atlantic cores have shown that the three methods give approximately similar results. A sudden strong decrease in the carbonate content of some north Atlantic cores, such as 552A (Shackleton *et al.* 1984), in the late Pliocene about 2.4 million years ago suggests this was a time of increased ice rafting of clastic sediment, and therefore of increased continental glaciation in N. America and Europe.

1.3 CAUSE OF THE CLIMATIC CHANGES

Many different theories have been put forward to explain why the Quaternary was generally much colder than most earlier periods of geological time and why the climate fluctuated from cold to warm in many parts of the world. The earlier of these were summarized by Charlesworth (1959, p. 1532), but most are not worth repeating because the evidence from deep sea cores has recently shown that one particular theory (the astronomical theory) can account for most of the climatic change inferred from oceanic successions. In the nineteenth century, pioneer workers such as Croll

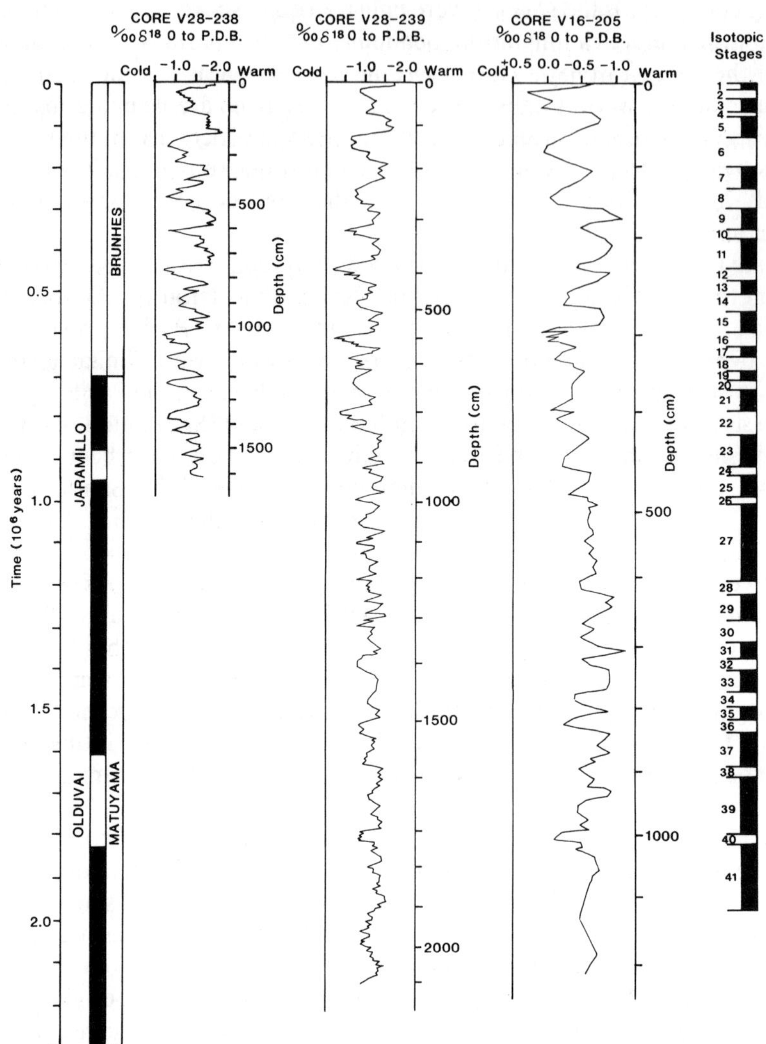

Fig. 1.2 — Oxygen isotope curves for oceanic cores covering long periods of Quaternary time and drawn to a common time scale (from Shackleton and Opdyke 1973, 1976 and Van Donk 1976). Originally published in part by Geological Society of America.

(1864, 1867) suggested that various perturbations of the earth's orbit around the sun affect the amount of solar radiation it receives and thus influence its climate. These insolation changes are related to cycles with periods of approximately 19 000, 23 000, 41 000 and 100 000 years, resulting from changes in the longitude of perihelion (precession of the equinoxes), the earth's obliquity (tilt of the axis of rotation relative to the plane of the orbit) and the eccentricity of the orbit (Lockwood 1980). Later Milankovitch (1920, 1930) calculated radiation curves for various latitudes, and although his results suggested dates for Quaternary ice ages very similar to those estimated previously for alpine areas by Penck and Brückner (1909), the theory was soon abandoned by most Quaternary geologists.

However, improved dating of the oxygen isotope changes in foraminiferal tests from deep ocean cores allowed Hays *et al.* (1976) to match cyclic changes in the isotope ratio with insolation changes at 65°N attributable to three of the four orbital cycles over the past 468 000 years, using frequency or spectral analysis (Fig. 1.3). This

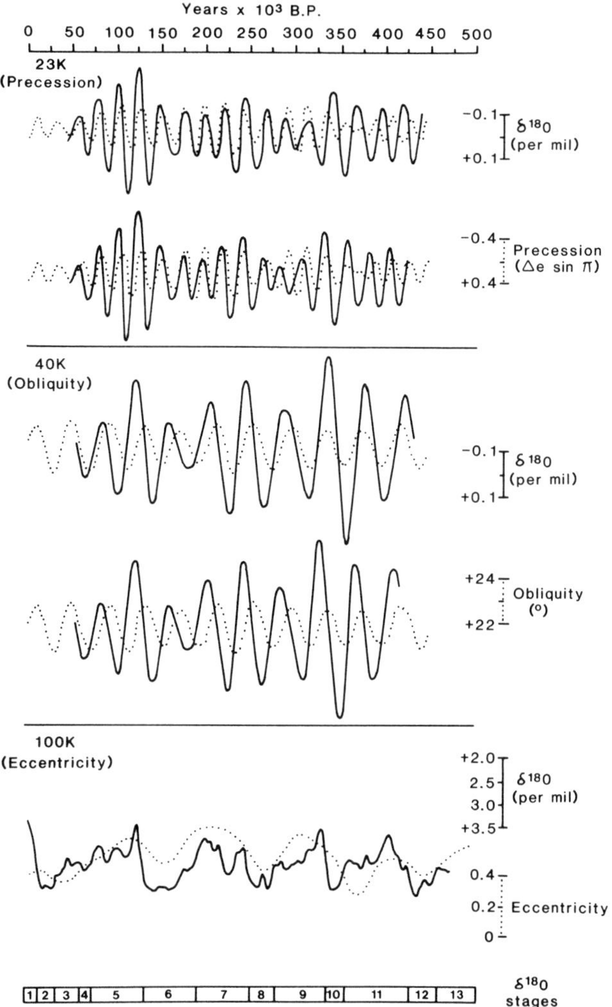

Fig. 1.3 — Variations in orbital data (precession, obliquity and eccentricity) for the last 500 000 years (dotted lines, from Vernekar 1972) compared with frequency components of climate derived from $\delta^{18}O$ variations (from Hays *et al.* 1976). The curves for $\sigma^{18}O$ for precession and obliquity are frequency components extracted by digital band-pass filters; that for eccentricity is the original unfiltered curve. The two sets of curves for precession and obliquity are for alternative time scales based on different interpolations between dated horizons in selected sediment cores.

led to a revival of the astronomical theory for climatic change, though it seems unlikely that there is a direct relationship between orbital cycles and climatic change because the maximum difference in total insolation over the last million years has been <0.6%. Imbrie *et al.* (1984) reported further evidence for a close relationship between orbital cycles and isotopic changes which enabled them to present a revised chronology for isotopic stage boundaries in core V28-238 over the past 780 000 years. Their dates are given in Table 1.1. Spectral analysis of the oxygen isotope ratios and

Table 1.1 — Revised dating of oxygen isotope stage boundaries in core V28-238 (from Imbrie *et al.* 1984)

Oxygen isotope stage boundary in V28-238	Revised dating (years B.P.×10^3)
1/2	12
2/3	24
3/4	59
4/5	71
5/6	128
6/7	186
7/8	245
8/9	303
9/10	339
10/11	362
11/12	423
12/13	478
13/14	524
14/15	565
15/16	620
16/17	659
17/18	689
18/19	726
19/20	736
20/21	763
21/22	790

carbonate content in dated Atlantic cores has shown that the climate of approximately the last 600 000 years has been dominated by the 100 000-year cycle related to orbital eccentricity. However, before about 600 000 years ago the 41 000-year tilt cycle dominated the climatic fluctuations. The change at approximately 600 000 years ago also led to stronger glaciations, which is puzzling because the 100 000-year cycle has an even weaker effect on insolation than the 41 000-year cycle. The increased glaciation may therefore have been related to rapid uplift of mountain ranges in Asia and western America at this time; the elevated surfaces would have extended the area of snow cover, which increased the albedo and thus lowered the overall temperature and extended the influence of continental glaciation. Tectonic activity may also have been responsible for the spread of northern hemisphere glaciers at 2.4 million years ago.

Insolation changes caused by orbital perturbation cycles must have occurred throughout the earth's history, but did not result in glaciations; indeed, it is now recognized that many examples of cyclic sedimentation in pre-Quaternary non-glacial rocks can be attributed to these cycles (Olsen 1984, Anderson 1984). The overall cooling that led to extensive glaciations during the insolation minima of the Quaternary must therefore relate to some other factor. As there were extensive glaciations also in the Permo-Carboniferous and late Precambrian, there may be another climatic cycle affecting the earth with a periodicity of approximately 250 million years. McCrea (1975) pointed out that the solar system passes through dust zones in one of the spiral arms of the galaxy at approximately this time interval, and the energy derived from accretion of dust particles by the sun would increase the overall level of radiation reaching the earth's surface sufficiently to produce glaciations by increasing evaporation from the oceans and thus increasing cloudiness and precipitation.

As well as the long-term changes, there have also been short-term climatic fluctuations which are not explained by the main cycles of orbital perturbation. These have been identified in detailed palaeontological and sedimentological records for the Holocene (the last 10 000 years) and some earlier periods, in historical records and, more directly, in long instrumental weather records extending over the last 2–3 centuries (Lamb 1977). For example, between about 1300 and 1850 A.D. there was a period (the 'Little Ice Age') when world temperatures were on average about 1.5°C lower than at present, and European valley glaciers pushed many kilometres further down their valleys than they do today. Short-term changes of this type may be attributable to other astronomical variables, such as (a) changes in the earth–sun distance as planetary alignments modify the sun's epitrochoidal orbit; this has a fundamental cycle of 19.857 years determined by Jupiter and Saturn, but is modulated by other planets on 59.6-, 178.7-, 317.7-, 893.6-, 2860- and 4448-year cycles, (b) the 18.6-year cycle of changes in inclination of the moon's orbit around the earth (the lunar nodal tide) (Currie 1981a, 1984, Currie and Fairbridge 1985), and (c) the 10–11-year solar sunspot cycle (Currie 1979, 1981b). The 'Little Ice Age', for example, may have been triggered by an alignment of the major planets commencing in 1306–1307 A.D., which increased the distance between the earth and the sun by $1\text{–}1.5 \times 10^6$ kilometres. However, all these suggestions need further investigation.

It has long been known that the carbon dioxide content of the atmosphere influences temperature by determining the amount of long-wave radiation trapped in the atmosphere. The Swedish physical chemist Arrhenius calculated (1896) that the CO_2 content of the 'Ice Age' atmosphere must have been 55–62% of the present value to allow the temperature to remain so low. The oceans have a buffering effect on atmospheric CO_2 content; as atmospheric CO_2 increases, more is dissolved in the surface water of oceans and is eventually incorporated into the organic matter and calcium carbonate of planktonic microorganisms, which are then deposited as part of the ocean floor sediment. During warmer (interglacial) periods of the Quaternary there would have been increased opportunity for the oceanic absorption of atmospheric CO_2, as the surface area of the oceans was greater, because less water was incorporated in glaciers and because less of the ocean surface was frozen than during glacials. Also more CO_2 would have been taken out of both the atmosphere and the oceans in interglacials by increased photosynthesis in green land plants; this would have led to more carbon being stored in the biosphere and as humus in soils, so that less was available to form atmospheric CO_2. All these effects make it difficult to understand how the atmospheric CO_2 content increased during interglacials and fluctuated as strongly during the Quaternary as it must have done to allow numerous glacial–interglacial cycles to occur. Changes in atmospheric CO_2 content must have resulted from some other process, which raises the possibility that they were a cause rather than an effect of climatic change.

Two types of explanation have been advanced for the increase in atmospheric CO_2 from glacial to interglacial periods, as at the beginning of the Holocene (Berger and Keir 1984, Broecker and Peng 1986). In one, the rising sea level caused an increase in atmospheric CO_2 by decreasing plant nutrients such as nitrogen and phosphorus, and thus decreasing the rate of photosynthesis in the sunlit upper layer of the ocean (Broecker 1982). Phosphorus was decreased by precipitation of phosphate in the more extensive shelf sediments, and nitrogen by the activity of denitrifying bacteria in the newly anaerobic flooded shelf areas. In the other theory, known as the coral reef hypothesis (Berger 1982), the transgression of shallow seas over shelves resulted in an increase in shelf carbonates, including coral reefs. This led to a decrease in pH and an increase in CO_2:

$$Ca^{2+} + 2HCO_3^- \rightarrow CaCO_3 + CO_2 + H_2O$$

The increased CO_2 would normally be absorbed by increased carbonate precipitation in the deeper parts of the oceans, but this was delayed during the transition from glacial to interglacial because deep ocean mixing was inhibited by a layer of warm, fresh ice meltwater on the surface. As a result the CO_2 escaped into the atmosphere. Once the normal rate of oceanic circulation returned, the excess atmospheric CO_2 was rapidly absorbed; this led to a rebound cooling (Berger and Killingley 1982), thus causing strong and fairly rapid late-glacial climatic fluctuations.

1.4 THE PLIO–PLEISTOCENE BOUNDARY

Because the Pleistocene was originally (though incorrectly) equated with the 'Ice Age', its lower boundary has usually been placed locally at the time when fossils provide the first evidence for a deterioration in climate. This point has been recognized from foraminifera and molluscs in shallow-water marine successions, as in Mediterranean areas and East Anglia (in the Red Crag), and from pollen in terrestrial deposits (e.g. in the Netherlands). However, subsequent dating has shown that this change occurred at different times, and may be equivalent to various cold stages in the ocean floor isotopic succession. It is consequently a poor indicator of an important chronostratigraphical boundary. Berggren and Van Couvering (1974) and Bowen (1978) suggested that one of the palaeomagnetic reversals (see 5.10) would be more suitable, because reversals occurred instantaneously throughout the world and can be identified in many different types of deposits. The most suitable reversal is probably the one marking the end of the Olduvai Normal Event (see Fig. 4.5), which has been dated to 1.61 million years ago. This is now accepted as the lower boundary of the Pleistocene by many Quaternary geologists, especially those working on deep oceanic sediments, but it is also true that many palaeontologists working on terrestrial successions do not accept it. The latest formal definition (Aguirre and Pasini 1985) places the boundary within a fairly broad zone of faunal change (Fig. 1.4) at the base of a marl overlying the sapropelic bed e in the coastal section at Vrica

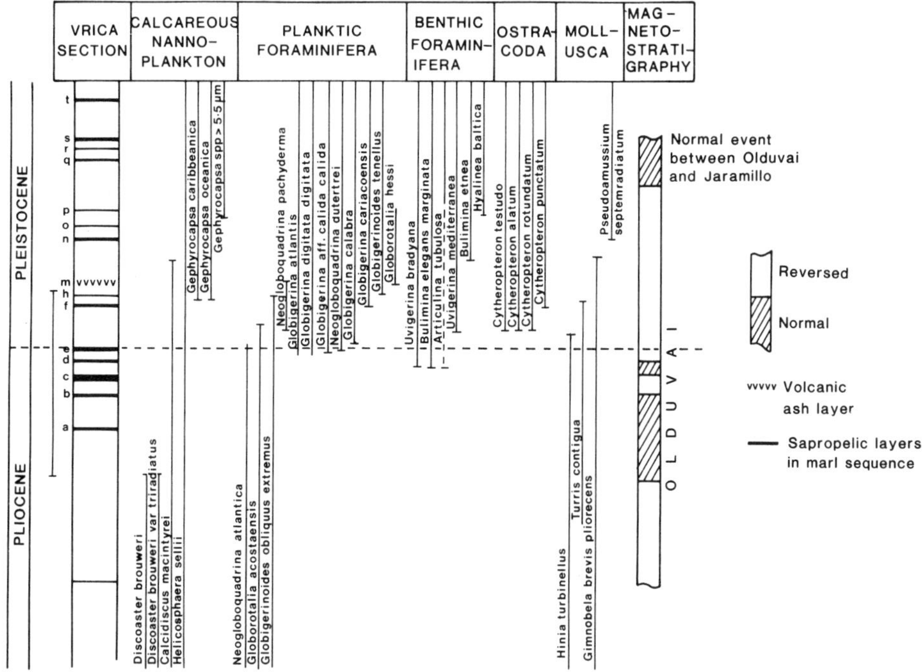

Fig. 1.4 — Faunal changes close to the Pliocene–Pleistocene boundary as defined in the Vrica section, southern Italy (from Aguirre and Pasini 1985). Reproduced by permission of the editor of *Episodes*.

(Calabria, Italy); however, this horizon is imprecisely dated (about 1.60 million years ago) and the faunal changes occurring at it are related to a local climatic change, and may even be based partly on misidentified species (Jenkins 1987), so it is unlikely to be a popular suggestion.

1.5 LIMITATIONS OF THE OCEANIC SEQUENCE

Most Quaternary geologists now regard the oceanic succession as a global 'yardstick' for major climatic changes during the last few million years. Certainly it has shown that the Quaternary, however defined, was much more complex climatically than was previously thought. But it has several aspects which severely limit its usefulness. First, it is impossible to correlate the oceanic deposits with those on land or on the floor of shelf seas except by direct dating, and as we shall see in Chapter 5 there is no dating method suitable for all continental Quaternary deposits. Second, the resolution of climatic changes in oceanic sediments is limited by their rate of sedimentation, by bioturbation of the sediments after their deposition, and by the rate of circulation of ocean waters. Complete ocean mixing takes 1000–1500 years, so that climatic changes resulting in warm or cold periods shorter than this can never be detected. However, it is difficult to obtain samples that are separated by such a short time interval, because of the bioturbation and slow sedimentation rates. Where the sedimentation rate is rapid and bioturbation minimal, so that the resolution is optimal, the length of core recoverable by normal piston sampling (usually 10–15 m) spans only part of the Quaternary; the more expensive hydraulic piston cores are usually necessary for sediments older than about 250 000 years. A third difficulty with the oceanic record is that it is sometimes incomplete because of periods of non-deposition or erosion, though this is a small problem compared with the gaps occurring in terrestrial Quaternary successions.

1.6 EVIDENCE OF CLIMATIC CHANGES FROM CONTINENTAL DEPOSITS

The earliest evidence that the Quaternary climate was at times colder than the present came from the realization that glaciers had once been more extensive in some parts of the world than they are today. This was first inferred in the late eighteenth and early nineteenth centuries in mountainous countries, such as Switzerland and Norway, which still have small glaciers. The conclusion was based on the occurrence of large blocks (erratics) of rock types some distance from their known outcrops, and the presence of parallel striations on bedrock surfaces. Both are often associated with heterogeneous deposits of mixed origin, which were thought to have been left by the glaciers when they receded. However, some early geologists felt that all these features could be explained by ice floes, provided the sea level was high enough to cover all the areas affected. The biblical flood provided supposed corroboration of this theory, and the deposits consequently became known as diluvium or drift, the latter term reflecting the idea of drifting ice floes. As a result the land-ice theory, accepted by scientists and even the general public in alpine areas by the 1820s, was not accepted in Britain, USA and other countries without remnants of glaciers until the late nineteenth century. Agassiz introduced the idea to British geologists in the early 1840s (Boylan 1981); Dean Buckland and others were quickly convinced, but Lyell and other famous British and American geologists clung to the sea-ice theory for several decades. This probably explains why the term drift became entrenched in British literature and persists on the legends of British geological maps even to the present day.

The first glacialists inferred only one 'Ice Age' when glaciers had covered much of north-west Europe and northern parts of USA, but Collomb (1847), Ramsay (1852), Morlot (1855) and others soon presented evidence for two or more glaciations in certain areas, and Heer (1865) found deposits containing the remains of warmth-loving plants between two different 'diluvial' accumulations in Switzerland. Heer described these fossiliferous beds as interglacial and concluded that they indicated one or more periods when the intense cold of the 'Ice Age' was punctuated by warmer periods with a climate similar to that of the present day.

The preliminary geological mapping of Britain in mid-Victorian times showed that the 'drift deposits' could often be subdivided lithologically by colour, by the presence of different erratic suites or by gravelly or sandy layers between beds of 'boulder clay'. This also led to the idea of multiple glaciation, though it is now realized that the deposits left by a single ice advance can vary laterally and vertically, so the lithological differences do not necessarily indicate separate ice advances. Interglacial deposits with thermophilous plant or animal remains between glacial sediments provided firmer evidence for climatic fluctuations, but some famous British geologists remained monoglacialists even until the 1950s, and explained the fossiliferous layers as large erratics of preglacial sediment incorporated into the boulder clay during a single glaciation.

The study of alpine glaciations by Penck and Brückner (1909) was one of the most influential in Quaternary geology. In the main river valleys draining the Alps, they recognized a succession of gravelly deposits forming gently sloping terraces, the surfaces of which occur at various levels on the valley sides (Fig. 1.5), suggesting that

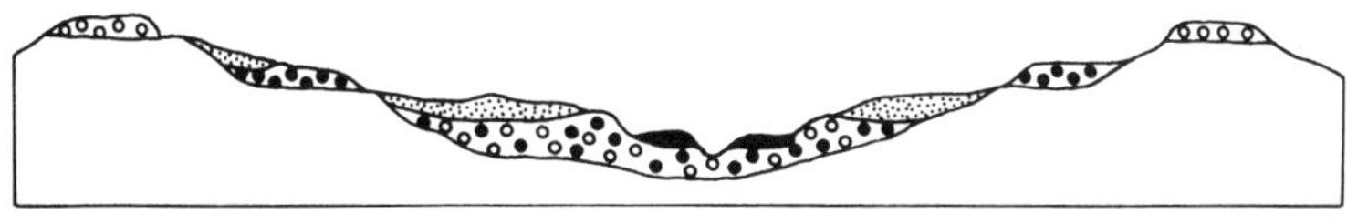

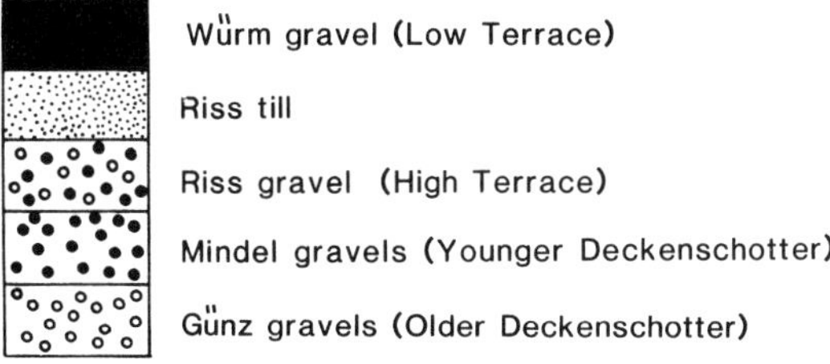

Fig. 1.5 — Schematic section through a Swiss valley, showing sequence of gravel terraces deposited during successive cold stages with intervening episodes of down-cutting (from Heim 1919).

episodes of terrace formation (or aggradation) were punctuated by periods when the river was eroding and down-cutting through earlier deposits. From the presence of erratics in the gravels and the occasional occurrence of buried soils between successive gravels (Fig. 1.6), they inferred that the terraces represent cold periods

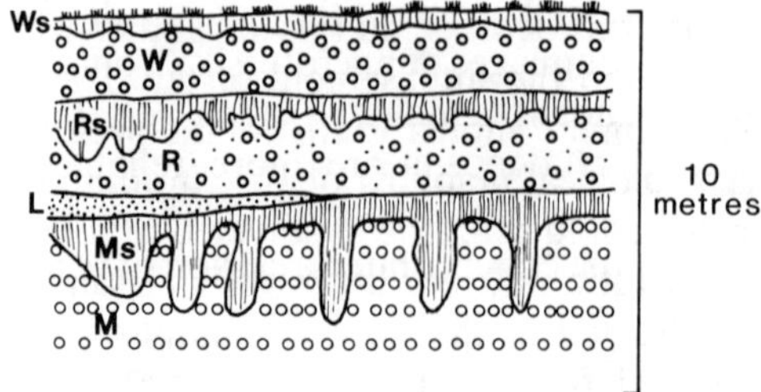

Fig. 1.6 — Section south of Munich, S. Germany, showing three glacial gravels with intervening soils (from Penck and Brückner 1909). W=Würm, R=Riss, M=Mindel, subscript s denotes soil developed on each gravel, L= loess.

when glaciers occupied higher reaches of the valleys, bringing coarse rock fragments which were then transported by meltwater issuing from the ice margin. Initially they identified four such cold periods, which they named after rivers draining the northern alpine foreland; in chronological (as well as alphabetical) order these were the Günz, Mindel, Riss and Würm. Later work (Eberl 1930, Schaefer 1953) showed that the first three of these could be divided into two substages, and the Würm into three, also that there were two earlier glaciations (the Biber and Donau), the later of which could be further divided into three substages. This implied a fairly complex series of climatic oscillations, though Schaefer (1953) showed that some of the down-cutting episodes coincided with periods of cold rather than 'interglacial' climate. But the idea of four glaciations persisted in many parts of the world and the Günz–Mindel-Riss–Würm succession became accepted almost worldwide as a standard for the Quaternary. The terms are in fact still used in many countries to indicate the last (Würm) major cold period (116 000 to 10 000 years ago approximately) and any succession of discernible earlier cold periods. The interglacials between them were named Günz/Mindel, Mindel/Riss and Riss/Würm.

Palaeontological evidence for climatic change is provided by many fossil groups found in various types of continental Quaternary sediment. The earliest evidence was from leaves, seeds and other plant macrofossils found in fluvial, lacustrine and peaty accumulations. However, these remains are rarely abundant and well-preserved. An important advance in Quaternary palaeobotany came in the years between World Wars I and II through the introduction of methods for extracting and identifying pollen grain types (West 1977, Moore and Webb 1978). After allowing for differences in the production, dispersion, accumulation and preservation of pollen types, it is possible to infer regional and local vegetation covers of past periods and changes in these with time from comparison of the assemblages found in successive horizons. The changes are interpreted mainly as resulting from climatic changes, though soil type, grazing by animals and (in the last few thousand years) human activities also influence pollen assemblages.

The main animal fossils providing evidence for climatic change during the Quaternary are molluscs, foraminifera and ostracods in shallow marine sediments, and molluscs, ostracods, coleoptera (beetles) and vertebrate remains (bones and teeth) in freshwater and terrestrial deposits. As with plant remains, the larger animal fossils are rarely very abundant, and climatic inferences drawn from small numbers of specimens are often unreliable because they may be derived from earlier deposits. Inferences drawn from assemblages of microfossils, from the large numbers of small molluscs or from the abundant remains of small vertebrates (e.g. rodent bones) found in some Quaternary deposits are more reliable, but demand specialist ecological knowledge of the groups involved.

A basic assumption in the climatic interpretation of Quaternary fossils is that the ecological requirements of a fossil species were the same as those of the same species today, or of the nearest living relative if the fossil is now extinct. However, the ecology of some species could have changed with time, and present distributions of many plants and animals have been influenced by man, so considerable care is required before climatic inferences are drawn. Where small numbers of species each represented by a few specimens are involved, the risk of error is greater than where large populations of many different species are identified and the relative abundance and ecological significance of each species is used to weight the result.

Because the Quaternary was much shorter than earlier geological periods, evolutionary changes are much less valuable in zonation and correlation. Many extinctions did occur, often as a result of climatic effects, but true worldwide extinctions were less common than local ones caused by migrations under the influence of climatic changes. Typically, cold Quaternary periods caused thermophilous species to migrate from high- to low-latitude regions, and during warm periods the reverse occurred. Some climate-induced migrations were fairly orderly, but many were also influenced by sea-level changes and consequent modifications in the distribution of land and sea. During cold periods the sea level was lowered eustatically because large amounts of water were incorporated into land-based glaciers, but it rose again when the glaciers melted in warm periods. However, other factors also influenced local sea levels, especially the glacio-isostatic depression of some areas beneath thick ice sheets and their slow uplift (rebound) on melting. At the end of a glacial period the eustatic rise of sea level was faster than the glacio-isostatic rebound in many areas, so some glaciated areas were inundated early in post-glacial times and later re-emerged, whereas unglaciated areas originally slightly higher remained dry for longer but were later submerged. Land bridges over which plants and animals could migrate to higher latitudes after cold periods therefore appeared at various times and sometimes disappeared before some species had successfully migrated.

In north-west Europe interglacials were periods of forest development on land surfaces, and can be divided into four zones (Turner and West 1968):

Zone IV (Post-temperate), dominated by boreal trees, such as *Betula* (birch) and *Pinus* (pine).
Zone III (Late-temperate), with mixed oak forest but also including some temperate trees that migrate more slowly from warmer regions (e.g. *Carpinus* (hornbeam)).
Zone II (Early-temperate), with mixed oak forest, i.e. *Quercus* (oak), *Ulmus* (elm), *Tilia* (lime), *Corylus* (hazel), *Alnus* (alder), and subsidiary *Pinus* and *Betula*).
Zone I (Pre-temperate), with mainly boreal trees (*Pinus*, *Betula*).

Non-arboreal pollen (grasses, herbs) is more abundant in zones I and IV than II and III, indicating that the birch–pine woodland at the beginning and end of an interglacial was more open, with common grassy areas, than the mixed oak forest during the warmest parts of the interglacial. Fig. 1.7 shows the relative abundance of different pollen types through a typical interglacial.

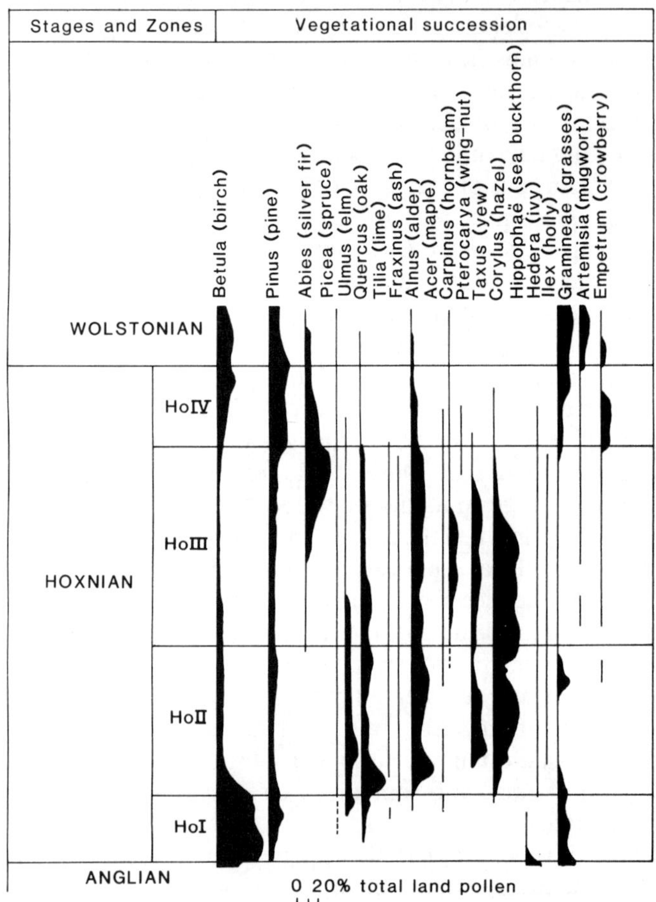

Fig. 1.7 — Frequency of main pollen types in a typical NW Europe interglacial succession, the Hoxnian at Marks Tey, England (from Turner 1970). Reproduced by permission of the Royal Society, London.

In contrast, the vegetation of cold Quaternary periods in north-west Europe was either grassland (steppe) or tundra (mosses, algae, lichens) with episodes of arctic desert when it was coldest. Small numbers of boreal trees (*Betula, Pinus* and *Salix* (willow)) and shrubs (*Juniperus* (juniper) and *Hippophäe* (sea buckthorn)) were present at times, especially towards the close of each cold period (the late-glacial periods), and a range of herbs was often present in the grassland areas. From palaeobotanical evidence, the cold periods were also diversified by short episodes of fairly warm climate with patchy woodland of *Betula, Pinus* and *Picea* (spruce). Coleoptera from these interstadial episodes suggest that summer temperatures were just as high as in interglacials (Coope 1977), so that the main reason why temperate forest did not appear in interstadials was that they were too short (and not necessarily too cool) for other trees to have time to migrate northwards from southern Europe. Radiocarbon dating of some interstadials during the last cold stage in Britain (the Devensian Stage) suggests that they often lasted only 1000–2000 years. The coldest periods between the interstadials are sometimes referred to as stadials.

Although the distinctions between glacials, interglacials, stadials and interstadials, as defined on palaeobotanical evidence in Europe, can be applied to some other mid-latitude parts of the world, such as northern USA, they do not necessarily apply in tropical or polar regions. The main worldwide effect of major climatic changes was to compress the earth's climatic zones towards the equator in cold periods and to expand them towards the poles in warm periods. In mid-latitude regions this zonal movement resulted in fluctuations from polar desert to temperate forest, but in tropical regions the climate of the Quaternary was continuously warm and in polar regions it was continuously cold. Consequently deposits dating from the same period of the Quaternary may contain typical interglacial fossil assemblages in some land areas, typical interstadial assemblages in others and steppe or tundra assemblages (often termed 'full-glacial' assemblages) elsewhere. This means that the climatic changes used to subdivide the Quaternary are relevant only in mid-latitude regions, but even there they are likely to be diachronous because the palaeontological evidence for them depends upon the rather slow migration rates of trees and other groups. Coleoptera seem to provide the best evidence for climatic changes in continental deposits, mainly because they are more mobile than other groups and migrate quickly in response to climatic and other environmental changes.

1.7 LONG CONTINENTAL QUATERNARY SEQUENCES

Although most continental Quaternary sequences are incomplete and difficult to correlate with the 'yardstick' of deep oceanic successions, fairly complete sequences have now been traced in two main terrestrial environments, lake or swamp basins and the loess steppes. Both of these provide climatic curves showing a strong resemblance to those derived from the oxygen isotope measurements on deep sea cores.

A long lacustrine sequence from a peat swamp at Tenaghi-Philippon in Macedonia (Greece) was described by Van der Hammen *et al.* (1971). Climatic changes were traced by variations in the ratios of arboreal pollen in the peat to that of grass and herbs, and by the abundance of oak pollen during warm periods but a predominance of pine pollen in cooler intervals. The upper part of the 120-m-long core was dated by radiocarbon, showing that the most recent increases in tree pollen and appearance of oak coincided with the boundary between oceanic isotope stages 1 and 2 (the

Pleistocene/Holocene boundary). Similar changes in pollen assemblages deeper in the core suggested correlations with oceanic oxygen isotope stages as old as stage 17 (Fig. 1.8).

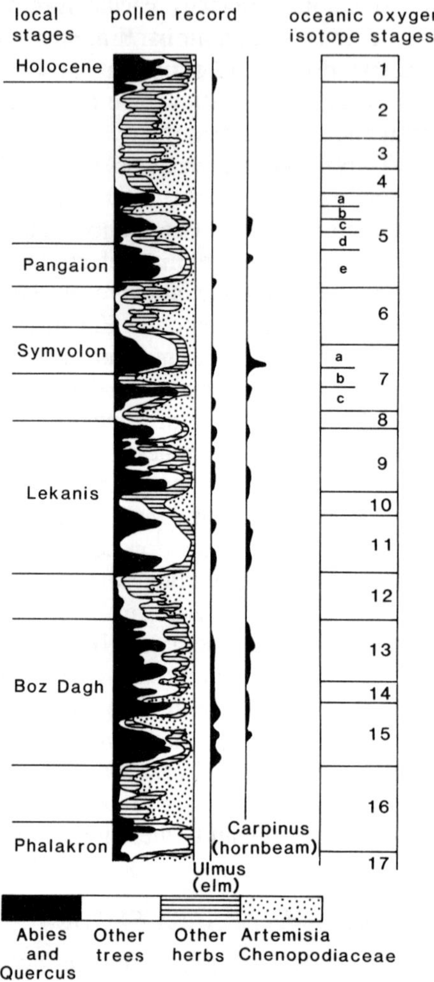

Fig. 1.8 — Pollen record of the 120-m-long Tenaghi-Philippon peat bog section, and likely correlation with the oceanic oxygen isotope stages (from Van der Hammen *et al.* 1971 and Kukla 1977). Published by permission of Elsevier Science Publishers.

More recently even longer lacustrine sequences have been obtained from intermontane basins in the tropical Andes, such as the high plain of Bogotá. Van der Hammen and González (1960) had earlier shown that Quaternary temperature fluctuations in the montane tropical Andes of Colombia were similar in magnitude to those of northern temperate regions such as north-west Europe, and that the very thick successions (up to 900 m in some basins) can be dated by potassium–argon and fission-track measurements on interbedded volcanic ashes. Pollen analysis of one of the longest cores (from Funza near Bogotá), covering the last 3.5 million years, has indicated 27 major climatic cycles (Hooghiemstra 1984); these can be correlated in detail with the oceanic succession, especially Pacific core V28-239 (Fig. 1.9) and north Atlantic core 552A, which covered a similar time span (Shackleton *et al.* 1984). The long pollen record indicated very cold periods around 3.4–3.5 million years ago and from 2.5 to 2.2 million years ago; the latter corresponds with the first evidence of ice rafting in the north Atlantic (see 1.2).

In some parts of the world, such as central and eastern Europe (Kukla 1977), northern China (Liu Tungsheng *et al.* 1982) and Soviet Central Asia (Dodonov 1981, Lazarenko *et al.* 1981), there are very thick (up to 300 m) deposits of windblown silt (loess). Palaeomagnetic dating has shown that, although most of the loess has accumulated during approximately the last million years (Pécsi 1984), in some areas it covers the last 2.4 million years. Like the Andean lacustrine successions, it therefore spans the Plio–Pleistocene boundary. As fossils in the loess indicate that it accumulated under cold conditions, the coincidence of the age of the oldest loess with the late Pliocene cold period when ice rafting first occurred in the north Atlantic is perhaps significant. In all the main loess areas the succession is divided by buried soils, which often contain fossils indicating that the soils formed in warmer conditions than the intervening episodes of loess deposition. The loess-soil sequences can be correlated fairly well with the oceanic oxygen isotope stages (Fig. 1.10), at least for the last million years (Kukla 1977), thus providing some confirmation of the complex history of Quaternary climatic changes obtained from the ocean floor and from the thick lacustrine successions.

Yet other evidence for past climatic change is provided by cores through thick polar ice caps, such as those of Greenland and Antarctica. Because winter snow accumulations are compacted annually into thin ice layers, these cores provide a very detailed record, which gives better resolution of short-term changes than do oceanic sediments. The longest cores so far obtained (1400–3000 m) cover only the last 100 000–160 000 years, but dating is more difficult than with ocean sediments. Oxygen isotope ratios and deuterium content (Jouzel *et al.* 1987) are both used to estimate past temperatures, and dating has been based on a physical model of ice formation and glacial flow (Dansgaard *et al.* 1969, Lorius *et al.* 1985). Unlike oxygen isotope changes in equatorial planktonic foraminifera, in which decreases of ^{18}O correlate with increased water temperatures, increases of ^{18}O in polar ice indicate higher air temperatures at the time of ice accumulation. This is probably because during precipitation water containing the heavier isotope (^{18}O) condenses more easily than that containing ^{16}O, since its vapour pressure is slightly less; as cooling proceeds, water vapour depleted in ^{18}O is then condensed at progressively higher latitudes (Dansgaard *et al.* 1975).

Mörner (1972, 1974) criticized the dating technique used in this type of investigation, but other methods based on, for example, volcanic debris incorporated in certain ice layers (Hammer *et al.* 1978) have corroborated the ages derived from the glaciological flow model. Results from a 1390-m-long ice core from Camp Century on the Greenland ice cap suggested higher temperatures from 120 000 to 73 000 years ago than between 73 000 and 10 000, and a final warm episode since 10 000 years ago

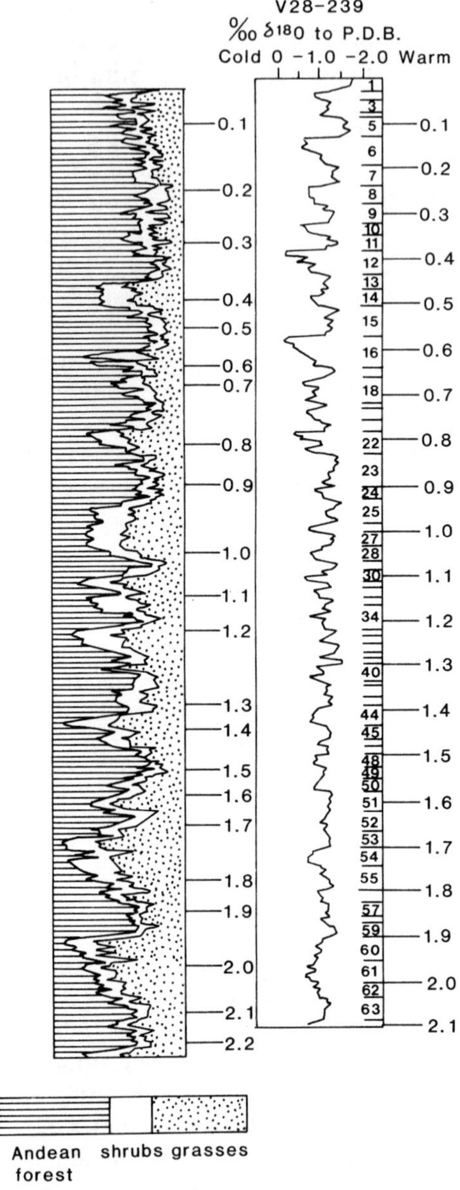

Fig. 1.9 — Pollen record for the last two million years from Funza, Colombia, compared with the oxygen isotope record from Pacific core V28-239. Ages in millions of years shown to the right of each core. Isotope stages 1–39 in core V28–239 from Shackleton and Opdyke (1976), and 40–63 from Hooghiemstra (1984). Redrawn from Hooghiemstra (1984).

(Dansgaard *et al.* 1969). Similar patterns of climatic change have been obtained from the Devon Island glacier in Arctic Canada (Paterson *et al.* 1977, Fisher 1979), and from a 2100-m-long core from Vostok in Antarctica (Jouzel *et al.* 1987). Despite the

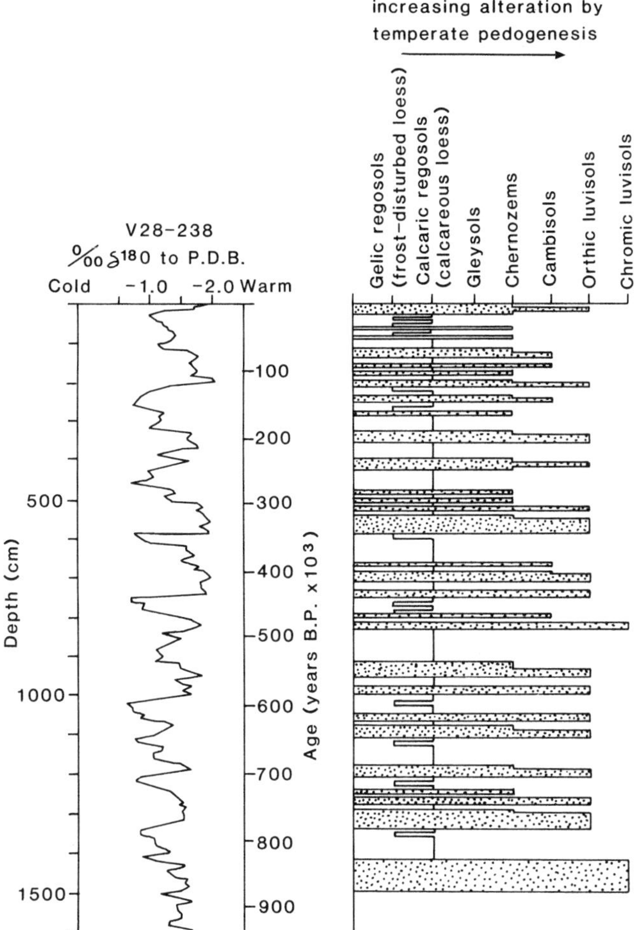

Fig. 1.10 — Sequence of loess deposits and buried soils in central and eastern Europe (right), and likely correlation with oxygen isotope stages in Pacific core V28-238 (left). Stippled soils show different extents of temperate pedogenesis (from Kukla 1977 and Morrison 1978). Reproduced by permission of GeoBooks.

problem of imprecise dating, these changes agree quite well with other terrestrial and oceanic evidence for climatic changes over the same period of time, except that the warming at the beginning of the last interglacial (oceanic stage 5) seems to have occurred at 140 000 years ago rather than 130 000 years ago as in the oceanic record. Short-term fluctuations indicated by the ice cores, such as the 'Little Ice Age' and interstadials towards the end of the last cold stage, are also dated to times similar to those indicated by other terrestrial evidence.

One advantage of the ice cores is the potentially high resolution they offer. This suggests that once the dating problem is overcome they may be used to investigate in detail the relationships between temperature changes and orbital or other astronomical cycles. Also, as ice contains dust and air bubbles formed at the time it accumulated, it is possible to use the cores to measure and date changes in the dust and CO_2 contents of the atmosphere. This will allow the relationship between past temperature changes and atmospheric composition to be investigated. Measurements on air bubbles in the Vostok core have already shown that atmospheric CO_2 changes occurred simultaneously with or slightly before temperature changes at glacial to interglacial transitions, but lagged behind the cooling after the last interglacial by as much as 10000 years. Barnola *et al.* (1987) suggested that this implies control of atmospheric CO_2 by two types of changes in oceanic circulation. As the CO_2 increase may have predated the temperature increase at the beginning of the last interglacial, and as both southern and northern hemisphere glaciations were synchronous with the CO_2 changes as well as the insolation changes for 65°N, it also seems likely that the CO_2 increases actually caused the temperature increases, perhaps by amplifying in some way the weak insolation changes resulting from orbital perturbations (Genthon *et al.* 1987).

1.8 THE BRITISH QUATERNARY SEQUENCE

For a long while the British Quaternary was subdivided according to the alpine sequence of glacial stages, on the assumption that the last main glaciation of Britain was equivalent to the Würm, and that successively earlier glacials were the Riss, Mindel and Günz. This approach, which Kukla (1977) and Bowen (1978) have called the 'count downwards from the top' method of correlation, is quite unreliable, but it is still widely used in Quaternary geology. It overlooks the possible existence of major hiatuses in the succession, and ignores the evidence for substages within the four main alpine stages.

After the Second World War, pollen studies of interglacial deposits at several sites in England led to a new method of subdividing the British Quaternary, which was originally formalized by West (1963) and later modified by Mitchell *et al.* (1973). The pollen studies showed that, although the interglacial vegetation sequence is broadly similar at all interglacial sites (giving part or all of the succession of four zones recognized by Turner and West 1968), minor differences allowed the sites to be grouped in a way that seemed to make stratigraphic sense. The main distinguishing characteristics arose from differences in the relative abundance of certain components of the mixed oak forest in some zones, the immigration of certain genera of temperate trees during the Late-temperate zone, the periodic reappearance of some genera that had been characteristic of late Tertiary floras but are now extinct in Britain, and the occurrence of characteristic genera in late-glacial deposits preceding some interglacials.

The different interglacials distinguished in this way in Britain are named after type sites (Table 1.2), but almost all interglacial sites are isolated from one another and their stratigraphic interrelationships are far from clear. Most of the terrestrial interglacial deposits are lacustrine, fluvial, beach or cave sediments, all of which are of very limited lateral extent. Usually the only deposits extensive enough to allow correlation between isolated interglacial sites are tills and other sediments of cold periods, most of which are devoid of indigenous fossils and liable to change rapidly in lithology, so that they are quite unreliable as marker horizons.

Another problem with using vegetation sequences to differentiate Quaternary

Table 1.2 — British Quaternary stages, type sites and main deposits (based on Mitchell *et al.* 1973 and Funnell *et al.* 1979)

Temperate stages	Cold stages	Type site	Main deposits
Holocene (=Flandrian)			Alluvium, peat, hillwash
	Devensian	Four Ashes, Staffordshire	Till, loess, glacial and fluvial gravels, gelifluction deposits, coversand
Ipswichian		Bobbitshole, Ipswich	Lake and river deposits
	Wolstonian	Wolston, Warwickshire	Till, gravels, loess, gelifluction deposits
Hoxnian		Hoxne, Suffolk	Lake deposits
	Anglian	Corton Cliff, Suffolk	Till, gravels, loess
Cromerian		West Runton, Norfolk	Peat, estuarine sands
	Beestonian	Beeston, Norfolk	River gravels, sands
Pastonian		Paston, Norfolk	Peat, gravels, marine silts
	Pre-Pastonian	Paston, Norfolk	River gravels, marine sands
Bramertonian		Bramerton, Norfolk	Shelly marine sands (crag), beach gravels
	Baventian	Easton Bavents, Suffolk	Marine silts
Antian		Ludham borehole, Norfolk	Crag
	Thurnian	Ludham borehole, Norfolk	Marine silts
Ludhamian		Ludham borehole, Norfolk	Crag
	Pre-Ludhamian (=Waltonian) (? Pliocene)	Walton-on-the-Naze, Essex	Red Crag, marine silts

time intervals is the possibility of successive interglacials having completely indistinguishable pollen contents. This could lead to stratigraphic confusion through miscorrelation of interglacial sites, and over-simplification of the countrywide Quaternary succession. At present there is some suspicion of this in Britain, because the large number of sites dated to the last (Ipswichian) interglacial on the basis of similar pollen assemblages (though often attributable only to fragments of the full interglacial zonal sequence of Turner and West 1968) can be divided according to two distinctly different mammalian assemblages (Sutcliffe and Kowalski 1976, Bowen 1978). This problem still needs to be resolved, but it is clear that despite the greater understanding pollen studies have brought, they have not provided a completely satisfactory means of dating and correlating British Quaternary deposits.

Many of these problems would be overcome if more Quaternary deposits were dated directly (e.g. by isotopic methods) and referred to a complete sequence of Quaternary chronostratigraphic units, such as the 'yardstick' of oceanic oxygen isotope stages. Radiocarbon dating (see 5.2) has in fact achieved this for deposits up to about 50 000 years old (oceanic stages 1–3), but at present there is no equally satisfactory method for dating older deposits. At the same time, radiocarbon dating has shown that the climatic record obtained from some continental deposits is much more detailed than that from any of the deep ocean sediments; many of the minor climatic changes indicated by fossil assemblages in continental deposits cannot as yet be resolved in the ocean bottom cores. Some Quaternary geologists (e.g. Kukla 1977) advocate abandoning subdivisions based on continental sequences in favour of the oceanic succession, but until ways are found of resolving climatic changes more fully from the oceanic record, and of dating terrestrial deposits so that they can be correlated with the oceanic sequence, this suggestion is premature. Also, it would be wrong to create oceanic type sites that are completely inaccessible to the majority of geologists, who have to work with continental deposits. At present there seems little choice other than to document local continental successions, which are difficult to date and correlate, and which the oceanic succession has shown to be usually very incomplete, but which often contain a detailed record of climatic events that are useful for correlation.

Just how incomplete many continental sequences, such as that of Britain, are remains to be seen. In the past there has been a strong tendency to ignore evidence for many climatic changes, because Quaternary geologists looked only for sufficient evidence to reinforce an over-simplified climatic model such as the alpine four-glaciation model. Since Mitchell *et al.* (1973) presented the succession of British Quaternary stages that forms the basis of Table 1.2, two new stages (the Bramertonian and Pre-Pastonian) have been formally proposed (Funnell *et al.* 1979) and evidence for several other possible additional stages has come to light in various parts of the country. This suggests that some evidence for a fuller sequence of Quaternary climatic changes is available in the form of deposits, episodes of soil development or erosive phases, but often passes unrecognized. A comparison of the British sequence with that in the Netherlands, based on palaeobotanical evidence (Zagwijn 1975a), which is unlikely to expose all the hiatuses, suggests that the sequence of stages proposed by Mitchell *et al.* (1973) does have large gaps (Fig. 1.11). Some of these may never be filled completely, but it is unlikely that the sequence will in future remain unaltered for long.

1.9 STRATEGY FOR QUATERNARY STRATIGRAPHIC INVESTIGATIONS

Because the evidence for past changes of climate (now used universally for subdividing the Quaternary) takes many different forms — palaeontological, sedimentological, pedological, geomorphological, archaeological and even historical — Quaternary stratigraphy cannot be regarded as simply the preserve of the geologist. It is indeed a multidisciplinary pursuit, and its exponents must have at least some appreciation of the value and limitations of the component disciplines. INQUA (International Association for the Study of the Quaternary) and equivalent national organizations, such as the Quaternary Research Association in Britain, the Friends of the Pleistocene in USA, CANQUA in Canada, DEUQUA in Germany, etc., have long recognized that the multidisciplinary approach is vital to Quaternary stratigraphy, and have encouraged interdisciplinary collaboration on projects, often of an international nature. This has led to important advances in our knowledge of Quaternary climates and stratigraphy. Looking back on work done by individual

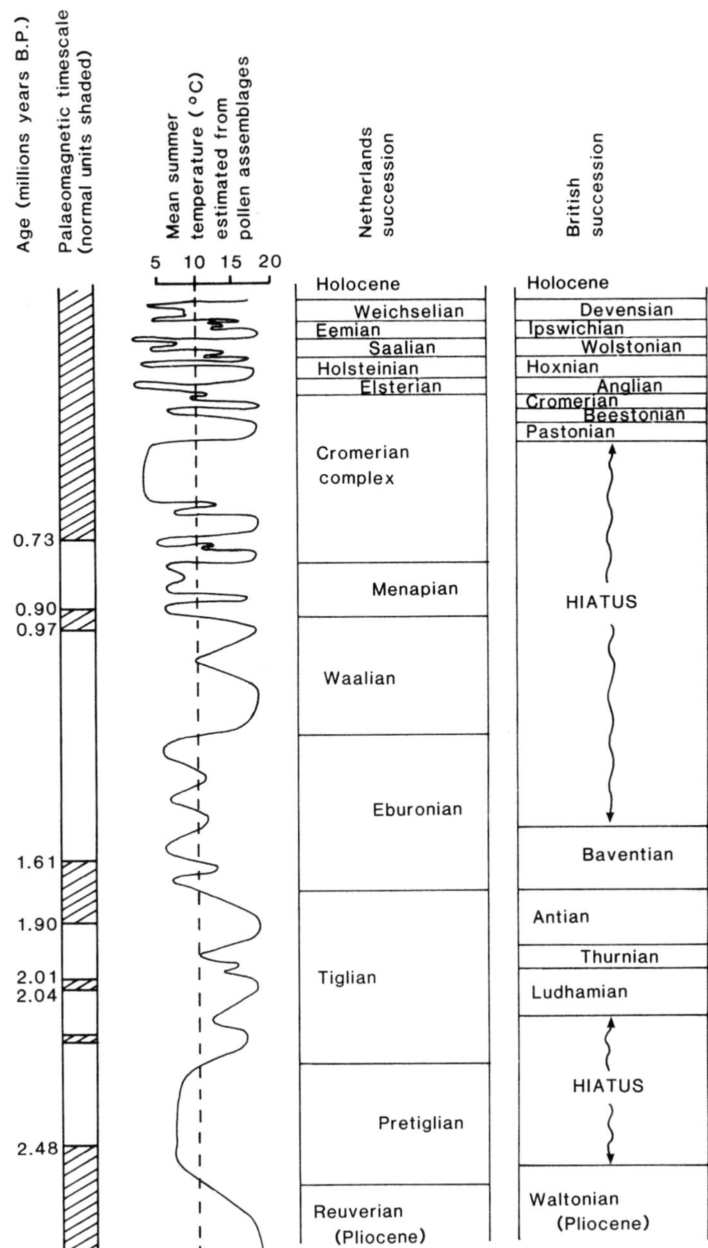

Fig. 1.11 — Likely correlation of Quaternary successions in Britain and the Netherlands (from Zagwijn 1975a).

specialists, for example in Britain before the Quaternary Research Association was formed in 1963, it is also possible to see how solo, single-disciplinary efforts frequently led to incorrect conclusions which actually delayed progress. More than with any other period of geological time, advances in our understanding of Quaternary stratigraphy and dating are therefore dependent upon cooperation between disciplines; a stratigraphic model that satisfies all interested parties is more likely to be correct than one based only on the evidence of one.

However, much can be gained from strict application and full understanding of stratigraphic principles (see Chapter 4). Because the stratigraphy of terrestrial Quaternary deposits is often very complex, many workers have uncritically employed various 'short cuts' to relative dating, which were simpler and quicker to apply than rigorous stratigraphical analysis. These led to erroneous conclusions, which delayed progress because they were accepted widely for many years and were often copied by others. Recent experience in several countries has shown that there is no short cut to a proper understanding of Quaternary stratigraphy. It is important that lithostratigraphical, biostratigraphical, climatostratigraphical, soil stratigraphical and other units (Chapter 4) are carefully defined and adequately distinguished within limited areas before national and international correlations are attempted. All should be placed in a chronostratigraphical framework as precisely as possible by the use of direct dating methods. Depositional, erosional, pedogenic and other Quaternary events should be stated to have occurred between the next oldest and next youngest events, with direct dating of all three given in years before present as precisely as possible. Dating and correlation by the 'count-from-the-top' procedure or other guesswork is misleading and unacceptable. It is often tempting to correlate similar events (e.g. periods of soil formation resulting in similar profile types, or interglacial deposits with similar fossil assemblages) in different areas. But as similar conditions were repeated many times over during the Quaternary, it is quite likely that such events were different in age.

However, having pleaded for stricter application of stratigraphic principles and more extensive use of direct dating methods, so that the age of each Quaternary event can be bracketed between known limits, it has to be admitted that the dating methods currently available are not completely adequate (see Chapter 5). All require certain types of samples, and some are more reliable than others, so in addition to other skills, the Quaternary scientist requires some appreciation of the methods available for dating and their various limitations.

2

Processes of Quaternary deposition and erosion

2.1 INTRODUCTION

In most parts of the world Quaternary deposits are different from those of earlier geological periods: they are essentially terrestrial in origin rather than marine. This can be attributed to three main factors:

(1) Because so much water was incorporated in glaciers, Quaternary sea levels were lower than in earlier periods and the proportion of the earth's surface occupied by land was consequently much greater.
(2) During cold stages of the Quaternary some of the land areas in mid- and high-latitudes were invaded by large ice sheets and others had permanently or seasonally frozen surface layers (permafrost), so that there was little vegetation to stabilize the soil. These areas were subject to special processes of erosion, which led to sediments unlike those deposited either beneath the sea or on land during most pre-Quaternary periods.
(3) The Quaternary was too short a period of geological time for any major changes to occur in the position of land masses and seas over the earth's surface. Consequently most present-day land areas have been so for most of the Quaternary.

Terrestrial deposits of any age are usually more difficult to subdivide, date and correlate than marine deposits, because their lithological characteristics are very variable and the fossils they contain are less evenly distributed. These difficulties are frequently magnified in Quaternary successions, which often present an almost bewildering variety of sediment types, many of them completely devoid of indigenous fossils. In this chapter the main processes of erosion and deposition occurring in cold and temperate Quaternary terrestrial environments are described, so that

Quaternary successions can be interpreted in terms of a local history of changing environmental conditions. Problems of correlation associated with different sediment types are commented upon, but the ultimate key to correlation (i.e. direct dating) is left to Chapter 5.

2.2 GLACIAL PROCESSES

2.2.1 Ice and glaciers

The ice in glaciers originates as snow, which is partially melted and compacted beneath successive falls. It accumulates mainly in upland areas where the snowfalls are heavy and melting is slow even in summer. Ice deforms plastically and spreads under its own weight to flow downhill and mould to irregular surfaces (Paterson 1981). The maximum velocity (usually tens to hundreds of metres per year) is at the top of the glacier, resulting in basal shear strain; this strain is proportional to the thickness of the ice and the slope of its surface. Ice may also slide downhill if melting occurs at its base. This happens because, although the basal layers of ice may be very cold (frequently colder than higher layers especially in summer), they are close to melting because of the pressure caused by overlying layers. Also small amounts of geothermal or frictional heat assist the basal melting because they are not conducted upwards. Plastic deformation and basal sliding allow glaciers to move slowly from upland accumulation areas to lowlands where the total snowfall would be too small and summer snowmelt too rapid for glacier ice to form. Temporary increases in basal sliding, giving velocities of several kilometres per year, are termed glacial surges (Meier and Post 1969).

Glaciers in cold continental regions, which are frozen to the surface beneath and move mainly by internal plastic deformation, are termed polar or cold-based glaciers; those in warmer (e.g. maritime) climates, which move mainly by basal sliding, are known as temperate or wet-based glaciers. Wet-based glaciers usually move more quickly and have more meltwater streams within as well as beneath them. Between the two extremes are intermediate types (sub-polar and sub-temperate), in which a decreasing proportion of the ice is at a temperature significantly less than the pressure-melting point. Sub-polar glaciers move mainly by plastic deformation, but basal sliding often occurs in their central parts. Sub-temperate glaciers move mainly by basal sliding, though their outer margins are often frozen to the subglacial surface in winter.

The total mass of ice in a glacier depends on the balance between accumulation in upland areas and ablation losses in lower reaches, the boundary between the two parts being termed the equilibrium line. Ablation includes melting, evaporation, wind erosion, and calving (formation of icebergs where a glacier enters the sea or a lake). Glaciers showing high rates of accumulation and ablation flow rapidly and are geomorphologically active in terms of eroding the subglacial surface, transporting the eroded material, and depositing it to form moraines and other features. When gross annual accumulation (the total volume of water added during the year between dates in successive summers when ablation reaches a maximum value) exceeds net ablation during the same year, the glacier has a positive mass balance. Methods of calculating mass balance are discussed in detail by Meier (1962) and Mayo *et al.* (1972).

Glaciers moving over their beds by flow or basal sliding are described as active. If the forward motion exceeds the rate of ablation at the ice margin, the margin advances; if it is less, the margin retreats. A positive mass balance, with high rates of accumulation and ablation, helps maintain activity. Movement may continue when the mass balance is negative, but not indefinitely. On gentle slopes or where low accumulation rates lead to a prolonged period of negative mass balance, movement may cease and the glacier is then said to be inactive or passive. If accumulation increases, activity may return. But when a glacier can no longer be fed by further accumulation it becomes dead (Ahlmann 1948). Dead ice may remain active if it is on a steep slope; it is then climatically dead but not dynamically dead. Stagnant ice is climatically and dynamically dead. Major climatic changes resulting in differences in upland snow accumulation control the size and activity of glaciers in the long term, though there is often a time lag of many thousand years. In the short term the effects of climatic changes on ablation rate are often reflected in the advance or retreat of the ice margin.

Glaciers vary in size, elevation and geomorphological situation (Embleton and King 1975). Cirque glaciers are upland ice masses occupying arcuate amphitheatre-shaped depressions on steep rock slopes (Plate 1); steep frost-shattered head and side walls lead down to a smoothed basin floor beneath the glacier, and there is often a low lip or threshold at the lower margin (Fig. 2.1). As cirque glaciers increase in size they overflow the threshold, and ice from several adjacent cirques may coalesce to form an alpine type of valley glacier on the valley floor below (Fig. 2.2). Outlet

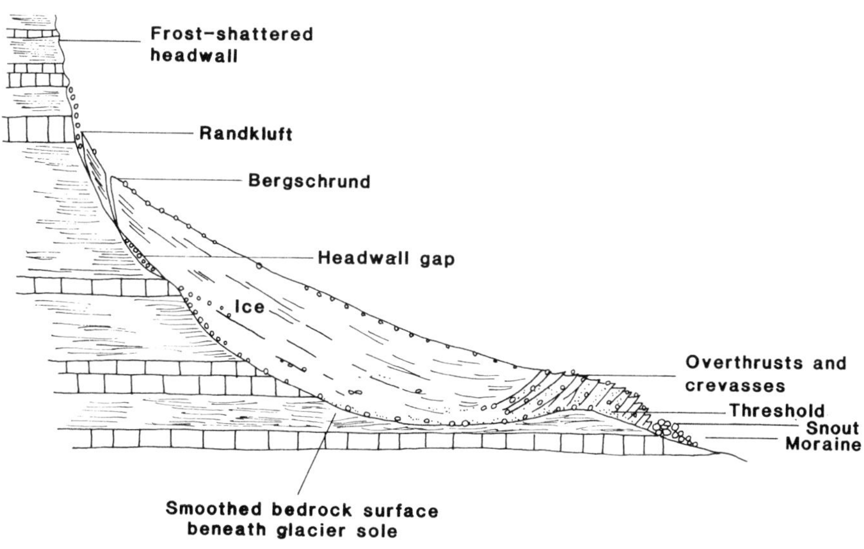

Fig. 2.1 — Main features of a typical cirque glacier.

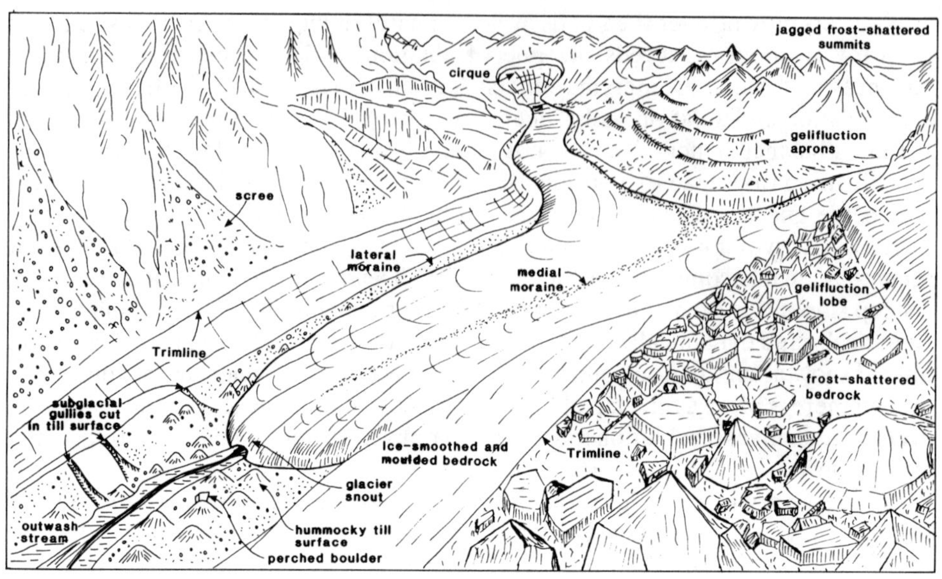

Fig. 2.2 — Main features of a typical alpine valley glacier.

valley glaciers are similar but are fed from a large mountain or plateau ice cap rather than from cirque glaciers. In high arctic regions small ice caps occurring on flat lowland surfaces have no significant outlet glaciers. Piedmont glaciers occur where valley glaciers spread onto unconfined lowlands. Where piedmont or other glaciers in high latitudes reach the sea, the floating parts are known as floating ice shelves or tongues. Ice shelves (e.g. the Ross Shelf) occur mainly in the Antarctic, and are nourished partly by snowfall on the shelf surface itself. The largest modern glaciers are the continental ice sheets of Antarctica and Greenland, which together account for 99% of the present total glacier ice. At the maximum of past glaciations (e.g. 18000 years ago), the Laurentide continental ice sheet in N. America was similar in size to the present Antarctic glacier, and the European continental ice sheet was about half this size (Fig. 2.3). Models of the Laurentide ice sheet and the British part of the European ice sheet have been produced by Sugden (1977) and Boulton *et al.* (1977), using evidence of flow lines, ice margins, profiles of modern glaciers, and palaeoclimatic data.

The altitude of the equilibrium line of cirque glaciers approximates to the snowline. So, if the mean annual temperature of the snowline in a certain region is known, the temperature decrease required to lower the snowline to the height of ancient cirques (as indicated by abandoned cirque basins) may be estimated from the present rate of temperature decrease with height. Using estimates of equilibrium line altitude and mass balance for Scottish cirques formed during the Loch Lomond Stadial (approximately 10000–11000 years ago), Sissons and Sutherland (1976) calculated both temperature and precipitation values for this final cold episode of the last (Devensian) cold stage. Their estimates of mean July and January temperatures at sea level were 6°C and −8°C respectively.

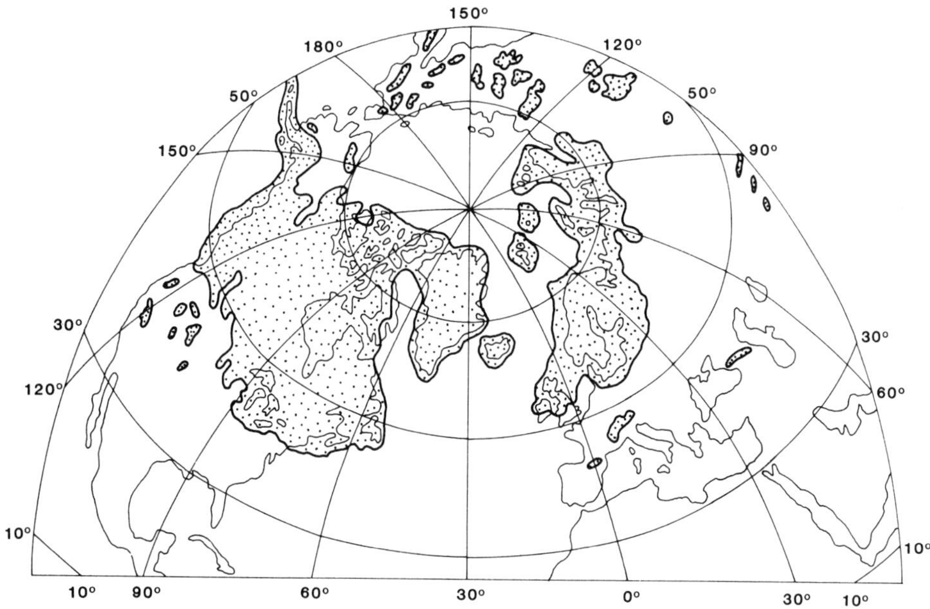

Fig. 2.3 — Maximum extent of northern hemisphere glaciers (from Denton and Hughes 1981 and Eyles 1985). Reproduced by permission of Pergamon Books Ltd.

2.2.2 Glacial erosion and deformation

Rock material is incorporated into glaciers by erosion of the sub-glacial surface and by deposition onto the ice surface from the atmosphere or by free-fall, gelifluction (see 2.4.3) or landslipping from valley sides above the ice margin. Hard rocks are extensively fractured by frost-shattering (see 2.8.6) before a glacier arrives, and the fragments are incorporated into the basal ice by regelation or refreezing of sub-glacial meltwater. They are also fractured and plucked beneath the ice, usually along bedding, cleavage or joint planes, and especially on the down-glacier side of obstructions. In addition, bedrock surfaces are striated by rock fragments within the ice, and smoothed by abrasion or moulded by debris-laden meltwater under pressure. In roches moutonnées the two processes of plucking and smoothing are juxtaposed (Fig. 2.4): on the up-glacier side pressure against a projecting mass of bedrock causes the basal ice to melt and lubricate movement, thus producing a smooth streamlined surface by abrasion; on the down-glacier side of the obstruction, decreased pressure allows regelation, and joint-bounded blocks are plucked because they are frozen into the basal layer of the glacier (Carol 1947). Bedrock surfaces moulded into troughs, bowls and deep potholes (moulins) by sub-glacial meltwater are often termed plastically moulded surfaces or p-forms (Dahl 1965); they usually occur in irregular patches where the meltwater streams, flowing partly within the ice, happened to contact the bedrock surface. Striations are better preserved on the surfaces of massive rocks (e.g. granite, limestone) and beneath a cover of deposits or soil than on bare surfaces of fissile or soft bedrock.

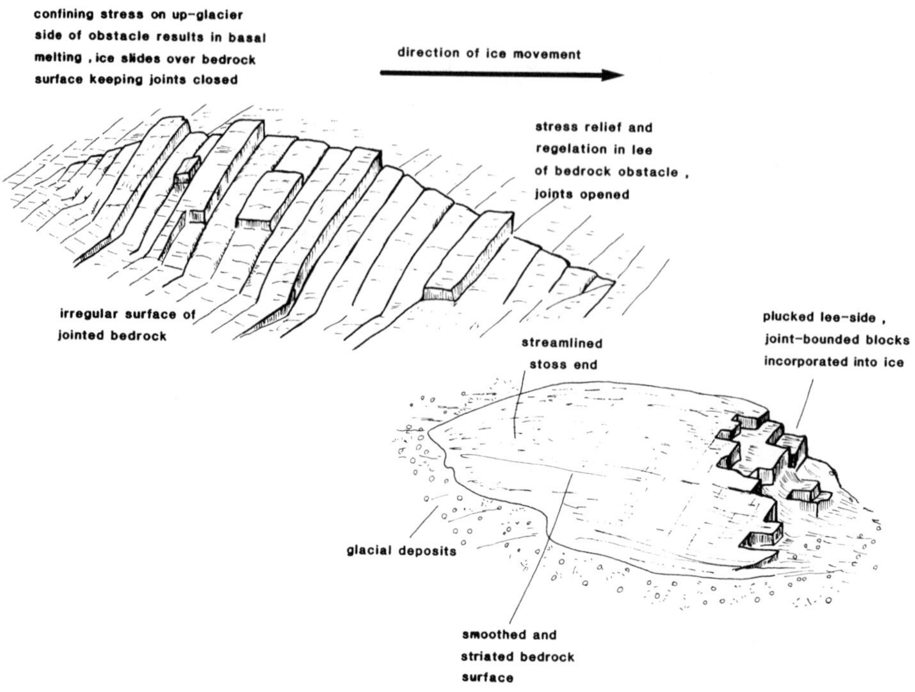

Fig. 2.4 — Formation of a roche moutonnée by smoothing and plucking of a bedrock obstacle.

Some of the rock debris incorporated into the basal ice layers is moved to higher parts of the glacier along gently inclined shear planes (Miller 1984), and eventually appears on the glacier surface. As the glacier moves on, fragments of characteristic rock types are transported variable distances from their original location. These plumes or 'trains' of indicator erratics can often be used to demonstrate the direction of ice movement, though multiple movements of clasts by ice or other transportation mechanisms may give erroneous results. From a given sub-glacial point-source (e.g. the outcrop of a mineral vein), the abundance of erratics near the glacier surface increases sharply to a maximum value some distance down-glacier, and then decreases exponentially with increasing distance from the source as the clasts are ground to fine powder and diluted with new material (Clark 1987). Half-distances (the distance over which the abundance of erratics declines to half the maximum value) are greatest for hard resistant rocks such as granite, and may be as little as a few hundred metres for softer rocks. In glaciated regions with isolated ore bodies in the bedrock, erratic trains are often used to help locate valuable ores (see 7.2.4); the axis of the train indicates the direction in which a mineral vein lies, and the abundance of erratics and their height above the bedrock surface suggest the distance it occurs up-glacier.

Soft sediments such as clays or older tills are mainly deformed beneath wet-based glaciers to produce streamlined landforms such as drumlins (oval mounds) or flutes (ridges separated by grooves) elongated in the direction of ice movement (Fig. 2.5). Erosion and incorporation of incoherent material probably occurs mainly when it is frozen beneath a cold-based glacier (Boulton 1979). Deformation of unconsolidated deposits also leads to the development of push-moraines in front of advancing glaciers. These steep-sided ridges extend parallel to the ice front (i.e. they are roughly transverse to the direction of ice movement), and the deposits within them are often isoclinally folded, reverse-faulted or thrusted, though the disturbances become weaker downwards and often terminate at a plane of décollement (Fig. 2.6). Push-moraines may be over-ridden and destroyed by further advance of the ice, and are thus best preserved near the maximum ice limit.

In upland areas of strong relief the effects of glacial erosion are often impressive, though they are usually the result of repeated frequent glaciations during the numerous cold stages of the Quaternary. Meandering river valleys are straightened, widened and deepened into U-shaped troughs with steep side walls, truncated spurs, and almost flat floors. The longitudinal profiles of glaciated valleys are less regular than those of river valleys, and often show alternating basins and ridges or rockbars with steep down-glacier margins. Glacial deepening of a main valley may leave less strongly eroded tributaries hanging high on the sides. Cirques or corries are often abundant on steep upland slopes, especially those which are well shaded and in the lee of prevailing winds. Enlargement of adjacent cirques produces narrow divides (arêtes), which are shortened as enlargement continues; horns remain at the intersection of three or more mature cirques, and coalescence of numerous cirque basins may eventually produce an irregular peneplain at a level a few hundred metres below the original upland surface.

Where glaciated valleys deeply excavated in hard bedrock are now flooded by the sea they are known as fjords. Coastlines with fjords (e.g. western Norway, southern Chile, southern New Zealand, southern Alaska) are usually close to extensive upland accumulation areas, from which large and very active glaciers can descend steeply to sea level. The longitudinal profiles of fjord valleys are often very irregular, with basins scoured to great depths and shallow rock thresholds, especially on the approach to the open sea where the glacier floated and ceased to scour (Fig. 2.7). The valley head is often high and steep, perhaps because of erosion by sub-glacial meltwater under hydrostatic pressure (Holtedahl 1967). Fjords usually consist of several straight sections of valley with sharp changes of direction, which are often determined by fracture patterns in the bedrock.

2.2.3 Glacial deposition

The eroded rock and sediment material carried by a glacier is deposited in various ways, usually forming quite complex sequences of glacial sediments. The various glacial facies associations were summarized by Eyles *et al.* (1983) and Edwards (1986). Much of the glacier load is in the basal ice, and is deposited almost directly onto the subglacial surface without being washed and sorted very much by meltwater. Some melting is probably important in the process of subglacial deposition, because wet-based glaciers usually carry a thinner layer of debris-rich basal ice than cold-based glaciers, despite the fact that they are more likely to pick up debris and cause erosion than cold-based glaciers. The sub-glacial sediment, known as till, may have any particle size distribution, and is often described in terms of a dominant

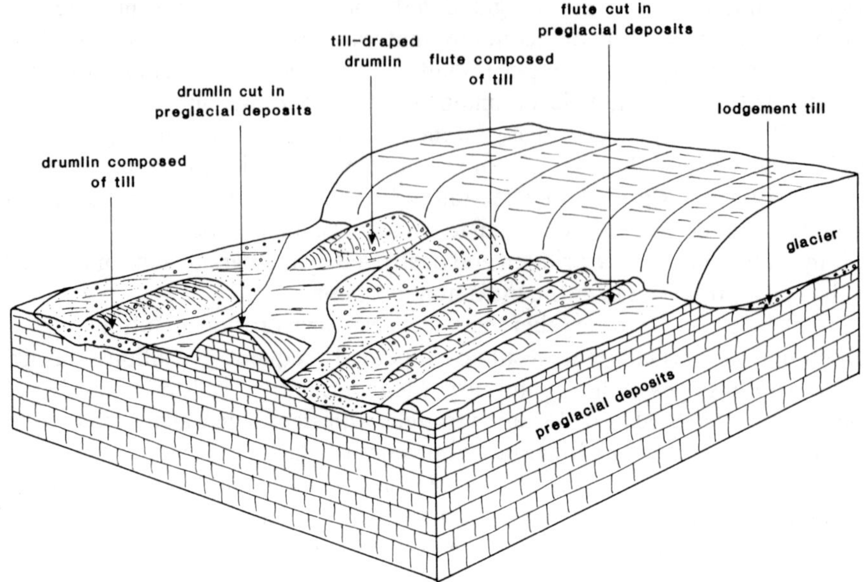

Fig. 2.5 — Formation of drumlins and flutes in glacial and preglacial deposits.

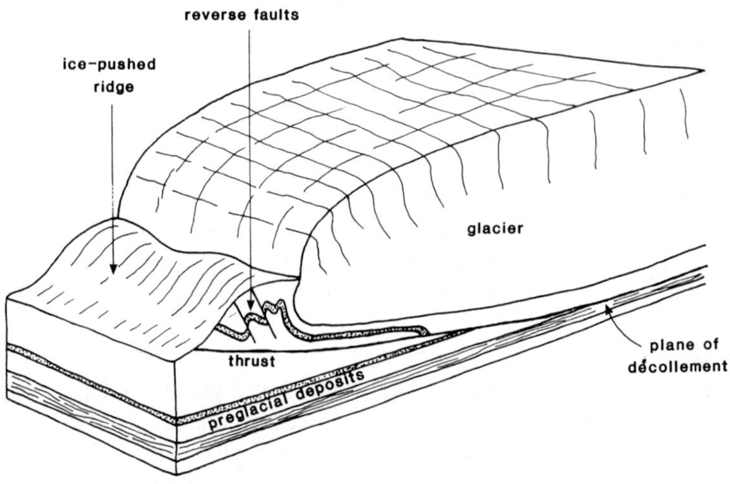

Fig. 2.6 — Structure of a push-moraine.

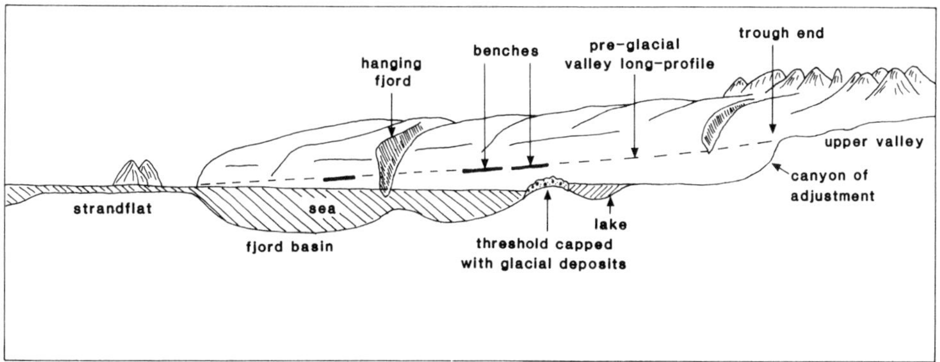

Fig. 2.7 — Features of a typical fjord (from Gjessing 1966).

constituent (e.g. chalky till) or the relative amounts of matrix (<2 mm) and larger clasts (e.g. matrix-dominant or clast-dominant). Boulder clay is a common type with conspicuous amounts of clay (<2 μm) and large clasts, but often also containing a wide range of particle sizes, so that the cumulative weight percentage size distribution curve (Fig. 2.8) has an almost uniform slope throughout (i.e. it is extremely

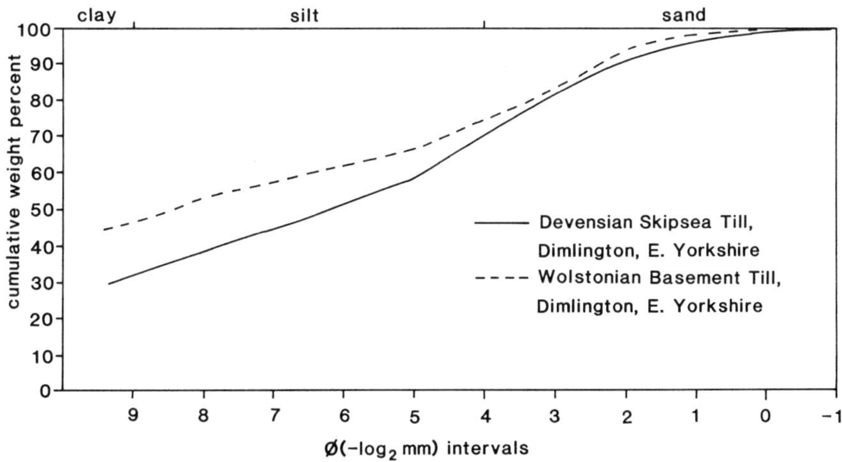

Fig. 2.8 — Typical particle size distributions of till (data from Madgett and Catt 1978).

poorly sorted). The clasts are derived either from local rocks or from more distant sources along the route of the glacier. Poorly sorted sediments containing large clasts in a fine matrix are not restricted to the glacial environment; for example, they can result from gelifluction or from subaerial or submarine debris flows (see 2.4.3).

Whether of glacial or other origin, they are termed diamictons (diamictites if lithified).

Till may be deposited in various ways, and the precise mode of deposition influences its characteristics. Till slowly smeared or plastered on the subglacial surface and derived from the basal layers of ice (lodgement till) is massive, firm and compact, overconsolidated by the weight of the glacier, and its larger particles (down to about fine sand size) are usually orientated with their longest axes parallel to the direction of ice movement (Holmes 1941, Donner and West 1956, Ostry and Deane 1963). Methods for measuring and interpreting till stone orientation were given by Andrews and Smith (1970), Andrews (1971) and Briggs (1977, Chapter 5). Andrews and Smith suggested that clast orientation results from the fine matrix flowing more rapidly than the larger clasts. But Lindsay (1970) stated that various sub-glacial, en-glacial or post-depositional processes could affect clast orientation, and suggested that glacial deformation should be compared with tectonic deformation, especially in terms of shear domains. With one active shear domain in the ice, clast long axes develop a single mode which is parallel to the direction of ice movement and plunges up-glacier. With two active shear domains, one dipping up-glacier and the other down-glacier, the clasts are aligned parallel to the intersection of the two domains, that is transverse to the direction of ice flow. This probably accounts for a subsidiary transverse peak often found in the long axis orientation patterns of clasts in tills (Fig. 2.9). However, as Penny and Catt (1967) showed, folding of till by a later

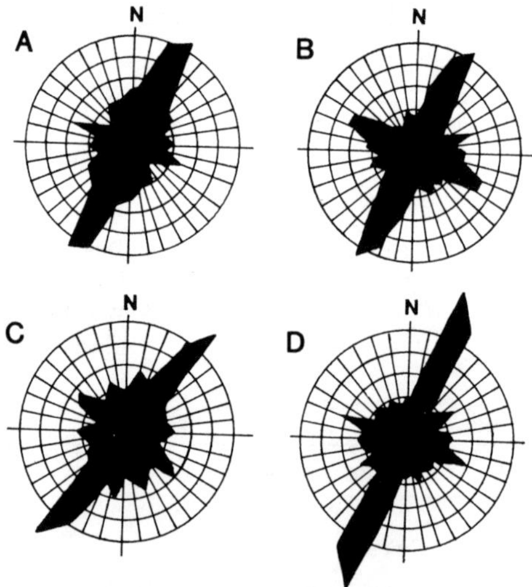

Fig. 2.9 — Orientation of long axes of stones in lodgement tills, east Yorkshire: A, Aldbrough; B, Hornsea; C. Barmston; D, North Landing, Flamborough (from Penny and Catt 1967).

readvance of ice may reorientate stones so that their long axes are transverse to the direction of the readvance. The preferred orientation of finer particles within the till matrix is usually studied in thin sections (Sitler and Chapman 1955, Penny and Catt

1967, Evenson 1971), though the orientation of magnetite grains can be measured from the anisotropy of magnetic susceptibility (Puranen 1977).

A second type of till, formed on the surface of a glacier by ablation (melting and evaporation), has been recognized for over a century (Goodchild 1875), and is usually termed ablation till. From observations of modern glaciers in Svalbard, Boulton (1970) recognized that ablation till may be modified by flow, creep or washing by meltwater, and that when a glacier stagnates, blocks of buried debris-rich ice may melt at the top or bottom to produce till which is neither plastered on by moving ice nor deformed by subsequent flow. Till redeposited as mudflows was earlier described as flow till (Hartshorne 1958, Boulton 1968), and this term is now widely used for any soft, uncompacted till material moved downslope or slightly reworked by various processes after its release from the glacier; lobes or patches of it may extend 1 km or more downhill from the ice margin. Flow may reorientate clasts so that their long axes are parallel to the local direction of flow rather than the original direction of ice movement.

Till released from sheets or blocks of stagnant ice beneath a confining cover which prevents subsequent flow or other deformation is termed melt-out till. This may be released beneath a layer of supra-glacial debris (supra-glacial melt-out till) or beneath ice (sub-glacial melt-out till) (Boulton 1972). Sub-glacial melt-out till and lodgement till are sometimes grouped as basal till (Francis 1975), as most sub-glacial melt-out till is derived from debris-rich basal layers of the glacier, though these may have been thrust into higher parts of the glacier along shear planes. Melt-out tills preserve a clast orientation inherited from the original ice, but they are rarely as compact as lodgement till, and usually form thin sheets interbedded with sorted and stratified sediments (Haldorsen and Shaw 1982); large clasts in some layers deform deposits beneath and may be draped by overlying layers (Fig. 2.10).

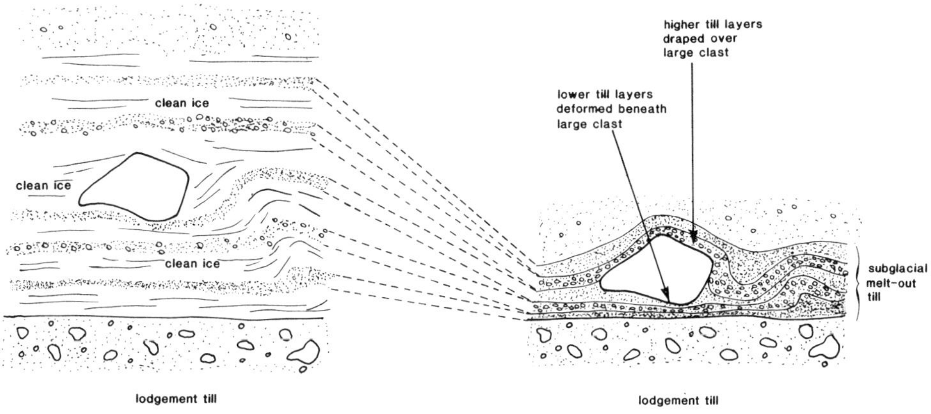

Fig. 2.10 — Formation of sub-glacial melt-out till.

Locally basal tills are composed almost entirely of fragmented local bedrock or unconsolidated preglacial sediment from beneath the glacier. In this material the original rock structure is replaced by a fabric imposed by the ice, even if it is not transported very far within the ice. These deposits are usually described as deformation till, though examples composed of crushed fragments of hard bedrock have been separated as comminution till.

Although tills are composed of material which has not been significantly reworked by moving water, till can be deposited in water, such as the sea or a lake, if it is dumped unmodified (*en masse*) from floating ice or from a glacier that terminates near the margin of the water body. This sediment is termed waterlain till. It is distinct from sediment accumulating in a completely or partially dispersed state on the sea- or lake-floor from floating ice, which is termed glaciomarine or glaciolacustrine sediment (see 2.2.7 and 2.2.6 respectively).

Two or more types of till may be deposited from a single ice sheet at any given site (Figs 2.11 and 2.12). Generally a basal lodgement, melt-out or deformation till is

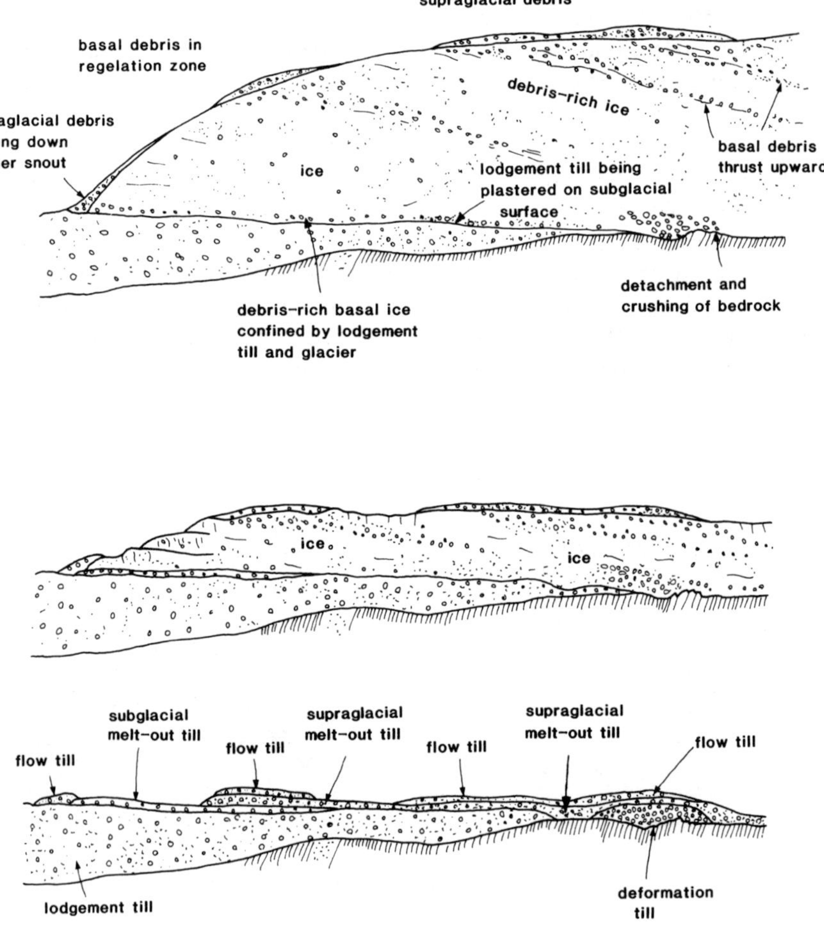

Fig. 2.11 — Formation of different till types from a cold-based glacier.

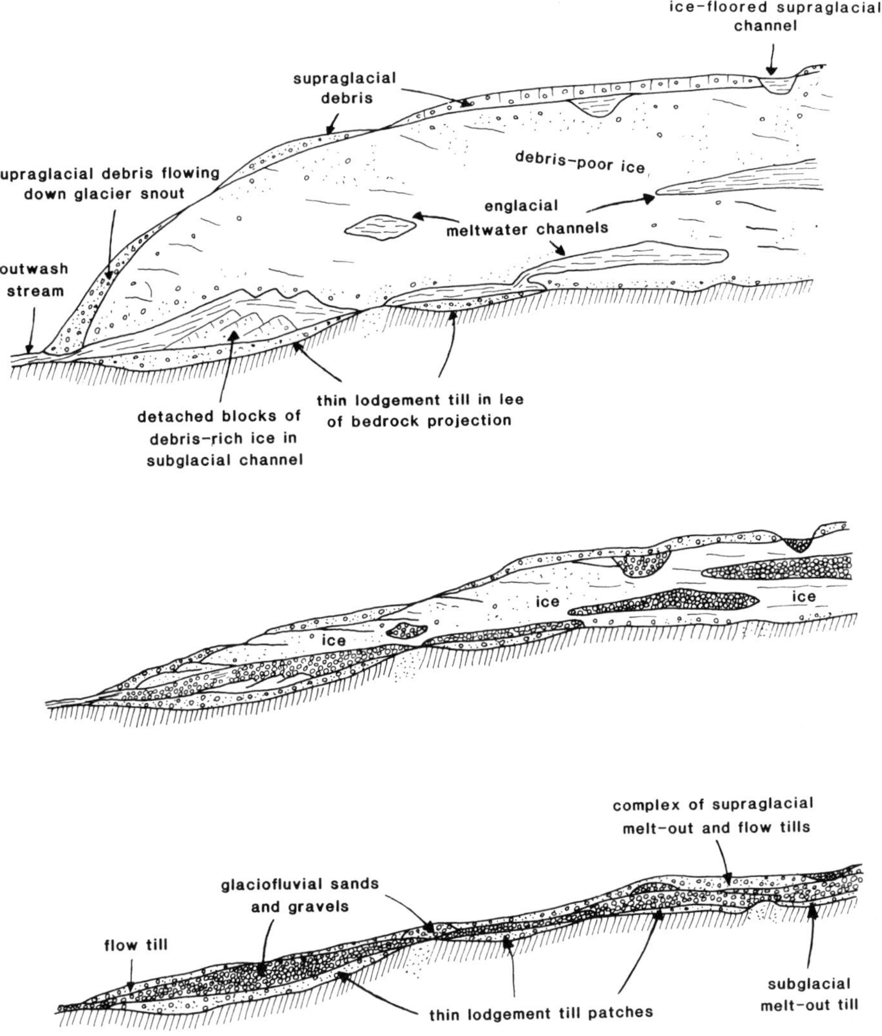

Fig. 2.12 — Formation of glacial gravel and till sequence from a wet-based glacier.

likely to be overlain by flow till or supra-glacial melt-out till, though the nature of the sub-glacial surface and the thermal regime of the glacier may influence the resulting sequence of till types. Cold-based glaciers which are frozen to the sub-glacial surface deposit mainly lodgement till possibly with small amounts of supra-glacial melt-out or flow till derived from basal debris thrust upwards through the glacier along inclined shear planes. Wet-based glaciers deposit only thin layers of lodgement till, usually on the down-glacier side of bedrock obstacles (Plate 2), and melt-out and flow tills are rare because the glacier moves rapidly especially on steep slopes and melts mainly by frontal retreat with meltwater streams sorting and redepositing most of the debris. Dead ice produces mainly melt-out and flow tills.

Fig. 2.13 — Drumlins west of Skipton, Aire Valley, North Yorkshire, England; the ice moved from left to right.

2.2.4 Geomorphological features of glacial deposits

The till surface left after the ice has completely melted may be a gently undulating plain or a complex of mounds, hollows and ridges. Oval mounds (drumlins) elongated in the direction of ice flow (Fig. 2.13) range in size from 5 to >100 m high and 50 m to several km long, with width:length ratios usually near 1:3. Large examples are often broader up-glacier. The smaller and more elongate examples may grade down-glacier into flutes or fluted moraines (Aario 1977, Hodgson 1986), which are parallel ridges up to 50 m wide and high (Fig. 2.5). Both drumlins and flutes tend to occur in swarms, especially within 20–100 km of the glacier margin. Some drumlins are composed of a thin layer of till smeared over a streamlined core of bedrock. Drift tails form on the down-glacier side of large bedrock obstacles or extend spurs at the confluence of deeply-incised main and tributary river valleys. Ridges parallel to the direction of ice movement may also form at the margins of valley glaciers (lateral moraines) or between two confluent valley glaciers (medial moraines).

Some ridges are elongated transverse to the direction of ice movement. These occur mainly at the ice margin as end- or terminal-moraines, but others termed Rogen moraines and De Geer (or cross-valley or washboard) moraines form occasionally beneath the ice sheet in transverse basal crevasses. Rogen moraines are larger than De Geer moraines, which are usually 1–3 m high, 10–15 m wide and 100 m–2 km long. De Geer moraines are often formed where ice grounds on the floor of a lake or the sea, and are then composed of deformation till, or disturbed glaciolacustrine or glaciomarine sediments. They are common in parts of Canada, Sweden and Finland.

2.2.5 Glaciofluvial deposits

Water from melting ice flows in tunnels beneath or within a glacier, in channels or crevasses on the ice surface, or as outwash streams away from the ice margin. The debris originally carried by the glacier is washed and sorted by meltwater, and then deposited as glaciofluvial sediments, which usually consist of stratified, uncompacted gravels or sands. When the adjacent ice melts, glaciofluvial sediments in supra-glacial, en-glacial and sub-glacial channels form sinuous ridges (eskers); Boulton (1972) summarized the shape, composition and structure of deposits formed in each of these situations, and further details of the sedimentary characteristics of eskers were given by Price (1973) and Saunderson (1975). When ice supporting the sediment melts, collapse may occur, leading to small-scale faulting, loss of stratification or the formation of a pitted surface. Fluvioglacial sediments deposited in en-glacial or ice-floored supra-glacial channels often overlie lodgement till or sub-glacial melt-out till, and flow till may occur over any fluvioglacial sediment, including proglacial outwash deposits. The complete sequence of tills and glaciofluvial sediments formed during a single ice advance may therefore be very complex and laterally variable. Chronological interpretation, such as the recognition of two or more separate advances from lithostratigraphy without independent dating and careful interpretation of the genesis and depositional significance of sedimentary units, is therefore impossible (Shaw 1987).

Beyond the margins of valley glaciers, outwash streams often deposit elongate sloping gravel terraces or valley trains; as the ice margin retreats, new trains are formed higher up the valley, and abandoned trains are then dissected by the meltwater stream (Fig. 2.14). Braided pro-glacial outwash streams emerging from

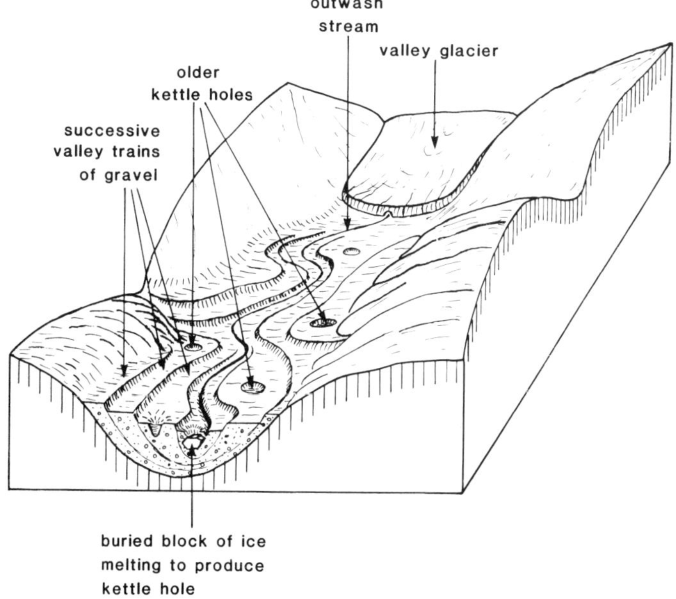

Fig. 2.14 — Deposition of valley trains with kettle holes in a glaciated valley.

larger ice sheets in unconfined lowland areas deposit extensive plains of fluvioglacial sediment known as sandar (singular=sandur). Both valley trains and sandar are usually coarsest and show the largest cross-bedded units close to the ice margin, where they may also contain blocks of ice that broke away from the glacier. If the blocks are buried in sediment before melting, they eventually collapse to form enclosed hollows (kettle holes) in the surface of the fluvioglacial deposits (Fig. 2.14). Sand and gravel deposited close to and in contact with an ice margin often form a belt of ridges, mounds and kettle holes known as a kame or kame complex (Francis 1975). Kames formed between the lateral margin of a valley glacier and the valley side are often termed kame terraces; when the ice melts the deposits are left as irregular terrace-like features on the valley side, usually with steep, embayed slopes marking the positions of the former glacier margins (Fig. 2.15).

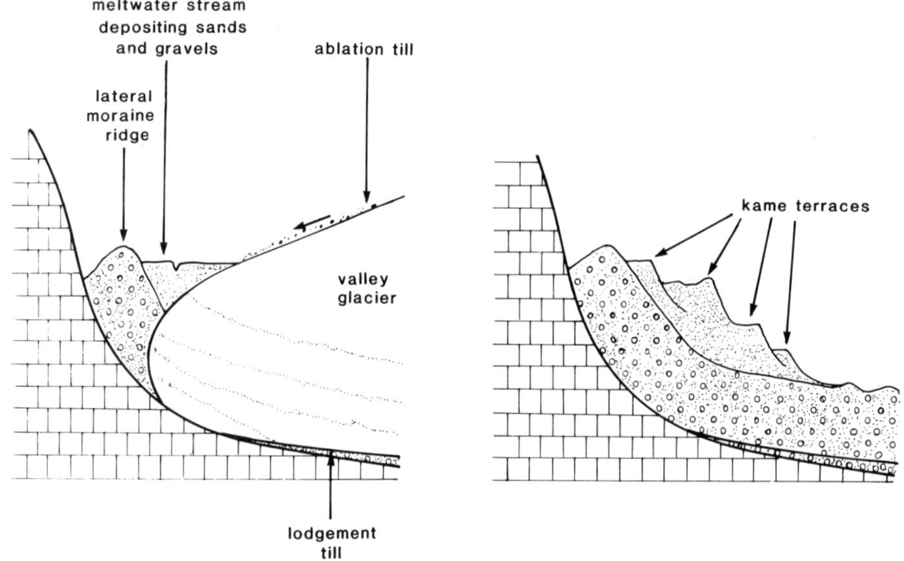

Fig. 2.15 — Cross-section of a glaciated valley to show formation of kame terraces.

The sedimentological characteristics of sandar, such as those in Iceland and Alaska, have been described by Bluck (1974), Boothroyd and Ashley (1975) and others, and are discussed in general reviews of the braided river environment by Miall (1977, 1978), Rust (1972a, 1978) and Bluck (1979). Near the ice margin there is often one or two outwash stream channels, but downstream these divide into many channels separated by elongate bars, which may be subject to wind deflation (see 2.3) or become vegetated if the climate is suitable. Proximal and distal reaches of sandar can be distinguished because of downstream changes in sediment grain size and types of channel bedform and interchannel bars. In proximal reaches, lozenge-shaped longitudinal bars up to 1 m high and several hundred metres long are composed of coarse gravels often with well-developed imbrication (upstream dip of clasts) or cross-bedding; sands with ripples and small dune bedforms are deposited only during periods of low water. In distal reaches (1–10 km from the ice front), sands or gravelly sands form lobate bars often covered with dunes or ripples. The bars are up to 300 m long, 150 m wide and 2 m high, and often terminate downstream in steep, sinuous faces, down which sand avalanches at times of high floodwater to produce planar cross-bedding. In the most distal reaches, sands usually give way to coarse silts forming low amplitude bars covered with ripples.

Miall (1978) defined various lithofacies for braided river sediments (Table 2.1), many of which occur in sandur deposits. They form three main groups, coded G (gravel), S (sand) and F (fines); lower case letter codes indicate distinctive structures or particle size characteristics. Miall also recognized six facies assemblages in braided river deposits, of which four are known in sandar (Table 2.2); these are named after

Table 2.1 — Lithofacies types of sandur deposits (from Miall 1978)

Facies code	Particle size	Sedimentary structures	Interpretation
Gm	Massive or crudely bedded gravel	Horizontal bedding, imbrication	Longitudinal bars and lag deposits
Gms	Massive, matrix-supported gravel	None	Proximal debris flows
Gt	Stratified gravel	Trough cross-bedding	Minor channel-fills
Gp	Stratified gravel	Planar cross-bedding	Linguoid bars
St	Medium to coarse sand, may be pebbly	Trough cross-bedding	Dunes of lower flow regimes
Sp	Medium to coarse sand, may be pebbly	Planar cross-bedding	Linguoid and transverse bars
Sr	Fine to coarse sand	Ripple-marks	Ripples of lower flow regimes
Sh	Fine to very coarse sand	Horizontal bedding	Planar bed flow
Sl	Fine sand	Low angle (<10°) cross-bedding	Scour-fills and crevasse splays
Se	Mixed	Crude cross-bedding	Scour-fills
Ss	Fine to coarse sand, may be pebbly	Broad shallow scours	Scour-fills
Sse, She, Spe	Sand	Analogous to Ss, Sh, Sp	Aeolian
Fl	Sand, silt, clay	Fine lamination, very small ripples	Overbank or waning flood deposits
Fsc	Silt, clay	Laminated to massive	Backswamp deposits
Fcf	Clay	Massive, with shells	Backswamp pond deposits
Fm	Silt, clay	Massive, desiccation cracks	Overbank or drape deposits
Fr	Silt, clay	Rootlets	Seatearth

Table 2.2 — Facies assemblages of outwash rivers (from Miall 1978 and Rust 1978)

Facies assemblage	Environment	Main facies	Subsidiary facies
Scott	Proximal, gravel-dominated rivers	Gm	Gp, Gt, Sp, St, Sr, Fl, Fm
Donjek	Medial, gravel–sand rivers	Gm, Gt, St	Gp, Sh, Sr, Sp, Fl, Fm
Platte	Distal, sand-dominated rivers	St, Sp	Sh, Sr, Ss, Gm, Fl, Fm
Slims	Distal, silt-dominated rivers	Fl, Fm	?

N. American rivers which show each assemblage. The Scott type is typical of proximal reaches and consists of gravel units formed by repeated aggradation of longitudinal bars, each of which shows an upward fining of clast size; sand occurs only in thin lenses, and fines (silt and clay) are rare; sand, silt and clay together form <10% of the total. In the Donjek type there is 10–90% gravel, with much interbedded sand; bar gravels are deposited in channels incised deeply into the sandur surface, sands or pebbly sands accumulate on slightly higher surfaces, and silts or clays are deposited in ponds formed in interchannel depressions. Upward-fining cycles are common. This type occurs within a few kilometres of the ice front. In distal reaches of sandar there are many shallow channels depositing sand with <10% gravel; this forms the Platte type. Abundant planar cross-bedding results from the migration of linguoid or lozenge-shaped bars; upward-fining cycles are rare. The Slims type occurs in the most distal reaches, where the sediment is mainly silt, which may be massive, laminated, or finely cross-bedded due to formation of ripples.

2.2.6 Glaciolacustrine deposits

Glaciolacustrine sediments accumulate in lakes occurring on, within, beneath or beyond the margins of glaciers. Many such lakes are temporary because they depend on ice for their existence, but some persist long after the ice has melted (e.g. in kettle holes or valleys dammed by end-moraines), so that normal lacustrine deposits or peat are deposited above the glaciolacustrine sediments. The water level in lakes impounded by cold-based glaciers is mainly controlled by the ice surface, and any overflow occurs through channels around or over the glacier. Lakes impounded by wet-based (temperate) glaciers can be drained also by sub-glacial or en-glacial channels; this may lead to rapid and sometimes catastrophic outbursts of water known as jökulhlaups (Nye 1976). Sediment entering a glacial lake from a meltwater stream, or direct from a glacier that terminates within or at the edge of a lake, is deposited in two main situations, near the strandline or further out on the floor of deeper parts of the lake. Strandline deposits consist mainly of coarse gravels forming spits, bars and irregular ridges (lake ramparts) produced by disturbance when ice is driven onshore by the wind. Gravel deposited at the lake margin from an inflowing meltwater stream usually forms a delta. If the stream comes directly from beneath, within or above a glacier, the delta may be supported from behind by ice, and when this melts the steep ice-contact slope may slump and cause faulting or other deformation of the ice-contact delta gravels (Fig. 2.16).

Typically glacial lake floor deposits beyond the delta front are fine, laminated

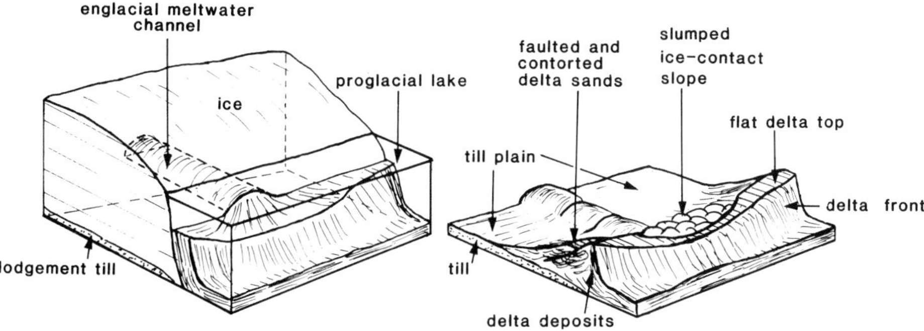

Fig. 2.16 — Formation of an ice-contact delta.

rhythmites because of periodic variations in sediment input and in processes of deposition (Fig. 2.17). Couplets of coarse (fine sand or coarse silt) and fine (clay or

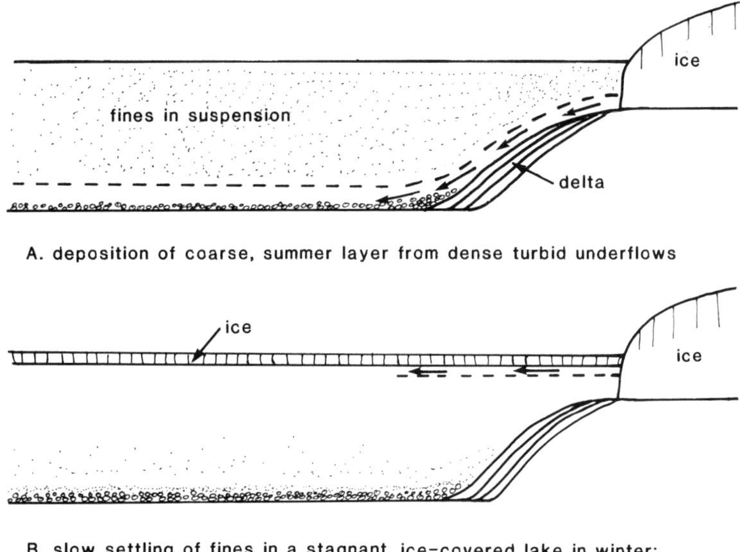

Fig. 2.17 — Deposition on a glacial lake floor.

fine silt) layers show either grading from one layer to the other or a sharp boundary between them. In varved clays each couplet represents a single year's deposition, and probably originates from turbid underflows of sediment-laden summer meltwater, which is colder and denser than the remainder of the lake water; grading occurs in distal portions of the lake floor, the coarse sediment settling out rapidly and the fine more slowly during the winter, often when the lake surface is sealed by ice and no further sediment can enter. On proximal parts of the lake floor the coarser layers are thicker, multilayered and often cross-bedded as a result of frequent sediment pulses during the summer (Banerjee 1973).

Varves are important in Quaternary geology for the opportunity they provide for high precision dating of the formation of glacial lakes and other glacial events (see 5.9), but some rhythmically laminated sediments are neither annual nor glaciolacustrine; in both glaciolacustrine and glaciomarine environments many laminations result from repeated turbidity currents with no seasonal control. If a glacial lake does not freeze over in winter, year-round turbidity currents produce multiple fining-upward laminae, with thin or impersistent clay layers. According to Ashley (1975), the main diagnostic features of varves are laterally persistent uniform clay layers and sharp boundaries between the winter clay layers and coarser overlying beds deposited by the next spring melt.

2.2.7 Glaciomarine deposits

Glaciomarine sediments accumulate where a glacier terminates in or near the sea, so that the composition of seafloor sediments is influenced by glacial detritus. Icebergs spread glacial detritus a long way from the glacier margin, where it is usually dispersed among normal marine sediment. The most obvious glacial constituents of glaciomarine sediments are far-travelled dropstones, though a few of these are not necessarily diagnostic of glaciomarine sediments because occasional stones may be dropped from floating vegetation. Beneath floating ice shelves and tongues, the sea floor sediments are often composed partly of waterlain till dropped from the underside of the ice; this resembles other till types in containing far-travelled stones in a massive, ill-sorted matrix, but it does not show preferred clast orientation and is not overconsolidated. It is usually accompanied by glaciomarine sediment derived mainly from the ice but dispersed and resorted by currents and debris flows (see 2.4.3) before deposition. However, distinguishing glaciomarine sediment from waterlain till is often difficult. Even the distinction between dispersed and resorted glaciomarine sediment and terrestrial basal till containing derived marine sediment can be problematical, and may lead to strong differences of interpretation, as illustrated by controversy over the origin of tills on the Isle of Man (Eyles and Eyles 1984, Thomas and Dackombe 1985). Glaciomarine sediments usually contain intact marine shells and other fossils indicating cold water. In contrast, derived marine fossils in tills are likely to be crushed or fractured, and are often mixed assemblages in terms of water temperature, depth, salinity or redox potential.

Inland from a floating ice shelf there is often a region (the stamukhi zone) in which soft sediments on the sea bed are sheared and gouged into ridges and elongate hollows by periodic grounding of the ice sheet (Barnes *et al.* 1987). This zone is separated from an inshore region, the fast ice zone where ice is permanently grounded, by a well-defined break (or 'knick-point') in the sub-glacial slope.

Meltwater containing large amounts of glacial detritus released from temperate glaciers terminating in or close to the sea often forms an overflow plume on the sea surface. Mixing of the plume with the denser saline water beneath is usually slow, but once sediment enters the saline layer it is flocculated and deposited fairly rapidly.

Together with the large seasonal and diurnal variations in the size and sediment content of the plume, this leads to fine lamination of the resulting glaciomarine deposits (Edwards 1986). The laminae become thinner and finer with increasing distance from the ice margin and eventually pass into unlaminated clays or fine diamictons with occasional dropstones.

2.3 AEOLIAN PROCESSES

2.3.1 Wind erosion

Wind is an important sediment transporting agent in areas where there is little vegetation to stabilize the ground surface, such as hot and cold deserts, bare mountain slopes, glacier surfaces, sea and lake shores, areas of recent subaerial deposition (e.g. glacial outwash plains, river foodplains and alluvial fans), and bare cultivated fields (Pye 1987). Air flow over the ground surface is usually turbulent rather than laminar, and consequently includes vertical velocity components at right angles to the main direction of flow, so that small particles can be lifted into the atmosphere. Here they may travel either long distances in suspension at various levels above the ground surface, or shorter distances by a series of hops (saltation), usually reaching<1 m above the surface. In addition some larger particles may roll or slide along the surface by the impact force of saltating grains, and between pure saltation and pure suspension some particles move with a random trajectory known as modified saltation (Pye 1987, p. 46).

Particles are initially entrained by the wind when they project above the general surface level and the drag force of the air moving over them overcomes the combined inertia of their mass and the binding forces between them and other particles beneath or on either side (Bagnold 1941). There is a square root relationship between the threshold wind velocity and grain diameter above about 80 μm (Fig. 2.18), but

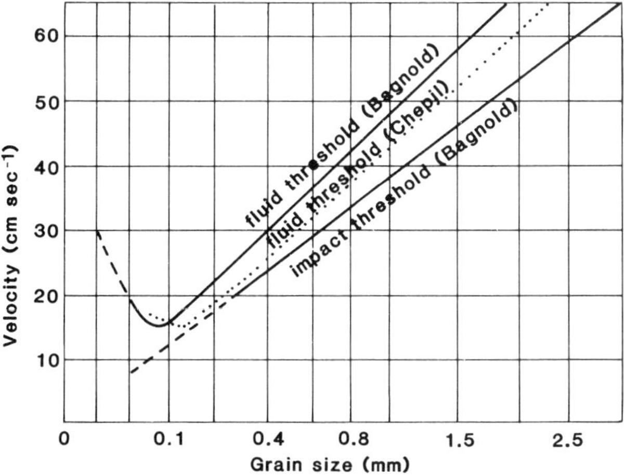

Fig. 2.18 — Relationship between grain size and wind velocity required to entrain grains (from Bagnold 1941 and Chepil 1945). Reproduced by permission of Methuen and Co. and Williams and Wilkins.

particles <80 μm require increased wind velocity for entrainment either because the drag is distributed over the whole surface and not carried by individual exposed grains or because of increased interparticle cohesion (Iversen and White 1982). Particle cohesion is affected by moisture content (Chepil 1956), electrostatic charges, cementing agents such as redeposited salts (Nickling 1984), microorganisms (Foster and Nicholson 1980) and clay crusts. As the intensity of erosion by wind varies with the cube of the wind velocity (Bagnold 1941) and inversely with the square of the moisture content of the surface layer (Chepil 1956), Chepil *et al.* (1963) suggested the following climatic index of wind erosion:

$$C = 100U^3/(P-E)^2$$

where U is the average annual wind velocity and $P-E$ is the effective precipitation index (precipitation minus evaporation) of Thornthwaite (1948). The value of C is often standardized to the average annual value measured at Garden City, Kansas, USA (i.e. 2.9).

The maximum diameter of particles with a specific gravity similar to quartz which can be carried in suspension at the highest frequently recorded wind speeds is about 200 μm. Larger grains may be entrained by high velocity gusts, but their mass is usually too great for them to remain in suspension for long, and they soon return to the surface. The hop trajectories of such saltating grains are determined by their initial upward velocity and changes in wind speed with height and time, but the mean hop distance is usually no more than a few metres.

When saltating particles return to the ground surface their momentum can move grains with diameters up to six times their own size, and also disturb finer particles, making it easier for them to be entrained as saltation or suspension load. This gives the slightly lower 'impact threshold' velocity curve shown in Fig. 2.18.

The atmospheric suspension load should have a modal size close to 80 μm because such particles require the least velocity for entrainment. But in practice the modal size is often <80 μm, because fine particles do not fall out of suspension as readily as coarse. The dust clouds frequently seen in and around modern deserts contain particles with median or modal sizes between 15 and 68 μm (Goudie 1978), and dust which has travelled distances of several thousand kilometres can have a modal size of 4 μm or less.

The wind is therefore quite effective in sorting particles of different sizes from an originally mixed size population. Particles >200 μm diameter travel only by saltation or surface rolling/sliding and consequently accumulate fairly close to their source. Particles <200 μm can be carried further in suspension but, of the suspension load, only particles <30 μm have settling speeds under gravity less than the minimum wind speed (15–20 cm sec^{-1}) capable of entraining grains of any size. As a result particles in the 30–200 μm size range do not remain in suspension for long, and are likely to be redeposited as soon as the wind slackens, though the finest in this range are occasionally carried as much as 300 km. Particles <30 μm can remain in suspension much longer and may be carried to heights of several kilometres by strong turbulence within cyclonic disturbances. This enables them to travel hundreds or even thousands of kilometres, but they are consequently so dispersed that they hardly ever form deposits of any significant thickness.

In addition to dry sedimentation under gravity, wind-transported particles may be deposited by inclusion in raindrops or snow. This is a very effective way of depositing particles of all sizes, though those $<1\ \mu m$ may escape light rain (Twomey 1977). However, in practice it does not seem to account for any large ancient or modern aeolian deposits. This is probably because most aeolian sediment is entrained in arid areas and is deposited by reduction in wind velocity before it reaches regions of frequent rainfall. Surfaces of dry sediment or bare rock trap wind-transported particles less effectively than moist or vegetated surfaces and water bodies. Settling may also occur preferentially in the lee of topographic obstacles where wind velocity and turbulence decrease (Jackson and Hunt 1975). Reported concentrations of dust in the atmosphere range from 0.01 to $10^5\ \mu g\ m^{-3}$ (Pye 1987), and measured rates of deposition on land range from less than 10 to over 200 t km^{-2} yr^{-1} (Yaalon and Ganor 1975); however, the highest rate calculated for oceanic areas is 4.5 t km^{-2} yr^{-1} (Janacek and Rea 1985). If the deposited dust has a bulk density of 1.5 g cm^{-3}, then 1.0 t km^{-2} gives a thickness of 0.7 mm.

2.3.2 Aeolian deposits

Because the saltation load and coarser components of the suspension load are transported much shorter distances than finer particles in suspension, most aeolian deposits of substantial area and thickness are either sands of local origin or silty deposits derived from distances of up to a few hundred kilometres. The most common Quaternary aeolian deposits, originating in the cold periglacial deserts principally during cold stages, are coversands and loess. Hot deserts were less important either as sources of silt ('hot loess') or as sites for deposition of aeolian dune sands; in fact, in most hot deserts, areas of aeolian erosion greatly exceed those of accumulation. Small accumulations of aeolian sand also originate in coastal regions by blowing of beach deposits; they are most abundant in areas of large tidal range where extensive littoral sediments are exposed to deflation at low tide.

Deposits of aeolian clay occur in parts of Australia, Texas, Senegal and Algeria. In southeastern parts of Australia, such as western Victoria and the riverine plain of New South Wales, they form dunes and thin sheets (Bowler 1973, Dare-Edwards 1984), and are known as parna or clay dunes. Many of the deposits lie on the down-wind side of lake basins and alluvial plains which dry out seasonally. Desiccation of the clayey lacustrine and alluvial sediments produces sand- and silt-sized pellets, which are then entrained and transported short distances by the wind. The clay is thus carried as aggregates rather than discrete clay-sized particles. Radiocarbon dating has shown that the main period of parna formation in Australia was between 10 000 and 20 000 years ago; this coincides with the last major glacial episode in other parts of the world, but in south-east Australia it was a time of marked aridity.

Surfaces from which sand and finer particles have been removed by the wind are known as deflation surfaces. They are often marked by a lag gravel, which may contain wind-faceted pebbles. These are shaped by abrasion, which produces one or more smooth surfaces inclined at a low angle rising down-wind. Typical wind-faceted pebbles have three abrasion surfaces (dreikanter). In both periglacial and hot deserts the lag gravel with wind-faceted stones may contribute to a dense stony mosaic on the ground surface, known as a desert pavement. Surface washing of fine particles by storm run-off, uplift of stones by shrink–swell movements in clay-enriched Bt soil horizons (see 3.2.1), and other processes are also involved in the formation of many desert pavements, however (Cooke 1970). Ventifacts include wind-faceted pebbles and cobbles, and also rock outcrops shaped (e.g. fretted) by aeolian abrasion.

2.3.3 Loess

Loess is probably the single most abundant Quaternary deposit on land. Keilhack (1920) estimated that it covers >26 million km^2 (about 20% of the earth's present land surface), but he was thinking only of fairly thick deposits, and if layers as thin as 20–30 cm are included, the total area would probably be more than twice his estimate. The thickest known loess deposits (up to 330 m) occur in northern China, and accumulations >200 m thick are known from Soviet Central Asia (Tadzhikistan and Uzbekistan). Deposits >15 m thick also occur in eastern Europe, central northern USA, Kashmir, the Siberian steppes and New Zealand. Thinner deposits are known from northwest Europe (including southern Britain), Spain, Italy, Yugoslavia, north Africa, Israel, Iran, Iraq, Saudi Arabia, Pakistan, south-east India, north-west USA (including Alaska), Canada, Mexico, south-west Greenland, Iceland, Argentina and western Australia (Fig. 2.19).

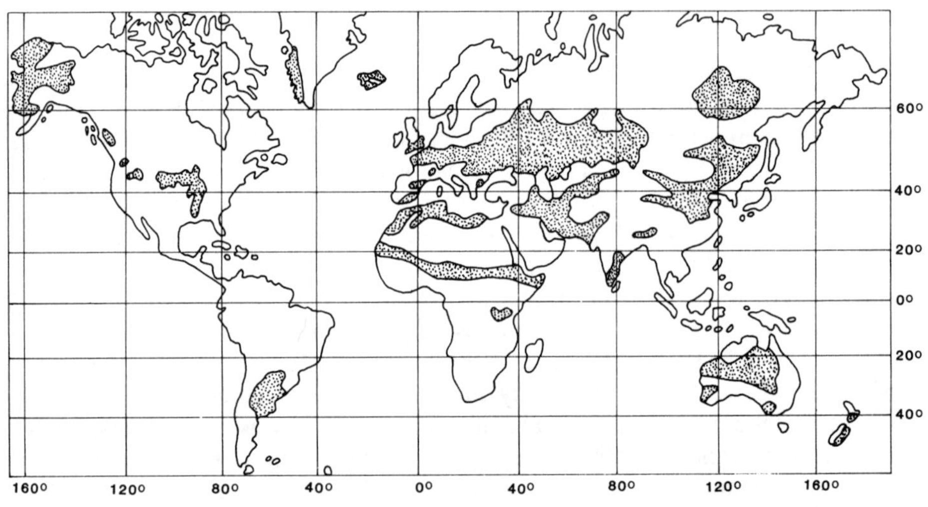

Fig. 2.19 — World distribuition of loess deposits (from various sources).

Loess is usually a yellowish calcareous silt, which is unconsolidated, unbedded and structureless when freshly cut, but often develops deep vertical fissures on exposure (Plate 3). It is characteristically a Quaternary material, though a few hard silty rocks (loessites) are known from the late Precambrian of Norway and some Upper Palaeozoic and Triassic formations (Edwards 1979). The carbonate content is usually 10–15%, but may exceed 40% in some Mediterranean and Middle Eastern accumulations which Smalley and Krinsley (1978) termed carbonate loess. The carbonate is either dispersed through the deposit as detrital silt particles, or secondarily concentrated as irregular brown nodules (loess dolls) or white coatings on the walls of fissures and fine cylindrical channels. The modal particle size is usually between 20 and 60 μm, the clay (<2 μm) content<20%, and sand (>63 μm) content <10% (Fig. 2.20). The bones of typical steppe animals (mammoth, reindeer, voles)

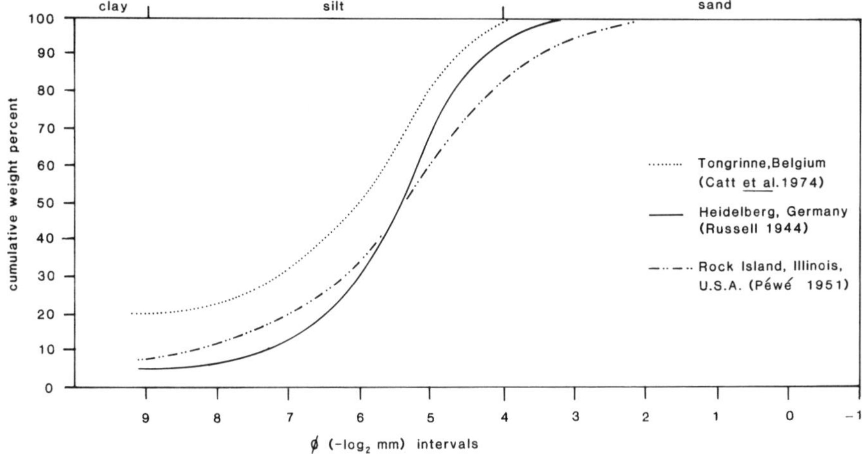

Fig. 2.20 — Particle size distribution of loess from three localities.

and shells of cold-tolerant terrestrial molluscs, such as *Pupilla muscorum, Columella columella, Vallonia costata* and *Cathaica pulveratrix* (Fig. 2.21), often indicate deposition on cold, dry land surfaces, though fossils suggesting other (e.g. fluvial) environments are occasionally present, and probably indicate secondary reworking.

Loess usually occurs at the surface, forming extensive blankets of fairly uniform thickness, which cover all but the most recent facets of the landscape and tend to smooth out any irregularities in the underlying surface. This implies quite recent deposition by wind, as no other transportation process can account for material of such uniform particle size distribution and thickness occurring in such diverse physiographic situations. The original surface of loess deposits is usually even, though dune-like features (pahas in USA and gredas in slavonic countries) occur occasionally, and a dense valley pattern (loess canyons) is often deeply incised into thick loess deposits (Bariss and Bronger 1981). Loess is in fact very prone to water erosion, because the low clay content allows disaggregation, and the dispersed silt particles are very easily moved by flowing water. However, it is less subject to wind erosion. This is because it is difficult for wind to entrain particles<80 μm unless they are disturbed by saltating sand grains, and in areas blanketed by thick loess deposits there are few sand grains available for entrainment. However, localized silt entrainment by wind may result from surface disturbance by vehicles or animals.

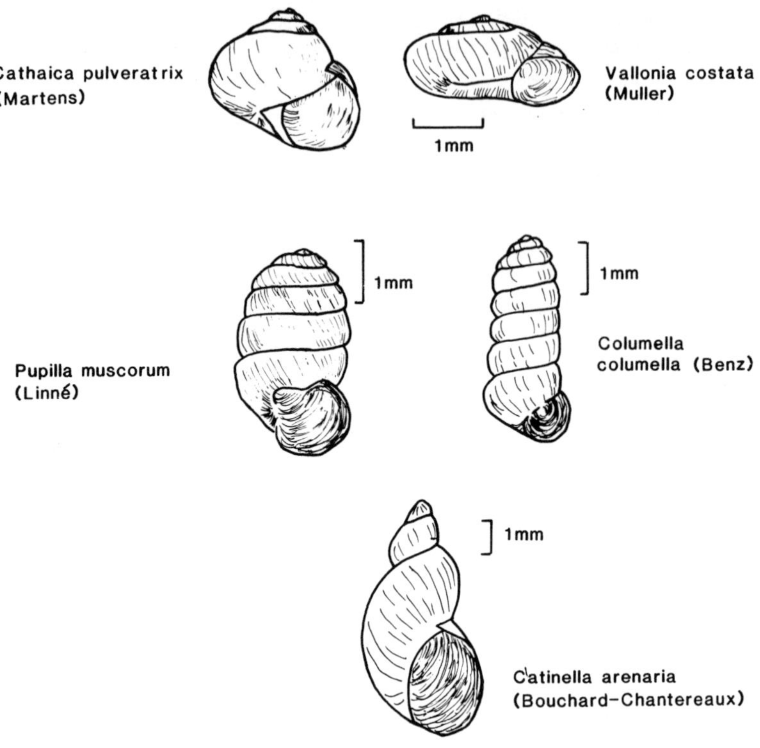

Fig. 2.21 — Typical loess molluscs.

Although loess is readily disaggregated by water, it is surprisingly firm when moist or dry, with the result that both naturally and artificially cut sections up to about 5 m high remain vertical indefinitely. Higher sections are less stable because the blocks separated by vertical tension cracks break away along inclined slip planes (Lohnes and Handy 1968). The firm consistence of loess has been attributed to secondary carbonate cementation (Snowden and Priddy 1968), but it is unlikely that this has more than local significance because it would not allow the rapid disaggregation on flooding that leads to intense fluvial incision. SEM examination of freshly broken surfaces of loess shows that the silt particles are often propped apart by clay bridges, in which the individual clay flakes are orientated perpendicular to the surfaces of the silt grains (Derbyshire and Mellors 1986). These give the deposit a stable but quite open structure, thus accounting for its characteristic low bulk density (usually 1.25–1.65 $g\,cm^{-3}$). It is likely that dispersion of the clay bridges on saturation allows the open structure to collapse and the material to flow under its own weight.

Loess deposits in many parts of the world have been dated by palaeomagnetism and, for the youngest loesses, by the radiocarbon and thermoluminescence methods. Buried soils provide the most convenient means of subdividing loess successions in many areas; they can also be dated palaeomagnetically, and often contain terrestrial molluscs indicating a warmer and more humid climate than during loess deposition.

In China (Heller and Liu Tungsheng 1984) and Soviet Central Asia (Dodonov 1984) the oldest loess layers are about 2.4 million years old from palaeomagnetic evidence (Fig. 2.22), and may therefore be late Pliocene rather than Pleistocene. However, these deposits are often redder and richer in clay than typical loess, and may be strongly weathered or reworked loess. Most of the typical loess in Asia and Europe is no older than about 1.0 million years (Pécsi 1984), and the most recent layers are clearly correlated with the later part of oceanic Stage 2 (24 000–12 000 years ago), the time when glaciers throughout the world were at their maximum extent. The youngest (Peoria) loess in USA is also dated by radiocarbon to the period between 25 000 and about 11 000 years ago (McKay 1979), and locally contains a buried soil (the Jules Soil of Frye *et al.* 1974) formed between 16 500 and 15 500 years ago. In central Europe, where the stratigraphy of loess, interbedded fluvial deposits and buried soils is now quite well known, loess layers deposited over the last 0.9 million years have been correlated with each of the cold oceanic isotopic stages between 2 and 22 (Fig. 1.10). The correlation of earlier loess-like layers in Europe and Asia with the oceanic sequence is not yet possible, mainly because the oceanic stages before about 1 million years ago are less well defined, but it is clear that most loess in regions away from the hot deserts of the world was deposited during the coldest periods of the Pleistocene. Deposits of 'hot loess' within and close to hot arid regions have not usually been so carefully dated or subdivided stratigraphically, but at Netivot in the Negev Desert (Israel) there is no clear relationship between loess deposition over the last 140 000 years and past cold periods (Fig. 2.23) (Bruins and Yaalon 1981). Indeed, the particle size and mineralogical similarities of the Negev loess to modern aeolian dust in the area (Yaalon and Ginzbourg 1966) suggest that it is still accumulating; the same is rarely true of loess in regions away from hot deserts.

2.3.4 Origin of loess

The origin of the abundant silt particles in loess has long been debated. Few sediment types are as rich in coarse silt (20–60 μm) as loess, and although this feature can be largely attributed to wind-sorting, there is so much loess in some regions that one or more distinctive Quaternary processes of silt production must be envisaged. Most of the silt particles are angular quartz fragments, and these were originally attributed to frost-shattering of the larger quartz grains found in other common sedimentary, igneous and metamorphic rock types (Wood 1882). Recent support for this idea has been given by Zeuner (1949), Moss *et al.* (1981), Konischev (1982) and Pye and Paine (1984), and it may well explain much of the loessial silt in areas such as northern China, which were often very cold during the Quaternary but not extensively glaciated. On the other hand, Smalley (1966) showed that glacial grinding of quartzose rocks can produce silt particles similar to those in loess, and the deposits of some modern glaciers, such as the Broggi Glacier in Peru (Manecki *et al.* 1980), contain abundant angular quartz silt. So it is very likely that much of the loess in Europe and USA contains silt grains derived from the large Pleistocene N. European and Laurentide ice caps. Silt-laden glacial outwash plains (sandar) are specially prone to seasonal wind erosion and dust-storms (Péwé 1951), and in some areas there is a strong mineralogical similarity between loess and glacial sediments of the same age (Catt *et al.* 1974).

To explain the small deposits of 'hot loess' in deserts, Smalley and Vita-Finzi

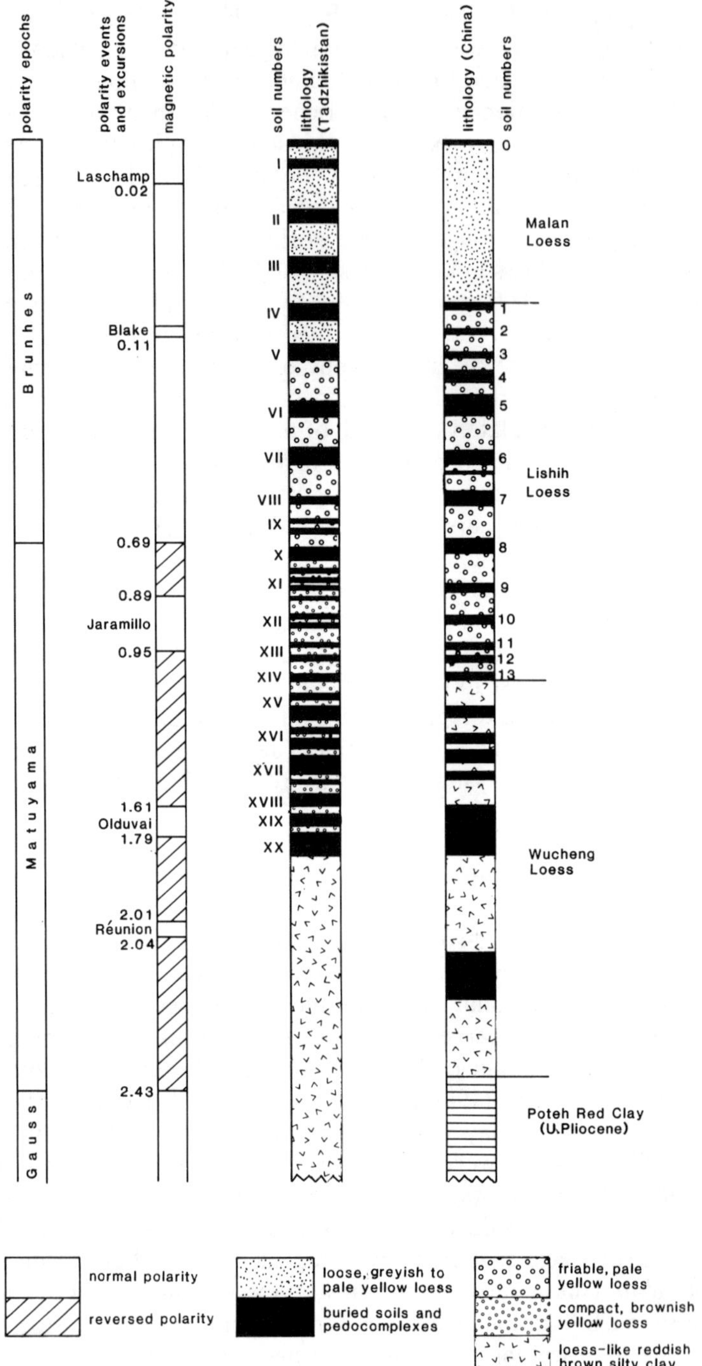

Fig. 2.22 — Loess sequences in Soviet Central Asia and China dated by palaeomagnetic measurements (from Dodonov 1981, and Heller and Liu Tungsheng 1984, by permission of the Royal Astronomical Society).

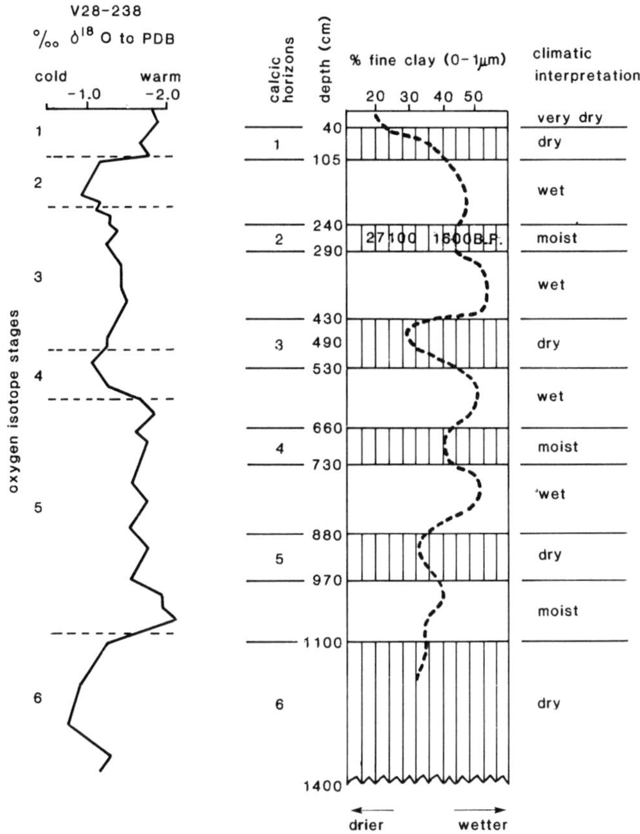

Fig. 2.23 — Sequence of loess and buried soils at Netivot, Israel (based partly on Bruins and Yaalon 1981).

(1968) suggested that spalling by grain-to-grain impacts of angular sand grains during aeolian transportation can produce quartz silt. Early aeolian abrasion experiments (Kuenen 1960) suggested that spalling gives little silt in the 20–60 μm range, though Whalley *et al.* (1982) did produce some in this way. Silt can also come from aqueous abrasion in rivers (Whalley 1979) and beaches, but most of this is <25 μm (Rogers *et al.* 1963). Quartz crystals often contain cracks and other defects, sometimes produced originally by the transformation from high- to low-temperature crystal forms during cooling of igneous rocks, and these can be exploited by various weathering processes to produce silt particles. In deserts an important physical weathering process known to produce silt by fracturing of larger grains is salt-weathering, that is the force exerted during crystallization of salts from solution (Goudie *et al.* 1979). In tropical and Mediterranean soils the same fractures may be exploited by chemical weathering (Nahon and Trompette 1982), dissolution occurring preferentially along the defects to divide a single sand grain into several angular silt particles. Finally, when weathered by either physical or chemical processes, schists provide another source of ready-made quartz silt particles.

Any of these processes could have been important locally in producing silt that was eventually incorporated into loess, but the main processes worldwide were probably frost-shattering and glacial crushing for periglacial loess and salt-weathering in the case of 'hot' or 'desert' loess. Frost-shattering was probably the dominant process in Asia, and glacial crushing the main process in producing silt for the loess of northern Europe and N. America.

Apart from aeolian sorting of the silt immediately before deposition, disaggregation and preliminary sorting by ephemeral streams is also an important part of loess formation in many areas. In deserts intermittent floods spread silt and clay across the floors of wadis and the surfaces of alluvial fans, and when the flood ceases a thin film of clay is often left on the surface above thicker layers of silt beneath. As this clay film dries to a crust, it cracks and curls, thus exposing the underlying silt to disturbance by saltating sand grains and to entrainment by the wind. Similarly, the role of meltwater in dispersing glacial debris and concentrating finer grains on the surfaces of proglacial outwash plains, where they are exposed to the wind, is perhaps as important in the formation of periglacial loess as the wind transportation itself.

Another important but controversial aspect of the origin of loess is the conditions in which it was deposited. The silt carried in suspension in the atmosphere was mainly deposited where winds slackened, and the deposit is consequently often thicker in the lee of bedrock and other obstacles. Rain or snow may occasionally have assisted deposition, but it is unlikely that rain played a major role in the accumulation of thick deposits, because frequent rainfall would remove the easily eroded silt directly into rivers and then into the sea. In fact many land areas notably devoid of loess, such as the coastal regions of western Europe, eastern and western USA, Japan and the humid tropics (Fig. 2.19), are those which probably enjoyed a wet oceanic climate throughout the Quaternary. The fine tubular concretions of secondary carbonate often seen in loess probably formed around the decaying rootlets of grasses and other plants, the above-ground parts of which could have helped trap the wind-borne dust. Also, accumulation of silt may have been assisted by adhesion to loess surfaces moistened by capillary rise (Cegla 1969), and most of the calcium in the carbonate concretions could have come in solutions rising from below by capillary action, assisted by fairly rapid evaporation from the surface. This suggests arid or semi-arid climatic conditions for loess accumulation. In parts of Asia, such as Kashmir and Soviet Central Asia, suitably arid conditions may have arisen when late Cenozoic tectonic activity produced mountain ranges which blocked the monsoon rains (Pye 1987).

Some carbonate concretions in loess are composed of calcium which has been leached downwards, but these are usually related to an episode of humid soil development long after deposition of the loess, because they are restricted to a fairly narrow horizon beneath decalcified layers. Many other concretions in loess are not so clearly associated with subsequent pedogenesis, and must be related to movement of groundwater during or soon after deposition. Smalley (1971) referred to these two types as 'contemporary' and 'original' accumulations respectively. Near the surface of accumulating loess, the increased carbon dioxide content resulting from oxidation of plant residues may have precipitated calcium from rising solutions to form the 'original' concretions.

The very porous nature of loess, with clay bridges propping coarser particles apart, leading to a tendency to collapse when saturated (hydroconsolidation), is similar to the structure of surface soil horizons, and may have originated by some processes to which soils are subject, such as penetration by plant roots, repeated freezing and thawing, or wetting and drying. Because of its environment of deposition, there is probably no part of any loess sequence which cannot be regarded as influenced by contemporaneous pedogenesis. To some extent the effects of soil development in a dry environment during deposition may be modified by diagenetic changes after burial (e.g. loss of organic matter by oxidation) or by later pedogenesis in a different environment consequent upon a climatic change. But it is likely that most of the important characteristics of loess are inherited from its origin as a terrestrial sediment, which was influenced throughout by a limited range of soil-forming processes because it was deposited slowly over quite long periods in a cold arid environment. This environment repeatedly characterized extensive mid-latitude regions during the Pleistocene, but is probably much more limited in extent today.

2.3.5 Aeolian sands

Periglacial aeolian sands or coversands are less widespread than loess, but do cover quite large areas of the Netherlands (Maarleveld 1960), Belgium (Paepe and Vanhoorne 1967) and England (Perrin *et al.* 1974, Wilson *et al.* 1981). In northern Belgium a wide area of coversands deposited mainly in the Weichselian is separated from a region of contemporaneous loess to the south by a narrow intermediate zone of mixed aeolian sand and silt known as sandloess. Thorez *et al.* 1970). Down-wind transitions from aeolian sand through sandloess to loess have also been reported from northern China, Israel and the USA. Pye (1987, p. 208) suggested that the intermediate sandloess deposits resulted from the transportation process known as modified saltation. Similar mixed deposits in England (Fig. 2.24) are often termed coverloam, but they are usually too thin to show whether the coversand and loess were deposited together, or at different times and then subsequently mixed by cryoturbation and other processes of superficial disturbance.

As sand is blown much shorter distances than silt, the occurrence of coversands depends upon local sources of sand. In modern periglacial environments, such as arctic Canada (Good and Bryant 1985), the source is often the glaciofluvial or fluvial sands deposited by seasonal streams, and repeated fluvial and aeolian reworking leads to mixed sand bodies in which cross-stratified fluvial sands merge laterally into planar bedded aeolian sands, the latter often containing deflation horizons with ventifacts. The flat bedding, ripple lamination or faint crinkly stratification seen in many coversands probably originates by alternate deflation of dry sand above a wetting front and slow accretion of sand, which adheres to a surface moistened by capillary rise from a water-table or a thawing layer of subsurface permafrost. Adhesion of saltating sand to a moist surface (the ‘fly-paper mechanism’) is known to produce flat or crinkly lamination (Kocurek and Fielder 1982). If the land surface is persistently damp, the amount of sand available for aeolian transport is limited, and this inhibits dune formation. As some capillary rise can occur in most fine to medium sands (Trewzecki 1972), dunes are unlikely to form in coversand subject to permafrost, because seasonal thawing of ground ice moistens the sand surface. The inland dunes on some coversands in Europe may therefore have formed in a late episode

Fig. 2.24 — Distribution of loess, coversand and coverloam in England and Wales, based upon Soil Survey of England and Wales (1983) Copyright Cambridge University Press.

after the disappearance of permafrost but before the sand surface was stabilised by growth of vegetation.

Coversand is usually yellow (Plate 4), unfossiliferous and moderately well or well sorted (Fig. 2.25), though usually not quite as well sorted as coastal dune sands, which are often derived from well-sorted beach sand. A lack of bedding in some coversands may result from disturbance by frost or plant roots soon after deposition, or from deposition with snow (niveo-aeolian sand). The mean particle size of coversand is usually between 0.1 and 0.4 mm, depending on sources and wind strength; some niveo-aeolian sands are much coarser and poorly sorted, however (Ballantyne and Whittington 1987).

Aeolian sands of Quaternary age are also common in low-latitude desert regions. Because of the frequent migration of climatic zones during the Quaternary, many subaerial dunes formed in hot deserts in earlier periods are now stable or even

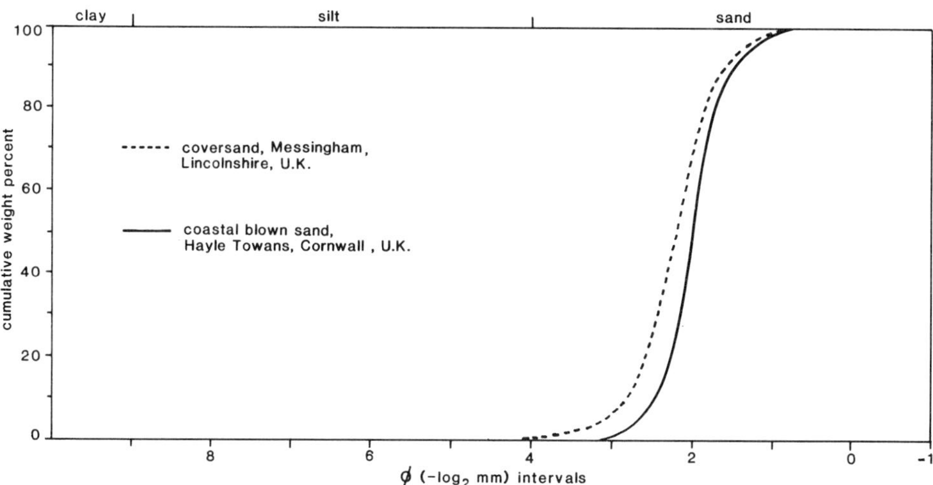

Fig. 2.25 — Particle size distributions of coversand (data kindly provided by L. C. George) and coastal blown sand.

covered with vegetation, as for example in parts of Africa (Grove 1969, Fryberger 1980), Australia (Mabbutt 1977) and USA (Smith 1965). Their occurrence, and thus the former extent of arid zones, is usually most clearly indicated by aerial photographs or satellite imagery.

2.4 EROSION AND DEPOSITION ON SUBAERIAL SLOPES

Many Quaternary deposits result from down-slope movement of unconsolidated sediments, loose fragments of hard bedrock or soil materials. Various processes are involved in both cold and temperate climatic conditions. They are usually divided into processes in which particles are transported in a dispersed or largely dispersed state, and processes involving movement of material *en masse* (i.e. mass wasting). Transportation of dispersed particles depends upon an abundance of surface water (runoff) and is typical of humid, hot or temperate regions. In contrast, mass wasting of various types occurs in many different climatic zones. It includes rapid movements along a limited number of shear surfaces (landslides), and slow movement by viscous flow or shear distributed over numerous planes (creep). Slope deposits may therefore show any degree of structural reorganization from almost none (landslides of coherent rock) to development of a completely new set of spatial relationships between the primary particles (as in colluvium or hillwash). As a result some have few or no lithological features distinguishing them from source materials up-slope.

2.4.1 Soil erosion by runoff

Down-slope movement of particles in a dispersed state results from the two stage process of (a) detachment of individual primary particles from the aggregates occurring in most soils, and (b) their transport down-slope by runoff, or that part of the rainfall flowing over the surface because it is in excess of the infiltration capacity of the soil (Morgan 1986). Detachment results mainly from raindrop impact, and to a lesser extent from runoff itself, especially where this is concentrated into rills or gullies. Flow velocities in rills are typically 0.5–1.0 m sec^{-1}, and raindrop velocities may reach 9 m sec^{-1}, both of which are sufficient to detach particles, especially in sandy or silty soils with little clay, humus or other interparticle binding agents. However, the flow rates in shallow sheets of runoff with infinite width (overland flow or sheet flow) are typically 0.01 m sec^{-1}, which is too low for detachment. Rills can be obliterated by cultivation or natural disturbance of the soil surface; if they develop into more permanent features, they are termed gullies (with ephemeral streams) or river channels (with permanent streams). The distinction between rill erosion and interrill erosion by overland flow may be difficult to make, because lines of concentrated flow often develop within thin sheets before any rills appear (Moss *et al.* 1982). The critical flow velocity required to entrain detached particles is usually least for a grain size of 0.2 mm (Savat 1982), though it decreases slightly for particles <0.2 mm in cohesionless soils.

Once entrained, particles are transported until the flow velocity falls below the value for settling under gravity, which according to Stokes' Law depends mainly on the particle size. As a result there is a marked sorting effect on eroded particles, coarse sand being deposited near the slope foot, where there is an initial check to the flow velocity in rills and gullies, fine sand and silt being carried further, and clay often failing to settle until the water stagnates in a temporary or permanent lake.

Soil erodibility (resistance to erosion) is very variable, and depends upon particle size distribution, infiltration capacity and the strength of interparticle bonds. The most erodible soils are often those with a high (>40%) silt content (Richter and Negendank 1977), low organic matter content (<2% organic C), or low (<30%) clay content (Evans 1980), because their aggregates are weakly bound and easily break down to the constituent primary particles. However, the stability of soil aggregates also depends upon their water content, the mineralogical composition of the clay, the cations dissolved in the water and occurring at exchange sites on the clays, the occurrence of cementing agents such as iron oxides or calcium carbonate, and the activities of soil organisms.

Indices of soil erodibility are based either on measures of some or all of these properties, or on the response of soil to natural or simulated rainfall (Bryan 1968, Wischmeier *et al.* 1971, Wischmeier and Smith 1978). A widely used soil erodibility index (K) is measured in the field from the amount of soil lost (from a bare plot 22 m long and of 5° slope) per unit of EI_{30} (the kinetic energy of the maximum 30-minute intensity of a rainstorm). K can also be estimated from the soil's particle size distribution, organic matter content, structure and permeability, using the nomograph in Fig. 2.26, though the agreement between measured and estimated values is better for some soil types than others, and for some climatic regions than others. With some soils it is even difficult to predict soil behaviour from measured values of K. For example, there are often complex interactions between clays and soil water of different compositions (Thornes 1980). Clays generally lose strength with increasing water content, but some can hydrate and gain strength through hydrogen bonding (thixotropic behaviour). In smectite clays, replacement of adsorbed calcium and magnesium by sodium increases swelling and the likelihood of aggregate collapse, but this effect is counteracted if the total ion concentration in the water is increased (Arulanandan *et al.* 1975).

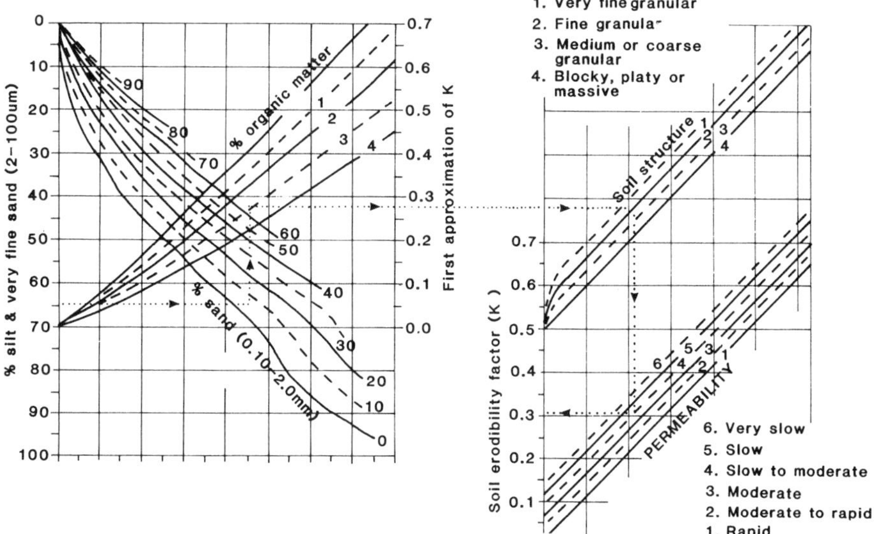

Fig. 2.26 — Nomograph for estimating soil erodibility (K) (from Wischmeier *et al.* 1971). With appropriate data, enter scale at left and proceed to points representing the soil's sand (0.10–2.0 mm) percentage, organic matter content, structure and permeability, in that order. The dotted line illustrates procedure for a soil with 65% silt plus very fine sand (2–100 μm), 5% sand (0.10–2.0 mm), 2.8% organic matter, fine granular structure, and slow to moderate permeability: result K=0.31.

Soil properties often vary with depth below the surface, and infiltration capacity as a factor in erodibility may be limited by a particular horizon with low permeability. Such horizons may be inherited from the geological history of deposition at the site (e.g. less permeable clay underlying a more permeable loamy surface deposit), from long-term pedological processes (e.g. a less permeable clay-enriched Bt horizon beneath a clay-depleted E horizon), from incorrect cultivation procedures (e.g. a less permeable plough pan or surface layer compacted by heavy machinery), or from formation of a less permeable surface crust. On fine sandy or silty soils with a weak structure because of insufficient clay and organic matter, raindrop impact on a previously saturated surface causes collapse and dispersion of aggregates (Farres 1978); clay particles rise to the surface and the dispersed silt or fine sand particles beneath are rearranged into a closely packed layer. As the soil dries out afterwards, these two layers contract into a hard crust 1–3 mm thick, which is much less permeable than the original surface (Morin *et al.* 1981), and is often the main cause of erosion of silty (e.g. loess) soils.

The rate of soil erosion depends upon the erosivity of rainfall, the slope geometry, and its plant cover, as well as the erodibility of the soil. According to Morgan (1986), two types of rainfall event are strongly erosive: (a) short intense storms which exceed the infiltration capacity of the soil, and (b) longer, low-intensity storms which saturate the soil. In some circumstances antecedent precipitation may therefore be important in that it determines how near to saturation the soil is before a storm arrives. Estimates of the minimum rainfall intensity required to cause erosion range from 25 mm hr^{-1} (Hudson 1981) to as little as 2 mm hr^{-1} if the soil has previously developed an impermeable crust (Fullen 1985). The relationship between erosion and slope is expressed by the equation:

$$Q_s \propto \tan^m\theta \, L^n$$

where Q_s is soil lost per unit area, θ is the gradient angle, and L is the slope length. In the USA, Zingg (1940) found that $m = 1.4$ and $n = 0.6$. These values seem to be valid in many situations, but they are probably affected by rainfall intensity, soil particle size distribution, plant cover, and slope shape. D'Souza and Morgan (1976) obtained m values of 0.14 for concave slopes, 0.4 for straight slopes and 0.5 m for convex slopes.

A vegetation cover usually decreases erosion by intercepting raindrops, improving soil structure and infiltration rates, providing a protective cover of litter on the soil surface, binding the soil with roots, and decreasing the velocity of any runoff. However, a tall tree canopy can increase the kinetic energy of light rainfall by allowing the small drops to coalesce into large drips, and this can increase erosion if the surface is not protected by a continuous litter layer (Mosley 1982, Wiersum 1985).

2.4.2 Hillwash deposits

The footslope colluvium or hillwash deposit resulting from repeated runoff and erosion events is usually unbedded, though it may contain diffuse lines of stones, and horizons containing charcoal, terrestrial gastropods or human artifacts can help date the main episodes of deposition (Bell 1983). There is often an irregular distribution of organic matter with depth, either because of irregular erosion of topsoil and subsoil up-slope or because of stable episodes when humus accumulated *in situ*. In colluvium derived from loess the different effects of rainsplash and sheetflow have been distinguished by micromorphological studies (Mücher and De Ploey 1977, Mücher *et al.* 1981). In many temperate regions, deposition of colluvium occurred during the main episodes of arable farming from the Neolithic onwards, because it depended mainly on erosion of disturbed soil on slopes with little stabilizing vegetation cover. Colluvium becomes finer down-slope and may eventually interdigitate with bedded alluvial or lacustrine deposits, though it is often deposited against minor obstacles such as walls, hedges, earthbanks or river levées. The flat or gently sloping surfaces built up by deposition are included in the features known as lynchets; however, other areas of decreased slope occur in eroded sites, forming negative lynchets, as opposed to positive lynchets in depositional sites (Fig. 2.27), or where a slope was deliberately terraced to assist cultivation and prevent erosion (strip lynchets).

2.4.3 Mass movement

Slow down-slope movement of soil or incoherent sediment *en masse*, without significant disaggregation and dispersion of individual particles but often incorporating small pieces of hard rock, occurs by two main processes: creep, and flow or solifluction. These depend mainly on seasonal fluctuations in ground temperature and moisture content. Creep involves the upward heaving of material at right angles to a slope and subsequent collapse under gravity (Fig. 2.28), so that a small net down-

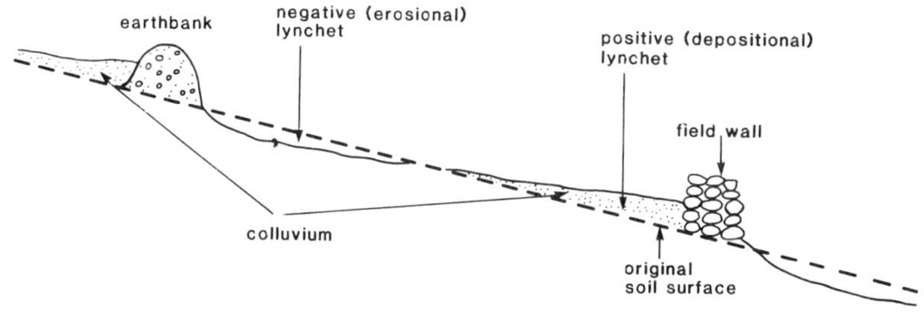

Fig. 2.27 — Formation of positive and negative lynchets.

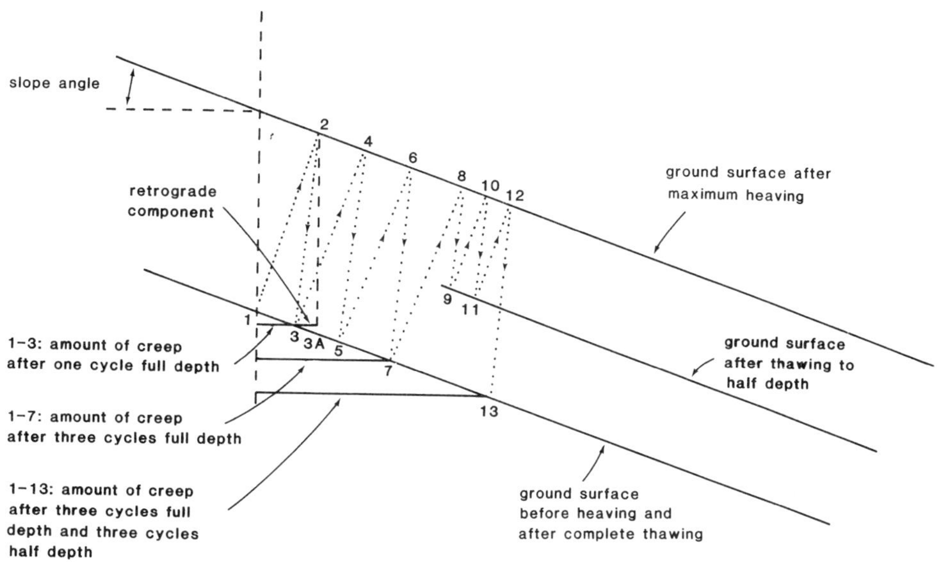

Fig. 2.28 — Down-slope creep of particles during freeze–thaw cycles: 1–3A — one cycle maximum potential movement; 1–3 — one cycle actual movement; 1–7 — three cycles to full depth; 1–13 — three cycles to full depth followed by three cycles to half depth (from Washburn 1979).

slope movement is achieved (Washburn 1979, p. 198). The initial heaving can occur in temperate climatic conditions by soil disturbance (faunal activity, tree-fall, soil cultivation) and possibly also by expansion during the wetting of clays. However, because of cohesion in clays, swelling and shrinking may cause little down-slope movement; when it shrinks the soil merely retraces the swelling movement perpendicular to the slope. Heaving can also occur in arctic climates, particularly by the formation of pipkrake (needles of ice developing just below and elongated perpendicular to the surface) and by frost-heaving (increase of volume on freezing, especially when water is drawn to the freezing front from below). On slopes composed principally of coarse rock material (e.g. screes), down-slope movement may also result from repeated daily thermal expansion and contraction of blocks; movement involving coarse particles with little or no matrix of fine earth (<2 mm) is often termed talus creep.

Solifluction or flow of water-saturated soil (Andersson 1906), usually over a low permeability layer beneath, can also occur in various climates. In tropical regions it often affects deep soil mantles over less permeable bedrock, which have been saturated by intense rainstorms. In periglacial regions the impermeable layer is usually the permafrost table (see 2.8.1), and the mobile layer is the thawed surface layer (or active layer), 1–2 m thick and saturated with meltwater from snow or ground ice. Dylik (1951) suggested the term congeliflaction for this movement over permafrost. However, solifluction can also occur during the thawing of seasonally frozen surface layers (i.e. frozen subsoil does not persist through the summer), and Baulig (1956) used gelifluction to include both types of solifluction in cold regions. In practice, solifluction (viscous flow) usually occurs in conjunction with other processes of erosion, such as runoff, creep and various types of more rapid but localized mass movement such as mudflows, but the resulting heterogeneous deposits are most conveniently described as solifluction deposits. In periglacial regions the combined movement of material by gelifluction and frost creep may reach 1 m per year, though it is spasmodic. It has been observed on slopes as gentle as 1–1.5°, and is more widespread in maritime than continental periglacial regions. Temperate or tropical solifluction probably occurs only on steeper slopes than this. Where flow is the main process, the rate of movement decreases with depth below the surface.

Solifluction deposits are extremely variable in composition, reflecting the nature of the source materials up-slope, and therefore cannot be correlated from site to site on lithological properties. Larger clasts are often orientated with their longest axes parallel to the slope (Harris 1981), but this may be replaced down-slope by a transverse preferred orientation near the margin of the deposit. There is often a crude stratification parallel to the slope, and small folds (drag structures), sometimes overturned down-slope, or rolled masses of different materials may occur. The deposits form thin sheets with steep lobate or tongued margins (Plate 5), especially in periglacial regions (Benedict 1976).

Most of the deposits mapped as 'head' or 'trail' in Britain (Fig. 2.29) have a gelifluction origin, though some may be periglacial mudflows (Catt 1987, Harris 1987). The clasts are often angular because of frost-shattering, and frost structures, such as involutions and ice-wedge casts, are common. Although initially vertical, the wedges may be distorted or inclined with their broader tops down-slope because of renewed movement after they were formed. Gelifluction deposits in southern England composed mainly of frost-shattered chalk are termed Coombe Deposits; they occur extensively on the floors of dry chalkland valleys and also form aprons and fans at the foot of the Chalk scarp (Horton *et al.* 1981). As in other gelifluction deposits, loess deposited just before or during the episode of slope movement is often a subsidiary constituent, and fossil snails indicate dry and very cold conditions.

In some upland areas the gelifluction deposits derived partly from coarsely jointed bedrock (e.g. granite) and lying on moderate or steep slopes are often later eroded by runoff, which removes fine (often sandy or silty) constituents to leave a

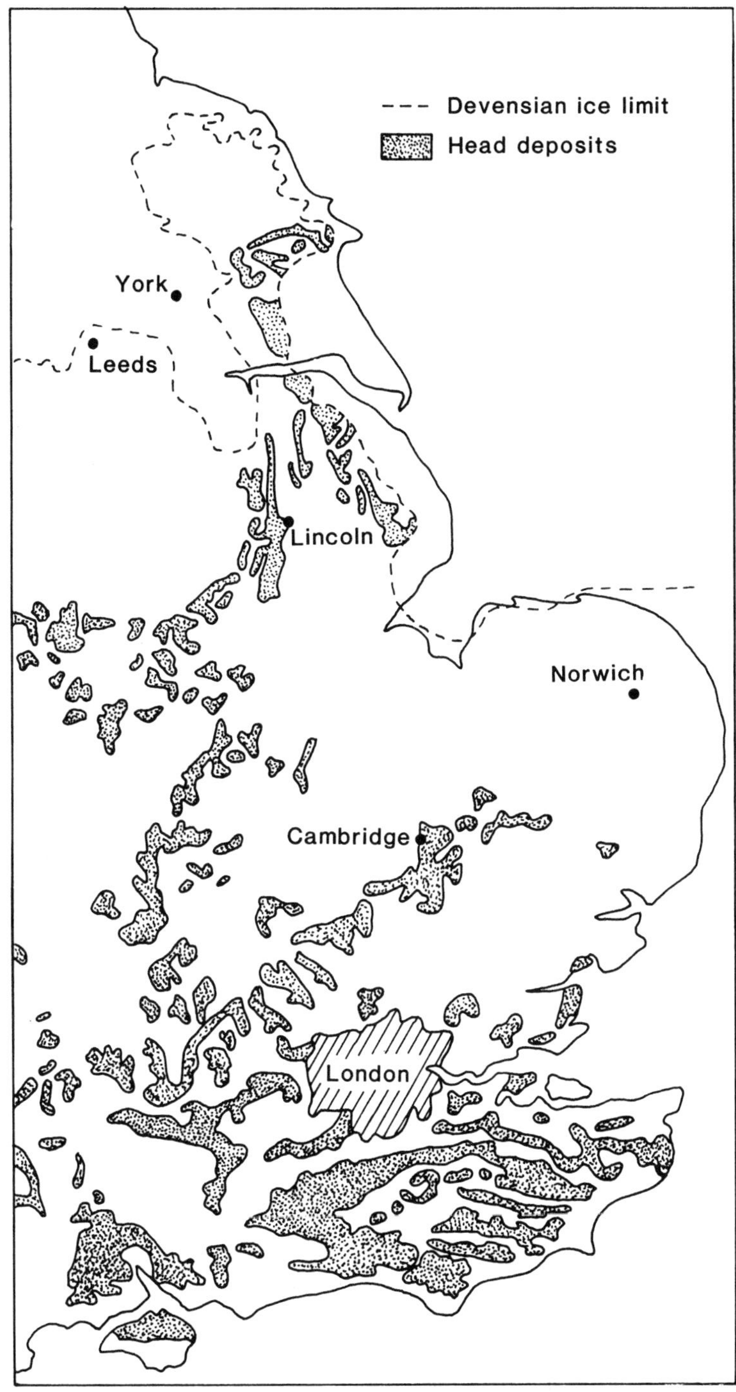

Fig. 2.29 — Distribution of head in eastern England, based upon mapping by Soil Survey of England and Wales (1983) (from Catt 1987).

surface residue of large angular blocks. Some of the blocks are also lifted to the surface by frost-heaving, a periglacial process by which stones are raised as much as the fine matrix when freezing occurs, but are prevented from returning to their original position because cavities beneath them are filled with matrix that is either heaved laterally or thaws and slumps before the stones are released by thawing. The areas covered by these blocks are termed block fields, and may resemble scree surfaces, but are usually less steep and unlike screes are not backed by a vertical bedrock cliff. On the summit areas, eroded cores of undisturbed bedrock may be left as upstanding blocks or tors (Plate 6).

Rock glaciers (White 1976) are tongue-shaped masses of angular frost-shattered rock occurring in mountain areas, such as the central Andes and Swiss Alps. They resemble small valley glaciers but have no ice visible on the surface. Active examples move slowly downhill, usually at rates of <1 m per year, and have a core of either fairly clean ice or mixed coarse and fine rock debris with interstitial ice. Those with a core of clear ice may be true glaciers covered with an unusually thick layer of coarse ablation till, but this is an unlikely origin for most rock glaciers because they do not produce meltwater or the proglacial outwash trains typical of valley glaciers. The surface of a rock glacier is usually a series of arcuate ridges resulting from the down-slope flow, and the margins are steep.

Rapid mass movements include down-slope movements along a shear plane which is either shallow and approximately parallel to the land surface (translational landslides) or deeper-seated and curved (rotational landslides), rapid sudden flows of saturated fine soil or sediment (mudflows) or stony material (debris flows), avalanches, and free fall under gravity from a very steep or vertical rock face (rockfalls, screes). Movement usually occurs spasmodically and over a more limited area than slower mass movements.

Landslides and rockfalls involve masses of hard rock or cohesive sediment, which are not changed in character by the movement and do not contribute to recognizably new sediments. Many occur on surfaces over-steepened by excavation or glacial erosion (e.g. the sides of glaciated valleys). Translational slides occur in rock masses cut by faults, steep bedding planes or master joints, and in soft sediments along planes of weakness such as the boundary between sand and wet clay. Many translational slides in temperate regions originated as gelifluction deposits in earlier cold periods, their reactivation resulting from loading of the upper part or excavation and unloading of the toe of the gelifluction lobe. Rotational slides (Fig. 2.30) are common in clays, and are often preceded by development of steeply inclined tension cracks at the top of the slope; they may be triggered by loading of the top or unloading of the slope foot (e.g. by marine or fluvial erosion).

Individual rockfalls may consist of blocks of almost any size, depending on the spacing of planes of weakness and the extent of physical weathering processes such as frost-shattering. Steep slopes cut in well-fissured rock produce large amounts of fairly small blocks, especially when subject to intense frost action; some massive, poorly fissured rocks may produce rockfalls only when affected by frost. Most large screes or taluses on natural slopes in temperate regions were therefore formed mainly during earlier episodes of cold climate; in Britain, for example, active talus formation is probably limited to upland areas in the north (Ballantyne 1987). Taluses contain angular blocks which often become larger down-slope, and the foot of the

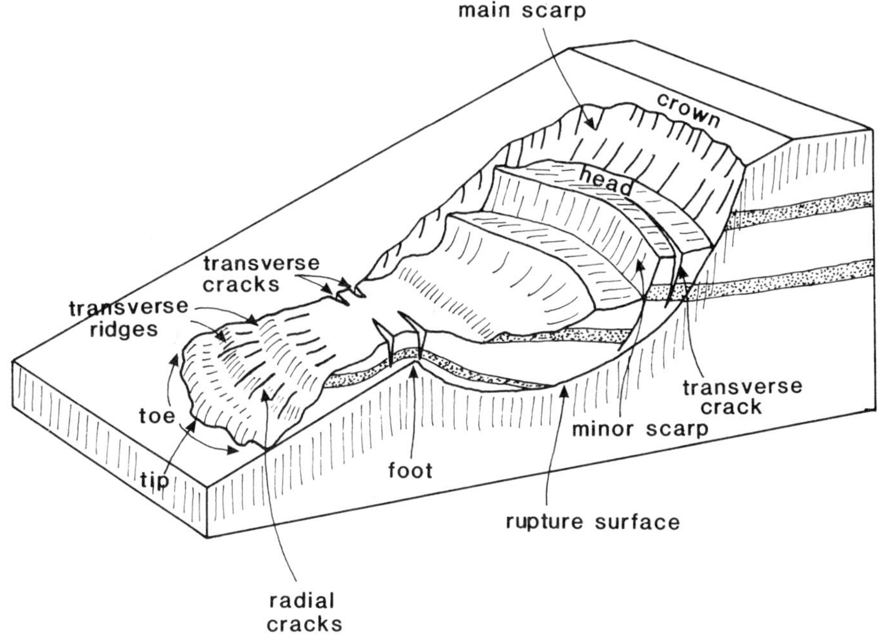

Fig. 2.30 — Features of rotational landslide (from Varnes 1958).

scree may be built into an arcuate ridge or protalus rampart composed of blocks which have slid over winter snowpatches (Washburn 1979, p. 234). Stratification is usually absent, but some fine screes composed of flat shale or slate fragments (grèzes litées) are quite well stratified, with interbedded coarse and fine layers dipping at up to 30° parallel to the slope. These probably result from seasonal redistribution of the fallen rock fragments by sliding, creep and sheetwash, processes resulting from the slow permeability of the material. Screes derived from less fissile bedrock show less evidence of later movement following the initial free fall under gravity, though a little creep, rolling or sliding of blocks may occur.

Mudflows are rapid down-slope movements of clay-rich sediment saturated with water from rain or melting snow (Gascoyne 1978). Overconsolidated clays may contribute to mudflows if they are exposed to alternate wet and dry conditions; desiccation is necessary for these sediments to crack and form small fragments, which disaggregate and make a plastic paste on rewetting. Unvegetated slopes are more prone to mudflows than those with a stabilizing cover of grass, shrubs or trees. Consequently they were much more extensive during cold periods of the Quaternary when there was little vegetation. They are normally initiated on steep (>30°) slopes, but once mobile they can probably spread several kilometres over even more gentle slopes than gelifluction deposits. Most mudflows are thin (<1.5 m) and tongue-shaped because they are directed along a pre-existing valley, but valley-side mudflows are thicker and wider; both can have a fairly steep and high (up to 5 m) lobate margin. Although movement is quite rapid (5–100 m sec^{-1}), the mud is usually fairly dense and viscous (Rodine and Johnson 1976), and can carry a load of quite large stones. Flows with coarse constituents are termed debris flows (Hampton 1975). Despite this load-carrying ability, mudflows and debris flows accomplish little or no erosion. Lighter clasts may rise to the surface during flow and form a stony crust on the stabilized deposit. The most extensive debris flows are volcanic in origin (lahars); these are several metres thick, 50–100 km long, and often contain blocks up to 3 m across.

Peat accumulations occurring on slopes even as gentle as 2° are likely to flow or slide downhill, especially after heavy rain or following removal of the down-slope margin by fluvial erosion or peat-cutting. In Ireland these have been termed bog flows or bog bursts (Alexander *et al.* 1986).

On steep mountain slopes avalanches containing snow, ice, earth and rock debris occur when the slope can no longer support the increasing weight of fallen snow, especially in spring when melting begins, or when it is disturbed by earthquakes. Movement initially involves free fall, flow and sliding, but often becomes so rapid on long slopes (>300 km hr^{-1}) that the mixture is fluidized by or supported on a cushion of trapped air (Shreve 1966, Kent 1966). Narrow erosion scars are produced down the slope, and the debris is deposited at the slope foot as a tongue-shaped mass of porous ill-sorted material containing large angular blocks; this may extend across a valley floor and even some distance up the opposing valley side (Rapp 1959). In these avalanche boulder tongues the blocks are deposited within snow, and are consequently left resting precariously on one another when the snow melts.

2.5 FLUVIAL PROCESSES

A larger proportion of the earth's present-day land surface is influenced by rivers than any other means of erosion. Rivers drain almost 70% of the land area, and move a total volume of water per year equivalent to a layer 28 cm deep over the entire land surface. They carry at least 15×10^9 tonnes of solid and dissolved material from the land to the sea each year (Milliman and Meade 1983), which is enough to lower the entire land surface of the earth by approximately 1 m every 15 000 years. However, individual river basins have calculated denudation rates ranging from 1 m 1000 yr^{-1} to 1 m 100 000 yr^{-1} (Corbel 1959). Erosion is much greater in mountain regions than in lowlands (Stoddart 1969), and also in areas with extensive loess deposits such as south-east Asia and southern USA (Strakhov 1967). Suspended sediment is greater in tropical than temperate or arctic regions, but tropical rivers carry less in solution than temperate rivers, probably because the soils are older and more strongly weathered and leached (Gibbs 1970). Fig. 2.31 shows the regional variation in annual sediment load of rivers. Because of human activities leading to extensive soil erosion, present rates of fluvial erosion may be greater than in the past, though the generally lower sea level during the Quaternary may also have increased rates of erosion over those of earlier periods.

Rivers, transferring water from the continents to the oceans, are supplied by flow from the ground surface (runoff), from the soil and rocks via springs, from the meltwater of glaciers and from the overflow of lakes. Thus river flow is not necessarily immediately related to precipitation, in particular because there is often a delay after precipitation while groundwater is being recharged before it contributes to spring flow. Once water infiltrates the soil it flows vertically down to the saturated

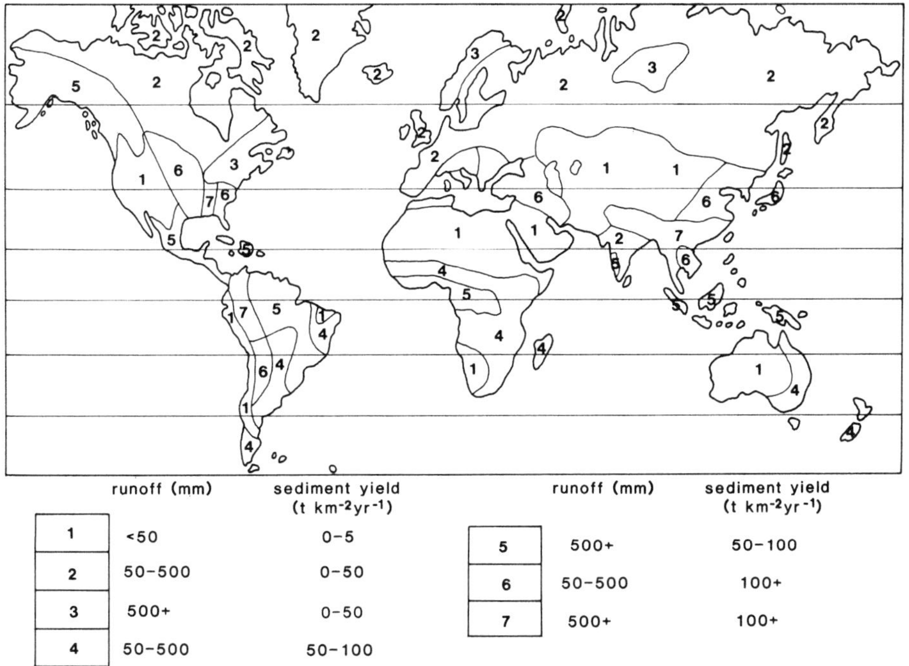

Fig. 2.31 — World rivers classified by sediment load (from Petts 1984). Reprinted by permission of John Wiley & Sons Ltd.

zone at the water table or flows laterally through the unsaturated zone above (Fig. 2.32), either in soil horizons close to the surface (throughflow) or in deeper aerated layers between the soil and the water table (interflow). On hill-slopes in humid temperate areas, throughflow is probably the most important way in which water is transferred from precipitation into rivers (Kirkby 1969).

2.5.1 River erosion

Once water is flowing in a permanent or ephemeral channel it is capable of various erosional processes (Schumm 1977). These include abrasion by particles suspended in the water (corrasion), the pressure of air and water driven along planes of weakness to lift rock or soft sediment from the channel floor and sides (evorsion), cavitation by the implosion of bubbles in foam produced by turbulent flow, and dissolution of soluble rock materials (corrosion), especially by aggressive acidic water which has passed through peat or other acidic soils. The particles in a river channel are moved either in suspension or as a coarser bed-load rolling or saltating along the bed. As the flow velocity increases, larger particles are incorporated into the bed-load and finer parts of the bed-load are transferred to suspension. Variations in discharge (volume of flow per unit time) and flow velocity, which determine the total amount of sediment moved by the river, depend on rates of water supply to the basin (mainly precipitation), rates of runoff, throughflow, interflow and groundwater flow, and various characteristics of the drainage basin itself. Characteristics

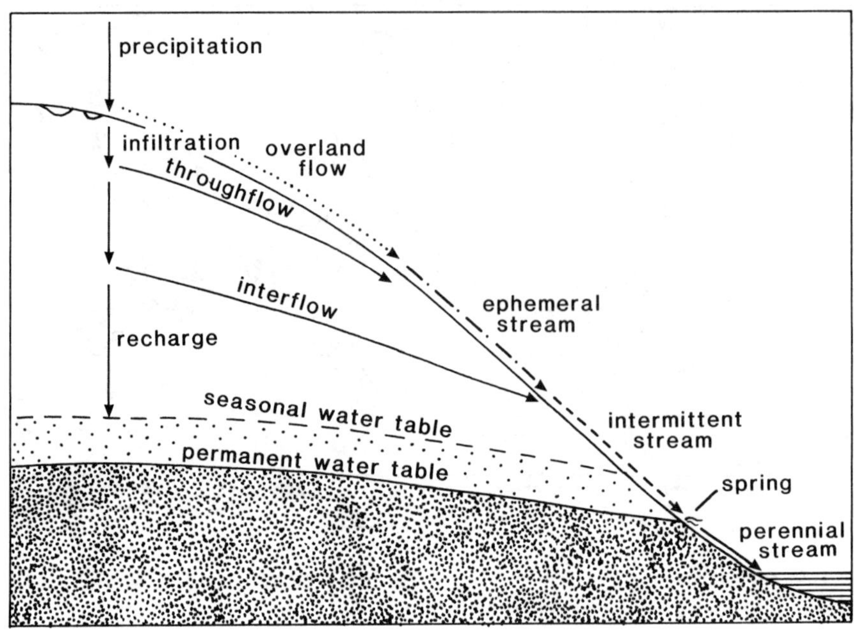

Fig. 2.32 — Water flow routes into a drainage basin (from Derbyshire *et al.* 1979). Reproduced by permission of Butterworth and Co. (Publishers) Ltd.

such as the nature of rocks and soils within the basin, the vegetation and land use mainly influence the different types of flow before water enters the river, but other (morphometric) basin characteristics affect flow within the river.

The morphometric variables of drainage basins are topographic attributes of the basin as a whole, of its total channel network or of individual parts of channels. The basin itself is delimited by a watershed line drawn from large-scale maps with closely spaced topographic contours or from aerial photographs. This gives the basin area (Horton 1945), basin perimeter (Smith 1950), basin relief (Strahler 1952), basin length (Schumm 1956), basin width (Doornkamp and King 1971) and relief ratio (basin relief/basin length) (Schumm 1956). The channel pattern is then drawn from streams mapped in the field, and segments of channels are ordered. Various methods of ordering have been suggested (Gregory and Walling 1973, pp. 41–5), but the one most commonly used is that of Strahler (1957): all fingertip tributaries are designated 1st-order streams; two 1st-order streams unite to form a 2nd-order stream segment, two 2nd orders to form a 3rd order, etc. (Fig. 2.33). From this the number and length of 1st-, 2nd-, 3rd-order, etc., segments, the total length of the net, and length ratios of each order (Horton 1945) may be calculated. Other important factors are the bifurcation ratio (ratio of number of segments of a given order to that of the next higher order), stream frequency (total number of segments per unit of basin area), mean link length (total length of net divided by number of links), drainage density (total length of net divided by basin area), lemniscate ratio (basin length^2 divided by $4 \times$ basin area) (Chorley *et al.* 1957), basin elongation (diameter of circle with same

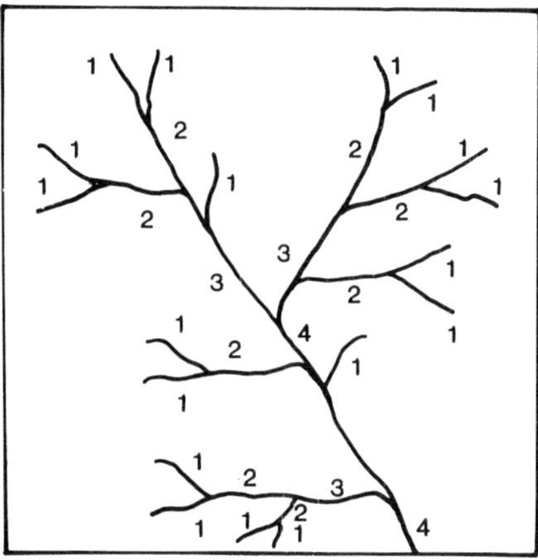

Fig. 2.33 — Method of stream ordering (from Strahler 1957).

area as basin divided by basin length) (Schumm 1956), and ruggedness number (drainage density × basin relief divided by 528) (Strahler 1958). All these variables can be used for comparison of basins.

Drainage density increases with increasing precipitation, with decreasing vegetation density, or decreasing permeability of surface deposits, and reaches a maximum in badlands (Smith 1958). Strahler (1957) suggested classes of drainage densities (Table 2.3), but much depends on the methods used to measure channel length; a 'blue-line' density based on streams marked on published maps is often slightly less than one based on field observations and considerably less than one based on contour crenulations (i.e. including dry valleys), especially in limestone areas.

Table 2.3 — Classes of drainage density (Strahler 1957)

Density Class	km/km^2
Coarse	<5.0
Medium	5.0–13.7
Fine	13.7–155.3
Ultrafine	>155.3

The overall shape of the drainage network within a basin is difficult to quantify, and has usually been described in qualitative terms (Fig. 2.34). However, preferred

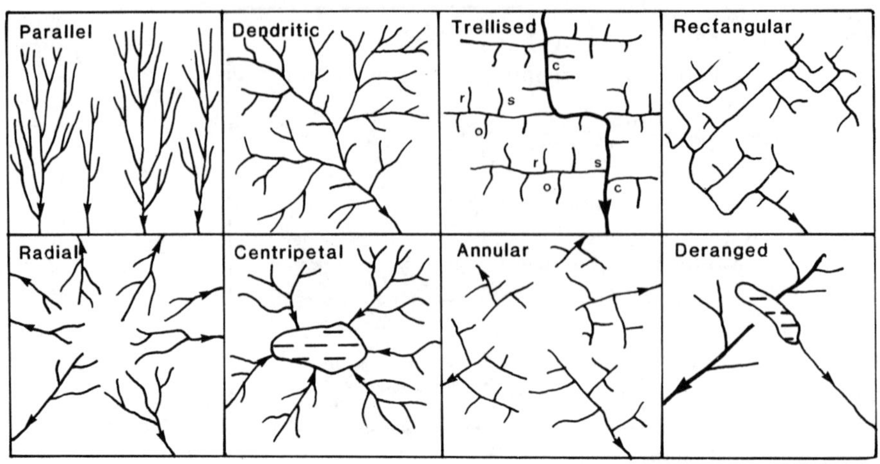

Fig. 2.34 — Classes of drainage pattern (based on Gregory and Walling 1973). (In trellised drainage, c=consequent stream, s=subsequent, r=resequent, o=obsequent).

orientation of stream segments (e.g. control by joint patterns) may be established by measuring the direction of arbitrary lengths of segment and plotting the results as a vectorial rosette (Milton 1965). Also deviations of a stream course from a cardinal direction may be measured at equally spaced points along its length (Schick 1965). Bifurcation ratios are usually between 3.0 and 5.0 in basins where geological structure exerts little influence on drainage, and are largest in areas of steeply dipping strata with many streams following the strike of less resistant beds.

The shape of channel segments has been classified qualitatively into single-thread, which may be either straight or meandering, and multithread, which are either anastomosing or braided (Leopold and Wolman 1957, Leopold *et al.* 1964, Chapter 7). Many rivers have separate reaches of two or more types, and individual reaches may show seasonal changes of characteristics, so the four types are probably members of a continuous series. Multithread streams have numerous channels which divide and rejoin, the junctions occurring at distances many times the channel width; braided streams show frequent changes of channel position, whereas anastomosing streams have more stable channels.

Single-thread channels are seldom straight for more than about ten times their width, and the line of greatest depth (talweg) swings from side to side even in straight channels, because sediment is deposited unevenly to form alternating pools and shallows (riffles). In meandering streams the pools occur below eroding concave banks at the points of maximum curvature. The channel cross-section is here strongly asymmetric because sediment is deposited on the opposite (convex) bank to form a crescentic point bar (Sundborg 1956, p. 288). Leopold and Wolman (1960) proposed measures for quantitative description of meandering channels, and Brice (1964) suggested an index for the extent of braiding based on the total length of interchannel bars or islands in a certain length of reach, but quantitative description of channel shape is complicated by the frequent changes in time and space. Speight (1965) suggested that overall channel geometry for the whole river can be expressed by spectral analysis of measurements taken at regular intervals throughout its length.

2.5.2 Fluvial deposits

Because the fine suspension load of a river travels faster than the coarse bed-load, and there is also some reduction in particle size by continued abrasion, fluvial sediments generally become finer and better sorted downstream. However, this trend may be modified by localized inputs from earlier alluvium or other eroded deposits, by sediment from tributaries, or by human influences. For example, soil erosion following Neolithic or Bronze Age deforestation in lowland Britain resulted in deposition of loamy alluvium up to 5 m thick, which often overlies coarser or finer sediments deposited before such human interference began. Another common effect of human interference is the bank erosion resulting from injudicious straightening and steepening of channels (Richards 1986).

The bedforms of fluvial sediments include lozenge-shaped longitudinal bars in gravels deposited by braided streams, and ripples, dunes, transverse bars and large, persistent sand flats in finer (sandy) deposits of multithread and single-thread streams (Collinson 1986). The bedforms present depend mainly upon flow velocity and mean particle size of the sediment (Fig. 2.35). Bars, dunes and ripples form

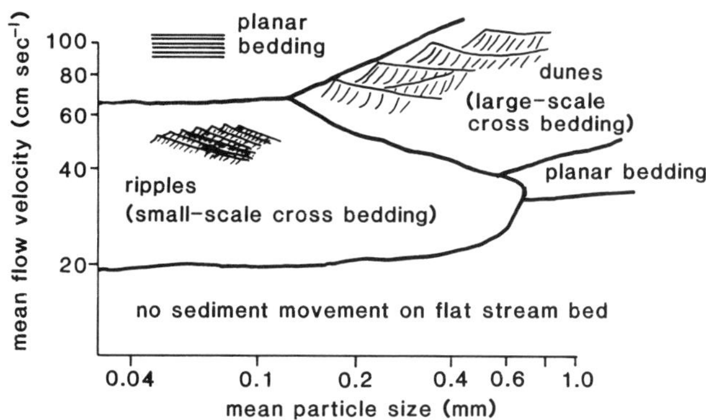

Fig. 2.35 — Influence of sediment grain size and flow velocity on fluvial bedforms in water 20 cm deep (from Richards 1986).

cross-bedded sediments by down-stream advance of their slip faces, and planar bedding occurs in high energy single-thread rivers and in coarse sands deposited by shallow streams of moderate energy (Allen 1970, 1983). Micaceous sands are often parallel-laminated because the platy particles inhibit formation of ripples (Manz 1978). Large dunes sometimes have smaller ones on their surface. Dunes and ripples have either straight or wavy crests; the former produce tabular cross-bedding, the latter trough-stratified sets (Fig. 2.36). Point bar sediments of meandering streams

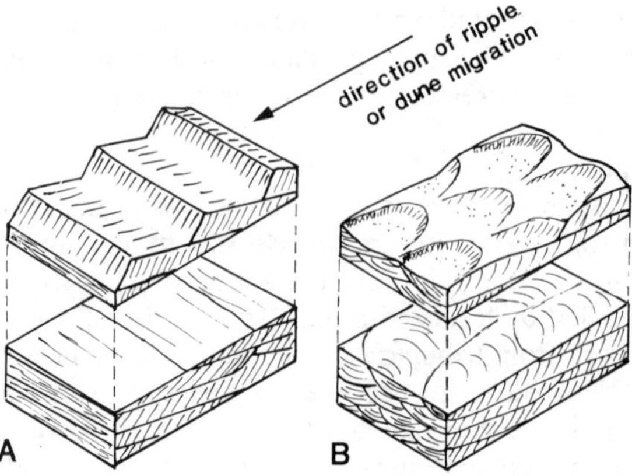

Fig. 2.36 — Fluvial sediment structures associated with migration of (A) straight-crested bedforms, giving tabular cross-stratification, and (B) curve-crested bedforms, giving trough cross-stratification (from Allen 1970). Reproduced by permission of George Allen and Unwin.

usually become finer upwards (Bernard and Major 1963), and may have scroll-shaped sand ridges (scrollbars) on their surface, marking the paths of earlier meanders (Hickin 1974). Dunes are the main bedforms on lower parts of point bars. Palaeocurrent directions estimated from channel orientation or cross-bedding are more widely dispersed in deposits of meandering streams than in those of less sinuous rivers (Kelling 1968). Current directions are also indicated in fluvial gravels by the long axes of pebbles, which are preferentially orientated transverse to the direction of water flow (Rust 1972b), and by blade-shaped particles which dip upstream (imbricate structure).

Multithread rivers develop where the supply of coarse sediment is too great for the existing flow, and there is consequently rapid deposition of bed-load (Doeglas 1962, Boothroyd and Ashley 1975). Typical situations for braided channels are where flow is checked as a fast mountain stream reaches a plain, or where abundant coarse sediment is supplied by a melting glacier or by repeated gelifluction down the valley sides. Anastomosing channels occur in areas of very gentle down-stream slope, such as swamps and delta tops; they also occur in semi-arid regions in response to decreasing discharge (Rust 1981); deposition is mainly by vertical accretion of the channel floor and formation of channel-side levées during periods of overbank flooding (Smith 1983).

Whereas braided rivers tend only to build up the valley floor by deposition of coarse sediment, single-thread rivers are capable of valley floor erosion as well as some deposition. In headwater regions this erosion is mainly headward and downward, principally because of the steep gradient and rapid flow. Lower in the valley, downward erosion of the floor is exceeded by valley widening, principally though undercutting of the sides by laterally migrating meanders (Klimek 1974), which also deposit point bars to build up a meander plain (Fig. 2.37). During occasional short periods of greatly increased flow, the channel overflows to turn this into a floodplain. Fine sand and coarse silt are deposited by the turbulent flow near the channel to form

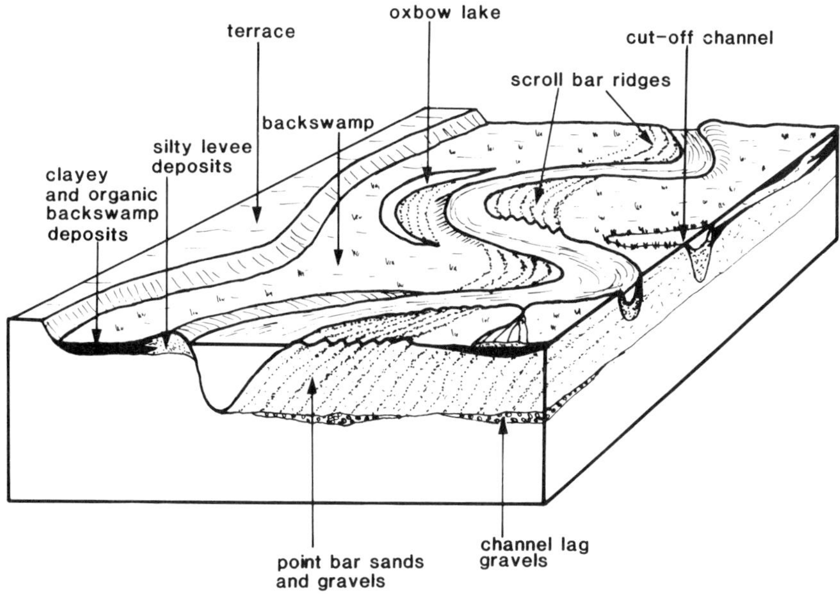

Fig. 2.37 — Sedimentary features of a river floodplain.

levées; finer silt and clay are carried beyond mainly by sheet flow, and are deposited intermittently to form finely laminated overbank sediments. The relative importance of channel and overbank sediments in the formation of river plains depends mainly on the frequency of flooding. Breaches of levées (or avulsion events) lead to changes in channel position during periods of increased discharge, especially when the channel is almost filled with sediment. On the lower, poorly drained backswamp areas of the floodplain beyond the levées, peat and shelly lacustrine sediments may accumulate in marshy areas or temporary ponds, including the ox-bow lakes formed when narrow necks between meanders are breached by cut-off channels. Overbank deposits become thinner and finer away from the channel, and often show desiccation cracks and raindrop prints. The term alluvium includes all fluvial sediments; further subdivision is based mainly on particle size and site of deposition (channel, overbank, etc.).

Alluvial fans are large depositional features formed by braided streams where a river emerges from a confined, steep valley into a basin or onto the floodplain of a larger river or a coastal or lake plain. The fan surface is concave upwards, the slope decreasing towards the toe, but is often divided into segments, each of which has a fairly constant gradient. Particle size usually decreases down-slope, but some layers within the fan may be coarser than others. The commonest situation of alluvial fans is at tectonically active margins of basins in desert areas (Bull 1964, 1972, Denny 1967), where mass movements such as debris flows (see 2.4.3) are often important subsidiary depositional processes. However, fans can also occur in wetter regions of strong relief, especially where the relief results from an active fault line. If the source area lacks fine sediment, these humid fans are deposited mainly by streams and sheetfloods with little or no influence of mass movement; they have gentle gradients, and range in size from 100 m to >100 km across. On the larger examples surface flow may decrease down the fan or even disappear because of infiltration into the coarse, permeable deposits. A sparse vegetation cover is often an important prerequisite for supply of coarse sediment to produce a fan, and in humid temperate regions, such as Britain, the largest examples are currently inactive and probably date from cold stages of the Quaternary, when there was little vegetation and large volumes of sediment were carried by upland periglacial rivers (Pounder and Macklin 1985) or outwash streams from valley glaciers.

The relative proportions of coarse (sand, gravel) and fine (silt, clay) deposits, their interrelationships and the extent to which coarse units are interconnected in alluvial sequences are collectively known as alluvial architecture (Allen 1978). This is influenced by several factors, including the ratio of bed-load to suspension load, floodplain width and the frequency of avulsion events. Where there is a large bed-load of coarse sediment, the channels migrate rapidly and very little of the fine sediment resulting from deposition of suspension load is preserved (Allen 1965), but where the load is mainly fine, channels are more stable so that both channel sands and finer overbank deposits are preserved. The classic pattern of channel deposits overlying an erosion surface, fining upwards, and showing an upward change from coarse cross-bedding to parallel or ripple lamination (Bernard and Major 1963) is now known to be an oversimplification. Many channel infills show more complex facies sequences, and the classic sequence can also result from declining flow in an unconfined sheetflood (Collinson 1978), though sheetflood deposits are generally thinner (<3 m) and laterally more extensive than channel-fills.

2.5.3 River terraces

River terraces are gently sloping surfaces extending parallel to the valley axis at levels above that of the present river. They can originate by processes of either deposition (aggradation) or erosion. Both types may be discordant with the slope of the present river, and may pass below the present valley floor as buried channels, especially towards the river mouth where large sea-level changes during the Quaternary had their greatest effect on deposition and erosion (Fig. 2.38).

The present long profiles of river valleys are concave upwards and approach zero gradient at the base level or lowest level to which water can flow (usually sea level). There have been several attempts to define the typical ('graded') long profile by equations of exponential, logarithmic, power or more complex forms (Broscoe 1959, Tanner 1971), but in practice long profiles usually consist of several component curves related to various earlier base levels. Knickpoints occur at the places where two former long profiles intersect, and may result in waterfalls or rapids, especially if they occur in hard bedrock. Terraces are parts of former long profiles which are partly or wholly separated from the present long profile by a vertical distance resulting from one or more episodes of down-cutting. Edges of terraces are therefore usually erosion features.

Depositional terraces are remnants of a former valley floor which resulted from continuing alluvial deposition because of the river's decreasing power to transport sediment, either through decreasing discharge or through increasing sediment

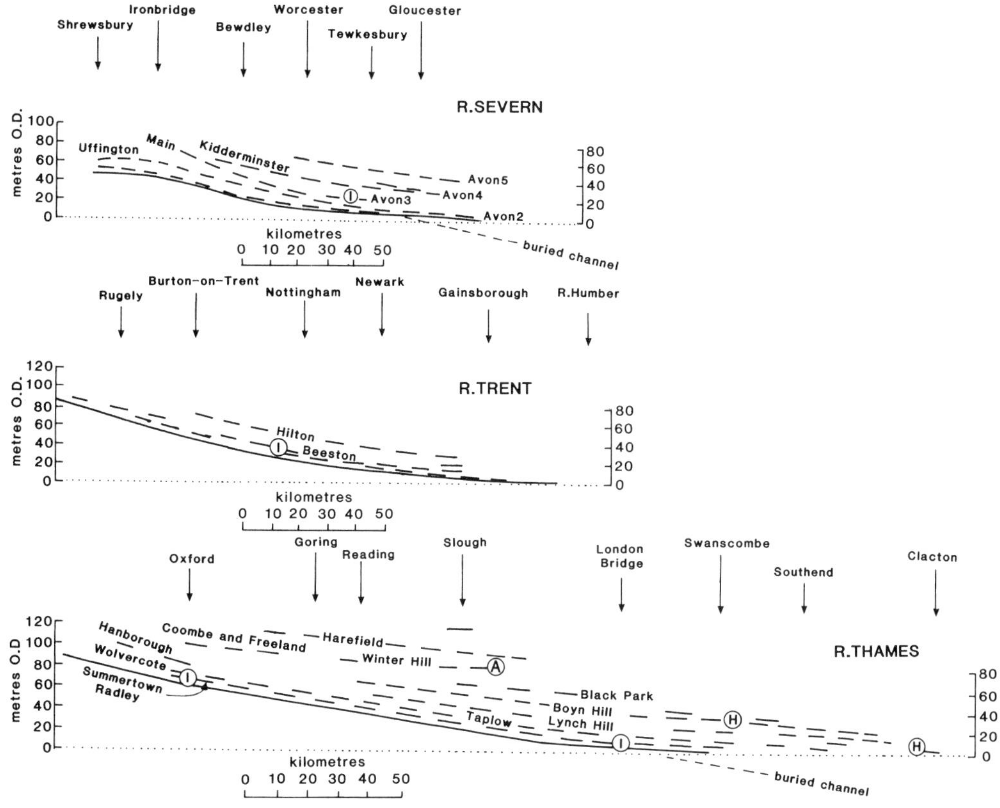

Fig. 2.38 — Long profiles and terraces of three English rivers (from Clayton 1977). I=Ipswichian, H=Hoxnian, A=Anglian.

supply. Subsequent down-cutting and dissection of the valley fill resulted from a decrease in sediment supply, an increase in discharge, or lowering of base level. If down-cutting is rapid, paired terraces are left on either side of the valley. Unpaired or single terraces imply slower down-cutting, allowing more time for lateral erosion.

Although younger terraces usually occur at lower levels than older terraces because of progressive down-cutting, rapid aggradation may refill a valley to produce a depositional terrace at a slightly higher level than earlier terraces. This may occur in upper reaches of a valley during a cold period as a result of sediment inputs from a glacier or valley-side gelifluction, or in lower reaches during a warm period when the sea rises to drown areas previously graded towards to a low base level. The latter were termed thalassostatic terraces by Zeuner (1946).

Repeated cycles of aggradation and down-cutting resulting from fluctuations of discharge or sediment input, often related to climatic oscillations, result in cut-and-fill terraces (Fig. 2.39) (Quinn 1957). Depositional terraces may be modified by later surface incision (e.g. gullying) or irregularly lowered by weathering of either the

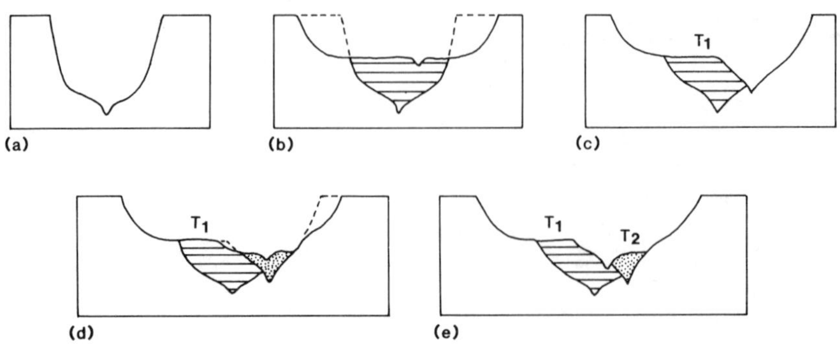

Fig. 2.39 — Formation of cut-and-fill terraces (from Quinn 1957).

terrace deposit itself or the bedrock (e.g. limestone) beneath. Some idea of the possible complexity of depositional and erosional processes within a single major Quaternary climatic cycle (interglacial–periglacial period–interglacial) is provided by the reconstruction of events in the Thames Valley (Fig. 2.40) by Green and McGregor (1980).

Erosional terraces are cut by a meandering stream either in bedrock (rock-cut terraces) or in valley-fill deposits (fill-cut terraces). Both can be paired or single terraces, but many paired rock-cut terraces have a structural origin, resulting from outcrops of hard bedrock strata on the valley sides (Fig. 2.41).

The age of many river terraces, especially those of erosional origin, is very difficult to determine. Like any erosion surface, the age of an erosional terrace is bracketed by the date of the youngest deposit it transects and the date of the oldest deposit overlying it. However, this rule rarely gives a very precise estimate of age. Channel deposits of depositional terraces rarely contain well-developed fossil assemblages useful for dating; usually there are only isolated bones or other resistant specimens which often may be derived from earlier deposits. Backswamp deposits are usually richer in indigenous fossils, especially molluscs, plant and insect remains, but it is often possible for deposition to occur in small ponds or streams on flat backswamp areas long after the terrace was originally formed. Correlation and relative dating of terraces by height, a technique often used in the past, is very unreliable. Within a single basin, separate terraces can often be distinguished by plotting their heights on a long profile and by petrographic studies such as clast analysis (Gibbard 1977, Green *et al.* 1982), but correlation of this type between basins is impossible.

2.5.4 Valley asymmetry

Many river valleys are asymmetric, but there are several possible reasons for this. On gently dipping strata, channels are cut along the outcrops of less resistant or less permeable beds (e.g. clays), and slowly migrate in the direction of dip to form a gentle forced slipoff slope on the surface of the underlying resistant bed and a steep, undercut slope subject to landslipping in the overlying resistant bed (Fig. 2.42).

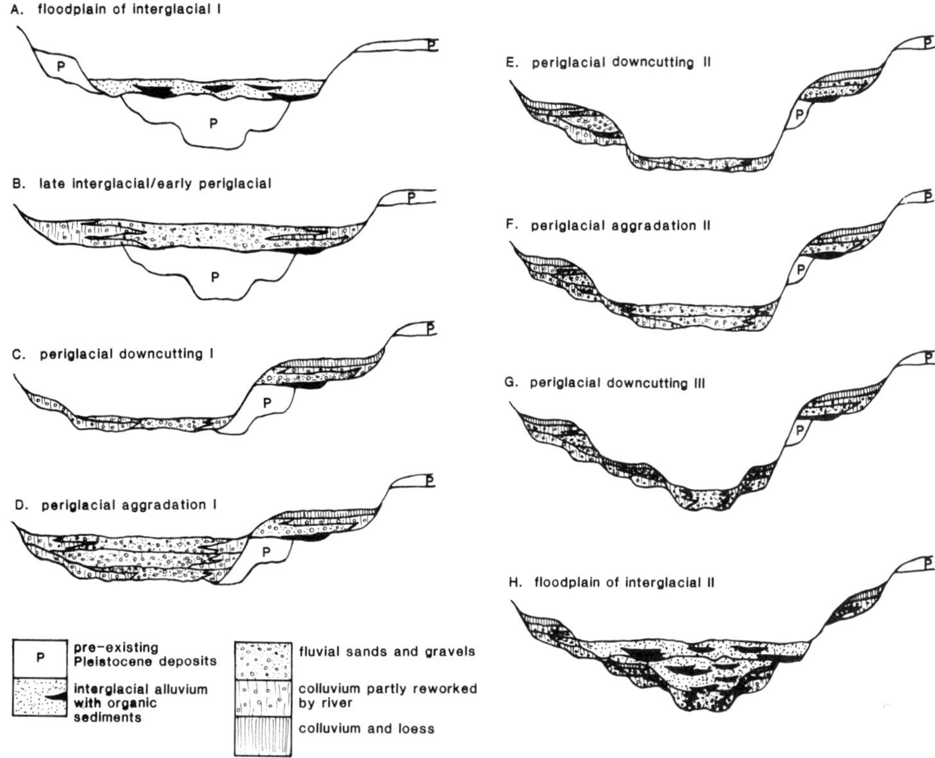

Fig. 2.40 — Scheme of Thames terrace development during a single periglacial episode between two warm interglacials (from Green and McGregor 1980). Reproduced by permission of Academic Press Inc.

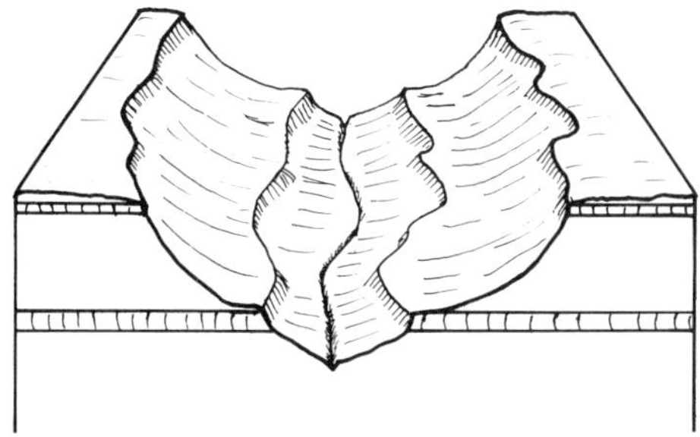

Fig. 2.41 — Structural river terraces.

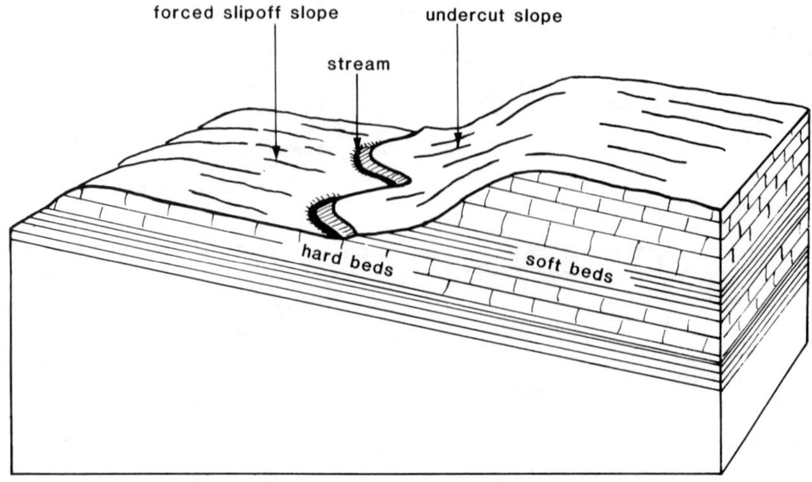

Fig. 2.42 — Formation of asymmetrical valley by uniclinal shifting of stream course.

Other valleys are asymmetric because of recent (neotectonic) tilting (Bridgland 1985), or because of an asymmetric distribution of fluvial or other sediments. For example, meandering in a narrow valley will leave a gentle meander slipoff slope covered with point bar sediments on one side and a steep undercut slope with no sediments or perhaps localized mass wastage deposits on the other (Fig. 2.43). In

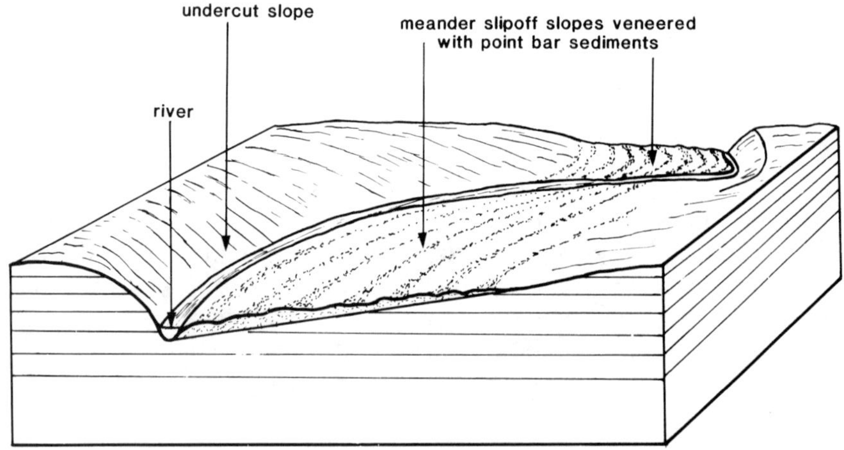

Fig. 2.43 — Formation of asymmetrical valley by meandering stream.

periglacial regions asymmetry can also arise by unequal gelifluction rates on opposite valley sides (Fig. 2.44). In mid-latitude regions of the northern hemisphere, south- or

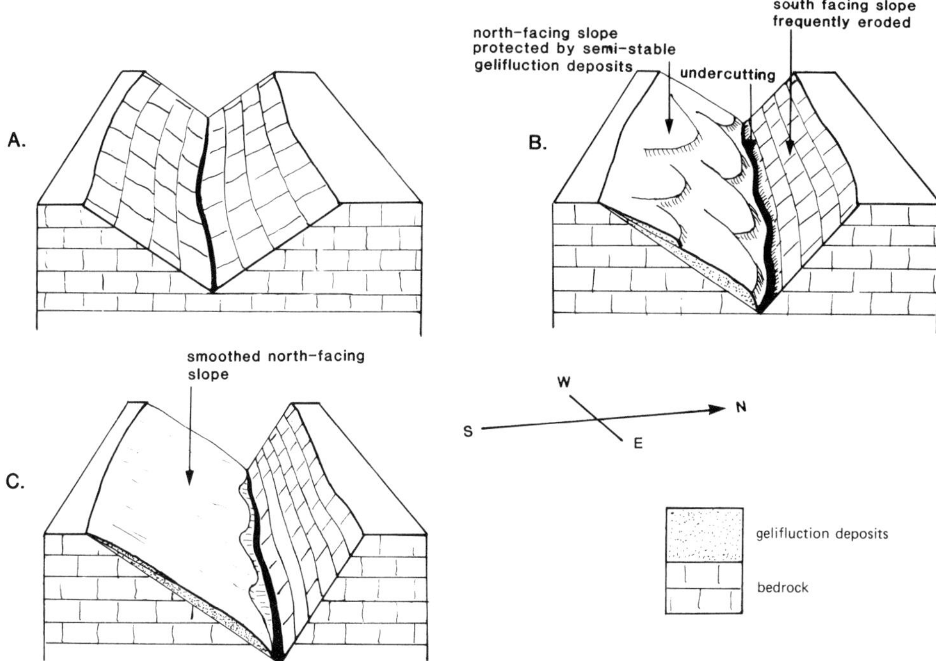

Fig. 2.44 — Formation of asymmetrical valley by unequal periglacial erosion resulting from repeated thawing of south-facing valley side and removal of the gelifluction deposits by stream erosion.

west-facing slopes are often steeper (Fig. 2.45), because during the Quaternary cold periods they received more insolation and thawed more frequently than those in the shade for much of the day. This led to more frequent erosion of the sunlit slopes by gelifluction, and the accumulated material was removed along the valley by periodic meltwater floods; in contrast, the gelifluction deposits on the opposite slope were more stable and as they accumulated tended to force the stream towards the sunlit slope, thus undercutting and steepening it (Ollier and Thomasson 1957). However, other northern hemisphere valleys, especially in higher latitudes, have steeper north- or east-facing slopes, suggesting that other periglacial processes may result in asymmetry (Currey 1964). Vegetation differences also may be important (Price 1971).

2.5.5 Peneplains

Before the Quaternary fluctuations of climate and sea level, base level was constant for long periods and many rivers probably developed gently sloping long profiles and broad floodplains. Some features inherited from these periods are still visible in the

Fig. 2.45 — Asymmetrical valley cut in Chalk, Little Hampden, near Princes Risborough, Buckinghamshire, England. Note the pale coloured soil on the steeper south-facing valley side, indicating Chalk close to the surface; thick, non-chalky gelifluction deposits remain on the north-facing slope (left).

present landscape, especially in low-latitude continental areas little affected by Quaternary glaciation, periglacial processes and coastal rejuvenation of rivers. Coalescence of adjacent floodplains produced a panplain (Crickmay 1933), which expanded upstream by slow removal of terrace and interfluve remnants. Inland, interfluve areas insufficiently resistant to persist as isolated monadnocks were progressively lowered by mass-wasting to form pediments, or gentle slopes on which removal of material by mass-wasting was balanced by weathering and soil formation (Penck 1953). Often the upper margins of pediments are separated from weak scarps at the margins of interfluve remnants by breaks in slope, though these do not indicate any changes in bedrock lithology. Glacis are similar to pediments, but are usually smaller and are cut in less resistant bedrock than the upland (interfluve) remnants; the break of slope at the upper margin is usually stronger, and the cross-profile is more distinctively concave than that of a pediment. Extensive areas of coalesced pediments produced a pediplain, and the coalescence of panplains and pediplains produced a flat or gentle undulating surface of considerable extent known as a peneplain. Most peneplains are covered by a deep residual soil, but if this has been partially stripped by subsequent erosion, leaving pockets of the weathered mantle between areas of virtually unaltered bedrock, the surface is termed an etchplain (Thomas 1974, 1986, Adams 1975).

Remnants of ancient peneplains and etchplains do occur in mid- and high-latitude regions, for example in Sweden (Lidmar-Bergström 1982), but many upland plains attributed to peneplains (e.g. in Britain) do not have a deep residual soil cover and have been so modified by glacial and periglacial erosion that their exact origin is obscure. Some are undoubtedly structural surfaces exhumed by various processes of erosion. The 'mid-Tertiary peneplain' of the Chalk outcrop in southern England (Wooldridge and Linton 1955) has, for example, been reinterpreted as part of an exhumed early Tertiary marine erosion surface gently folded by alpine earth movements (Moffat *et al.* 1986).

2.6 LACUSTRINE DEPOSITS

Lake basins vary considerably in geometry and origin (Hutchinson 1957), many forming as a result of tectonic activity, volcanism or glaciation (Allen and Collinson 1986). Most modern lakes originated in the Quaternary, and very few have persisted since the Tertiary; Lake Baikal in USSR is probably the oldest, but has existed only since the Miocene. However, many lakes preserve a good record of Quaternary events, because they have fairly high sedimentation rates on account of being completely surrounded by land, and because they are less buffered from climatic changes than the oceans. If this record spans much or all of the Quaternary, it provides a very detailed and useful comparison with the deep oceanic succession (Van der Hammen 1978, Hooghiemstra 1984). Climatic changes are indicated by pollen or diatom sequences, by the composition of the sediments and by stratigraphic, geomorphological and archaeological evidence for variation in lake level.

In open lakes (those with outflowing as well as inflowing rivers) sedimentation is usually dominated by influx of river-borne clastic material. Coarse detrital inputs are usually deposited close to the lake shore as deltas (Gilbert 1885) or alluvial fans, though some may be carried into deeper water by subaqueous slumps, slides or debris flows. Sediment-laden underflows may produce channels and levée-like features on the lake floor. Clay is often carried further into an open lake than in the sea because the lower salinity causes less flocculation. The waters of closed lakes are extremely variable in chemical composition, however; total salinity, for example, can range from almost zero to over 25%, depending on sources of inflowing water and the rate of evaporation, and pH ranges from <2 in some volcanic lakes to >12 in 'soda lakes'. Evaporite minerals, calcium carbonate and organic material (both allochthonous and autochthonous) are common constituents of lacustrine sediments, variations in amounts often resulting in conspicuous layering.

In temperate regions the water of closed non-saline lakes circulates twice a year (dimictic lakes) because of density changes resulting from seasonal variation in temperature (Ruttner 1963). Similar changes also occur in artificial reservoirs (Petts 1984). The maximum water density is reached at 4°C, so one 'turn over' of water occurs in spring as the surface water warms up to 4° and sinks, and another occurs in autumn as the warm surface water cools to 4° (Fig. 2.46). Summer and winter are stagnation periods with dense water underlying less dense water at $>4°$ and $<4°$ respectively. Biological production is greatest in the warm upper layer (epilimnion) in summer, but in autumn the detritus of dead organisms settles into the lower layer (hypolimnion) and is slowly deposited on the lake floor during the winter stagnation period. Oxygen is also carried down and oxidizes part of the organic matter, but amounts are usually too small to prevent anaerobic bottom conditions from develop-

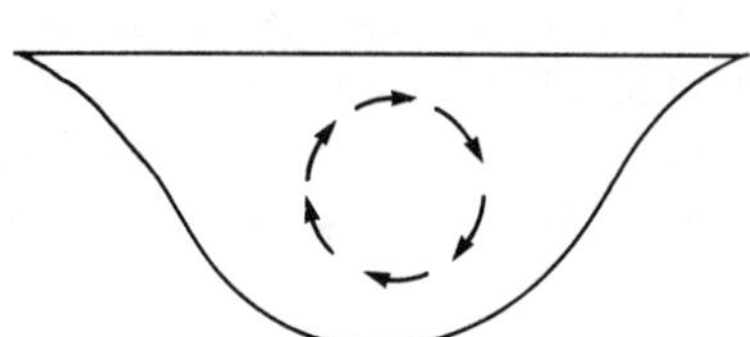

spring circulation: uniform temperature >4°C: deposition of inorganic sediment in aerobic bottom conditions.

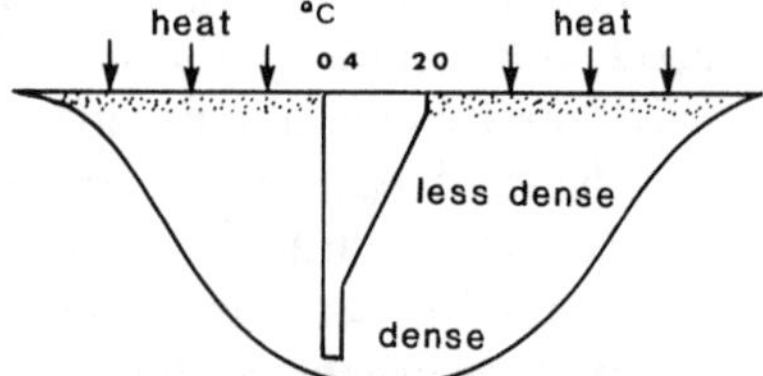

summer stagnation caused by thermal stratification: bottom water near 4° C: rapid growth of organisms in warm surface water.

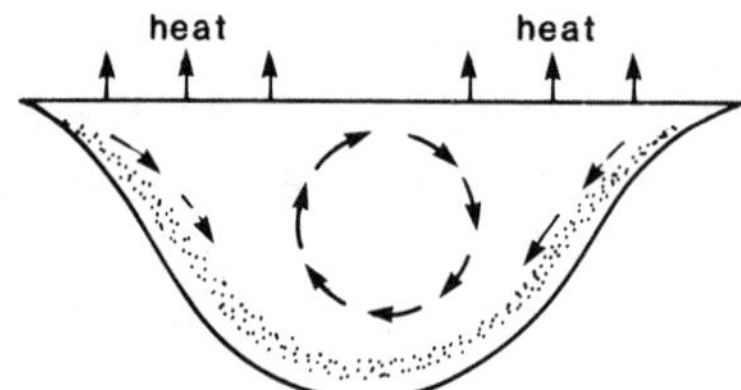

autumn circulation caused by cooling and sinking of surface layers: temperatures gradually approach 4°C throughout, and dead organisms sink to bottom.

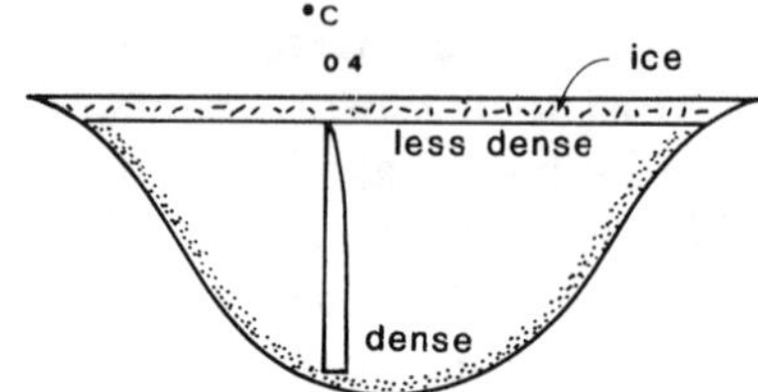

winter stagnation,with all water at 4°C or less: deposition of organic sediment in anoxic bottom conditions.

Fig. 2.46 — Seasonal circulation in a temperate, non-saline lake.

ing. At an Eh of about 0.2 volts, Fe^{2+}, Mn, P and NH_4 dissolve in the bottom water, and may be carried upwards at the spring 'turn over' to provide nutrients for the next summer's production.

In arctic regions lakes are covered by ice for much of the year and the water is permanently <4°C, so no mixing occurs (amictic lakes). In the tropics, there is also no mixing, but here the cause is a permanent temperature stratification, with the surface water never cooling sufficiently to sink; in such oligomictic lakes the bottom waters are strongly anaerobic, and pyrite (FeS_2) often forms in the sediment (Bloomfield *et al.* 1970). In meromictic lakes 'turn over' is prevented by the presence of heavy saline water in the bottom.

Sedimentation usually results in shallowing of the lake, unless crustal downwarping keeps pace with deposition, as in Lake Baikal and other very old lakes. As Theinemann (1928) originally pointed out, shallowing can lead to eutrophication (enrichment in nitrogen and other nutrients) because there is insufficient oxygen to consume each year's production, and anaerobic conditions lead to increasing amounts of nutrients in each successive spring 'turn over'. Contamination by runoff from arable land, farmyards or sewage works can also cause eutrophication locally.

Accumulations of autochthonous organic matter in anoxic lake floor sediments are termed sapropel; they are essentially amorphous, have a C/N ratio >10 (Hansen 1959), and are often microlaminated because there are no organisms to disturb the sediment by burrowing. Dark-brown or black organic gel (dy) may form locally. Transported (allochthonous) organic accumulations with incompletely decomposed fragments of plant and animal remains are termed gyttja. This has a C/N ratio <10, and unlike sapropel or dy does not give a brown solution when boiled in alkali. If many plant remains are coarse and identifiable, indicating rapid deposition probably in shallow water, the deposit is termed detritus gyttja. Gyttja clay is clay containing 3–6% gyttja; clay gyttja contains 6–12% gyttja. Gyttja with abundant calcium carbonate is termed lime gyttja, and shell gyttja contains mollusc shells. In detritus mud, much of the organic matter mixed with fine inorganic sediment is recognizable plant remains.

Amounts of carbonate in lacustrine deposits are mainly related to seasonal changes. In summer, photosynthesis by phytoplankton removes carbon dioxide from the epilimnion. This causes dissociation of bicarbonate and increases the pH. The combined effect of increased alkalinity and higher temperature is to precipitate calcium carbonate. Some of this is redissolved in the colder hypolimnion, but much is deposited as a thin pale-coloured layer on the lake floor. Dark-coloured, carbonate-poor layers accumulate during the winter when fine detrital constituents and organic matter settle out. Where there is little disturbance of the bottom sediments, finely laminated deposits with annual couplets may result from these processes. Carbonate is also accumulated as invertebrate shells or by plants such as mosses and algae (stoneworts). Some lacustrine marls are composed almost entirely of the spiral oogonia of the alga known as *Chara*.

Other major biogenic components of some lake deposits are the siliceous tests of diatoms (unicellular algae). These are concentrated in the fine, white or pale-coloured deposit termed diatomite, kieselguhr, randanite or tripolite, which typically has a very low bulk density (0.4–0.8 g cm^{-3}) and high porosity (70–90%). Often they are concentrated in the summer layers of annually laminated beds in temperate lakes (Saarnisto 1986). Lacustrine faunas are often less diverse than marine faunas, because they are under greater stress on account of the sensitivity of lake waters to frequent climatic changes.

Formation of evaporite minerals in closed lakes of hot semi-arid regions depends upon the source and composition of the inflow, and on subsequent changes in the water chemistry as a result of evaporation and precipitation of the less soluble compounds (carbonates and gypsum). Concentration of the original inflow by up to 1000 times is often necessary to reach saturation with respect to more soluble minerals (Allen and Collinson 1986). This is achieved by evaporation, and by formation of brines by localized dissolution of efflorescent crusts. Minerals such as halite (NaCl), mirabilite ($Na_2SO_4.10H_2O$) and trona ($HNa_3(CO_3)_2.2H_2O$) are precipitated either from the lake water or from occluded brines within the lake floor sediments. Soda lakes, in which trona and natron ($Na_2CO_3.10H_2O$) are precipitated from very alkaline water, result from inflows which are deficient in Ca and Mg, or become depleted in these elements by precipitation of carbonates, followed by removal of sulphate ions as precipitated sulphides in a reducing hypolimnion.

In many arid and semi-arid low-latitude regions there is evidence for alternating expansion and contraction of lakes during the Quaternary. Recent contraction of previously more extensive lakes is indicated by exposed lacustrine sediments, or by geomorphological features such as abandoned lake shorelines, cliffs, beaches and overflow channels. Desiccated lake basins resulting from increased aridity are often covered by sand dunes (Grove and Warren 1968). Although there are several possible reasons for desiccation of lakes, many of the changes in lake size reflect past variations in precipitation associated with the migration of climatic zones in response to expansion and contraction of the polar ice caps. Wet periods are often termed pluvials and dry periods interpluvials. It was originally assumed that these correlated universally with the glacials and interglacials respectively of higher latitudes. Recent dating has shown that, although this is true in some areas, the pluvials of other regions (e.g. E. Africa) coincide with the warmer intervals of mid-latitudes (Goudie 1977, Street and Grove 1976, 1979).

2.7 PEAT DEPOSITS

Peat is an autochthonous organic deposit formed at sites (mires) where plants grow and their remains can accumulate because waterlogging prevents oxidation and decomposition. Plants which grow permanently submerged in shallow water, such as reeds, form limnic peats; these develop in almost completely infilled lakes or locally in shallow lake margins. Plants growing partially submerged between high and low water marks form telmatic peats; in eutrophic conditions with abundant nutrients, the main plant types are tall fen sedges, fen mosses and other sedges such as *Cladium*, but in oligotrophic conditions these are replaced by the bog moss *Sphagnum* and the cotton-grass *Eriophorum vaginatum*. Terrestrial peats form at or above high water, either where soil drainage is poor because the mire is in a valley or hollow with a high groundwater table (topogenous peat) or where there is a low permeability subsurface horizon (soligenous peat), or where high rainfall and low evaporation keep the soil wet despite the absence of a high water table or low permeability subsurface horizon (ombrogenous peat). In eutrophic conditions, terrestrial peats are formed by small sedges (e.g. *Parvocaricetum*) or fen-woodland (alder or birch). In oligotrophic conditions, heather (*Calluna*), shrubs (e.g. *Myrica*, *Vaccinium*), grasses (e.g. *Molinia*), rushes (e.g. *Scirpus*) and hummock-forming species of *Sphagnum* are the main plants involved.

Peat decomposes at variable rates as it accumulates and is buried beneath subsequent layers. Von Post (1924) devised a field test for assessing the degree of decomposition. This involves (a) squeezing a sample at natural moisture content in the closed hand, and observing the colour of the liquid expressed and the proportion extruded between the fingers, and (b) assessing how distinct the plant residues are. Table 2.4 summarizes the characteristics of the ten degrees of decomposition on the Von Post scale.

Troels-Smith (1955) proposed a more detailed system of peat classification, based on components, degree of decomposition (humification) and physical properties. The degree of humification is assessed by adding a small sample of the peat to a few millilitres of dilute potassium hydroxide solution and observing the brownness of the liquid when it is absorbed on a filter paper. The components are described in terms of botanical composition and the size of the main organic materials: turfa contains coarse (>2 mm) fragments; detritus contains smaller fragments (0.1–2 mm); and limus contains mainly fragments <0.1 mm with microscopic structure only. The physical properties include colour (moist and after drying), structure (granular, felted or fibrous), carbonate content, elasticity (recovery of shape after squeezing), and stratification. Lamination results from changes of climate and water regime

Table 2.4 — Scale for assessing the degree of decomposition of peat (modified from Von Post 1924)

Nature of liquid expressed by squeezing	Proportion of peat extruded between fingers	Nature of plant residues	Degree of decomposition
Clear, colourless	None	Plant structure unaltered; fibrous, elastic	1. Undecomposed
Almost clear, yellow-brown	None	Plant structure distinct; almost unaltered	2. Almost undecomposed
Slightly turbid, brown	None	Plant structure distinct; most remains easily identifiable	3. Very weakly decomposed
Strong turbid, brown	None	Plant structure distinct; most remains identifiable	4. Weakly decomposed
Strongly turbid, contains a little peat in suspension	Very little	Plant structure clear but becoming indistinct; most remains difficult to identify	5. Moderately decomposed
Muddy, much peat in suspension	One third	Plant structure indistinct but clearer in the squeezed residue than in the undisturbed peat; most remains unidentifiable	6. Well decomposed
Strongly muddy	One half	Plant structure indistinct but recognizable; few remains identifiable	7. Strongly decomposed
Thick mud, little free water	Two thirds	Plant structure very indistinct; only resistant remains such as root fibres and wood identifiable	8. Very strongly decomposed
No free water	Nearly all	Plant structure almost unrecognizable; almost no identifiable remains	9. Almost completely decomposed
No free water	All	Plant structure unrecognizable; completely amorphous	10. Completely decomposed

during growth of the peat. For example, dark humified layers formed from pale ombrogenous peat indicate periods of surface drying and therefore less precipitation; if they are overlain by less humified peat formed in wetter conditions, they are termed recurrence surfaces (Godwin 1954). However, similar layers in other types of peat may indicate non-climatic changes, such as lowering of the water-table.

Table 2.5 summarizes the properties used in the Troels-Smith peat classification. A notation system is based on the size of components (capital T, D or L for turfa, detritus or limus), their botanical composition (e.g. lower case 'b' for bryophytica, indicating moss), a superscript number 0–4 for position on a five-point scale of humification, and a number 0–4 for the proportion of the organic component to the inorganic mineral constituents clay (As), silt (Ag) etc. Thus a pure unhumified coarse moss peat is designated $Tb^0 4$, and a partly humified coarse peat containing 80% woody material and 20% coarse mineral sand is designated $Tl^2 3$, Gs1.

2.8 PERIGLACIAL EROSION AND SOIL DISTURBANCE

The term 'periglacial' has been variously used for the climate of areas around major ice sheets (Loziński 1909), for a climatic zone with specified temperature and

Table 2.5 — Properties used to classify peats and mixed peat/inorganic sediments (based on Troels-Smith 1955)

Class	Element	Symbol	Description
Turfa	*T. bryophytica*	Tb^{0-4}	Moss remains >2 mm
	T. lignosa	Tl^{0-4}	Woody roots, stems, branches, etc.
	T. herbacea	Th^{0-4}	Non-woody herbaceous roots, stems, etc.
Detritus	*D. lignosus*	Dl^{0-4}	Fragments of woody plants <2 mm
	D. herbosus	Dh^{0-4}	Fragments of non-woody plants <2 mm
Limus	*L. detrituosus*	Ld^{0-4}	Plant fragments <0.1 mm
	L. siliceus organogenes	Lso	Siliceous organisms (e.g. diatoms)
	L. calcareus	Lc	Calcareous marl (e.g. *Chara* oogonia)
	L. ferrugineus	Lf	Iron oxides
Argilla		As	Mineral particles of clay (<2 μm)
		Ag	Mineral particles of silt (2–60 μm)
Grana		Ga	Mineral particles of fine sand (60–600 μm)
		Gs	Mineral particles of coarse sand (600 μm–2 mm)
		Gg	Mineral particles of gravel (>2 mm)

precipitation ranges (Wilson 1969), for areas with perennially frozen ground (Péwé 1969), and for an environment in which cold climate, non-glacial processes (especially those resulting from ground freezing) have produced distinctive landforms and deposits (Ballantyne 1987). It is also loosely applied to cold periods of the Quaternary in mid- and high-latitude regions of the earth not invaded by glaciers.

2.8.1 Permafrost and ground ice

Perennially frozen ground or permafrost is commonly defined as ground that remains frozen through at least one summer (French 1976, p. 47), though continuity of subsoil freezing for much longer periods is usually implied and may well be necessary for the development of characteristic soil features able to persist after the climate has improved. Like glaciers, permafrost was more extensive in cold stages of the Quaternary than in warm stages, but in many areas permafrost lasted much longer than the ice sheets. This is because glaciers take many thousands of years to grow and spread from upland accumulation areas to the lowlands, whereas permafrost develops as soon as it is cold enough, probably at a mean annual air temperature of −4°C or less (Black 1976).

Present-day permafrost reaches a maximum thickness of >1400 metres in Siberia (Grave 1968), and where it is much thinner (<50 m approximately) it is often patchy (discontinuous permafrost). Much of the discontinuous permafrost in Asia and northern Canada (Fig. 2.47) is probably a decaying relic of the Würm/Wisconsinan cold stage, as it occurs in regions with a mean annual air temperature as high as −1°C and may not be in equilibrium with the present climate. During the summer, upper layers of permafrost may thaw, especially in coarse, freely-drained sediments which do not contain much ice because they retain little water against gravity. The maximum depth of thawing is termed the permafrost table, and the thickness of the thawed or active layer decreases with increasing latitude and shortness of the

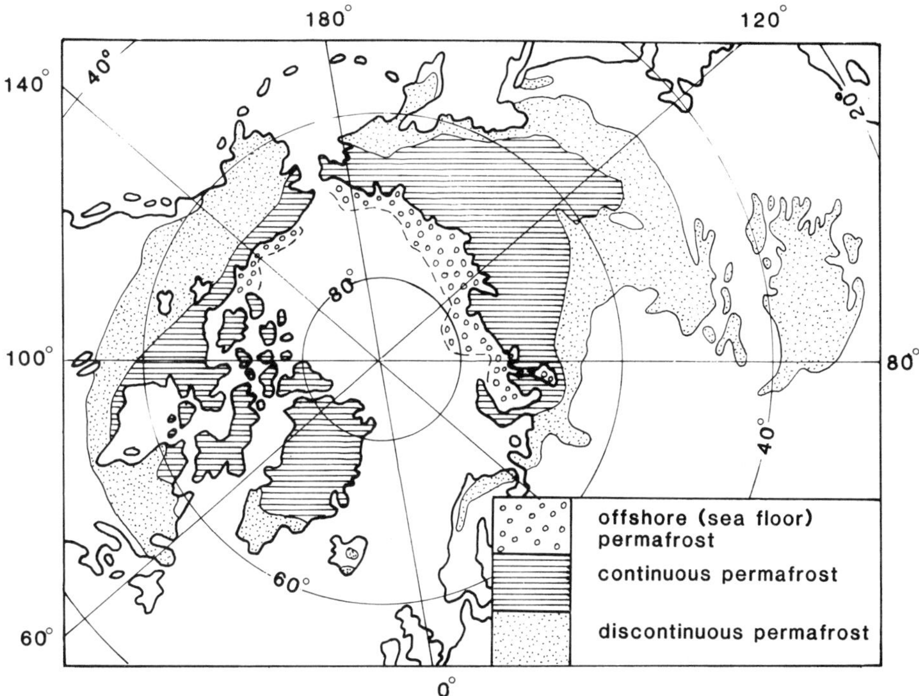

Fig. 2.47 — Distribution of permafrost in the northern hemisphere (compiled by T. L. Péwé from various sources, from Washburn 1979).

summer thaw period. Refreezing of the thawed layer in winter may be incomplete, leaving an unfrozen talik above the permafrost table. Taliks can also occur within permafrost, especially in regions where it is discontinuous. Several geophysical methods have been used to determine the depth and character of modern permafrost (Scott *et al.* 1979).

Ground ice forms in seasonally or perennially frozen ground either by freezing of water held in the original pores or by supersaturation with water drawn to a freezing surface or injected under artesian pressure (Mackay and Black 1973). Some ground ice may also originate by burial of surface ice (e.g. blocks of glacier ice or naleds) beneath fresh sediment. Ground ice is most abundant in upper parts of the permafrost, where it forms thin veins, acicular aggregates (pipkrake), lenses or massive beds up to several metres thick, or wedges which taper downwards from a maximum width of several metres near the ground surface. Ground ice wedges (Black 1974) are characteristic features of permafrost, which are commonly preserved as ice wedge casts long after the permafrost has completely dispersed (Fig. 2.48). The casts are preserved because the sediments on either side are deformed by growth of the ice wedge or because on melting, the walls collapse into the wedge or the cavity is filled with new sediment. Wind-blown sand is a common fill material in areas where the mean annual precipitation is less than 100 mm (French

Fig. 2.48 — Ice wedge cast in late Devensian Sherburn Sands, East Heslerton, North Yorkshire, England.

1976); the resulting features are termed sand wedge casts (Péwé 1959). At the present day, ice wedges form in areas where the mean annual air temperature is less than approximately −8°C (i.e. colder than the conditions required for permafrost) and there is little winter precipitation (Williams 1975).

Ice wedges often occupy cracks originating by thermal contraction of frozen ground (frost cracks), which form when there are rapid (e.g. over-night) falls of temperature to below −15°C. The largest frost and ice wedges form in clays, peats and other fine deposits, but they are rarely well-preserved as casts because on thawing these materials flow and destroy the wedges; casts are more frequently preserved in coarse sediments such as gravels (Black 1976) (Fig. 2.48). Syngenetic ice wedges result from repeated cracking beneath a surface that is intermittently raised by deposition of fresh sediment, such as fluvial gravel on a periglacial river floodplain

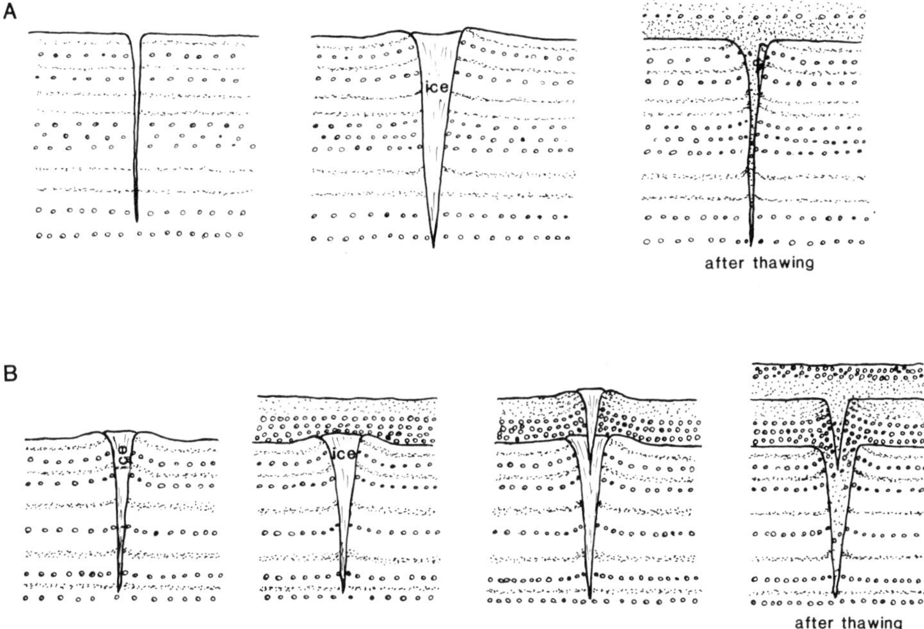

Fig. 2.49 — Formation of (A) epigenetic and (B) syngenetic ice wedges.

(Fig. 2.49). Epigenetic wedges develop beneath a stable land surface. Either type may be truncated by erosion during or after development, but once a crack or wedge has formed, it acts as a line of weakness which may determine where further cracking occurs either at the same or at a higher stratigraphic level.

2.8.2 Periglacial soil patterns

Frost cracks, ice wedges and ice wedge casts (including sand wedge casts) often extend laterally to form polygonal patterns in plan. Individual polygons range from 1 m to >100 m across, the largest often forming by rapid refreezing of a seasonally thawed active layer, though these are less often preserved as relict casts. Sand wedge polygons often produce remarkably clear soil or crop patterns in aerial photographs (Fig. 2.50). Crudely rectangular or other less regular patterns of periglacial cracks and wedges are often termed nets; these may originate by deformation of regular polygons through gelifluction on a slope, a process that eventually leads to formation of stripes running parallel to the direction of maximum slope (Washburn 1956).

Lateral compression resulting from contraction in frost cracking or the growth of ice wedges often leads to doming of the soil within each polygon. Stones lifted to the surface by frost heaving (Washburn 1979, pp. 80–91) then slide down the domed surface and accumulate in the marginal furrows (Fig. 2.51). This process of stone-sorting results in sorted polygons, nets or stripes. In non-sorted patterns the marginal furrows often contain concentrations of vegetation (e.g. mosses or even small shrubs), because water accumulates there during periods of summer melting. Lateral

Fig. 2.50 — Aerial photograph of ice wedge polygons, Breckland, Norfolk, England; the ice wedge casts penetrate Chalk, and are filled with coversand. Cambridge University Collection, Crown Copyright.

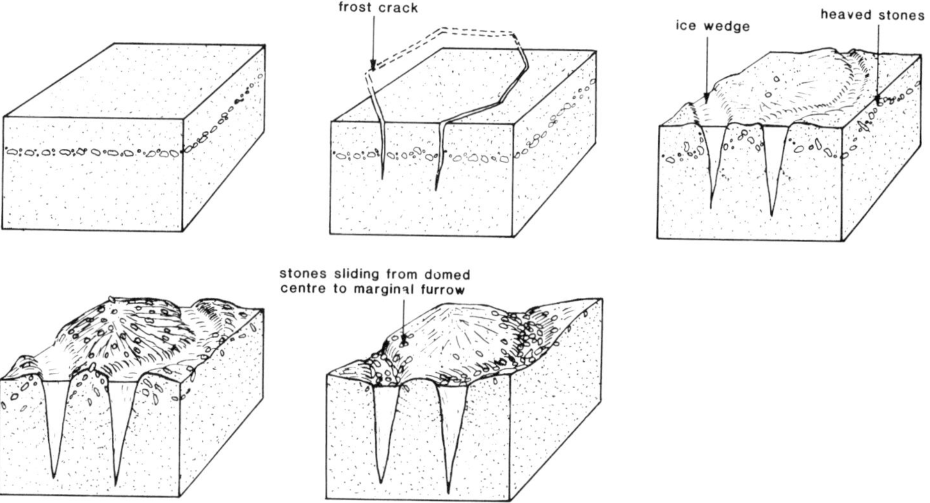

Fig. 2.51 — Formation of sorted polygons.

compression may also orientate flat stones so that they stand vertically in the margins.

Localized frost heaving of soil results in isolated circular domed areas up to approximately 3 metres in diameter, which may be sorted or non-sorted. The domed surface of these mudboils or circles is often covered by smaller polygonal dilation cracks. Fine stonefree material heaved to the surface through a layer of stones results in a type of sorted circle known as a debris island. Hummocks or thúfurs are non-sorted circles or nets, 1–2 metres across and up to 50 centimetres high, which form in peat or fine mineral soil in vegetated tundra or forest environments; they are widespread in periglacial regions with permafrost, but also occur in sub-polar and alpine areas with a mean annual air temperature up to 6°C. Together with small sorted circles, nets and stripes, they even occur locally in some highland areas of northern Britain (Ballantyne 1987).

Vertical displacements of sediment *en masse* by frost are often seen in vertical sections as cryoturbations or involutions (Sharp 1942). These range from irregular, almost random contortions to regularly spaced pockets or flask-shaped intrusions of an upper bed into a lower (Figs 2.52–2.54). Some authorities use the term involution only for the more regular features, whereas others use the two terms synonymously for all these types of disturbance. The flask-shaped pocket involutions probably originate by sinking of a denser, usually coarser sediment into soft saturated material below. This load-casting may occur in a thawed active layer above permafrost, and the uniform level of the flat bottoms seen in many relict involutions may indicate the position of the former permafrost table (Watson 1977). However, it can also occur in poorly drained sites in warm or temperate climates, so involutions are not as clear an indication of former permafrost as, for example, ice wedge casts. Other cryoturbations may result from flow under pressure generated in taliks between the permafrost

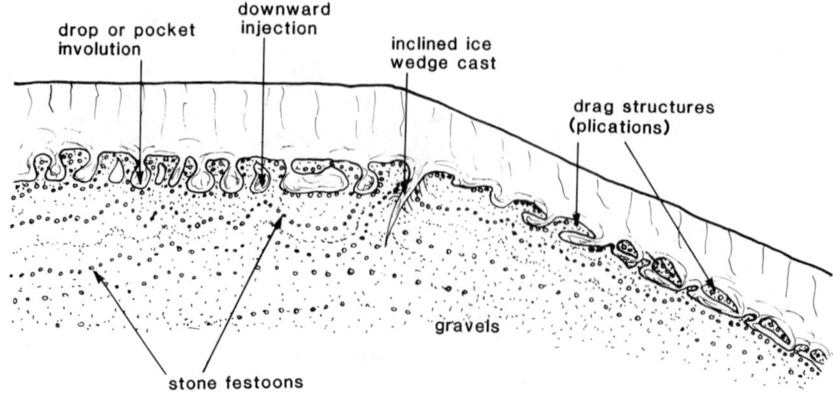

Fig. 2.52 — Effects of cryoturbation on level and sloping surfaces in a fine deposit over gravels.

Fig. 2.53 — Involutions in late Devensian loess over frost-shattered Chalk, Pegwell Bay, Kent, England.

Fig. 2.54 — Involutions in late Devensian gelifluction deposits, Marsworth, Buckinghamshire, England.

table and the down-freezing surface of an active layer, or from volume changes in clayey sediments as layer silicates dehydrate and rehydrate on freezing and thawing (Hobbs 1974, pp. 347–9). In stony deposits cryoturbations often show reorientation of stones as festoons parallel to the structures, many of the stones standing almost vertically.

2.8.3 Pingos and palsas

Large lenses of ground ice cause mounds or ridges to form on the surface. Those formed in peat bogs are termed palsas (Åhman 1976), and are up to 10 metres high, 30 metres across and 150 metres long. Others formed in inorganic sediments or bedrock are termed pingos (Porsild 1938), and are often much larger, up to 70 metres high and more than a kilometre across. The surfaces of ground ice mounds are often broken by radial and concentric dilation cracks, and as the ice lens melts beneath the most open parts of the cracks, the crest of the mound initially collapses into a central depression. Further thawing of the ice core then leaves a thermokarst depression surrounded by a low circular or elliptical rampart. In peat, even this ridge may collapse to leave the bog surface with little or no evidence of the former ice lens. However, the depression and rampart persist much longer in pingos, and those relict from the last cold stage often retain small lakes in which peat and lacustrine sediments have accumulated for much of the Holocene. The earliest of these lake sediments provides a minimum age for melting of the pingo ice lens (Watson 1972). Two types of contemporary pingo are distinguished (Mackay 1978): (a) the closed-system or Mackenzie type of pingo, which forms by eventual freezing and expansion of water trapped, for example, on a lake floor by progressive freezing from top, bottom and sides, (b) the open-system or East Greenland type, which is usually smaller and formed by freezing of water injected upwards into permafrost from an aquifer under artesian pressure (Fig. 2.55).

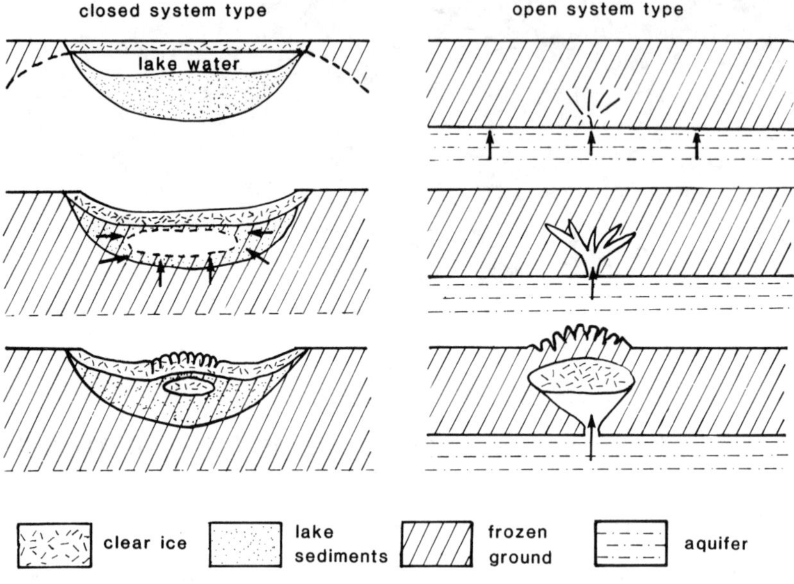

Fig. 2.55 — Formation of closed- and open-system pingos.

2.8.4 Naleds

Naleds or icings are accumulations of ice formed on the ground surface where river or spring water freezes. They are favoured by underlying permafrost and are usually tongue-shaped parallel to a valley, gully or fault; some reach several metres in thickness, and on wide floodplains may occupy many square kilometres (Ferrians *et al.* 1969). A broad shallow depression is left in underlying (e.g. alluvial) sediments after the ice has melted; this is usually eroded or buried by subsequent deposition of sediment, but some naled depressions are preserved (Coxon 1978). If burial occurs before completion of melting, subsequent collapse may result in the formation of enclosed hollows resembling the kettle holes formed by melting of buried ice in glaciofluvial gravels (Catt *et al.* 1982).

2.8.5 Thermokarst features

Thawing of ground ice as a result of a climatic amelioration, fires or the disturbance of a vegetation or peat cover causes the ground surface to collapse, creating thermokarst phenomena. Initially collapse is localized, with small thaw lakes forming in the collapsed areas (Hopkins 1949); as water has a greater specific heat than ice, the lakes progressively increase in size and may coalesce to form alases several kilometres across. Thaw lakes formed at the intersections of ice wedge polygons are often connected by waterfilled troughs along the edges of the polygons to form beaded drainage. Some elliptical thaw lakes are preferentially orientated parallel to bedrock structures or predominant wind directions (Price 1968).

2.8.6 Gelifraction and nivation

Frost-shattering or gelifraction of even the hardest rocks is possible because the force generated by the volume increase when water freezes exceeds their tensile strength by up to ten times (Washburn 1979, p. 73). However, shattering is easier in porous or strongly cleaved rocks, such as chalk (Williams 1980, 1987) or shales, especially if waterfilled pores on the rock surface are sealed by rapid freezing so that internal pressures are not readily released.

A snow cover usually insulates rock surfaces from gelifraction. However, at the margin of a snowpatch, especially one over impermeable permafrost, gelifraction is often accelerated by the frequent supply of meltwater, which also encourages removal of the rock fragments by gelifluction and other down-slope movements (Ballantyne 1978). In hillside hollows where snowpatches form frequently, this process of erosion, termed nivation, enlarges the hollow along the slope to form a bench or terrace (cryoplanation or altiplanation terrace) (Reger and Péwé 1976). In rocks which are easily shattered, nivation can increase the depth of hollows by as much as a metre per year; cryoplanation terraces probably take thousands of years to form and may be 2–3 kilometres wide and 10–15 kilometres long. If a hollow retains some snow through successive summers it becomes a cirque or niche glacier.

Where hard jointed bedrock overlies softer sediment (e.g. clay) on an escarpment or upper valley side, ground ice may widen the joints to form fissures or gulls (Hollingworth *et al.* 1944, Kellaway and Taylor 1953). These may be filled with aeolian sediment such as loess (Worssam 1981) or with frost-shattered rock debris. Blocks of the hard caprock may be rotated to increase the valleyward dip progressively as the valley is approached (Fig. 2.56). Within these cambered strata some gulls may develop into minor reverse faults to give dip and fault structure. Upward squeezing of the underlying soft strata into the valley floor forms an anticlinal valley bulge, on the margins of which the basal layers of the caprock may be upturned against the direction of dip imposed by cambering. Some valley bulging results from unloading of the overconsolidated clay when it is exposed by valley erosion either in a temperate climate or beneath a glacier (Kellaway 1972), but Horswill *et al.* (1976) maintained that ground freezing superimposed on the effects of stress relief is necessary to account for the extent of cambering and valley bulging in the English Midlands.

2.9 KARST EROSION AND DISTURBANCE

Karst features (Cvijic 1893, Jennings 1985) are characteristic of regions with thick, fairly soluble surface bedrock strata (mainly limestone but locally gypsum or other evaporites), moderate to heavy precipitation, a considerable elevation above sea

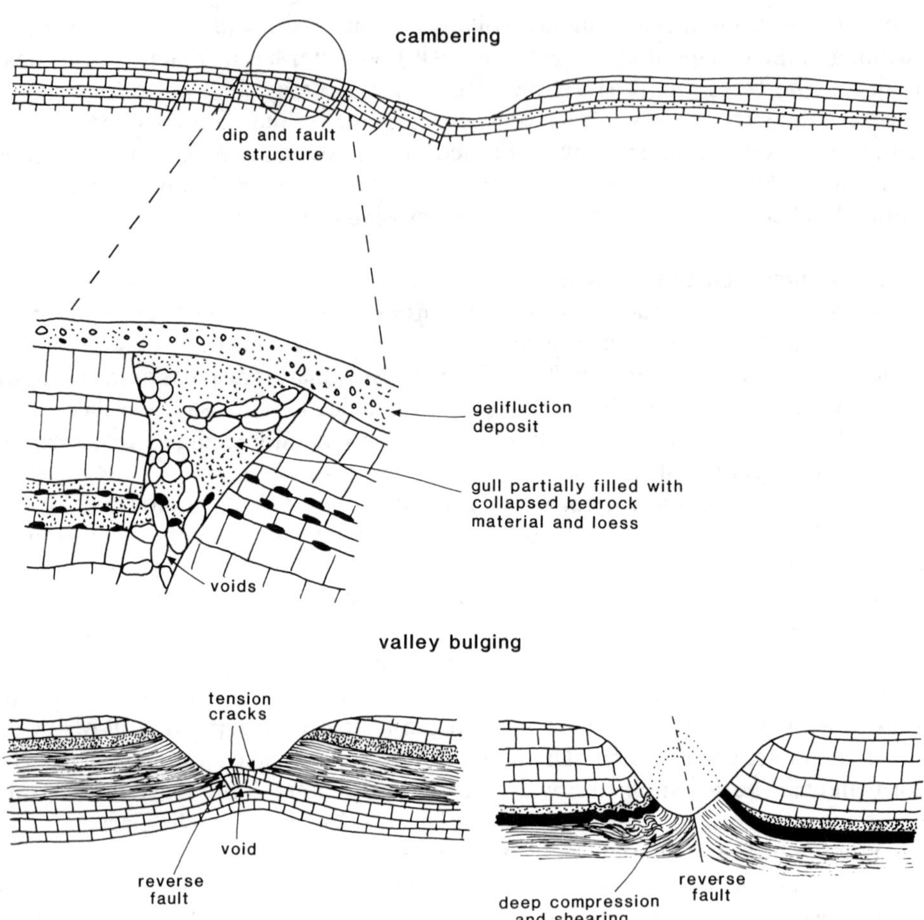

Fig. 2.56 — Structures associated with frost action in valleys cut in flat-bedded sedimentary rocks of variable lithology (from Hollingworth *et al.* 1944).

level and fairly deep water-table, so that most drainage is underground rather than on the surface. The soluble rock is usually also well-jointed but quite strong, so that large underground cavities can be formed and maintained. Surface runoff is carried underground through swallow holes or ponors, which develop by erosion, dissolution and collapse into circular or oval, funnel-shaped hollows termed sinkholes (Plate 7); elongated hollows developed along enlarged fissures are termed dolines. Enlargement and coalescence of adjacent sinkholes and dolines forms extensive irregular depressions termed uvalas. Caverns form below the surface, mainly in upper parts of the phreatic (saturated) zone, but also in the vadose (unsaturated) zone above; roof collapse, initially forming small light-holes, may eventually contribute to further irregular lowering of the ground surface. Protracted dissolution of the soluble rock eventually exposes less soluble strata beneath. Normal surface erosion is then re-established on this surface, though residual hills (hums) of the soluble rock usually persist between the new streams.

Blind-valleys form at the contact between soluble and insoluble rocks, especially where the latter are soft and of low permeability (e.g. clays). The streams that cut them often emerge from caverns at the foot of a high limestone wall. Semi-blind valleys extend a short distance onto the limestone, usually as steep-sided karst canyons resulting from collapse of the cavern roof or erosion by a steep, fast-flowing stream. More extensive valley networks on mid-latitude limestone outcrops are often completely dry, and are usually inherited from past cold periods when the rock was rendered impermeable by permafrost.

Dissolution of limestone beneath a cover of other permeable sediments or a deep weathered mantle in humid tropical regions (e.g. Jamaica) often produces a series of closely-spaced hills with flat or gently rounded, accordant summits, known as cupola-karst. Steep-sided depressions or cockpits often occur between the cupolas.

Karren or lapies are small-scale surface features resulting from partial dissolution of rock at the surface or beneath a thin soil cover. They include grikes, formed by enlargement of vertical or steeply inclined joints (Jones 1965), and the intervening rock surfaces (clints), which are often etched by shallow bowl-shaped weathering pits or irregular elongate depressions (rockrills). Zanjones (Monroe 1964) or karst lanes form by enlargement of grikes.

Calcium carbonate is often redeposited in limestone karst regions when the water carrying calcium and bicarbonate ions evaporates or loses carbon dioxide to the atmosphere or to aquatic plants such as algae. Slow redeposition in subsurface caverns produces solid flowstones or dripstones (roof-pendant stalactites and upward-growing stalagmite sheets and pillars on the cavern floor), but subaerial deposition especially near springs and waterfalls (Plate 8) produces soft, porous tufa (Pentecost 1981).

Sinkholes are often concentrated along fracture zones or lie just beyond the edge of insoluble, low permeability strata (e.g. clays) overlying the more soluble rock (Fig. 2.57). Runoff produces surface streams on the less permeable formation, and these disappear underground when they reach the outcrop of the soluble rock. However, sediment carried from the less soluble rock may fill and eventually block some sinkholes, so that they become inactive and may intermittently form small lakes. Aeolian sediment and collapsing, sliding or flowing remnants of the insoluble beds also contribute to the infilling. The location of solution features is also influenced by lithological features of both the soluble rock and any covering strata (Edmonds 1983).

Climatic changes during the Quaternary probably affected the rate of dissolution and surface lowering in some karst regions. They also affected growth of flowstones (or speleothems) in caverns; for example, uranium-series dating of speleothems from caverns in north-west England showed that the main periods of formation coincided with oceanic interglacial isotope stages 1, 5, 7 and 9, whereas glacial stages 2 and 6 were periods of zero growth (Gascoyne *et al.* 1983). The main geomorphological effect of climatic changes was re-establishment of surface drainage in areas where rocks were rendered uniformly impermeable by permafrost in cold stages. Together with intense gelifraction and abundant meltwater provided by snow and permafrost in summer thaw seasons, this resulted in rapid valley development in

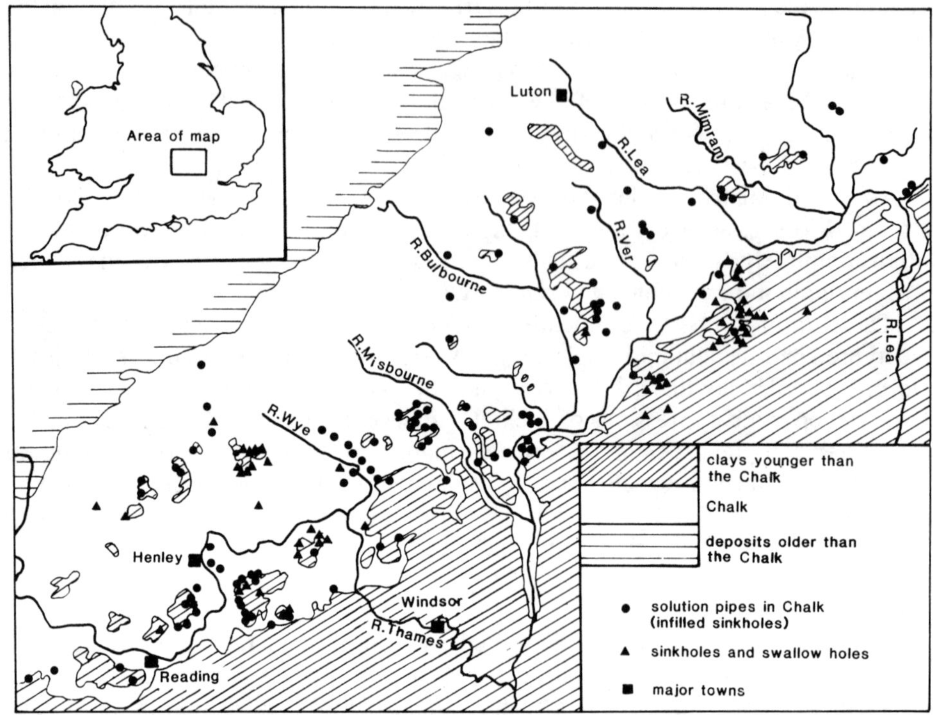

Fig. 2.57 — Distribution of solution features on the Chiltern Hills, England, in relation to outcrops of impermeable clays overlying the Chalk (from Edmonds 1983). Reproduced by permission of the Geological Society from Quaterly Journal of Engineering Geology Volume 16, 1983.

periglacial limestone regions, such as the English chalklands (Catt and Hodgson 1976), and the drainage patterns persisted into the Holocene as a scarcely modified network of relict dry valleys.

2.10 COASTAL EROSION AND DEPOSITION

Marine erosion on hard rock coasts results from corrosion (chemical weathering, especially of limestone), corrasion (abrasion by rock fragments moved by waves and currents) and hydraulic action (compression of air pockets by breaking waves). These processes operate over a narrow vertical zone to create a steep cliff and gently sloping wave-cut platform. The steepness of the cliff is determined by the balance between mass-wasting (e.g. landslipping) of the slope and removal of the resulting debris from the wave-cut platform by wave activity. Effective removal allows waves to undercut the cliff, which remains almost vertical and recedes fairly rapidly. If the rock is strong enough to resist collapse despite undercutting, a notch forms at or just above mean sea level. Caves are excavated along lines of weakness; air compressed in a cave by waves may create a blowhole between the end of the cave and the ground surface above. In soft sediments mass-wasting is more rapid, and features such as a steep profile, caves and notches are short-lived; recession is rapid. On periglacial shores, the rates of erosion and formation of wave-cut platforms are greatly increased by repeated growth of ice in rock fissures (Dawson 1980, Dawson *et al.* 1987). This suggests that many wave-cut platforms previously attributed to interglacials may have formed instead during cold stages of the Quaternary (Fairbridge 1977).

Deposition in the littoral zone (between the highest level reached by storm waves and the base of sediment movement by the waves) usually results in landward coarsening of sediment. During storms, material of all sizes is carried by waves towards the upper margin, but finer sediment is returned seawards by the slightly weaker backwash. The sediment may form a thin impersistent veneer on the wave-cut platform, or accumulate as a thick beach where it is concentrated locally or where there is a rapid supply of sand or coarser sediment eroded from the cliff. Beach deposits are often horizontally bedded, but may show ripple cross-bedding or gently dipping planar cross-bedding; they usually have well sorted and slightly negatively skewed size distributions, and many grains are well rounded because of repeated abrasion in the high energy surf. Coarse shingle and storm accumulations of cobbles create steeper beach profiles (often $>20°$) than finer deposits such as sand (usually $<3°$).

If there is no change of mean sea level, a coastline either retreats through erosion or advances by continued deposition of beach sediment, growth of biogenic (e.g. coral) reefs, or formation of deltas near the mouths of rivers carrying abundant detritus. As the highest parts of beaches are composed of the coarsest material, an advancing or prograding shore results in a coastal plain covered by subparallel shingle ridges. If extensive deposits are exposed at low tide, sand is deflated by onshore winds and redeposited as coastal dunes, which eventually may be built to heights of over 30 metres. Together with coarse storm ridges on upper parts of the beach, these constitute a coastal barrier, which protects any older parts of the coastal plain from inundation during all but the most violent storms (Hageman 1969, Kraft and John 1979).

The Quaternary glaciations resulted in large worldwide eustatic falls of sea level because very large amounts of water were incorporated into ice sheets. After each cold stage the melting of ice sheets resulted in approximately equivalent sea-level rises. The extent of the fall during each glaciation is uncertain, mainly because the evidence is now mostly submerged, though the difference in oxygen isotope ratios of benthonic foraminifera between oceanic stages 1 (Holocene) and 2 (maximum of the last glaciation) (Shackleton 1977), and the estimates of total ice volumes at times of glacial maximum (Denton and Hughes 1981), suggest a glacial lowering of at least 160 metres. Interglacial sea levels are also uncertain, though most were probably within a few metres of present sea level, because no interglacial benthonic foraminifera have oxygen isotope ratios significantly lighter than those of the Holocene (Shackleton 1987).

Superimposed on the eustatic sea-level changes during the Quaternary were various isostatic changes, which were more localized in effect. In areas which were actually covered by ice, the weight of it depressed the crust, and when it subsequently melted, the crust rose again. The amount of this glacio-isostatic movement was proportional to the weight of ice in any area, and therefore less at the margins of ice sheets than near the centres of accumulation. The movement was slower than the glacio-eustatic changes of sea level, with the result that, for example, an area originally at sea level and then eventually depressed isostatically by the same total amount as the eustatic fall in sea level would remain above sea level for much of the early part of the glaciation but lie below sea level during — and for some time after — the post-glacial eustatic rise. Other isostatic changes of sea level resulted from long-term tectonic movements, such as the Cenozoic subsidence of the North Sea basin, and from changes in the amount of water in ocean basins (Bloom 1967, Clark *et al.* 1978).

Yet other factors affecting sea level are changes in the geoid caused by various terrestrial and extra-terrestrial factors influencing the earth's gravitational field (Mörner 1976a), and more locally the compaction of recent sediments such as peat (Pinot 1979). The earlier concept of evaluating past eustatic changes on 'stable' coastlines unaffected by glacio-isostatic changes is therefore unworkable; few coastlines are stable in any sense. Also, many earlier curves portraying the Holocene eustatic sea-level rise and subsequent fluctuations are misleadingly precise, and recent papers merely emphasize caution (Tooley 1982, 1985, Devoy 1982, Kidson 1982, Shennan 1982, 1986). The most useful coastlines for evaluating past changes are probably those beyond the effects of glacio-isostatic changes and subject to constant tectonic uplift, such as parts of the Californian and New Zealand coastlines. These show flights of marine platforms, many of which can be dated by their associated deposits.

Another result of the recently appreciated complexity of Quaternary sea-level change is that the chronocorrelation of raised beaches or marine platforms purely on the basis of height is very unreliable, especially over long distances. Previously, correlations based on height were used extensively in Quaternary geology, but it is quite common for deposits of the same age to occur at different heights, and for deposits of different ages in separate regions to occur at approximately the same height.

3

Soil development during the Quaternary

3.1 DEFINITION AND FORMATION OF SOILS

It is regrettable that the word 'soil' has acquired several different meanings. To the civil engineer it is any soft, unconsolidated rock material, often Quaternary in age but possibly older. To the farmer or gardener it is the uppermost layer of the earth's surface, often darkened by humus or homogenized by cultivation, in which crops grow. To the botanist, it can include any medium from which plants can extract the necessary nutrients for living.

However, to most geologists, geomorphologists and soil scientists, 'soil' means those layers of the earth's crust which show evidence of modification through contact with the biosphere and atmosphere. This modification might include the many effects of physical or chemical weathering on hard rock or unconsolidated sediment, the incorporation of humus (decomposing plant material), disturbance of sedimentary layering by plant roots, burrowing animals or frost action, or the downward leaching of soluble materials. It is in this sense that the word 'soil' is used in this book. The various processes likely to affect upper layers of the earth's crust immediately beneath the interface with the atmosphere are considered in detail by Duchaufour (1982), Bonneau and Souchier (1982), Birkeland (1984) and McRae (1988).

The thickness of soil material showing evidence of modification below the earth's surface may range from a few centimetres to several tens of metres. It depends on many factors, such as how stable the land surface is (i.e. the amounts of deposition or erosion in the recent past, and therefore how long the soil has taken to form), the composition of the rock material at the surface (i.e. how easily it is altered), and the climate (i.e. how aggressive are the processes of modification). Soils which have formed over a short period of time since the last episode of erosion, have developed from an inert parent material (e.g. hard quartzite), or have formed in a cool dry climate are usually very shallow, whereas ones which have been developing from a very weatherable parent material (e.g. soft limestone or an ultrabasic igneous rock) over a long period of time in a warm wet climate are very thick.

In addition to these three factors (time, parent material and climate), Jenny (1941) identified two other factors determining the properties of a soil, namely relief and organisms (vegetation, animals and man). Consequently,

$$\text{soil } (S) \text{ or a single soil property } (s) = f(cl, o, r, p, t)$$

where cl=climate, o=organisms, r=relief, p=parent material and t=time. If cl, o, r and p remain constant or vary in ways that have negligible effects (Jenny 1961), the only factor determining soil characteristics, such as the extent to which humus has been incorporated, or the amount of an element that has been leached away, is time (t). The rate at which these soil-forming processes occur (i.e. the amount of change per unit time) is then termed a chronofunction. Similarly, if length of soil-forming period (t), parent material (p), relief (r) and the effects of organisms (o) remain constant, the effects of changing climatic factors (e.g. increasing temperature or rainfall) on soil properties are known as climofunctions. Other functions are termed biofunctions (o variable), topofunctions (r variable) and lithofunctions (p variable). Sequences of soils in which relief varies but the other four genetic factors are constant are termed toposequences; sequences in which only parent material varies are termed lithosequences; other sequences are known as chronosequences, biosequences and climosequences.

Chronofunctions are the easiest of the functions to express in mathematical terms, either graphically or as quantitative rates (Bockheim 1980), but their precision depends upon accurate assessment of the lengths of soil-forming periods. Other soil-forming factors are more difficult to quantify, partly because they are often interrelated; for example, climate may depend partly upon relief (height above sea level), and in turn relief may be related to geology and therefore often to parent material. Another problem is that it is often difficult to know how constant the factors climate and organisms were during the period of soil development. Jenny (1941, 1980), Yaalon (1975) and Birkeland (1984) have reviewed existing knowledge relating to the various functions.

Because so many complex factors could have been involved in the formation of any particular soil type, it is often a difficult and lengthy job to evaluate any one factor that might be of interest in Quaternary geology (e.g. how long the soil took to form, or under what climatic conditions). The work involves careful recording of the field characteristics of the soil and of its relationships to other soils and to various parent materials. It also includes a wide range of possible laboratory investigations, such as chemical and mineralogical analyses, examination of thin sections, palaeontological studies (e.g. pollen analyses), and the application of several dating techniques. Ideally the relationships between measured soil properties and conditions of soil formation are then evaluated from known functions. Where quantitative evaluation of this type is impossible, however, qualitative interpretation of soil properties is sometimes possible.

3.2 SOIL HORIZONS

Soils can usually be divided into a succession of distinct layers roughly parallel to the ground surface and therefore often unconformable with rock structures, such as inclined bedding, folds, or slaty cleavage (Fig. 3.1). These horizons are distinguished in the field by differences of: colour (including mottling characteristics); particle size distribution of the fine earth (<2 mm); abundance and type of stones (>2 mm); humus content; pH and carbonate content; size, shape and degree of development of the natural semi-permanent aggregates (peds) separated from each other by voids or natural planes of weakness; shape, size and abundance of voids (pores and fissures); consistence (strength, degree of cementation, stickiness and plasticity); size, abundance and type of roots and other soil flora (fungi, algae); abundance and type of soil animals and their faecal pellets; the presence of different types of crystals, nodules, concretions, coatings on ped surfaces or pans (thin, hard horizons of precipitated iron, manganese or humus). Hodgson (1976) gave further details of these characteristics, including criteria for their recognition and classification. Colours are usually described according to the Soil Color Charts of the Munsell Color Company Inc., of Baltimore, Maryland 21218, USA. Particle size classes are defined in Fig. 3.2.

Differences between soil horizons may result from: (a) decreasing effects of weathering with increasing depth below the ground surface, (b) translocation of solid particles vertically downwards to give depleted upper (eluvial) horizons and enriched lower (illuvial) horizons, (c) translocation of soluble constituents and their reprecipitation either lower down (in humid climates) or close to the surface (because of evaporation in dry climates), (d) the presence of a permanent or seasonal water-table close to the ground surface, causing reduction of Fe^{3+} to Fe^{2+} and development of greyish colours, often as mottles, (e) superimposition of the effects of soil development in present environmental conditions upon those of pedogenesis in an earlier episode of different conditions, and (f) original inhomogeneity of the soil parent material, either within a single formation (e.g. interbedded clays and sands resulting from rapid alternations of sea bottom conditions during deposition) or by deposition of a thin recent sediment on an erosion surface transecting a much older formation. Inhomogeneity of soil parent material is extremely common, especially in mid-latitude lowlands, and the original lithological boundaries often control the extent of subsequent pedogenetic alterations, such as the depth at which dissolved iron or calcium carbonate is reprecipitated.

3.2.1 Horizon designation

Different soil horizons are designated using notation systems which often vary slightly between countries, though most are based on the system proposed by the International Society of Soil Science (1967). The system used by the Soil Survey of England and Wales is summarized by Avery (1980). Horizons composed mainly of unconsolidated inorganic mineral material are designated A, B and C from the surface downwards, and continuous hard bedrock which cannot be dug with a spade by R. Subsurface horizons containing less organic matter, clay or iron than the immediately underlying horizon (because these constituents have been translocated downwards) are designated E (for eluvial). Organic horizons (>20% organic matter if the mineral fraction contains no clay, >30% organic matter if the mineral fraction is 50% or more clay) are designated O if composed of peat accumulating under wet conditions, L if composed of fresh, dry leaf litter deposited in the past year, F if composed of partly decayed leaf litter in which some of the original plant structures

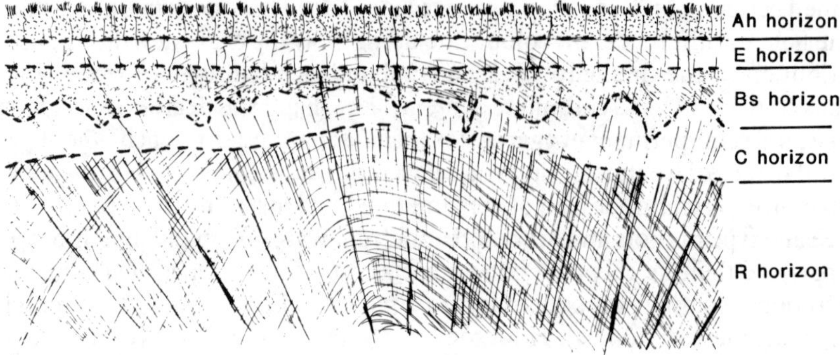

Fig. 3.1 — Soil horizons superimposed on an anticline in slates with vertical cleavage.

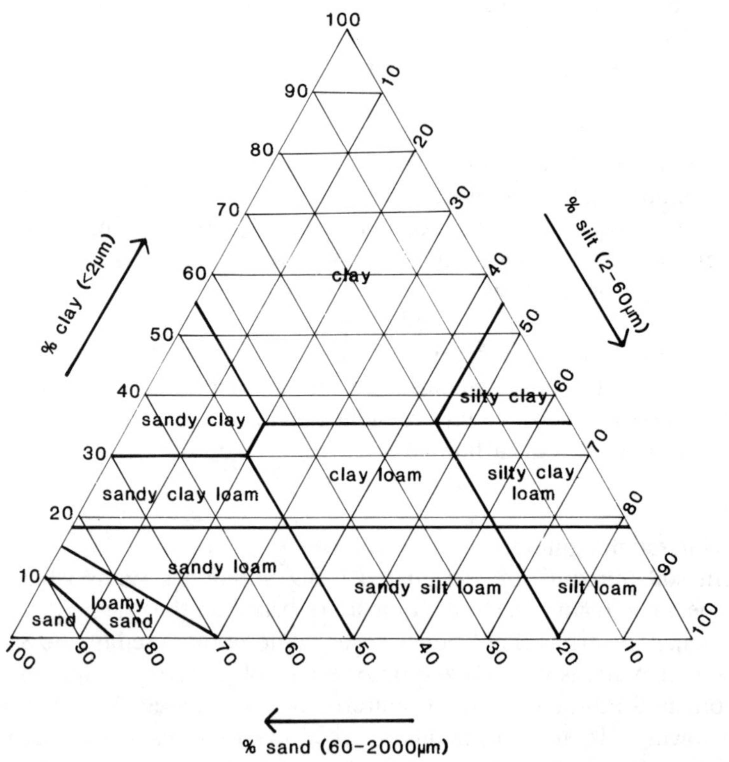

Fig. 3.2 — Particle size classes for <2 mm fractions (from Hodgson 1976).

are still visible, or H if composed of more decayed litter with no plant structures visible.

A horizons show incorporation of humus (Ah horizon), disturbance by cultivation (Ap) or both. E horizons may have a pale colour determined mainly by the colour of uncoated mineral grains (Ea), a greyish colour with brown ferruginous mottles or nodules caused by periodic saturation leading to reduction and segregation of iron (Eg), or enough evenly distributed iron oxide to give a uniform brownish colour but with laboratory evidence that clay has been translocated into horizons beneath (Eb).

B horizons lack rock structure (e.g. original bedding) and may contain illuvial accumulations of silicate clay (Bt), amorphous iron and aluminium (Bs) or humus (Bh). Other B horizons show alteration of the parent material by (a) reduction and segregation of iron (gleying) to give greyish and rusty mottling (Bg horizons), or (b) removal of carbonate, development of peds or formation of clay and iron and aluminium oxides through mineral weathering *in situ* (Bw horizons).

C horizons usually consist of unconsolidated inorganic material which retains rock structure and lacks the properties of any overlying A, E or B horizons, but may be gleyed (Cg), or enriched with at least 1% secondary carbonate (Ck) or with gypsum (Cgy). Weakly consolidated C horizons, coherent enough to limit root penetration, are termed Cr horizons; those continuously cemented with secondary iron, alumina, silica, carbonate or humus so that they resist root penetration are termed Cm; and those made compact, dense and brittle by frost action without cementation are designated Cx (or fragipans).

3.3 SOIL PROFILES AND SOIL CLASSIFICATION

The succession of horizons from the ground surface at any site down to the lowest level at which there is any evidence of parent material modification is known as the soil profile. This is usually described over a small horizontal area, commonly 1 m^2, so that lateral variation is minimized. The American concept of 'pedon' is similar (Soil Survey Staff 1975). The profile or pedon is the smallest unit of soil classification.

3.3.1 Soil series

Soil profiles with a limited range of characteristics of the properties, thickness and vertical sequence of horizons are grouped as a single soil series. As originally applied in the USA and subsequently in Britain, each soil series represented an area of land within which the soil was developed on a single parent material (e.g. Keuper Marl) and had similar profile morphology; series were consequently named after appropriate local place names. However, the desire to compare and systematize soil properties led to a classification of series into higher categories based mainly on genetic concepts. Unfortunately each country has developed its own system of higher classification of soils, and at present there is no universally accepted grouping. The soil series concept consequently changed from the original mapping unit to a taxonomic unit. This change was hastened by the fact that in many areas subject to the rapid depositional, erosional and pedogenetic changes resulting from Quaternary climatic oscillations it is impossible to portray the distribution of individual series at scales of 1:25 000 or smaller. Soil units shown on maps covering significant areas of the country are therefore often composite, perhaps containing several series, though the units are usually named after the one or two most abundant series, and the map legend may contain information about the relative abundance of different series in each unit.

In the classification now used in England and Wales (Clayden and Hollis 1984), each soil series has a unique definition consisting of terms indicating its parent material type and lithology, its particle size class, peaty or extremely calcareous nature (if appropriate), any distinctive colour or mineralogical properties, and its affiliation to the next higher category in the classification hierarchy (i.e. soil subgroup). Although many features inherited from the parent materials are important in this system of series differentiation, some characteristics considered important by geologists play little or no role. Chronostratigraphic or geochronological age is ignored, except that a distinction is maintained between soils developed in Quaternary (drift) deposits and otherwise similar soils in pre-Quaternary formations. Conditions of deposition are also ignored, except where they lead to certain criteria of colour (e.g. the redness of redbeds) or mineralogy (e.g. the presence of pyrite in marine clays leading to formation of a sulphuric soil horizon).

3.3.2 Higher categories of soil classification

Processes of soil formation are subordinate to properties of parent materials in the differentiation of soil series in England and Wales, USA and many other countries in mid-latitude parts of the world, but the reverse is true in characterizing and separating the various higher categories. In the system used in England and Wales (Avery 1980) the higher categories are called soil subgroups, soil groups and major soil groups (in order of increasing size). In the American Soil Taxonomy (Soil Survey Staff 1975) they are subgroups, great groups, suborders and orders (again in order of increasing size). Soil Taxonomy uses a completely new nomenclature. Names of orders (Table 3.1) end in '-sol', and immediately before this contain a formative element or syllable used as an ending for the names of suborders, great groups and subgroups within each order. Names of suborders have two syllables, the formative element preceded by a syllable denoting the main diagnostic properties of the soils. Names of great groups consist of the names of the suborders to which they belong preceded by one or two further syllables suggesting additional diagnostic properties. Names of subgroups consist of the name of a great group plus one or more adjectives; the adjective 'typic' is used for subgroups with clearly expressed properties thought to typify the great group to which it belongs and with no properties transitional to other great groups. Intergrade subgroups have subsidiary properties of another order, suborder or great group, which are denoted by an adjective derived from the name of that taxon. In this system there are 10 orders, 47 suborders and 230 great groups.

The American system of classification is frequently criticized for its complex and often rather obscure nomenclature. However, it is the closest approach yet to a comprehensive system of soil taxonomy based on measurable soil properties that reflect genetic processes conditioned by environmental factors. The Canadian system (Canada Soil Survey Committee 1978) is also based on these principles, and manages to avoid the worst of the nomenclature problems, but is not so comprehensive as the American system because it is designed only for soils occurring in Canada.

Table 3.1 — Approximate equivalents of the F.A.O. world soil map units in the American and English systems of soil classification

F.A.O soil units	American soil orders	Major soil groups in England and Wales
Acrisols	Ultisols	—
Cambisols	Inceptisols	Brown soils
Chernozems	Mollisols	—
Podzoluvisols	Ultisols	—
Rendzinas	Mollisols	Lithomorphic soils
Ferralsols	Oxisols	—
Gleysols	Mollisols	Surface water gley soils
Phaeozems	Mollisols	—
Lithosols	Entisols	Lithomorphic soils
Fluvisols	Entisols	Groundwater gley and raw gley soils
Kastanozems	Mollisols	—
Luvisols	Alfisols	Brown soils
Greyzems	Mollisols	—
Nitosols	Alfisols	—
Histosols	Histosols	Peat soils
Podzols	Spodosols	Podzolic soils
Arenosols	Entisols	—
Regosols	Entisols	Terrestrial raw soils
Solonetz	Aridisols	—
Andosols	Inceptisols	—
Rankers	Entisols	Lithomorphic soils
Vertisols	Vertisols	Pelosols
Planosols	Alfisols	—
Xerosols	Aridisols	—
Yermosols	Aridisols	—
Solonchaks	Aridisols	—
—	—	Man-made soils

The Food and Agriculture Organization (F.A.O.) of the United Nations (1974a) devised a system of soil classification for its world soil map, which probably comes closest to being an international reference system, but is not based completely on a taxonomy related to genesis and measurable properties. The complete map was published in 18 sheets at a scale of 1:5 000 000, which of course does not permit individual soil series to be shown. Instead the legend is divided into 26 units (nouns), which are roughly equivalent in status to the major soil groups of the English classification or the soil orders of the American system (Table 3.1), and are differentiated mainly by genetic processes and features important in crop production. Most of the F.A.O. units are subdivided using any one of up to nine possible adjectives, which refer either to subordinate properties similar to those characterizing other units (e.g. "gleyic" for soils showing slight evidence of gleying but not enough for them to be classed as Gleysols), or to other special properties, such as "gelic" for permanently frozen subsoils, "dystric" for acidic soils lacking important plant nutrients, or "eutric" for neutral or alkaline soils well supplied with nutrients. This gives a total of 106 F.A.O. map units throughout the world. However, the soil information from different regions is very variable. As with other world soil maps, parts of the F.A.O. map in areas with little direct soil information are based on inferences drawn from geological, climatic and natural vegetation data.

Table 3.1 lists the 26 units of the F.A.O. system and their rough equivalents in terms of soil orders in America and major soil groups in England and Wales. In all three systems the units are usually identified by one or more diagnostic horizons, which are defined mainly by criteria evaluated in the field, but also to some extent by laboratory analyses. Some of the diagnostic horizons are surface (A or H) horizons, known as epipedons in the American system, and some are subsurface (usually B) horizons, though of course any horizon may occur at the surface of a soil truncated by erosion. Many of the diagnostic horizons recognized in the American system have rough equivalents in the F.A.O. and English systems, though there are usually small differences in the definitive criteria. For complete definitions of the diagnostic horizons recognized in each of the three systems, the reader should refer to F.A.O. (1974a), Soil Survey Staff (1975) and Avery (1980); a summary is given by McRae (1988).

As an example of the use of the systems of higher soil classification used by F.A.O. and in the USA and England and Wales, we can consider the classification of soils common in N.W. Europe and north-eastern USA on late Pleistocene deposits such as loess or loamy tills. Many well-drained mineral soils in these areas have a light-coloured (weakly organic) A horizon (ochric diagnostic surface horizon), a clay-depleted E horizon (albic diagnostic subsurface horizon) and a brown, clay-enriched Bt horizon (argillic diagnostic subsurface horizon). As the parent materials contain moderate amounts of weatherable minerals and the soils have been weathered for a fairly short period (usually about 10 000 years) in a humid temperate climate, the profiles are neutral or slightly alkaline and fairly rich in bases (K, Na, Mg or Ca). In the USA these properties constitute the central concept of the Alfisol order, within which there are five suborders, the Aqualfs, Boralfs, Udalfs, Ustalfs and Xeralfs. These suborders are distinguished according to precisely defined moisture and temperature regimes. If the profile has a udic moisture regime (i.e. it is not affected by groundwater but receives enough rain and retains enough water against gravity and evapotranspiration to prevent dryness in any part of the profile for as many as 90 days per year, cumulative rather than consecutive), it is in the Udalf suborder. This suborder contains 10 great groups, the Agrudalfs, Natrudalfs, Ferrudalfs, Glossudalfs, Fraglossudalfs, Fragiudalfs, Paleudalfs, Rhodudalfs, Tropudalfs and Hapludalfs, which are distinguished on the presence or absence of other profile characteristics. For example, the Agrudalfs have an agric subsurface diagnostic horizon, formed under long cultivation which has weakened the structure of the topsoil so that the Bt horizon contains illuvial humus and silt as well as illuvial clay. In Glossudalfs the albic E horizon extends downwards into the Bt horizon as tongues (glossic features). In Fragiudalfs there is a fragipan diagnostic subsurface horizon (Cx horizon). Fraglossudalfs have both glossic features and a fragipan. Hapludalfs do not have agric horizons, glossic features or fragipans.

In the F.A.O. system, soils with an argillic diagnostic subsurface horizon are currently divided into Luvisols, Planosols, Nitosols and Podzoluvisols. Podzoluvisols show tonguing of the E horizon to the Bt; Nitosols lack an albic diagnostic subsurface horizon (E horizon); Planosols have an E horizon, but this shows evidence of gleying because the Bt horizon is so enriched with clay that it is only slowly permeable; Luvisols show none of these additional features. Luvisols are divided into eight subunits with the following adjectival prefixes: gleyic (showing grey colours or other evidence that subsoil horizons are saturated by groundwater for part of the year); plinthic (having ferruginous horizons within 125 cm of the surface, which harden irreversibly if exposed to repeated wetting and drying); ferric (having ferruginous segregations giving nodules up to 2 cm diameter or abundant coarse mottles with hues redder than 7.5 YR); albic (having an albic E horizon but without tonguing or the low permeability Bt horizon characteristic of Podzoluvisols and Planosols respectively); vertic (showing cracks 1 cm or more wide in dry periods); calcic (showing secondary carbonate enrichment in an A, B or C horizon over a thickness of at least 15 cm); chromic (having a Bt horizon with a uniform hue of 7.5 YR or redder); orthic (lacking the characteristic features of other Luvisol subunits). Additional F.A.O. soil units with argillic diagnostic horizons have recently been proposed (F.A.O. 1985a), but these are unlikely to appear on F.A.O. soil maps for many years.

In England and Wales loamy and sandy soils without grey or grey-mottled horizons within 40 cm of the surface but showing some evidence of weathering or clay illuviation are classified in the Brown soils great soil group. This contains eight soil groups, of which two have argillic diagnostic subsurface horizons, the argillic brown earths (Plate 9) and the paleo-argillic brown earths (Plate 10). Paleo-argillic B horizons, which are diagnostic of paleo-argillic brown earths, are formed in pre-Ipswichian deposits and have a dominant colour of 7.5 YR or redder (5 YR or redder if sandy) or many coarse mottles 5 YR or redder. Argillic B horizons are not so red and may be formed in deposits of any age, but should be >5 cm thick and extend below 30 cm or start within 1.2 m depth. Within each of these soil groups, there are three subgroups: (a) stagnogleyic argillic brown earths or stagnogleyic paleo-argillic brown earths (grey mottles caused by winter waterlogging appear at less than 70 cm but more than 40 cm depth, as a result of a perched water-table above a low permeability horizon); (b) gleyic subgroups (grey mottles at less than 70 cm but more than 40 cm depth as a result of a shallow water-table); (c) typical subgroups (no grey mottles within 70 cm depth). If grey mottles appear within 40 cm of the surface in otherwise similar soils, the profile is classified in one of two other major soil groups, the surface-water gley soils (perched water-table) or the groundwater gley soils (shallow groundwater table). In such extremely wet situations humus is likely to accumulate in the A horizon, and a distinction is drawn between profiles with a non-humose A horizon (<4.5% organic C) and a humose A. In the groundwater gley soils, profiles with loamy humose A horizons (other than those in alluvium) form the soil group of humic gley soils, and if they also have argillic horizons they form the soil subgroup of argillic humic gley soils. No paleo-argillic equivalents are known among the groundwater gley soils. In the surface-water gley soils, the humose/non-humose distinction gives rise to two soil groups, the stagnohumic gley soils and stagnogley soils respectively; both have paleo-argillic subgroups (paleo-argillic stagnohumic gley soils and paleo-argillic stagnogley soils respectively), but an argillic subgroup is known only within the stagnohumic gley soils.

3.4 SIGNIFICANCE OF SOIL CLASSIFICATION IN QUATERNARY GEOLOGY

Although most soil classification systems are designed as a basis for production of soil maps useful in agriculture, horticulture, silviculture or general land-use planning, both the classification systems and the maps based upon them have considerable value in reconstructing the Quaternary history of an area. By focussing attention on the nature and origin of thin soil horizons, the discipline of investigating, interpreting and eventually classifying profiles or pedons often reveals thin deposits which would be ignored in a conventional geological survey, indicates the age of the ground surface, or suggests climatic and other environmental changes which occurred during soil formation. When this discipline is combined with an appreciation of the distribution of the different soil series or higher units, and their relationship to geomorphological features, the earth scientist has an extremely useful store of knowledge relevant to the Quaternary history of a region.

Thin deposits which are likely to be recognized only in the upper metre or so of the soil profile include loess, coversand, volcanic ash, alluvium and various slope deposits accumulating in a range of environments (head or gelifluction deposits, colluvium or hillwash, mudflows). These may form distinct soil horizons, the boundaries of which were originally depositional boundaries, or may be incorporated into mixed horizons derived from two or more parent materials more or less homogenized by frost-churning, soil faunal activity or cultivation. The presence of loess is often indicated by an increase in coarse silt containing a range of far-travelled minerals (Catt 1978). Aeolian sand components may be more difficult to identify, because they are less likely to be mineralogically distinct from other local sandy deposits. The same is true of many slope deposits, which are also laterally variable because they are derived from whatever deposits happen to crop out on the slope above (see 2.4.3). Volcanic ash can often be identified, even in minute proportions, by the presence of glassy fragments or characteristic minerals, but volcanic constituents are often liable to disappear because they are very easily weathered.

In many soils, granulometric and mineralogical analyses of successive horizons indicate several deposits forming a layered sequence. However, rarely were all deposited before any pedogenesis began. More commonly there were long gaps between periods of subaerial deposition, so that pedogenesis alternated with sedimentation. Even more often, subaerial sedimentation of loess, blown sand, volcanic ash, alluvium or slopewash was slow enough for soil development to continue concurrently. In such circumstances, the A horizon of the soil, enriched with humus and homogenized by various possible processes, is progressively thickened to produce a profile in which topsoil characteristics may extend to several metres depth. This is known as an accretionary, aggrading or cumulative soil. Later the lower parts of the over-thickened A horizon may achieve B horizon characteristics, such as accumulations of illuvial clay. Where slow erosion is concurrent with soil development, as on bare cultivated fields subject to 'windblow' or slopewash under heavy rain, the profile becomes progressively thinner. The result is a degrading soil. If erosion exceeds the rate at which C horizon material is converted into a B horizon by weathering, leaching or illuviation, the B horizon is eventually lost and the resulting soil has only A and C horizons. This is often called an A/C soil.

The relative ages of ground surfaces are often indicated by the types of soil beneath. Many soil-forming processes are slow, and produce measurable effects in terms of the thickness, depth and composition of horizons only over periods of 10^3–10^7 years. For example, the total thickness of an argillic (Bt) horizon, the percentage illuvial clay it contains, and the depth of its upper boundary below the ground surface all tend to increase progressively with time. This is reflected in some differences between argillic and paleo-argillic brown earths in England, and between most Arg- (or Natr-) and Pale-great groups in the USA. Brown earths in England and Hapl-great groups in the USA have cambic instead of argillic B horizons, and are probably less mature than any soils with argillic horizons. On well-drained deposits of similar lithology but increasing age (e.g. successively older river terraces) one should therefore find the sequence brown earth→argillic brown earth→paleo-argillic brown earth in England, or Hapludalf→Natrudalf→Paleudalf or Hapludoll →Argiudoll→Paleudoll in the USA.

However, superimposed on time as a soil-forming factor during the Quaternary in all mid- and high-latitude regions were the rapid climatic changes described in Chapter 1. These led to changes in the types of some soil-forming processes and to an increase or decrease in the rates of others. Soils that were permanently or seasonally frozen in the greatly extended periglacial zones of Quaternary cold periods could undergo little or no chemical weathering, leaching or clay illuviation. Although there was little vegetation in such cold regions, any humus incorporated into the soil was oxidized more slowly than in warmer areas, and consequently accumulated, especially in hollows that remained wet during summer thaw periods. This allowed weak gleying or podzolization to occur locally. But the main soil-forming processes occurring in mid- and high-latitude regions during cold stages of the Quaternary were physical disruption and reorganization of coarser particles lying on or close to the land surface. These resulted from the action of frost in fracturing stones (gelifraction), heaving stones upwards, sorting them into surface patterns (polygons, nets, circles and stripes), and disturbing different layers so that they interpenetrate as involutions or cryoturbations and eventually become intimately mixed (Washburn 1979). Soils showing these features of physical weathering and reorganization are often called arctic structure soils (Mückenhausen 1977).

In contrast to soils formed in Quaternary stages when cold conditions extended to mid-latitude regions like Britain and northern USA, those of interglacial stages in the same regions were dominated by processes of fairly rapid weathering, leaching and illuviation. In parts of north-west Europe the Ipswichian (Eemian) Interglacial (equivalent to oceanic stage 5e, 115 000–128 000 years ago) and at least one earlier interglacial were slightly warmer than any part of the Holocene (Coope 1977; Mangerud *et al.* 1981). They were also longer than the Holocene and at least as humid. Consequently soils formed during these interglacials are likely to be more weathered, leached and richer in illuvial clay than any formed during the Holocene; this probably explains the characteristics of the paleo-argillic horizons in England and Wales.

Soils in which the effects of two or more periods of pedogenesis in different climatic (or other environmental) conditions are superimposed are known as polycyclic (Duchaufour 1982, p. 44), polymorphic (Simonson 1978), composite (Morrison 1978) or polygenetic (Butler 1959). These may occur in one parent material or a sequence of thin deposits. When the last period of pedogenesis is the current one, that is the soil has remained at the surface since before the last major climatic change, the effects of earlier periods are termed relict features, and the soil a relict soil. However, in tropical and subtropical regions where climatic changes during the Quaternary were small or non-existent, unburied soils can be extremely old without containing relict features. For these, Cremaschi (1987) has proposed the term vetusol.

In some isolated mid-latitude areas, deep weathering of igneous and metamorphic rocks, reaching depths of tens of metres and resembling that on extensive ancient peneplains of tropical continental regions, has been attributed to early Quaternary or late Tertiary pedogenesis. Two main types have often been recognized (Millot 1970, Hall 1985): (a) sandy gruss composed of coarse fragments of chemically little-altered primary minerals, and (b) clayey gruss dominated by fine secondary minerals, especially kaolinite, illite, haematite and gibbsite. Some deep weathering resulted from hypogene (hydrothermal) alteration, but where it is extensive on mid-latitude land surfaces and has a fairly sharp basal transition to fresh rock, it must be the result of either repeated episodes of interglacial pedogenesis or long-continued Tertiary soil formation. Hall (1985) suggested that the sandy gruss of NE Scotland is Pliocene or early Quaternary and the clayey gruss late Miocene or older, but such dating is based on very indirect evidence and is therefore uncertain.

Old, thick, strongly developed soils, such as many polycyclic and paleo-argillic soils, vetusols, and sandy or clayey gruss, are often termed 'residual soils' by civil engineers (e.g. Legget and Karrow 1983). In a strict sense, residual soils should be developed *in situ* from a single parent material, and no component should have been transported laterally to the site. In practice this is probably unknown, because lateral movement of soil material is very common, and even on extensive, completely flat surfaces there is usually some slow accretion of aeolian sediment. Many so-called residual soils in fact show clear evidence that at least part of the parent material was transported laterally, but the concept has some validity, especially in civil engineering, because many of the geotechnical properties of these soils can be attributed to protracted weathering and are different from those of less strongly developed soils or of unconsolidated, unweathered sediments found at comparable depths below the surface. For example, some typical residual soils, the laterites (McFarlane 1976) and bauxites of tropical regions, are dominated mineralogically by oxides of iron or aluminium respectively, and consequently behave differently from soils containing layer silicate clay minerals. Other residual soils have duricrust horizons (Goudie 1973), which are strongly cemented with iron oxides (ferricrete), aluminium oxides (alucrete), calcium carbonate (calcrete), dolomite (dolocrete), gypsum (gypcrete), silica (silcrete) or calcium phosphate.

Because of slower weathering rates and more extensive glacial and periglacial erosion in higher latitudes, most well developed residual soils occur in tropical and sub-tropical regions. In Britain the most extensive soils that could be classified as residual are those on upland Chalk plateaux in parts of southern England beyond the

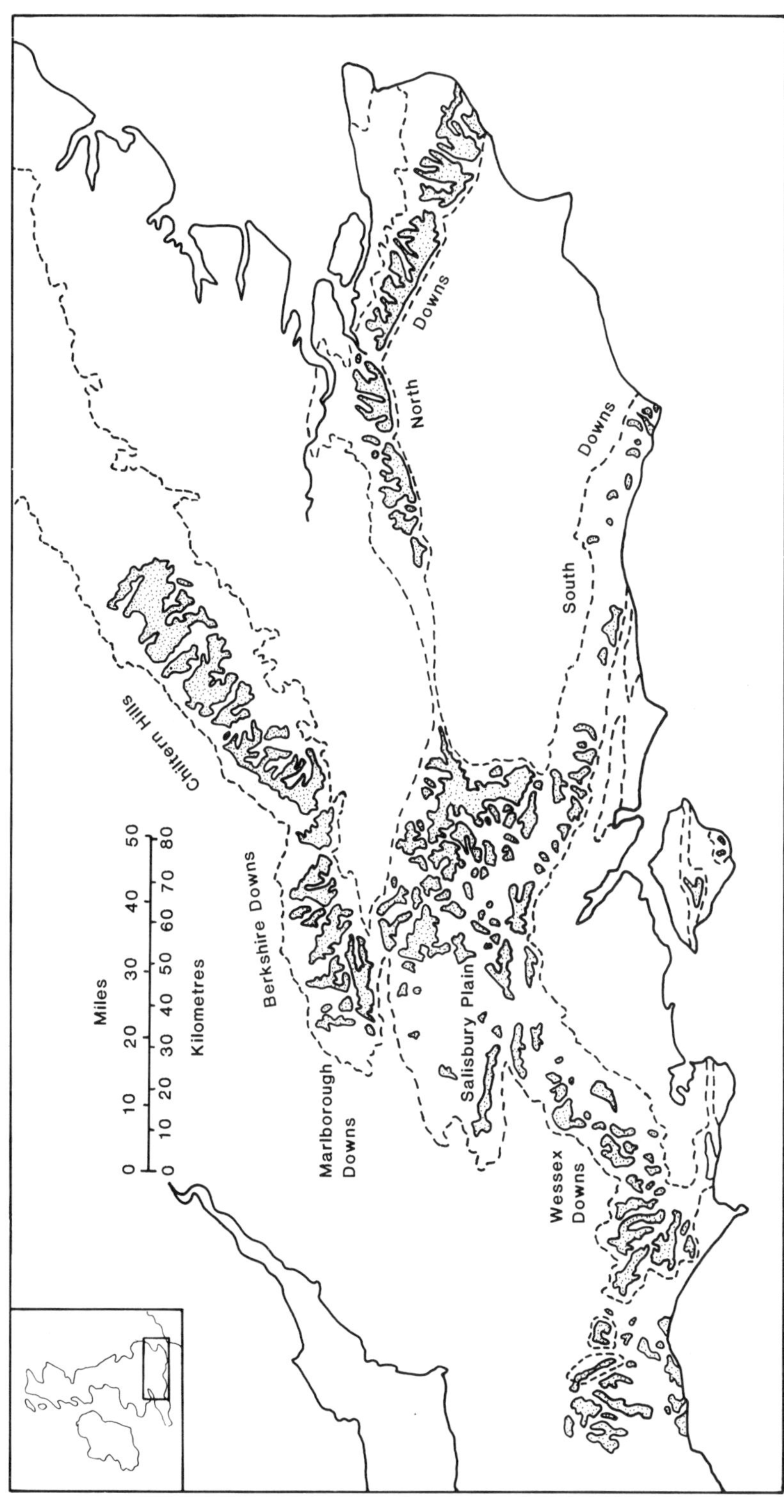

Fig. 3.3 — Distribution of residual soils (Clay-with-flints of British Geological Survey) on the Chalk outcrop in southern England (based on Soil Survey of England and Wales 1983).

limit of the most extensive (Anglian) glaciation (Fig. 3.3). These were initially mapped by the British Geological Survey as a distinct 'drift' deposit, termed Clay-with-flints. This was originally regarded simply as a weathered residue of the Upper Cretaceous Chalk; for example, Wooldridge and Linton (1955) referred to it as 'true residual Clay-with-flints'. However, the mineralogical composition and micromorphology of these soils show that they are formed in a thin (2–5 m) veneer of basal Tertiary deposits (usually Reading Beds Clay) overlying the Chalk, though some insoluble residue from the underlying Chalk was released by deep interglacial weathering and incorporated into the weathered clay veneer by cryoturbation in cold stages of the Quaternary (Catt and Hodgson 1976).

3.5 SOIL CATENAS AND TOPOFUNCTIONS

Many soil scientists have observed regular associations of soil types and geomorphological features such as slopes. Milne (1935) introduced the term catena for a 'grouping of soils which, while they fall wide apart in a natural system of classification on account of fundamental and morphological difference, are yet linked in their occurrence by conditions of topography and are repeated in the same relationships to each other wherever the same conditions are met'. The term later came to be used in different ways, leading to some confusion (Watson 1960). It is a broader concept than toposequence (Jenny 1941), which is limited to a sequence of soils in which only one of the five pedogenetic factors (relief) has varied. In practice many of the other pedogenetic factors (e.g. parent material) vary with relief, and their effects are included in the catena concept.

Simple catenas are derived from a single parent material, and their constituent soil types are differentiated by processes occurring as a result of the presence of a slope. Because water moves more rapidly through profiles on steeper parts of the slope, such soils are often better drained than those on plateaux or interfluves, footslopes and valley floors. This is often indicated by brown or red colours persisting to a greater depth below the ground surface, or by a smaller organic matter content. In most temperate and tropical climates, fine soil particles are moved from valley sides to the valley floor by slopewash; this often leads to progressive fining and thickening of the profiles down-slope, and to an increase in fine weathered constituents. As materials may also be carried down-slope in solution, these changes are often accompanied by changes in pH, cation exchange characteristics, salinity or amounts of redeposited iron and manganese.

In complex catenas some or all of these changes are superimposed on other differences resulting from inhomogeneity of the soil parent material (e.g. where gently dipping strata of different types form outcrops along the slope), or where various parts of the slope developed under different past soil-forming conditions (e.g. during different climatic periods of the Quaternary). Examples of these are illustrated in Fig. 3.4 and were discussed in detail by Ollier (1976). He recognized eight situations (mainly climatic regions) characterized by processes leading to certain types of catena:

(1) Cold dry regions, in which frost action and salt weathering dominate, leading to formation of lithosols.

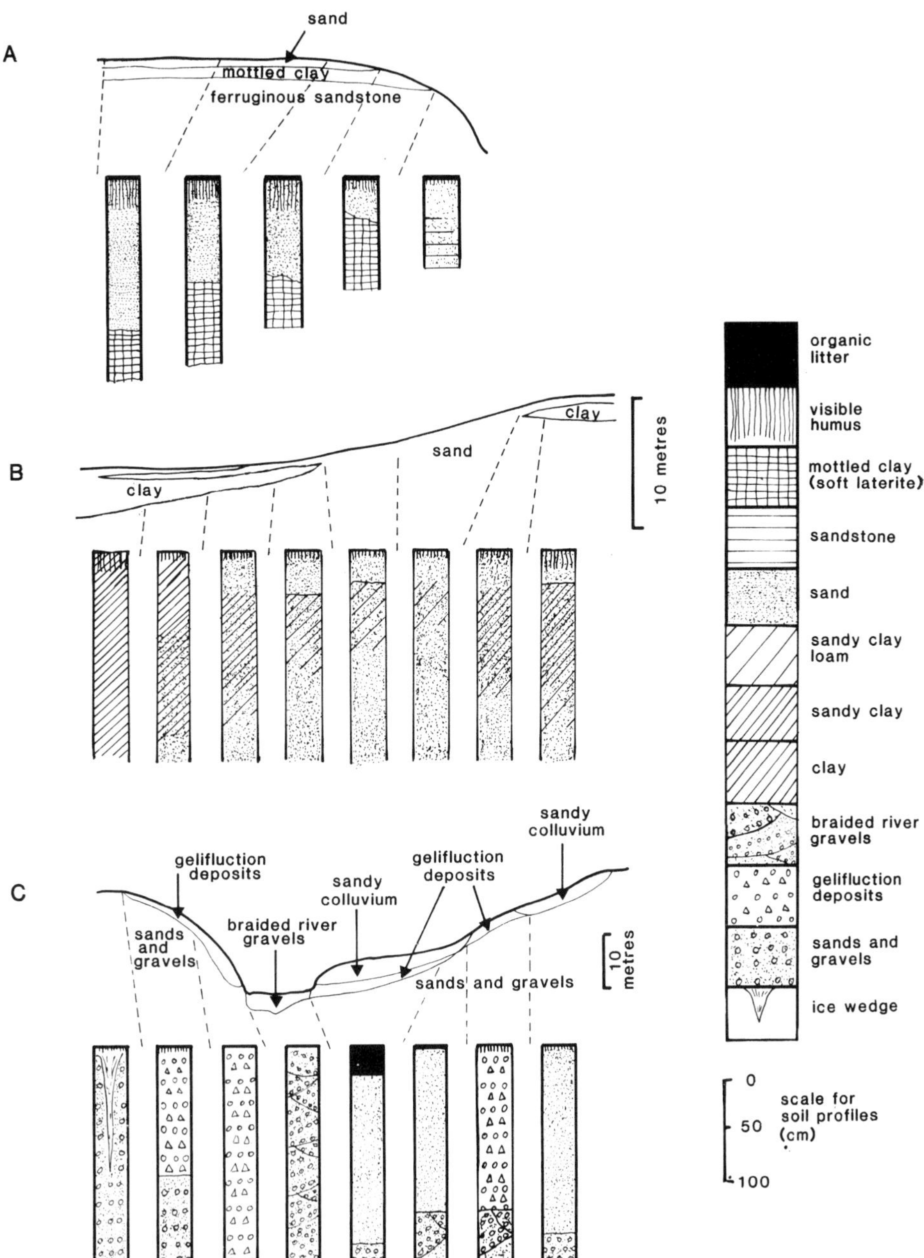

Fig. 3.4 — Examples of soil catenas in different climatic zones (from Ollier 1976). A: soils associated with a slope cutting a plateau laterite in Nigeria (Moss 1965), B: soils of the Netanya catena on sand dunes, Israel (Dan *et al.* 1968), C: soils associated with an asymmetric valley, north-west Banks Island, Arctic Canada (French 1971). Reproduced by permission of Elsevier Science Publishers.

(2) Cold wet regions, with gelifluction dominant, leading to lithosols and gleysols on lobes of mobile debris and organic accumulations (histosols) on valley floors.
(3) Hot dry regions, where wash caused by occasional storms is the dominant transport process, leading to lithosols on slopes and finer gleysols or salt-affected solonetz soils on valley floors.
(4) Tropical duricrust areas, with ferricrete occurring on plateaux and valley-side shelves; silcrete occurs in more arid areas and bauxite where there is continuous high rainfall.
(5) In other tropical areas, lower slopes often have sandy soils where throughflow has removed the clay fraction.
(6) Some rare sites, such as fixed sand-dunes, are very permeable and suffer little erosion or slopewash, so that catenary changes result mainly from hydrological factors.
(7) Landslide-dominated landscapes in wet areas with fairly steep slopes.
(8) All other situations, where erosion, deposition and pedogenesis interact on slopes in many different ways, and there is no apparent relationship between catenas and climate.

Various carefully chosen catenas have been used in attempts to calculate topofunctions, the mathematical relationships between (a) soil properties, such as grain size, organic matter content, thickness of A horizon or depth to an imperfectly drained (e.g. grey-mottled) horizon, and (b) relief factors, such as slope gradient or distance from the slope summit. Examples are provided by Walker (1966), Ruhe and Walker (1968), Walker *et al.* (1968a, 1968b), Dan *et al.* (1968), Kleiss (1970) and Vreeken (1973), based mainly on catenas in uniform aeolian sediment. The relationships reported are, however, variable (mainly linear or polynomial) and probably have local rather than general significance (Yaalon 1975).

3.6 BURIED SOILS

Soils formed during past periods were often buried beneath younger sediments or extrusive volcanic rocks. Before burial, many were truncated by erosion, often because the upper (A and E) horizons were loose and friable. In such circumstances the B horizon is sharply overlain by the new deposit. The erosion may result from fluvial, aeolian or glacial action, or movement on slopes especially under cold conditions (gelifluction). If deposition of the new sediment is initially slow and the A horizon is overthickened (as in an accretionary soil), there is a gradation from the buried A horizon into the overlying sediment, the latter becoming progressively less humose upwards. After burial a soil may be modified by various diagenetic processes, such as oxidation (decreasing the humus content), compression (lowering the porosity), deposition of iron or manganese from groundwater, deposition of calcium carbonate (usually from an overlying soil) or removal of soluble salts.

Because of these various effects during and after burial, buried soils are often quite unlike unburied equivalents, and may be difficult to recognize. Identification can be facilitated by one or more of the following:

(1) In thin sections, characteristic soil features, such as argillans in Bt horizons, humus coatings on sand grains in Bh horizons, droppings of soil animals, body fossils of soil organisms or typical soil pores, may be recognized (Fig. 3.5).

(2) Features seen in thin section and bulk properties of soils, such as chemical composition, particle size distribution and mineralogical composition, show characteristic changes with depth (depth functions) (Fig. 3.6), so measurements should be made at regular vertical intervals and compared with results for unburied soils.

(3) All soils vary laterally in characteristic ways because of changes in parent material, drainage or other factors. These changes are often related to geomorphological features, such as slopes, and can be explained in terms of the processes producing soil catenas (see 3.5). Any exposure of a presumed buried soil should therefore be traced laterally as far as possible to locate catenary and other lateral changes.

Buried soils are preserved most frequently in areas subject to repeated aeolian sedimentation (e.g. in loess or coversand successions), probably because the change from a stable land surface with soil development to aeolian deposition involves less environmental adjustment than a change to marine, fluvial, lacustrine or glacial deposition. In regions such as northern China (Heller and Liu Tungsheng 1984), Soviet Central Asia (Dodonov 1984) and central Europe (Kukla 1977), where the entire Quaternary and even the late Pliocene is represented by loess, there are sequences of up to 40 buried soils. From molluscan evidence, the soils seem to represent warm humid episodes and the intervening loess layers cold dry periods, which correlate well with the warm and cold stages respectively of the oceanic oxygen isotope sequence (Kukla 1977) (Fig. 1.10). Pye (1984) pointed to small differences in the loess-soil sequences of these major loess regions (Fig. 3.7), but they probably result from gaps in some of the successions, palaeoclimatic differences between the regions, or imprecise dating of some units.

Less complete sequences of Quaternary buried soils occur in areas of mixed aeolian and glacial deposition, such as Britain, central Europe, northern USA and New Zealand (Tables 3.2 to 3.5), or where there were temporary breaks in alluvial, lacustrine, shallow marine or slope deposition. In most areas where cold stages of the Quaternary resulted in glaciation, periglacial aeolian deposition, and the suppression of pedogenesis by chemical weathering, leaching and illuviation, the buried soils are assumed to represent interglacials (Plate 11) and interstadials; indeed over large areas, such as the mid-western USA, they are often the only evidence for warm stages.

From experience of buried soils in the south-western USA, Birkeland and Shroba (1974) suggested that buried soils should not necessarily be correlated with warm stages of the Quaternary; they emphasized the necessity for a stable land surface in soil formation, and showed that periods of stability are often unrelated to the established sequence of Quaternary climatic oscillations. Although it is true that in some areas buried soils do often represent periods of land surface stability unrelated

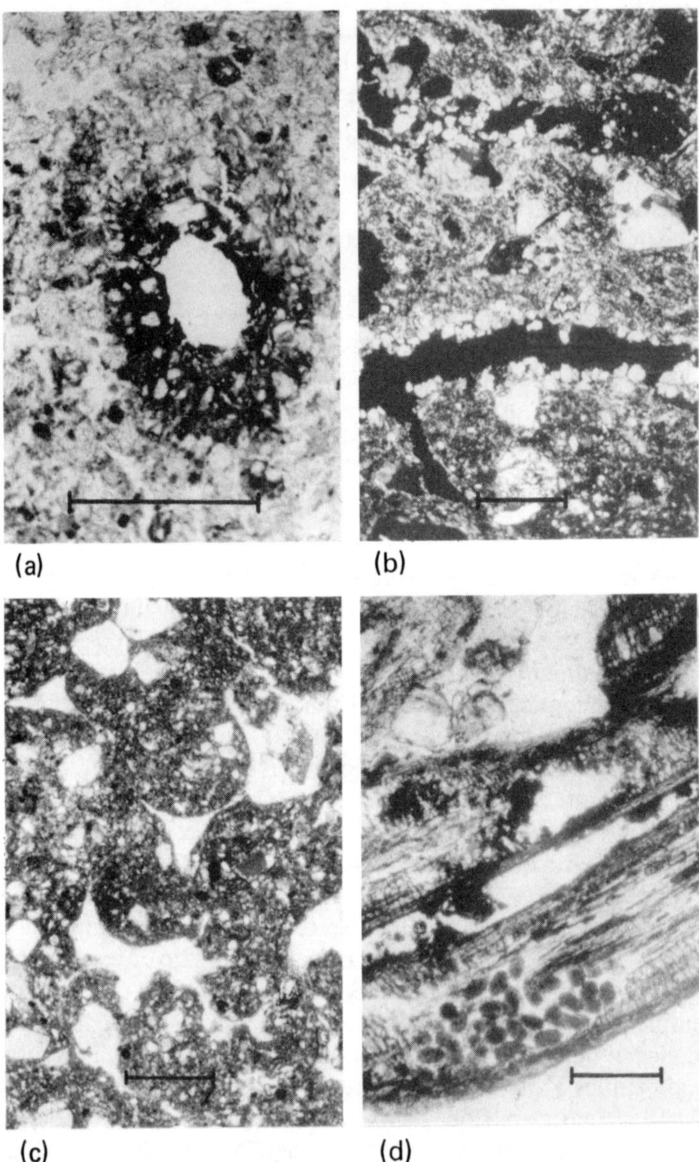

Fig. 3.5 — Characteristic micromorphological features of soil horizons: (a) pore with humus coating, (b) subsoil fissure lined with secondary calcite crystals, (c) earthworm excreta in topsoil, (d) excreta of oribatid mites on a conifer needle from the A horizon of a podzol. Each scale bar represents 0.5 mm.

to Quaternary climatic fluctuations, these are in the tropical and sub-tropical regions where the fluctuations were too weak to prevent chemical weathering, leaching and illuviation from continuing uninterrupted. At higher latitudes the climatic changes exerted a greater influence on pedogenetic processes. Here it was only in the warm

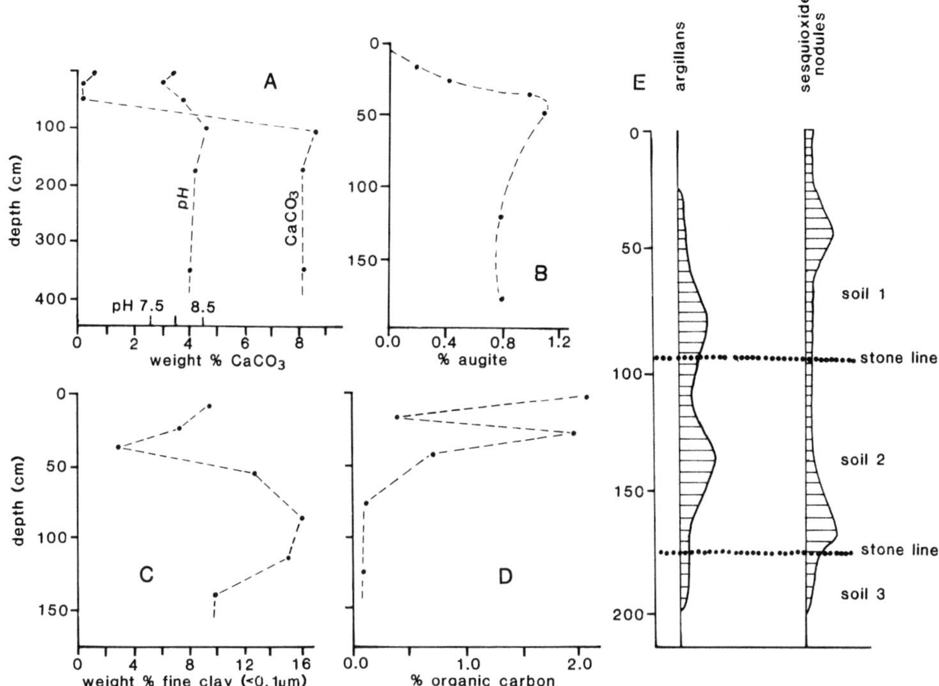

Fig. 3.6 — Depth functions for various soil components.

A: pH and calcium carbonate in a Holocene soil developed in late Devensian till, Holderness, E. England.

B: percentage augite in late Holocene humoferric podzol in Devensian coversand, Suffolk, E. England; the curve is an exact-fitting cubic spline (from Bateman and Catt 1985). Reproduced by permission of Catena Verlag.

C: percentage fine clay (<0.1 μm) in a buried early Holocene soil in Devensian loess, Pegwell Bay, south-east England (from Weir *et al.* 1971).

D: percentage organic carbon in humoferric podzol in Triassic sandstone, Clipstone Forest, E. England.

E: micromorphological features (argillans and sesquioxide nodules) in compound soil profile, Blackwood River valley, W. Australia; the three soils are separated by stone lines (from Finkl and Gilkes 1976). Reproduced by permission of Elsevier Science Publishers.

stages that land surfaces were sufficiently stable (under forest) and pedogenetic processes sufficiently rapid for deep, strongly altered soils to form; on the rare occasions when a land surface was stable during a cold stage the only soil types likely to form were arctic structure soils or very thin, weak podzols, brown earths, rendzinas or peats.

Buried soils are also quite common in volcanic areas, but they are not related to climatic changes because they essentially represent quiescent episodes between periods of lava extrusion or ash deposition.

3.7 DATING PERIODS OF SOIL DEVELOPMENT

The oldest possible date for the time when a buried soil started to form is indicated by the age of its parent material, and the youngest possible date for the time

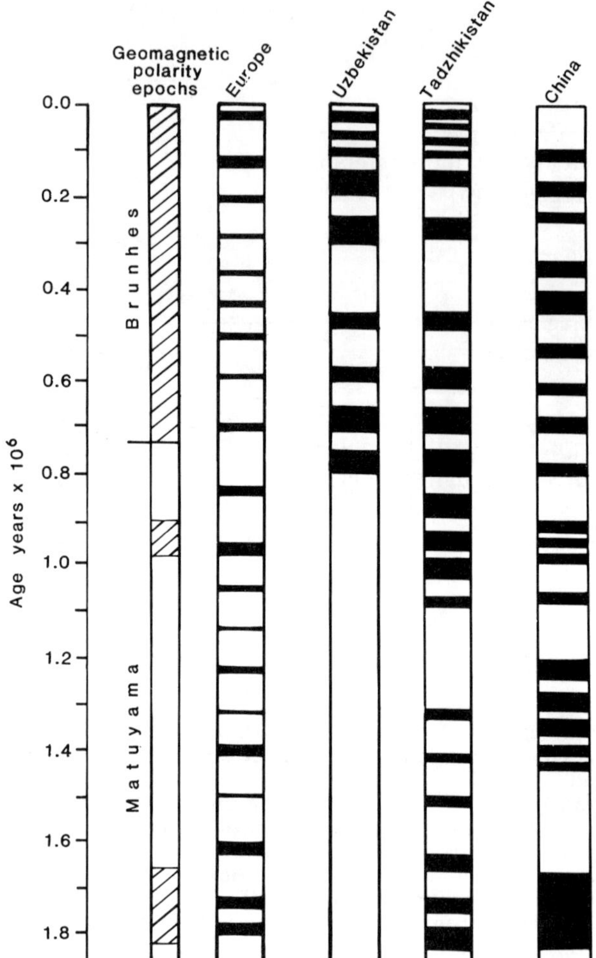

Fig. 3.7 — Sequences of buried soils (black) in the loess deposits of Europe and Asia (based on Pye 1984).

it ceased to continue forming is given by the age of the deposit overlying it. At any one site these two limits may give little indication of the actual start and finish of soil formation, but if the soil is traced laterally a much narrower age range may be indicated by applying the rule that the soil is younger than its youngest parent material but older than the oldest overlying deposit (Fig. 3.8). A more definite date for the termination of pedogenesis may be given by the age of an overlying deposit if it has a diffuse, gradational boundary with the soil's A horizon beneath, as this indicates that the last stage of pedogenesis coincided with burial. Other methods of determining the age of soils by laboratory analyses are discussed in Chapter 5, but these usually give either a single date for some time during the period of soil

Table 3.2 — Soil stratigraphic units in the British Quaternary (Rose *et al.* 1985); unnamed units also occur at other stratigraphic levels

Age (oceanic isotope stages)	Soils
Late Devensian (Windermere interstadial) (2)	Pitstone
Ipswichian interglacial (5)	Troutbeck
Wolstonian	
Hoxnian interglacial	
Early Anglian	Barham
Cromerian interglacial (possibly also Pastonian)	Valley Farm

formation, or an estimate of how long the soil took to form but with no indication of when it formed. So although some laboratory studies can help date a buried soil, they cannot substitute for careful evaluation of stratigraphic relationships in the field.

The upper age limit of unburied soils is of course the present. However, if they are polycyclic or composite soils with relict features inherited from an earlier period of different environmental conditions, it is necessary to date the end of that earlier period. This need not be the last known climatic or other environmental change, because the soil might have been buried before this change and exhumed after it. Morrison (1978) suggested that if the unburied composite soil is traced laterally to points where horizons containing the relict features are truncated by erosion surfaces, the relict features can be dated as older than the oldest of those erosion surfaces. But the erosion surfaces themselves are dated only by reference to deposits in the same way as soils are dated, so this may not help very much. It may therefore be more useful to trace the composite soil laterally even further until the two or more component soil stratigraphic units are separated by recognizable and datable deposits. Where the component units are separated by thin deposits but still partly overlap, they form subdivided (Morrison 1978) or compound soils (Duchaufour 1982), or more commonly pedocomplexes.

The term 'palaeosol' is often used for soils thought to date wholly or partly from earlier geological periods when soil-forming conditions differed from those of the present. As a loosely defined term simply meaning 'old soil' it has some value, but it has no universally accepted definition, and is used in several different senses (Catt 1986), including the equivalent of buried soil (however recent burial might have been), soil formed before the last cold period of the Pleistocene in mid-latitude regions, and soil formed before the Holocene. Further confusion results from the use of palaeosol for old unconsolidated sediments, such as the Mesozoic marine clays of the English Midlands (Legget and Karrow 1983, p. 42–2); this is an extension of the engineer's use of soil for any unconsolidated sediment. The main difficulty with the word 'palaeosol' comes in trying to find a definition acceptable both to pedologists working with relict soils on the present land surface, and to geologists dealing with buried soils. This is because:

(1) Most Quaternary buried soils are likely to emerge at the surface somewhere, and

Table 3.3 — Quaternary soil stratigraphic units in Europe (from various sources)

Stage (likely oceanic isotope stage)	Soils
Weichselian (2–4)	Mende Upper, Basaharc Base and Double, Kirchberg, Odderade, Brørup, Stillfried B
Eemian interglacial (5)	Bla, Elbeuf I, Rocourt, Upper Heitersheim, Erkelenz, Bilshausen, Lommatzsch, Naumburg, Nietulisko, Stillfried A, Wels I, Pilszcz, Mende Base
Warthe (6)	Rugen, Altenburg, Nieledew
Treenian interglacial (7)	Cla, Elbeuf II, Rheindalen, Wenningstedt, Rittmitz, Tomaszow, Wels II, Paks Sandy Forest
Drenthe (8)	
Dömnitzian interglacial (9)	Dla, Elbeuf III, Wegberg, Edderitz, Wels III
Fuhnian (10)	
Holsteinian interglacial (11)	Ela, Elbeuf IV, Profondeville, Lower Heitersheim, Gotha, Wels IV, Muglinov, Paks Marshy
Elsterian (12)	
Cromerian Complex (13)	Fla
(14)	
(15)	Gla, Paks Lower Double
(16)	
(17)	Hla, Paks Lower Double
(18)	
(19)	Ila, Paks-Dunakömlod, Krems 4
(20)	
(21)	Jla, Dunaföldvár 1, Krems 5
(22)	
(23)	Kla, Dunaföldvár 2, Krems 7b
(24)	
(25)	Lla, Dunaföldvár 3, Krems 7a
(26)	
(27)	Mla, Dunaföldvár 4, Krems 8
(28)	
(29)	Nla, Dunaföldvár 5, Krems 9
(30)	
(31)	Ola, Dunaföldvár 6, Krems 10

if one is a palaeosol so is the other. If soils buried very recently are palaeosols, then almost all unburied soils become palaeosols and the term has no special meaning; in effect all soils become palaeosols.

Table 3.4 — Soil stratigraphic units in central northern USA (Hallberg 1986)

Age (oceanic isotope stages)		Soils
Wisconsinan (2–4)		Farmdale, Sidney, Pleasant Grove, Chapin
Sangamonian (5)		Sangamon
Illinoian	(6–8)	Pike, Buzzards Roost, Ingham
Pre-Illinoian	(9–14)	Yarmouth
	(15)	Dysart
	(17)	Upland, Franklin
	(19)	Westburg
	(21)	Paleosol K
	(23–25)	Afton

Table 3.5 — Soil stratigraphic units in New Zealand (Leamy *et al.* 1973)

Age	South Island soils	North Island soils
Aranuian		
Otiran	Edievale, Pomahaka, Criffel, Amisfield, Alfern, Tinwald, Pukerau	Whanahuia, Kimbolton
Oturian interglacial	Romahapa, Pisa	Tapuae
Waimean		Stanway, Makino
Terangian interglacial		Tutaenui
Waimaungan		Warring

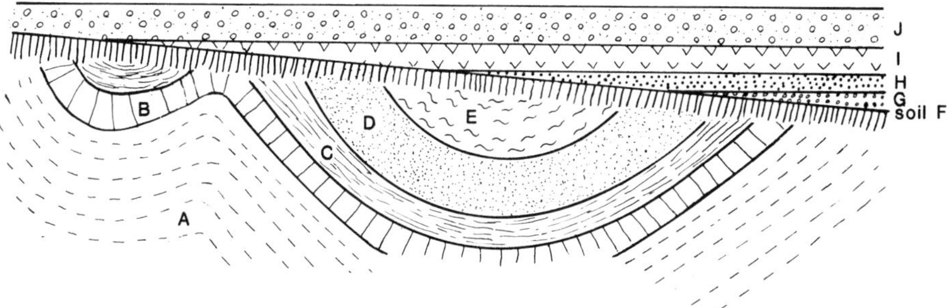

Fig. 3.8 — Stratigraphic interval of buried soil in relation to lithostratigraphical units. Soil F formed between deposition of units E and G, though much longer apparent intervals (A–J, B–I, etc.) might be inferred from observations at single exposures along the traverse.

(2) If an arbitrary age limit (e.g. 10 000 years ago) is placed on palaeosols (buried or unburied), there is immediately a major problem of dating, especially with unburied soils. This is best resolved by placing the age limit at the last major climatic change, so that relict soil features formed in the different climate before that date become diagnostic features of palaeosols. This often proves workable in a small region, but cannot be extended worldwide because climatic changes differed in magnitude from place to place, and in many areas (e.g. the tropics) may have been too weak to affect soil-forming processes. As a result, quite recent soils in high latitudes would become palaeosols but much older soils in low latitudes would not.

Instead of imposing on soils an arbitrary and unworkable distinction into palaeosols and others (? neosols), it is more important in Quaternary geology to reconstruct a detailed history for any buried or unburied soil, relating individual features to episodes of deposition, erosion and environmental changes affecting soil development, and also dating the beginning and end of pedogenesis as precisely as possible. As in other aspects of Quaternary geology, it is more important to bracket the timing of events like the start of soil formation within known limits than to guess the single most likely date between those limits.

3.8 CHRONOSEQUENCES

Soils of increasing age formed on a succession of lithologically similar deposits within an area or areas in which other soil-forming factors (climate, organisms and relief) were reasonably constant constitute a chronosequence. Vreeken (1975) recognized four types (Fig. 3.9):

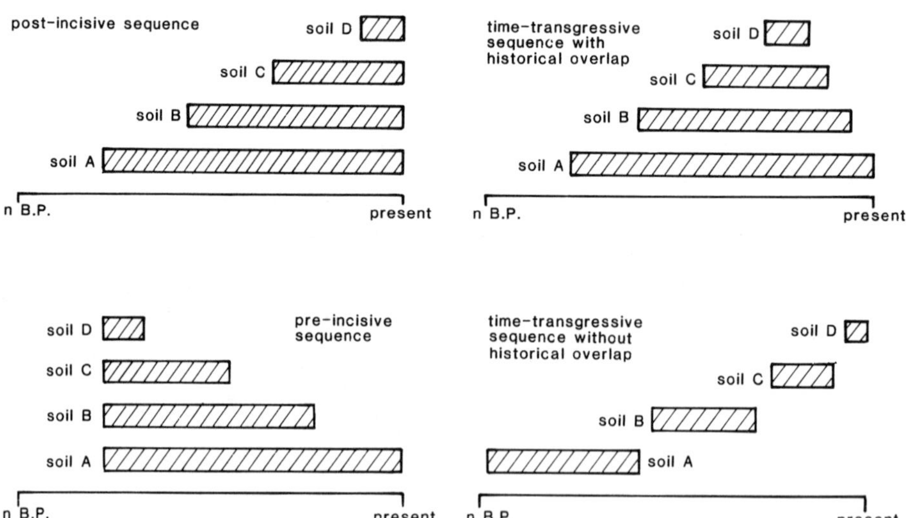

Fig. 3.9 — Four types of soil chronosequence (from Vreeken 1975). Reproduced by permission of the editor, Journal of Soil Science.

(1) Post-incisive chronosequence: the individual soils began forming at different times, and all of them either are still exposed or were simultaneously buried.
(2) Pre-incisive chronosequence: the individual soils began forming simultaneously, but were buried at different times, and one may still be exposed.
(3) Time-transgressive chronosequence without historical overlap: the individual soils began to form and ceased to form at different times, but none of the soil-forming intervals overlaps with another.
(4) Time-transgressive chronosequence with historical overlap: the individual soils began to form and ceased to form at different times, but two or more of the soil-forming intervals overlap in time.

Types (1) and (3) are the commonest, but if they are used to calculate pathways and rates of soil-forming processes, they suffer from the assumption that each component profile of the chronosequence developed in the same way and at the same rate. As environmental conditions changed frequently in many regions during the Quaternary, this is often an unjustified assumption; earlier soils in the chronosequence may not have gone through the same early history as later soils. With type (2), all the individual members experienced the same initial conditions, and if environmental change occurred later in formation of the sequence it should be revealed by the appearance of polycyclic soils among the members that were buried later. Consequently there is a better chance of establishing pathways of soil development and calculating rates of certain processes, but true pre-incisive chronosequences are probably quite rare. Vreeken argued that time-transgressive chronosequences with historical overlap (type (4)) are more common and the most valuable of the four types, though some soil properties in the sequence might show differences related to the length of time individual soils were buried and modified by diagenesis.

Without doubt the interpretation of all chronosequences is more problematic than first appears, and some types are more suitable for certain purposes than others. Despite this, it is clear from the study of known chronosequences that many soil properties initially change quite rapidly, and after some time the rate of change decreases as the soil property approaches a steady-state condition. This applies to the humus content of A horizons, the reddish colour development of B horizons, and the amount of Fe extracted from B horizons by sodium dithionite solution. The processes responsible for these properties are termed self-terminating processes. From 32 chronosequences in various climatic regions, Bockheim (1980) showed that the best correlation between these soil properties (y) and time (x) is the logarithmic chronofunction

$$y = a+(b \log x)$$

This could predict the relationship over short periods (500 yr) as well as long (10^6 yr). The rates of all soil-forming processes are very variable, and often depend upon internal soil factors as well as external. For example, for the same 32 chronosequences, Bockheim found that the rate of increase of the clay content of argillic (Bt) horizons correlates with the clay percentage of the parent material and with mean annual temperature. But in addition, studies of several individual chronosequences have suggested that other factors, such as high exchangeable sodium content and regular aeolian dust deposition on the soil surface, increase rates of clay illuviation (Muhs 1982, Peterson 1980), whereas very dry conditions seem to inhibit the process (Dan *et al.* 1982, Bockheim 1982).

Birkeland (1984) discussed rates of change of other soil morphological features, such as the build-up and loss of calcium carbonate, and of soil clay mineralogy. He also showed how some of the diagnostic horizons and soil orders of the American system of soil classification (Soil Survey Staff 1975) are related to the age of the land surface in parts of the USA and other countries, so that soil maps can be used to help group parent materials and parts of the landscape according to age. These relationships are summarized in Fig. 3.10.

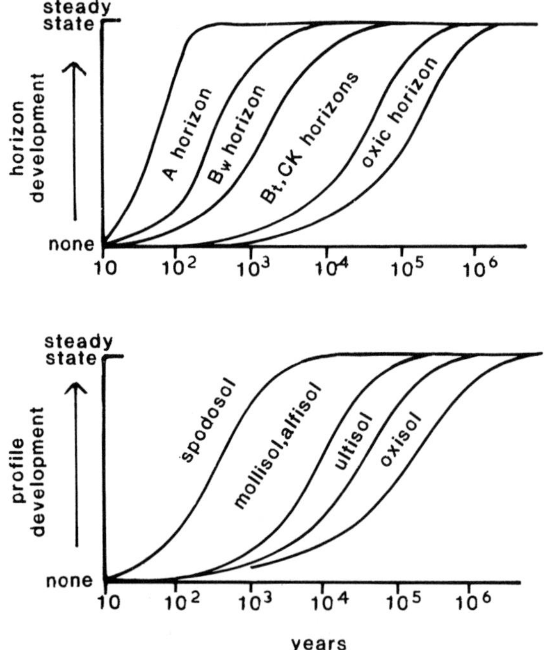

Fig. 3.10 — Time required to attain a steady state for different soil horizons (top) and various soil orders in the American soil taxonomy (bottom) (from Birkeland 1984).

3.8.1 Soil development indices

In estimating how long a soil took to form, it is useful to combine values for various pedogenic properties into a single index of overall profile development. Harden (1982) developed such an index based upon soil thickness and eight properties evaluated in the field (Table 3.6). The properties for each soil horizon are compared

Table 3.6 — Steps for quantification of soil horizon field properties in calculation of profile development index (Harden (1982)

Property	Example: Horizon property	Example: Parent material property
Rubefication: $X_r = 10[\text{hue } \Delta X_o) + (\text{chroma } \Delta X_o)]$ dry+moist colours of Munsell Chart	Horizon property:	Parent material property (X_o):
10 points for each increase in hue redness: 5 Y, 2.5 Y, 10 YR, 7.5 YR, 5 YR, 2.5 YR, 10 R, 5 R 10 points for each increase in chroma: 0, 1, 2, 3, 4, 5, 6, 7, 8 (for multiple colours take the average)	7.5 YR 5/4 dry 7.5 YR 4/5 moist $X_r = 10(1+2)$ dry$+10\ (1+3)$ moist $= 70$	10 YR 7/2 dry 10 YR 6/2 moist
Texture: $X_t = 10[(\text{particle size class } \Delta X_o) + (\text{stickiness } \Delta X_o) + (\text{plasticity } \Delta X_o)]$ 10 points for each particle size class line crossed towards the clay class on the triangular diagram of particle size classes (Fig. 3.2)	sandy clay loam: moderately sticky slightly plastic	sandy loam: non-sticky non-plastic
10 points for each increase in stickiness: non-sticky, slightly sticky, moderately sticky, very sticky 10 points for each increase in plasticity: non-plastic, slightly plastic, moderately plastic, very plastic	$X_t = 10(1+2+1)$ $= 40$	
Argillans: X_a = [(abundance+thickness+location) of class with most points] $+\frac{1}{2}$ [abundance value of all other secondary classes]	continuous thin grain bridgings few thick ped-face coatings common moderately thick grain bridgings	none
(see points table below)	$X_a = (50+10+20)+\frac{1}{2}(20+40)$ $= 110$	

Points	10	20	30	40	50
Abundance	rare	few	fairly common	common	continuous
Thickness	thin	moderately thick	—	—	—
Location	pore-filling	ped-face or grain-bridging	—	—	—

(If two classes have equal points, the one with maximum abundance points becomes the primary class)

Structure: X_s=[(grade+type) of primary structures]+$\frac{1}{2}$[(grade+type of secondary structures)]					primary: moderate prismatic secondary: weak blocky	none
Points	5	10	20	30	$X_s = (20+20)+\frac{1}{2}(10+10)$ $= 50$	
Grade		weak	moderate	strong		
Type	platy	blocky	prismatic	columnar		
Dry consistence: X_d=10 (dry consistence ΔX_o) 10 points for each increase in hardness: loose, soft, slightly hard, hard, very hard, extremely hard					very hard $X_d = 10\times4$ $= 40$	loose
Moist consistence: X_m=10 (moist consistence ΔX_o) 10 points for each increase in firmness: loose, very friable, friable, firm, very firm, extremely firm					firm $X_d = 10\times3$ $= 30$	loose
Melanization: X_v=10 (Munsell value ΔX_o) dry+moist colour 10 points for each decrease in value: 10, 9, 8, 7, 6, 5, 4, 3, 2, 1, 0					7.5 YR 5/4 dry 7.5 YR 4/5 moist $X_v = (10\times2)+(10\times2)$ $= 40$	10 YR 7/2 dry 10 YR 6/2 moist
pH: X_{pH}=pH ΔX_o difference between pH of horizon and parent material (if pH of horizon >pH of parent material, zero points are assigned)					7.2 $X_{pH} = 7.9-7.2$ $= 0.7$	7.9

with those of the parent material, as represented by the unaltered C horizon at the base of the profile or by fresh sediments elsewhere. Differences from the parent material are quantified as points, which are normalized on a 0–10 scale, summed and then divided by the number of measured properties to obtain first an index for each horizon. The horizon values are then weighted according to horizon thickness, and finally summed to obtain the profile development index. Using a chronosequence of soils on dated alluvial deposits of the Merced River in California (Marchand and Allwardt 1981), Harden showed that the logarithm of the profile development index increases linearly with the logarithm of the soil age (Fig. 3.11). Because many soils,

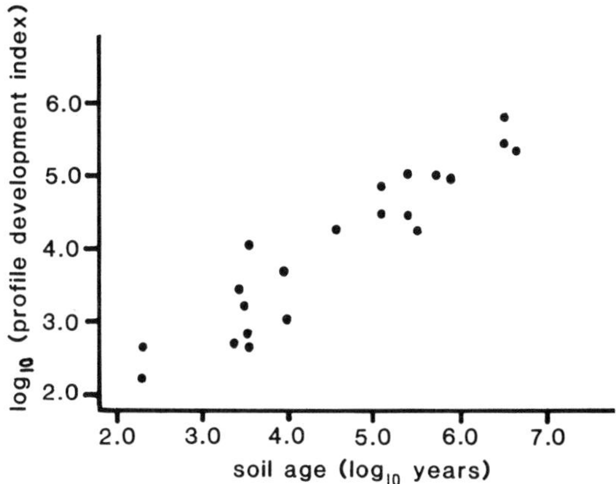

Fig. 3.11 — Relationship between profile development index and soil age on alluvial deposits of the Merced River, California (from Harden 1982). Reproduced by permission of Elsevier Science Publishers.

especially old ones, are likely to have suffered some erosion, estimates of substratum age based on Harden indices are likely to be minima. However, addition of clay to the profile, as part of an aeolian influx at some stage during profile development for example, can give greater indices than those for soils of the same age which have not received any influx.

By calculating profile indices for each of the eight properties individually, Harden (1982) was able to show that most properties in the Merced River chronosequence were significantly correlated with at least one other (Table 3.7). Argillans, texture, rubefication and consistence were more strongly correlated with soil age than other properties. This suggests that where only a limited number of soil properties can be evaluated, some combination of these four is likely to give the best indication of age, though the value of the Harden Index depends principally on the fact that it incorporates as many profile properties as can be measured.

3.9 CLIMATIC INTERPRETATION OF SOILS

As climate is one of the five factors influencing soil characteristics (Jenny 1941), it should be possible to infer climatic conditions at the time a buried or relict soil was

Table 3.7 — Correlation matrix for profile development indices of field properties and soil age in the Merced River chronosequence, based on 140 horizons from 21 profiles (Harden 1982)

	Argillans	Texture	Rubefication	Structure	Dry consistence	Moist consistence	Melanization (colour value)	Decrease of pH
Texture	0.86	—	—	—	—	—	—	—
Rubefication	0.87	0.81	—	—	—	—	—	—
Structure	0.17	0.15	0.07	—	—	—	—	—
Dry consistence	0.78	0.79	0.69	0.28	—	—	—	—
Moist consistence	0.65	0.62	0.56	0.30	0.84	—	—	—
Melanization (colour value)	0.00	0.65	0.11	0.03	0.00	0.21	—	—
Decrease of pH	0.30	0.37	0.43	0.19	0.12	0.10	0.02	—
$\log_{10}$ soil age	0.66	0.58	0.74	0.24	0.63	0.55	−0.08	0.31

formed, using existing knowledge from published climofunctions and other less quantitative relationships between soil properties and climatic factors. Unfortunately most published climofunctions are for organic matter content (organic C% or N%) or for the clay content and silica/sesquioxide ratios of soils developed from crystalline igneous rocks. These have limited value in calculating the climatic conditions under which many Quaternary buried or relict soils were formed, either because the soils are derived from other parent materials or because their organic matter content has since changed. However, organic matter is often preserved in waterlogged soils, and principles established in soils on igneous rocks are often applicable in a general sense to other soils, even though the same mathematical relationships cannot be applied.

3.9.1 Climatic significance of organic content

Both N and organic C contents increase with increasing rainfall (expressed as mean annual precipitation) and decrease with increasing mean annual temperature. As illustrated by work on American soils (Jenny 1941), the relationships are linear for rainfall (Fig. 3.12) and exponential for temperature (Fig. 3.13). Curves from various

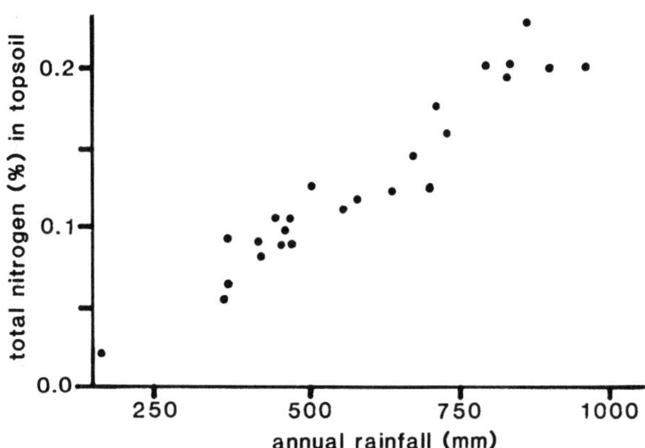

Fig. 3.12 — Relationship between topsoil nitrogen content and annual rainfall in soils of USA developed in loess (from Jenny 1941).

regions are approximately parallel, but for comparable precipitation and temperature values the amounts of C and N increase from temperate to equatorial regions (Jenny 1980). Nitrogen content decreases exponentially with depth in most types of soil profile, and the higher the rainfall, the deeper the penetration of nitrogen (Fig. 3.14). Part of the precipitation falling on the soil surface cannot be used by plants, as it is lost by runoff or evaporation. Runoff losses can be minimized by taking samples from level ground, but evaporation losses should be allowed for in any study of the relationships between rainfall and soil composition. Various indices have been suggested for this; a widely used factor is the NS Quotient of Meyer (1926), which is

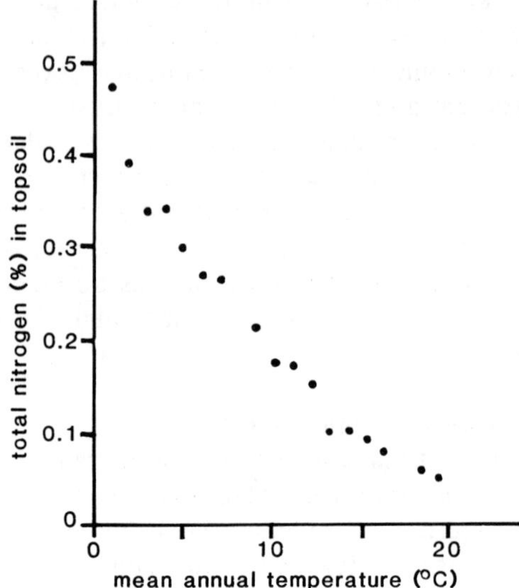

Fig. 3.13 — Relationship between topsoil nitrogen content and mean annual temperature in upland soils of semi-humid N. America (Canada to Louisiana) (from Jenny 1941).

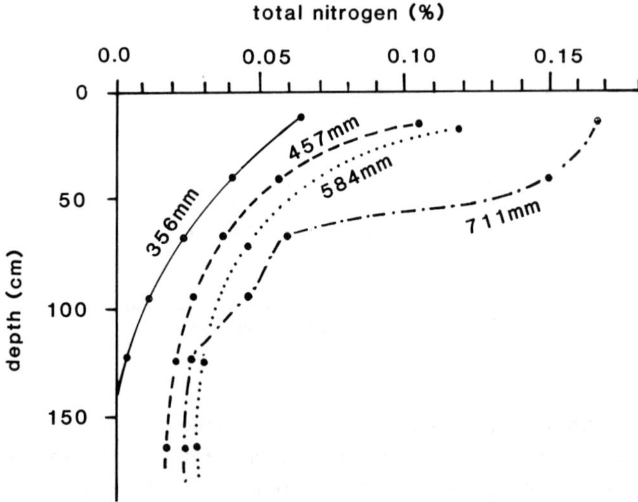

Fig. 3.14 — Depth functions for nitrogen content in soil profiles from regions of different rainfall (from Jenny 1941).

calculated by dividing precipitation (mm) by the absolute saturation deficit of air (mm Hg). Jenny (1941) integrated the effects of mean annual temperature and moisture (as NS Quotient) on the nitrogen content of loamy grassland soils of the Great Plains area from Canada to Mexico into the nitrogen-climate surface shown in Fig. 3.15. This shows that at constant temperature, soil nitrogen increases logarith-

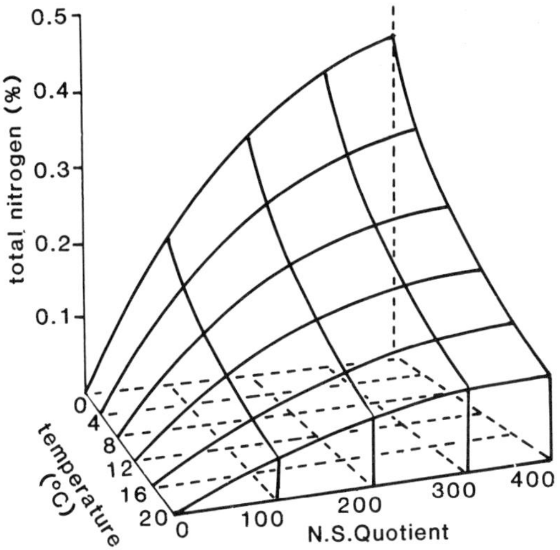

Fig. 3.15 — Relationship between topsoil nitrogen content, mean annual temperature and moisture (the NS Quotient of Meyer 1926) in virgin grassland soils derived from loess on the Great Plains, N. America (from Jenny 1941).

mically with NS Quotient, though the rate of increase depends on temperature, being greater at lower temperatures. At constant NS Quotient, nitrogen content decreases exponentially as the temperature increases; the rate of decrease depends on NS Quotient, being greater in the more humid regions.

3.9.2 Climatic significance of clay content

Although it is clear from the nature of soils in different climatic zones that much more clay is formed by weathering in hot and humid regions than in dry and cold areas, reliable relationships between clay content and climatic factors are best established in soils formed either from clay-free parent materials such as crystalline igneous rocks, or from loess, which has a fairly constant original clay content. Jenny (1935) found that, if soils in eastern USA are grouped according to the type of igneous parent material, for example basic rocks (Fig. 3.16), then the clay content of the top 1 m increases linearly with mean annual temperature. Clay content of soil also increases linearly with mean annual rainfall, as shown by the relationship between topsoil clay percentage of profiles in loess and rainfall in samples collected along the 11°C mean annual isotherm in Kansas and Missouri (Fig. 3.17). If an allowance for

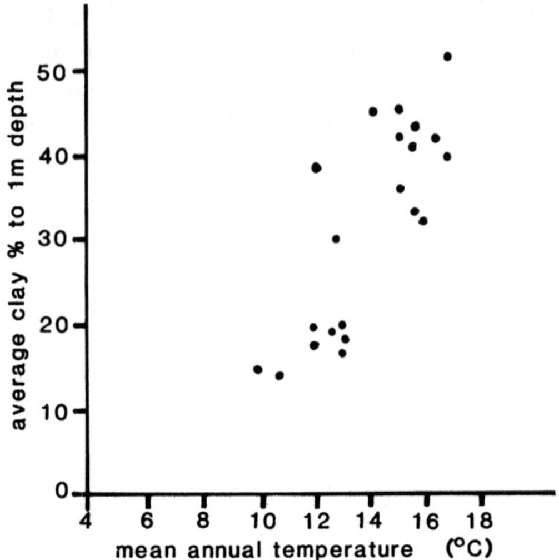

Fig. 3.16 — Relationship between mean annual temperature and clay content to 1 m depth in soils developed from basic igneous rocks in unglaciated parts of the eastern USA (correlation coefficient, r=0.81) (from Jenny 1941).

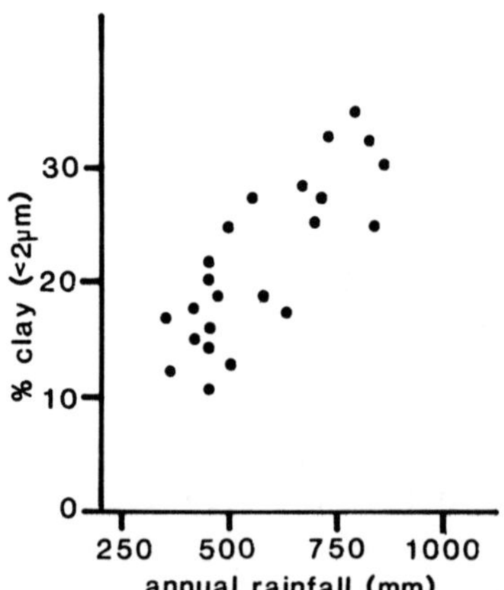

Fig. 3.17 — Relationship between mean annual rainfall and clay content of surface horizons (0–25 cm) in loess-derived soils along the 11°C isotherm in Kansas and Missouri, USA (correlation coefficient, r=0.82) (from Jenny 1941).

moisture differences in the soils from basic igneous rocks is made by adjusting their clay contents to an arbitrary constant value of 400 for the NS Quotient according to the clay–moisture relationship shown in Fig. 3.17, the clay–temperature function then becomes exponential (Fig. 3.18). The relationship between clay content

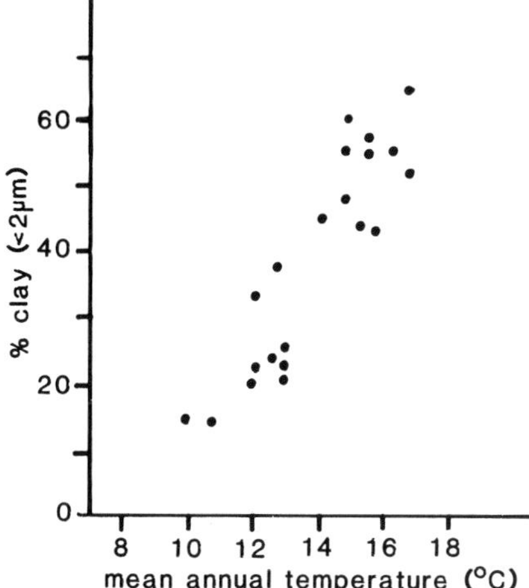

Fig. 3.18 — Relationship between mean annual temperature and clay content to 1 m depth in soils developed from basic igneous rocks in eastern USA; the clay content has been adjusted to an NS Quotient (Meyer 1926) of 400 on the basis of the clay–moisture relationship shown in Fig. 3.17 (from Jenny 1941).

(similarly adjusted to an NS Quotient of 400) and temperature in eastern USA soils derived from granite is also exponential (Fig. 3.19), though for a given temperature

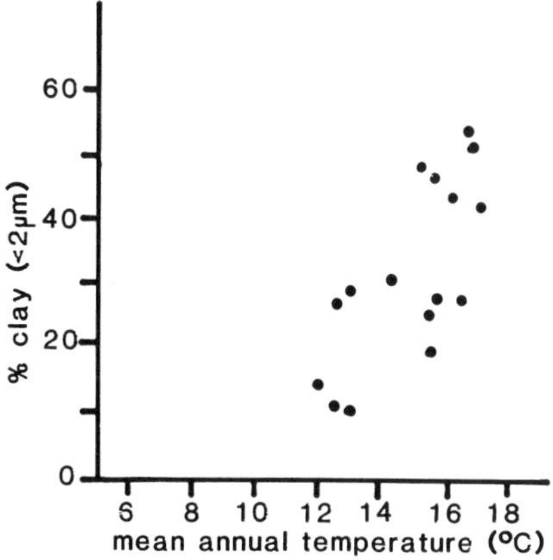

Fig. 3.19 — Relationship between mean annual temperature and clay content to 1 m depth in soils developed from granitic rocks in unglaciated parts of eastern USA; the clay content has been adjusted to an NS Quotient (Meyer 1926) of 400 on the basis of the clay–moisture relationship shown in Fig. 3.17 (from Jenny 1941).

the clay content is less than in the soils formed from basic rocks. Fig. 3.20 shows the clay–climate surface for the soils derived from granite in eastern USA. This shows that at constant temperature, clay content increases with moisture, but at a greater rate at a high temperature than at a low temperature; at constant NS Quotient, clay content increases exponentially with temperature, the effect being more pronounced in humid regions than in arid regions.

3.9.3 Climatic significance of silica/sesquioxide ratios

By making measurements in soils formed from crystalline rocks, the complication of distinguishing clay formed by weathering from that inherited from texturally-variable sedimentary parent materials is avoided. For the same reason, the effect of weathering and leaching on the ratios of SiO_2 to Fe_2O_3 and/or Al_2O_3 and their relationships to climatic factors can also be reliably evaluated only in soils derived from igneous rocks. As weathering and leaching proceed, SiO_2 is lost and the sesquioxide content of the residual soil increases proportionately. The ratios SiO_2/Fe_2O_3, SiO_2/Al_2O_3 and $SiO_2/Al_2O_3+Fe_2O_3$ in either the whole profile, the topsoil or its clay ($<2\ \mu m$) fraction decrease linearly, logarithmically or exponentially with increasing precipitation (Robinson and Holmes 1924, Craig and Halais 1934, Tanada 1951, Simonett 1960), and increase linearly with increasing temperature (Crowther 1931). Fig. 3.21 shows the effect of increasing precipitation on the SiO_2/Al_2O_3 ratio in soils developed over the last 10 000–17 000 years from the basaltic Pahala Ash in Hawaii (Hay and Jones 1972). The amounts of iron and aluminium extractable with oxalate or dithionite also increase with increasing precipitation (Singer 1966) (Fig. 3.22). These extractants distinguish iron and aluminium released by weathering from that remaining in primary minerals, but even this distinction does not clarify the extent of weathering in sedimentary soil parent materials, which often contain oxalate- or dithionite-extractable forms of iron and aluminium at the time of deposition.

3.9.4 Climatic significance of soil clay mineralogy

The loss of silica and bases and accumulation of residual sesquioxides during weathering and leaching also result in changes in the mineralogical composition of clay fractions. However, these effects are known mainly in semi-quantitative terms from the worldwide distribution of soil clays in relation to climatic zones. In soils formed from crystalline rocks, the trend to clay minerals containing less silica and bases (often illite→smectite→kaolinite or halloysite→iron and aluminium oxides and hydrated oxides) with increasing precipitation is stronger in tropical regions than in cooler temperate or polar regions (Loughnan 1969, Tardy *et al.* 1973, Marshall 1977). But this pattern is complicated by differences in composition of the parent rocks (Barshad 1966), in slope position and in site drainage characteristics. For example, on felsic rocks smectite is stable under lower mean annual precipitation than it is on mafic rocks. Palygorskite and sepiolite require a high soil pH and abundance of magnesium in solution (Singer and Norrish 1974), and therefore characterize soils in arid regions (Paquet and Millot 1973).

The small number of clay mineral studies of soils developed in Quaternary sediments in relation to climate and parent material composition generally support the conclusions based upon soils formed from crystalline rocks. For example, in soils

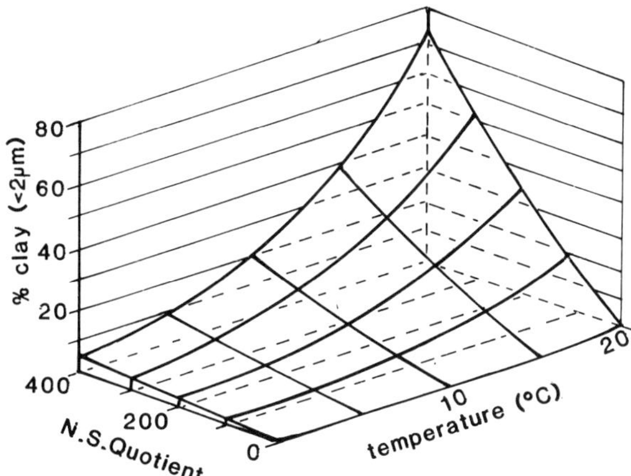

Fig. 3.20 — Relationship between mean clay content to 1 m depth, mean annual temperature and moisture (the NS Quotient of Meyer 1926) in soils derived from granitic rocks in eastern USA (from Jenny 1941).

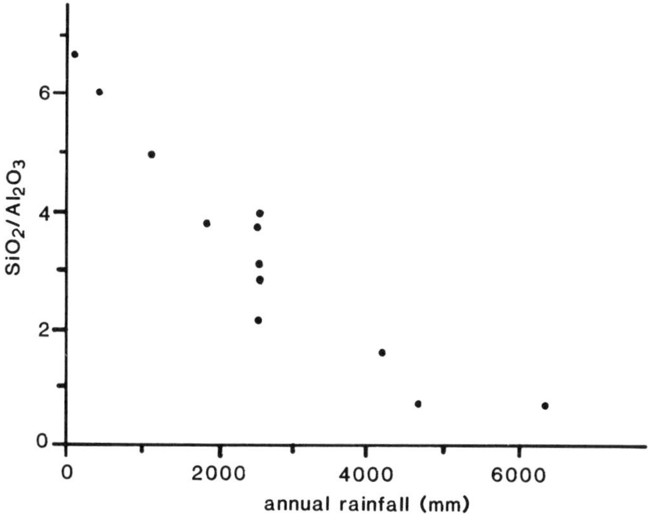

Fig. 3.21 — Relationship between mean annual rainfall and SiO_2/Al_2O_3 ratio in soils on the basaltic Pahala Ash in Hawaii (from Hay and Jones 1972). Reproduced by permission of the Geological Society of America.

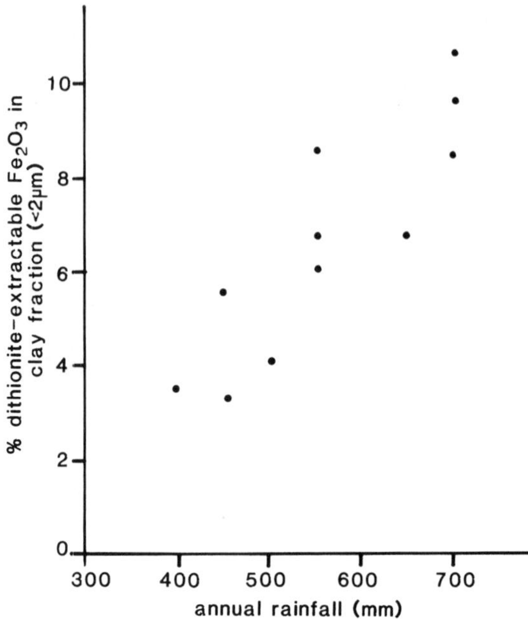

Fig. 3.22 — Relationship between mean annual rainfall and dithionite-extractable iron in the clay fraction of soils derived from basalt in Israel (from Singer 1966). Reproduced by permission of the editor of Journal of Soil Science.

derived from glacial deposits of various ages in the Sierra Nevada (California), Birkeland (1969) and Birkeland and Janda (1971) showed that smectite occurs up to about 400 mm annual precipitation on till of mixed lithology (granite, andesite and basalt) but is absent from soils on purely granite-derived till even in drier areas.

3.9.5 Climatic significance of clay illuviation

The amount of illuvial clay in argillic horizons and the thickness of such horizons depend on several factors. According to McKeague (1983), clay illuviation is favoured by a pH of 4.5–6.5 (or higher if associated with exchangeable sodium), small amounts of cementing and flocculating agents (carbonates, humus, sesquioxides, exchangeable Al, Mg, Ca), a system of fissures or channels such as those formed by dissolution of limestone clasts, and a seasonal rainfall distribution. Consequently it occurs mainly in moderately weathered soils of warm temperate regions or saline or alkaline soils of arid regions, but there is no clear relationship with climatic factors. Providing the structure of A and E horizons is stable, the particles illuviated into Bt horizons are exclusively fine clay (silicate clay with subsidiary but variable amounts of iron oxides), but as the soil structure weakens, fine clay is accompanied by increasing amounts of coarse clay and fine silt, sometimes with humus as well. This may occur under the influence of prolonged cultivation or deteriorating climate (decreasing temperature), both of which lead to loss of humus and weakening of inter-particle bonds. Although clay illuviation does not occur in most arctic soils

(Pastor and Bockheim 1980), it has been observed in some affected by seasonal frost (McKeague *et al.* 1973); during thawing, soil particles are dispersed by the high dielectric properties of the meltwater and are then carried downwards, sand and silt being redeposited in higher parts and clay in deeper parts of the profile (Van Vliet-Lanoë 1985).

3.9.6 Climatic significance of rubefication

Rubefication, or reddening of soils not derived from red parent materials, is often associated with a Mediterranean type of climate with hot dry summers. Guillet and Souchier (1982) stress also the importance of low organic matter content and a near neutral pH. Increasing redness (Munsell hues of 10 YR, 7.5 YR, 5 YR, 2.5 YR to 10 R) has often been related to increasing haematite content (e.g. Kemp 1985), and Kämpf and Schwertmann (1983) showed that haematite forms instead of goethite in Brazilian soils where the mean annual temperature exceeds 17°C and mean annual precipitation exceeds evapotranspiration by at least 900 mm. However, reddening can occur in coarse (e.g. sandy) soils at lower temperatures and higher annual precipitation values than in fine, clayey soils. In the alpine foreland of southern Germany, rubefied soils on Würm glaciofluvial gravels occur close to yellowish brown (10 YR) soils on clayey moraines of the same age, and their redness increases westwards as mean annual precipitation decreases from 1200 to 500 mm and mean annual temperature increases from 7 to 11°C (Schwertmann *et al.* 1982). This is probably because coarse soils are warmer and drier than fine soils in the same climatic regime.

3.9.7 Other features of climatic significance

Topsoil pH decreases either linearly or logarithmically with increasing precipitation or NS Quotient (Prescott 1931, Jenny and Leonard 1934, Kohnke *et al.* 1968, Jenny 1980). The correlation is weak if all parent materials are included (Fig. 3.23), but stronger if soils derived from a single parent material, such as loess (Fig. 3.24), are considered. Cation exchange capacity often increases with increasing precipitation (Fig. 3.25), and as pH decreases, the proportion of the total exchange capacity attributable to exchangeable acidity increases linearly with increasing precipitation (Jenny *et al.* 1968).

Shallow horizons containing secondary carbonate (Ck horizons) form in soils subject to a persistent moisture deficit in a prolonged dry season. However, there is no clear relationship between precipitation and depth to the top, thickness or carbonate content of Ck horizons. These properties are affected by the vegetation cover, particle size distribution and structure of the soil, and the calcium content of the parent material as well as present and past seasonal distributions of rainfall (Richmond 1962). In soils with a Bt horizon, any Ck horizon usually lies immediately beneath, because the illuvial clay is flocculated and redeposited in the presence of calcium carbonate. If there is a gap between the Bt and Ck horizons, it may indicate a climatic change to moister conditions after the Bt horizon started to form. If, however, the Ck horizon extends upwards into the Bt, it indicates a change to drier conditions (Birkeland 1984, p. 313). Similar relationships exist with horizons containing secondary gypsum (Cgy horizons) or other soluble salts, except that these form under more arid conditions than Ck horizons.

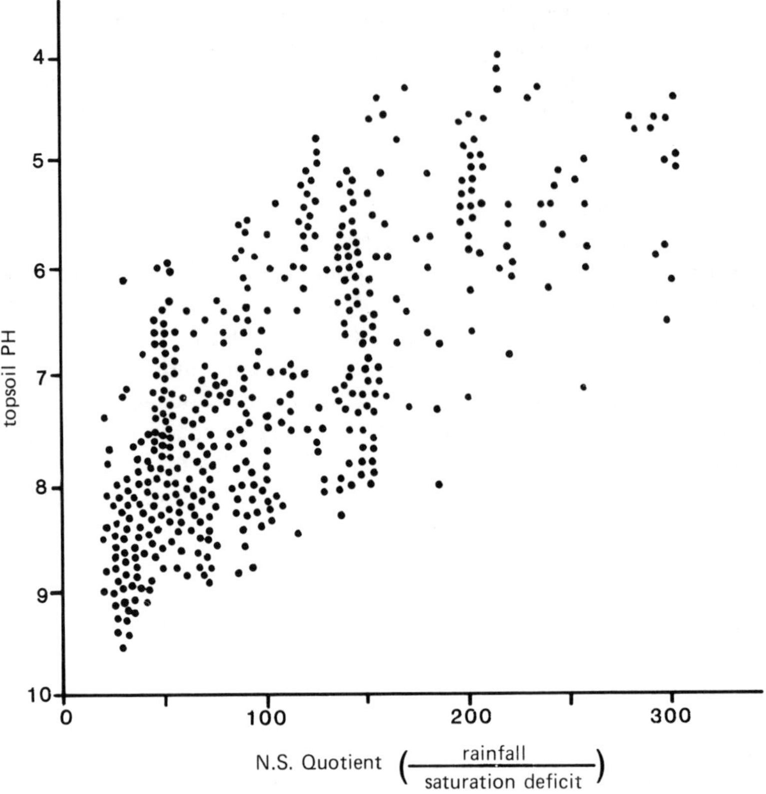

Fig. 3.23 — Relationship between topsoil pH and moisture (NS Quotient of Meyer 1926) in Australian soils (from Prescott 1931).

In natural soils unaffected by man, amounts of bicarbonate-soluble phosphorus often decrease with increasing rainfall (Walker and Syers 1976), though the actual amount present is also influenced by parent material, animals and the length of the soil-forming period.

3.9.8 Frost features

Structural features produced by frost action in soils, such as ice-wedge casts, cryoturbations, vertically orientated stones, fragipans and various types of patterned ground (see Chapter 2), often provide good evidence in mid-latitude regions for an earlier episode of periglacial climate. However, there are no clear relationships known between intensity of frost action and the size or abundance of such features. Effects of frost action seen in soil thin sections are reviewed by Mücher and Morozova (1983) and Van Vliet-Lanoë (1985). One of the clearest micromorphological effects of frost is the disruption of illuvial clay coats formed in an earlier, probably temperate, episode on the walls of old root channels and other voids. The coats are fractured into angular fragments (Plate 12), which are dissociated from the

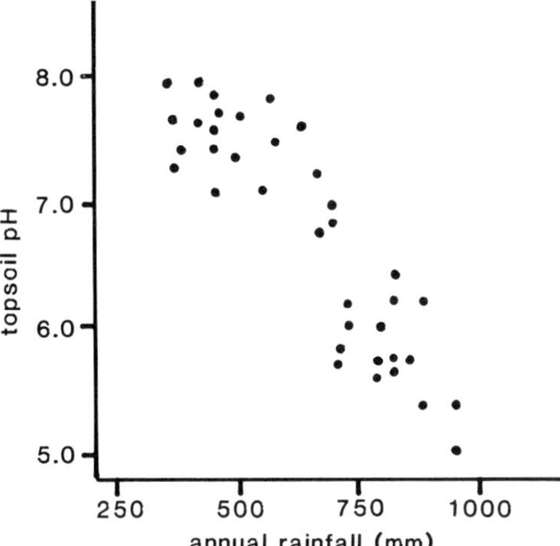

Fig. 3.24 — Relationship between topsoil pH and mean annual rainfall in virgin grassland soils derived from loess on the Great Plains, N. America (from Jenny and Leonard 1934).

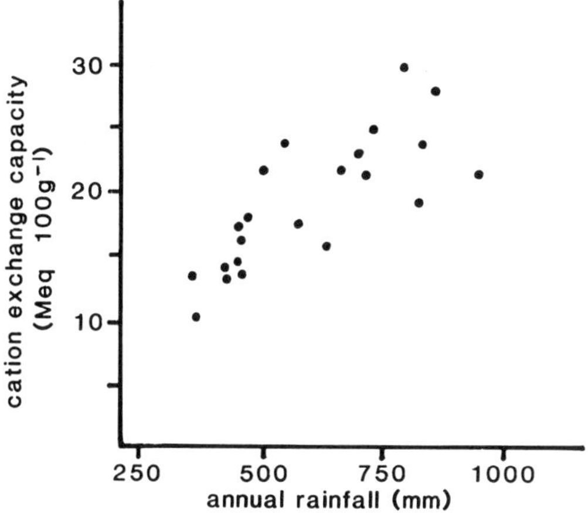

Fig. 3.25 — Relationship between cation exchange capacity and mean annual rainfall in virgin grassland soils derived from loess on the Great Plains, N. America (from Jenny and Leonard 1934).

voids and incorporated into the soil matrix (Jamagne 1972, Catt 1987). Another cryoturbation phenomenon is the cutting of plant tissues into silt-sized fragments by formation of ice needles and their translocation down fissures to produce organic accumulations deeper in the soil profile (Ellis 1983).

Some frost features can be confused with disturbance features formed in hot or temperate climates. For example, desiccation cracks formed in clayey soils of hot arid regions may superficially resemble ice-wedge casts, though ice-wedge casts are usually preserved in coarse rather than fine soils, and often show a characteristic upturning of adjacent beds because of the pressure caused by lateral expansion of the ice.

Many of the climatically significant features of temperate soils, such as organic carbon and nitrogen contents, pH, cation exchange capacity, Ck and Cgy horizons, are easily modified or even destroyed by climatic changes or by diagenetic processes after burial. Very often this effectively rules out their use for palaeoclimatic interpretation of buried or relict soils. Other characteristics, usually those which form more slowly, are more likely to survive in these situations. But at present they do not provide any reliable quantitative measure of palaeoclimate; most of the reliable climofunctions apply to the more transient soil properties. Usually it is only possible to build up a qualitative picture of the climate when a soil formed by investigating various climatically significant properties likely to have been preserved.

3.10 BIOLOGICAL INTERPRETATION OF SOILS

The biotic factors affecting soil characteristics are micro-organisms (bacteria, fungi, algae, actinomycetes, diatoms and viruses), higher plants, the invertebrate soil mesofauna (earthworms, enchytraeid worms, nematodes, mites, springtails, millipedes, beetles, termites, ants, gastropods, crayfish and sponges), vertebrates living in the soil (moles, rabbits, prairie dogs) or grazing on it (sheep, horses, cattle), and man. To a large extent some of these are as dependent upon other soil-forming factors (climate, parent material and relief) as the soil itself, and Crocker (1952) and Jenny (1958) have stressed that both soil and organisms should be regarded as a single ecosystem. To isolate higher plants as an independent factor in soil formation, Jenny (1941) defined it as the sum of plant disseminules able to reach the site during the period of soil formation rather than the actual vegetation at the site. For pedogenic periods including the present, this approximates to a complete list of the species in the surrounding region, though as Crocker (1952) pointed out it is often very difficult to decide the boundaries of a floral region. For older soils the best indication of vegetation as a pedogenic factor is likely to be obtained from a survey of regional pollen assemblages from nearby lake deposits.

3.10.1 Soil palaeontological evidence

The best evidence for the higher plants which actually lived in a soil in past periods is likely to be provided by resistant plant remains, mainly pollen grains and phytoliths. Pollen is best preserved in acidic and poorly drained soils. It is rapidly degraded in alkaline and well-drained soils, and the morphological features used to distinguish different genera and species are then lost. In well drained soils there is also a tendency for pollen to be illuviated slowly down the profile (Dimbleby 1985). This means that vegetational changes during profile development may be inferred from a comparison of pollen preserved at different depths in the profile. However, some pollen types are more prone to illuviation than others. Allowances must also be made for pollen that may have been blown to the site from distant sources (e.g. *Pinus* pollen), for differences in pollen production by different species, and for preferential preservation of certain types in certain soil conditions. Phytoliths are composed of amorphous silica (opal), and are consequently more likely to be preserved in soils. They are produced mainly by grasses and to some extent by trees. Many have characteristic morphologies, but it is often difficult to identify the species from which they come (Lutwick 1969, Rovner 1971). An abundance of phytoliths may indicate that a soil formed under grass rather than forest (Jones and Beavers 1964b, Wilding and Drees 1969), but it is difficult to give limiting values for each. Also amounts can vary with soil drainage status, and depth distribution through the profile may depend on soil type (Jones and Beavers 1964a).

Bones and teeth indicating the vertebrates that influenced development of a soil are occasionally preserved in its upper horizons, but they do not persist in active soils for very long, so isolated specimens may have been incorporated after development ceased. Gastropods are preserved only in calcareous soils, but do provide useful insights into ecological aspects, such as the nature of the vegetation and some climatic factors (J. G. Evans 1972). Beetles can also provide quite detailed palaeonvironmental evidence, but are usually preserved only in poorly drained soils. Sponges, diatoms and crayfish are also confined to poorly drained soils; sponges and diatoms leave fairly resistant siliceous residues, but the former presence of crayfish is usually indicated only by their burrows, often termed krotovinas. Other members of the soil mesofauna can often be identified from faecal pellets, which are best studied in thin sections (Babel 1975, Bullock *et al.* 1985).

3.10.2 Biological significance of soil properties

Although there are few reliable biofunctions, except perhaps for soil moisture in semi-arid environments (Noy-Meir 1974), several soil properties are known to have qualitative relationships with natural vegetation. Perhaps the most significant is the distribution of organic matter through the profile. In grassland soils, organic carbon and nitrogen contents do not decrease as rapidly with depth as in forest soils (Fig. 3.26), because grasses have a dense root system which is continually decaying and being regenerated, whereas tree roots decay infrequently and most of the soil organic matter under forest is added at the surface by leaf fall. For the same reason the pH and percentage base saturation of grassland soils are often greater than under forest (White and Riecken 1955), and because the chelating ability of arboreal decomposition products is often greater, Bt and Bs horizons are often more strongly developed under forest. The most extreme example of this is the localized deep podzolization ('eggcup-podzols') under specimens of the kauri pine (*Agathis australis*) in New Zealand (Crocker 1952, Gibbs et al. 1968), but increased mobilization of iron and aluminium has also been reported under other coniferous trees (De Kimpe and Martel 1976). Ugolini *et al.* (1981) distinguished podzols formed under various types of vegetation in northern Alaska using morphological, chemical and isotopic data. Ovington (1958a, 1958b) also showed that under conifers, soils often have less calcium and magnesium but more phosphorus, sodium and potassium than otherwise similar soils under deciduous trees.

However, it is impossible to use individual chemical properties to infer the vegetation present when an old (e.g. buried) soil was formed, unless strict comparison can be drawn with modern soils under natural vegetation. If, for example, a

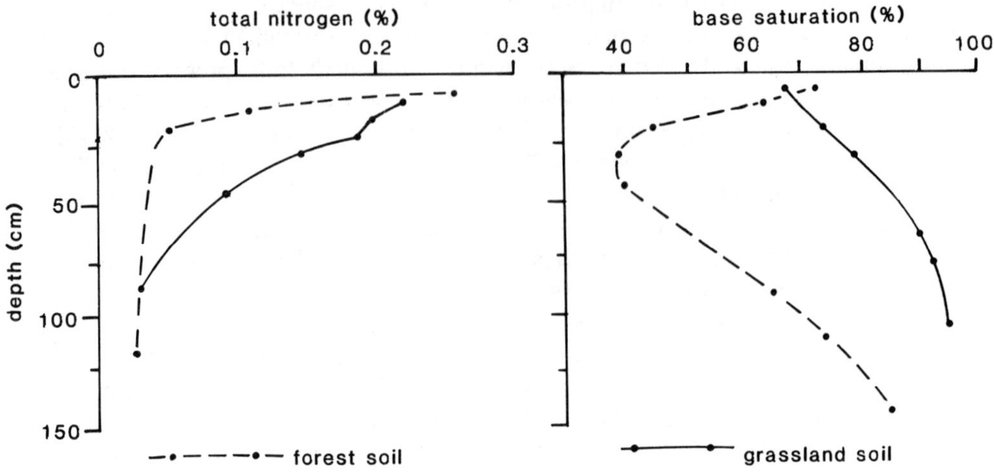

Fig. 3.26 — Depth functions for nitrogen content (left) and base saturation (right) in soils under forest and grassland (from White and Riecken 1955).

buried soil formed from the same parent material, for the same length of time and in a similar topographic situation to a nearby modern grassland soil shows several features consistently indicating forest rather than grassland vegetation, then it is reasonable to conclude that the buried soil formed under forest. But the same conclusion based upon a single property or without a strict comparison with a modern situation would be unreliable. The extent to which soil properties can resist change after burial or after an environmental change in a relict soil must also be considered. Properties such as pH and cation exchange capacity are likely to change very rapidly, whereas Bt and Bs horizons are more persistent. With respect to organic content in a relict soil, much depends on the way the climate changes. The turnover of soil organic matter (the rate at which carbon is cycled from atmospheric CO_2 through plants and the soil and then returned as CO_2 to the atmosphere) is much more rapid in temperate regions than in arctic areas, so the amount and distribution of organic matter in a temperate soil will persist longer after a change to periglacial conditions than the organic matter properties of an arctic soil will last after a return to temperate (e.g. interglacial) conditions.

Many relict soil features surviving vegetation changes have been described from parts of mid-western USA and Canada, where the prairie–forest boundary fluctuated to and fro during the late Wisconsinan and Holocene. For example, in soils which have recently changed from grassland to forest, the increased illuviation of clay and iron has often resulted in development of an E horizon within or at the base of the earlier thick grassland A horizon (Sawyer and Pawluk 1963, Dormaar and Lutwick 1966).

The pedological and soil-palaeontological evidence of the flora and fauna associated with a buried or relict soil can be used in combination to indicate climatic conditions, though the conclusions are usually rather tentative (e.g. Sorensen *et al.*

1976). One problem is that soil and vegetation can change progressively and simultaneously as interdependent parts of an ecosystem without the influence of a climatic change. For example, a change from brown earths with deciduous forest vegetation to podzols with a heathland flora, which occurred on sandy deposits in north-west Europe during both the Holocene and some interglacials, was originally attributed to a change to a cooler and wetter climate. However, Andersen (1966) suggested that progressive leaching and eventual depletion of bases would have the same effect, and in the Holocene this may have been related to human activities such as deforestation and primitive agriculture. Relict brown earth features in soils which have undergone this particular change include poorly preserved pollen of deciduous trees in deep subsoil horizons (Dimbleby 1985), illuvial clay accumulations in a Bt horizon beneath the podzol Bs, the burial of early (e.g. Mesolithic) artefacts in horizons now too acid for the earthworms that usually cause such burial (Keef *et al.* 1965), and fragments of fungal hyphae comminuted by oribatid mites, which are also unable to survive in a podzol (Andersen 1979).

4

Quaternary stratigraphic principles and methods

4.1 INTRODUCTION

Stratigraphy is a system of subdividing and ordering bodies of rock, including unconsolidated sediments and materials altered by soil-forming processes, into units based upon their properties. Many different properties are used to distinguish stratigraphical units; they are broadly divisible into properties expressing or related to age, and those based on material content or physical features. Stratigraphical principles and methods were originally developed to bring order to sedimentary rocks and the events recorded in them, but they can be applied to all earth materials to reconstruct earth history and define the distribution of earth resources.

To meet the need for uniform standards and procedures in defining and classifying bodies of rock, several codes of stratigraphical nomenclature have been published in different countries over the last half century. Those in the English language include: Committee on Stratigraphic Nomenclature (1933), American Commission on Stratigraphic Nomenclature (1961, 1970), George *et al.* (1969), Harland *et al.* (1972), International Subcommission on Stratigraphic Classification (1976), Holland *et al.* (1978), and North American Commission on Stratigraphic Nomenclature (1983). These show that stratigraphy has been undergoing frequent revision, and certainly will continue to do so. Consequently it is impossible to give a complete list of stratigraphical principles and terms which are agreed universally.

Working with sedimentary strata, early geologists formulated the simple law of superposition (a deposit is younger than the one on which it lies). Superposition is not applicable to deposits which are never seen in contact with one another nor to many metamorphic and intrusive igneous rocks; with these, other properties and criteria must be used to determine rock sequences. They include fossils, direct determinations of age by isotopic dating, magnetic and seismic properties, landforms or pedological features associated with the surface of a unit, and cross-cutting relationships (e.g. faults).

As units based on one property do not necessarily coincide with those based on others, different schemes of subdivision and ordering must be used independently, with distinctive terms to identify the different criteria involved. Thus lithological properties of rocks (chemical composition, mineralogy, particle size distribution, colour, bedding structures, geotechnical properties) are used as criteria for differentiating lithostratigraphical units, and the procedure of correlating (or demonstrating correspondence between) units at two or more sites by these properties is termed lithocorrelation. Similarly, the fossil content of sediments is used in various ways for biostratigraphy, and correlations based on fossils are termed biocorrelations. Chronostratigraphy employs direct or indirect estimates of rock age to establish chronocorrelations of chronostratigraphical rock units. Pedostratigraphy uses features resulting from soil development for pedocorrelation of pedostratigraphical units; morphostratigraphy uses landform features for morphocorrelation of morphostratigraphical units; and magnetostratigraphy uses magnetic properties of rocks and soils for magnetocorrelation of magnetostratigraphical units.

Chronostratigraphical units include all the rocks formed during a defined span of earth history. They are distinguished from the timespans themselves, which are termed geochronological units. If two rock bodies were formed during the same geochronological unit, they are isochronous, and are bounded above and below by synchronous surfaces. The term diachronous is applied either to a rock (e.g. lithostratigraphical) unit with lower and/or upper boundaries which are not synchronous or to a boundary which is not synchronous (i.e. its age changes from place to place). Thus all chronostratigraphical and geochronological units are isochronous, but some lithostratigraphical, biostratigraphical, pedostratigraphical and morphostratigraphical units are isochronous and others are diachronous. Successions of similar lithostratigraphical, biostratigraphical or pedostratigraphical units in two different areas are described as chronotaxial if they are also isochronous, but as homotaxial if they were formed during different periods of time.

Stratigraphical units and boundaries between them are formally defined at designated type sites, and are given a compound name consisting of the geographical site name and the rank of the unit, both with capital initial letters. However, many long established chronostratigraphical and geochronological units have well-known names of more diverse origins (e.g. Quaternary System as a chronostratigraphical unit, Quaternary Period as a geochronological unit). Also, biostratigraphical units are usually designated by names of one or more important biological taxa (e.g. *Calluna vulgaris* — Gramineae Pollen Assemblage Biozone). Detailed instructions for definition of formal stratigraphical units are given in the North American Stratigraphic Code (North American Commission on Stratigraphic Nomenclature 1983).

There is also room in stratigraphical nomenclature for informal units. Indeed, formal definition of stratigraphical units is appropriate only for units requiring stability of nomenclature, such as those likely to be recognized over large areas or having some other significance in the geological history of an area. Informal names (without capital letters) are more appropriate for less significant units, which may be thin, geologically unimportant, restricted in occurrence, or mentioned only casually.

4.2 IMPORTANCE OF STRATIGRAPHY IN QUATERNARY GEOLOGY

For a long while, lithostratigraphical, biostratigraphical, chronostratigraphical and geochronological units sufficed for the ordering, subdivision and description of pre-

Quaternary rocks. They were also used sometimes for Quaternary sediments, but it became clear that they do not cover some important aspects of Quaternary dating and correlation. Many of the additional units mentioned above were invented to make good these deficiencies, though they are also applicable to some pre-Quaternary problems. However, many Quaternary scientists, especially in disciplines other than geology, have been prepared to ignore many aspects of stratigraphy. This was partly in the hope of developing rapid, simple methods of dating and correlation, but it is also a result of the tedious and rather repetitive descriptions of a region that result if all types of stratigraphical unit are fully considered.

Despite the undoubted problem of presenting a full description and evaluation of all aspects of Quaternary stratigraphy, this approach does have the benefit of clarifying the relative values and limitations of the various stratigraphical units recognized. Without doubt, much confusion has arisen in the past from a failure to recognize the limitations of some forms of stratigraphy and from misapplication of simple stratigraphical principles. Examples of these are the frequent failures to realize that many lithostratigraphical and morphostratigraphical units may be diachronous, that terrestrial successions in particular may contain many breaks in deposition, and that many biostratigraphical successions are homotaxial rather than chronotaxial.

Far from being dispensable, a full consideration of all aspects of stratigraphy is therefore essential for correct interpretation of Quaternary successions and for regional, national and international correlations. Without it there are strong possibilities of incorrect dating and miscorrelation of depositional, erosional and soil-forming events. Despite the initial promise of numerous techniques proposed and used, often quite extensively, by Quaternary scientists, there are no satisfactory short-cuts to dating and correlation.

4.3 CHRONOSTRATIGRAPHY AND GEOCHRONOLOGY

Table 4.1 shows the geochronological (time) units commonly used in geology, and the equivalent chronostratigraphical units (the rocks deposited during those time units). Unfortunately there is still no universal agreement regarding the rank of time units such as the Quaternary, Pleistocene and Holocene. Charlesworth (1959) and Mitchell *et al.* (1973) described the Quaternary as an Era. However, Curry *et al.* (1978), following George *et al.* (1969), divided the Cenozoic Era into the Tertiary and Quaternary Sub-Eras, and as they subdivided the Tertiary into the Palaeogene and Neogene Periods, comparable subdivision of the Quaternary would make the Pleistocene and Holocene also into Periods. The Holocene Commission of INQUA defined the Holocene as the last 10 000 years, so it is much shorter than all pre-Quaternary Periods, which were 5–100 million years long approximately; indeed Mitchell *et al.* (1973) regarded it as equivalent to one of their stages (the Flandrian). This confusion has arisen because (a) there is a strong tendency for units to become shorter as one approaches the present on account of the greater detail available for recent events, though there is no agreement on how rapid this abbreviation process should be, and (b) chronostratigraphical boundaries are based on various different criteria through geological time.

A compromise status for the Quaternary is the rank of System or Period, divided

Table 4.1 — Ranks of chronostratigraphical and equivalent geochronological units (parentheses indicate term is rarely used)

Chronostratigraphical units	Geochronological units
(Aeonothem)	Aeon
(Erathem)	Era
System	Period
Series	Epoch
Stage	Age
Chronozone	(Chron)

into two Series or Epochs, the Pleistocene and Holocene. This avoids introducing the otherwise unused geochronological rank of Sub-Era, and avoids simultaneously ranking the Holocene as two chronostratigraphical units as diverse as Period and Stage, though it is still both a Series and a Stage.

By definition, chronostratigraphical units are bounded above and below by synchronous surfaces. Each unit represents all rocks worldwide formed during a specific time span (the equivalent geochronological unit). Units are based upon the time spans of lithostratigraphical, biostratigraphical, magnetostratigraphical or other units with a known time range. The base of each chronostratigraphical unit should be defined at a marker point in the type section for that boundary; this also serves as the top of the next older unit, so as to avoid overlaps or gaps between units. Geographical extension of a chronostratigraphical unit's boundary away from the type site is possible only by chronocorrelation based on dating with a similar precision to that at the type site; this can be achieved by direct methods (isotopic dating, thermoluminescence, electron spin resonance, palaeomagnetic, tephrochronology, varve counting, dendrochronology and amino acid dating with Quaternary deposits) or indirect methods, such as appearances or extinctions of biological species. In the Quaternary, other indirect methods, including biological and physical evidence for climatic change, degree of pedological alteration, lichenometry and archaeological evidence, have also been used for chronocorrelation. However, these are less reliable, as boundaries between units based on them are likely to be diachronous over long distances, though they may be almost isochronous over short distances. Much of the art of Quaternary chronocorrelation is knowing how far and in what circumstances these less reliable methods can be trusted. All these direct and indirect dating methods are discussed in Chapter 5.

Chronozones are non-hierarchical chronostratigraphical units of any size, though most are small, equivalent to or shorter than a stage. Together with the geochronological equivalent, chron, the chronozone is used mainly for thin marker beds in industrial investigations, such as basin analysis in petroleum exploration, and has not been used very much in Quaternary stratigraphy. Its upper and lower boundaries are often different from those of other ranked units, and are based on synchronous lithostratigraphical, biostratigraphical or magnetostratigraphical boundaries, which can usually be recognized throughout the area over which the chronozone extends.

Parts of chronostratigraphical units are often distinguished as lower, middle and upper, and equivalent parts of geochronological units are termed early, mid and late. Further subdivision is rarely required, though stages are often divided into substages where narrow chronozones cannot be defined. The Pleistocene is often divided for convenience into Lower, Middle and Upper (e.g. West 1977, Table 11.6), but the boundaries are not universally agreed, and many different schemes are applied locally.

Most chronostratigraphical units of series and lower ranks are known by geographical names related to a type site or type area, usually made into an adjective by the addition of '-an' or '-ian'. Some long established unit names of system and higher rank have more diverse origins, however (e.g. Quaternary, Cenozoic). All other types of stratigraphical unit are nouns rather than adjectives.

4.4 LITHOSTRATIGRAPHY

Lithostratigraphical units are bodies of sedimentary or extrusive igneous rocks, or their weakly metamorphosed equivalents, which are distinguished on the basis of lithological characteristics and generally form stratified sequences obeying the law of superposition. Lithological characteristics may include fossils as evidence for composition or conditions of deposition but not as evidence for age, and surface (outcrop) morphology as evidence for mode of deposition, composition or bedding structures but not as evidence of age. Upper and lower boundaries are drawn in accessible type sections where lithological character changes abruptly, though they may of necessity be drawn at an arbitrary point in a gradational zone (Fig. 4.1). The units should have

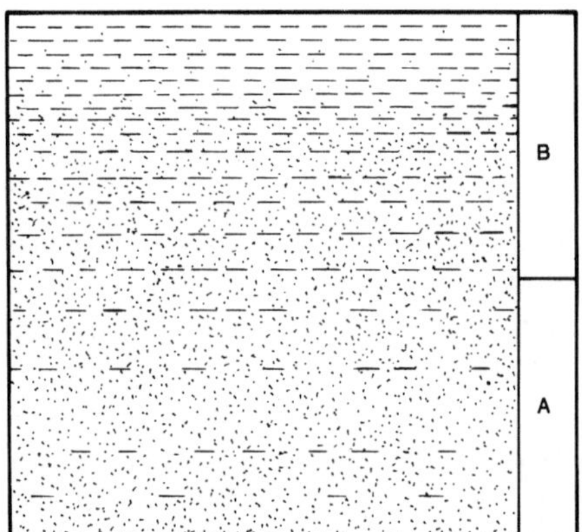

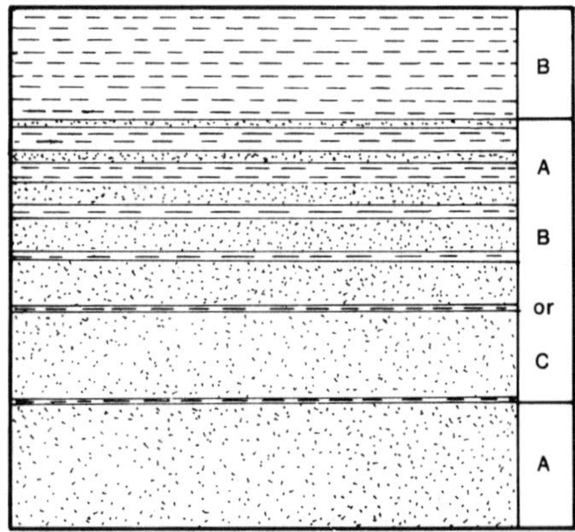

Fig. 4.1 — Horizontal boundaries between lithostratigraphical units (A, B, C) which grade vertically into one another by slow change in properties (left) or by alternation of bed types (right).

Plate 1. Cirque glacier in Vanoise National Park, Savoie, S.E. France.

Plate 2. Ice cave beneath Nigardsbreen glacier, S. Norway; ice movement is from right to left, and thin lodgement till is being deposited (left) on the down-glacier side of bedrock obstacles (right).

Plate 3. Verticle cliff of loess, bank of Missouri River, USA.

Plate 4. Coversand deposited during the Loch Lomond Stadial (10 000–11 000 years ago) in Lancashire, England; the Shirdley Hill Sands, Mere Sands Wood.

Plate 5. Thin solifluction tongue with steep margin, Savoy Alps, S.E. France.

Plate 6. Tors of Millstone Grit (Carboniferous sandstone), Brimham Rocks, Yorkshire, England.

Plate 7

Plate 8

Plate 7. Sinkhole in Carboniferous Limestone, Yorkshire, England; the 'Buttertubs' near Hawes.

Plate 8. Curtain of tufa deposited by waterfall; Janets Foss, Yorkshire, England.

Plate 9

Plate 10

Plate 9. Typical argillic brown earth (Hamble series) developed during the Holocene in late Devensian loess, Heathrow Airport, West London, England. Beneath the grey Ap horizon a thin Eb horizon overlies a slightly browner Bt horizon, and unweathered calcareous loess (paler yellowish brown C horizon) forms the lower third of the section.

Plate 10. Typical paleo-argillic brown earth developed over a long period of the Middle and Late Pleistocene in a thin layer of Reading Beds (Tertiary) mixed with flints from the underlying Chalk (U. Cretaceous). Note the redder colour of the Bt horizon compared with that in plate 9.

Plate 11. Succession of four reddened interglacial buried soils in the loess sequence at St. Pierre-les-Elbeuf, Normandy, France.

Plate 12. Thin section of paleo-argillic horizon (crossed polarizers) showing an angular fragment of illuvial clay coat (yellow), which has been dissociated from the void in which the clay accumulated; soil on Anglian till, Essendon, Hertfordshire, England.

Plate 11

Plate 12

Plate 13. Part of British Geological Survey 1:50000 sheet 80 (Kingston upon Hull); solid and drift edition. The till, glacial sand and gravel, and fluvioglacial sand and gravel were all deposited in the late Devensian (approximately 18000 years ago) by a glacier advancing southwestwards across a surface of Chalk (U. Cretaceous) with patches of marine beach gravel dating from an earlier interglacial. The western limit of the till indicates the approximate margin of the glacier. The fluvioglacial sand and gravel occupies a distinct channel, which probably originated within or near the surface of the glacier. The dry valley deposits on the Chalk occur mainly beyond the ice margin, and were formed principally by gelifluction during the late Devensian shortly before the glacier invaded the area. Holocene alluvium and peat have accumulated since the glaciation on the floors of valleys occupied by small streams, which follow courses initiated by the fluvioglacial drainage. Alluvium is also shown in small elongate hollows on the till surface, some of which may be kettle holes. As the till is thin near its western margin, it has locally collapsed into cavities formed by dissolution of the underlying Chalk (marked as swallow holes). The grid lines are 1 km apart. Reproduced by permission of the Director, British Geological Survey; base map reproduced from the Ordnance Survey map with permission of The Controller of H.M. Stationery Office, Crown copyright reserved.

Plate 14. Part of Soil Survey of England and Wales 1:25000 sheet TF 28 (Donington on Bain). As in plate 13, the late Devensian glacier advanced southwestwards across the Chalk dipslope of the Lincolnshire Wolds. Here it deposited only reddish clayey till (units eK and Fc). Elkington series (eK) occurs mainly in valleys and is less well drained (pelo-stagnogley soil) than Flint series (Fc), a stagnogleyic argillic brown earth. West of the ice margin the Chalk is covered mainly by a thin veneer of late Devensian loess, in which four soil types are distinguished: Andover series rolling phase (slopes <11°) (Ac_3), a brown rendzina, with extremely chalky material at <30 cm depth; Andover series steep phase (slopes >11°) (Ac_1), with profile characteristics similar to Ac_3; Panholes series (pH), a typical brown calcareous earth (i.e. resembling a rendzina but with a Bw horizon); Hamble series (hL), a typical argillic brown earth (i.e. with a Bt horizon). Unit We (Winchester series) is a typical paleo-argillic brown earth (i.e. with a thick, reddened interglacial Bt horizon) formed in pre-Ipswichian till or gelifluction deposits forming isolated erosion remnanats on higher parts of the Chalk interfluves. Devensian gelifluction deposits (the dry valley deposits of Plate 13) occur mainly in dry valleys cut into the Chalk, and are composed mainly of loess and frost-shattered chalk and flint fragments. Most of the soils in them are well drained typical brown calcareous earths, the Coombe series (Ct); however, in the lowest parts of some valleys poorly drained equivalents are separated as Gayton series (gN), a calcaro-cambic gley soil. Reproduced by permission of the Director, Soil Survey of England and Wales, copyright Lawes Agricultural Trust; base map reproduced from the Ordnance Survey map with permission of The Controller of H.M. Stationery Office, Crown copyright reserved.

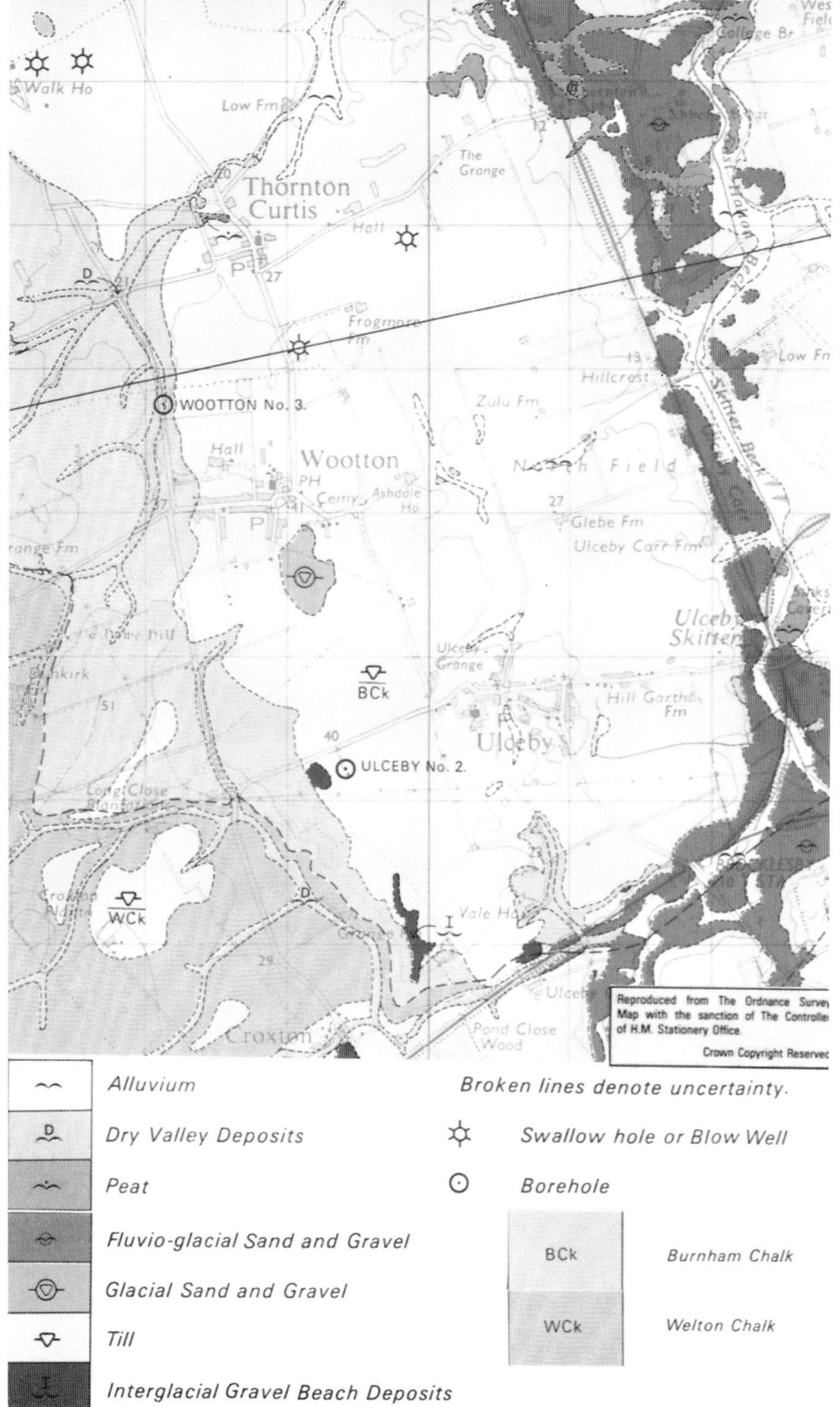

Walk Ho
Low Fm
The Grange
Thornton Curtis
Hall
27
Frogmore Fm
Hillcrest
Low Fm
WOOTTON No. 3.
Zulu Fm
Hall
Wootton
PH
Cemy
Ashdale Ho
P
27
Glebe Fm
Ulceby Carr Fm
Skitter Beck
BCk
Ulceby Grange
Hill Garth Fm
Ulceby
Ulceby Skitter
40
ULCEBY No. 2.
51
WCk
Vale Ho
29
Croxton
Pond Close Wood
Reproduced from The Ordnance Survey Map with the sanction of The Controller of H.M. Stationery Office.
Crown Copyright Reserved
Alluvium
Dry Valley Deposits
Peat
Fluvio-glacial Sand and Gravel
Glacial Sand and Gravel
Till
Interglacial Gravel Beach Deposits
Broken lines denote uncertainty.
Swallow hole or Blow Well
Borehole
BCk
Burnham Chalk
WCk
Welton Chalk

Plate 13

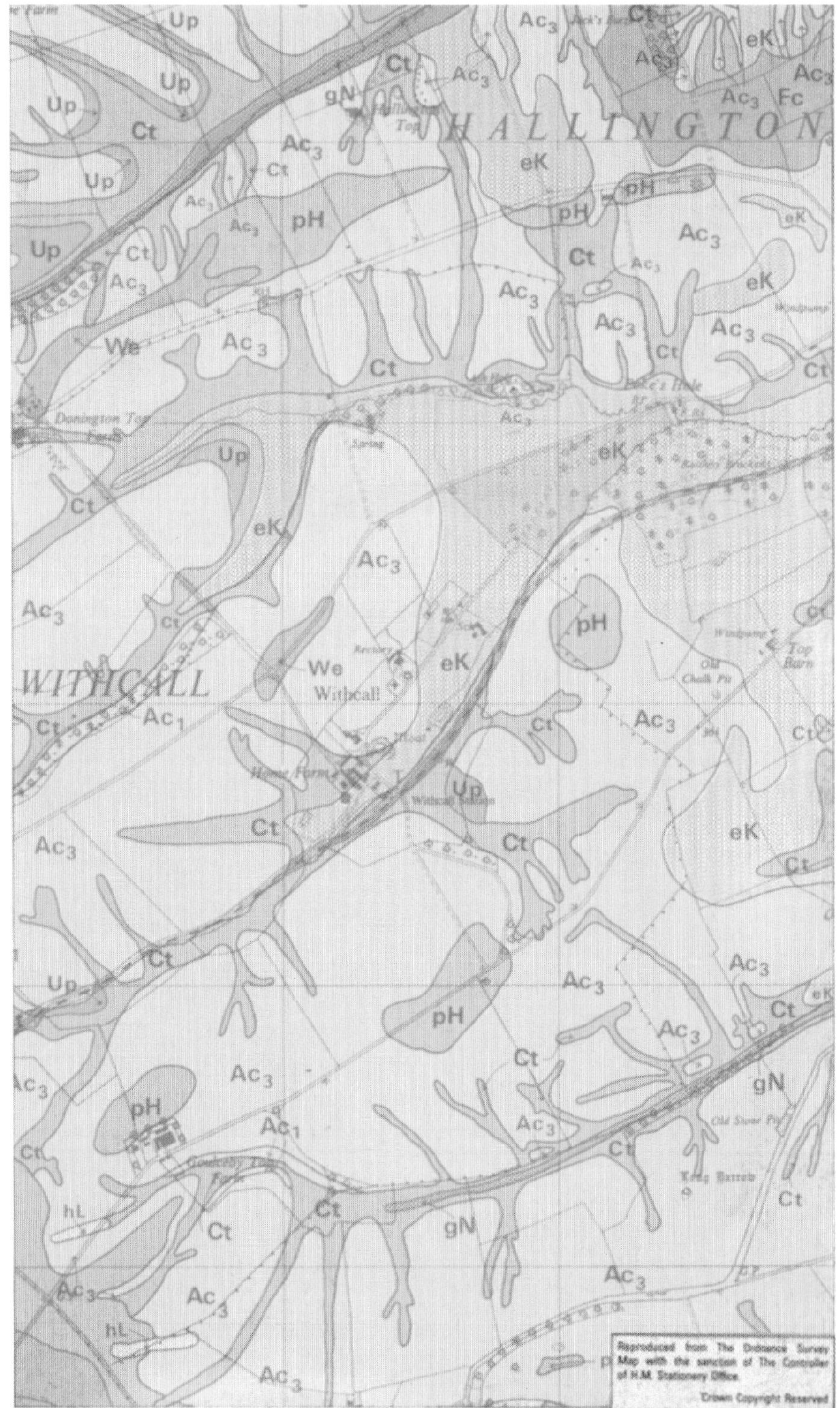
HALLINGTON
WITHCALL
Withcall
Donington Top Farm
Spring
Rectory
Moat
Home Farm
Withcall Station
Old Chalk Pit
Top Barn
Windpump
Old Stone Pit
Long Barrow
Up
Ct
gN
Ac3
Ac1
eK
pH
Fc
We
hL
Reproduced from The Ordnance Survey Map with the sanction of The Controller of H.M. Stationery Office.
Crown Copyright Reserved

Plate 14

regional validity. Many lithostratigraphical units and boundaries between them are diachronous, and some boundaries are unconformities. If two units grade laterally into one another or are intertongued, an arbitrary vertical boundary may be placed between them, or a third transitional unit is recognized if the zone of gradation or intertonguing is very extensive (Fig. 4.2).

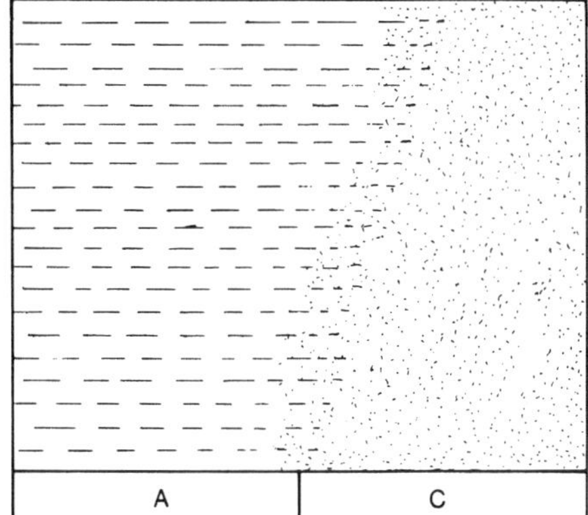

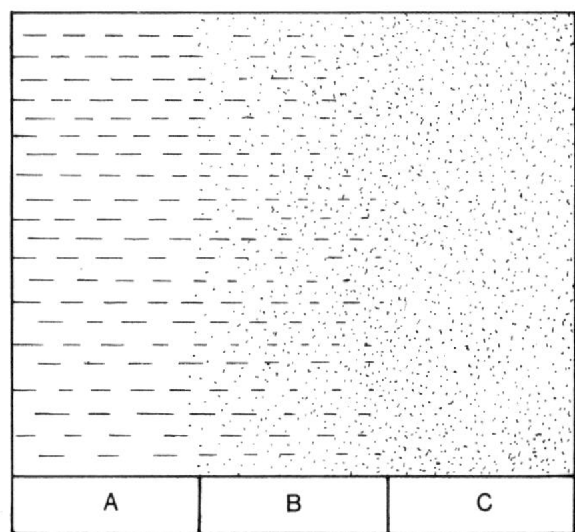

Fig. 4.2 — Vertical boundaries between lithostratigraphical units (A, B, C) which grade rapidly (left) or slowly (right) into one another.

The fundamental unit in lithostratigraphy is the formation. Each defined formation should be lithologically homogeneous within certain limits, and possess distinctive lithological characteristics which enable it to be consistently differentiated from other formations. However, in some instances these differentiating features may include extreme, though characteristic heterogeneity. Thickness is unimportant, as many formations thin out to a 'feather-edge', but regional continuity is essential, so that each formation can be mapped at the usual scale of published geological maps (1:10 000 to 1:100 000). Thin but extensive deposits which would be shown as a single line on maps and sections sometimes constitute formations, but usually are better classified as some lower lithostratigraphical unit (e.g. member or bed). Boundaries between formations are selected so as to divide the entire succession in a region into units of approximately similar overall size, and every deposit must belong to a formation. Formations may represent long or short time intervals, and may include breaks in deposition. Lithological features suitable as distinguishing characteristics of formations include particle size distribution, chemical or mineralogical composition, colour, geotechnical properties, and sedimentary structures. Electrical, seismic or other geophysical properties may be used to help recognize some formations, especially where they extend at depth below the ground surface, but should not be used as sole definitive criteria (North American Commission on Stratigraphic Nomenclature 1983).

Where it is useful to do so, a heterogeneous formation may be divided completely or partly into more homogeneous members, which should possess characteristics allowing differentiation from other parts of the formation. Members need not have the same lateral continuity as formations; for example, some may be lenses or reefs. However, members may extend laterally from one formation to another.

A bed is the smallest lithostratigraphical unit. It is usually 1 cm to a few metres thick, and where distinctive and widely distributed may be termed a marker bed. In volcanic lava sequences the equivalent of the bed is the individual flow.

Lithostratigraphical units higher in rank than formations are known as groups and supergroups. These are used mainly in small-scale mapping, including reconnaissance work where large units, which might subsequently be divided into formations, are recognized. The constituent formations within a group or the groups within a supergroup need not be the same everywhere. Supergroups may be assemblages of groups or of groups and formations.

Bodies of intrusive igneous or highly metamorphosed rocks are termed lithodemic units. These differ from lithostratigraphic units in not usually obeying the law of superposition (North American Commission on Stratigraphic Nomenclature 1983). They are very rarely required in the description of Quaternary sequences. The term complex is used for mixtures of igneous, sedimentary or metamorphic rocks where the mapping of each is impractical at ordinary mapping scales.

The North American Commission on Stratigraphic Nomenclature (1983) introduced the term allostratigraphical unit for mappable bodies of sedimentary rock bounded entirely by discontinuities. Internally these units may be lithologically uniform or non-uniform, and laterally or vertically adjacent units may be lithologically similar. Different allostratigraphical units may be (a) superposed units of similar lithology separated by disconformities, (b) lithologically similar units which are laterally contiguous but bounded by discontinuities, (c) lithologically similar units bounded by discontinuities and separated geographically, or (d) lithologically heterogeneous units which are bounded by discontinuities (Fig. 4.3). Many Quaternary deposits, such as glacial, fluvial, slope and aeolian sediments, are bounded by discontinuities and qualify as allostratigraphical units. The discontinuities between them may be disconformities marking episodes of non-deposition, unconformities (episodes of disturbance and/or erosion), soils or occasionally faults. There is certainly some value in distinguishing this type of stratigraphical unit from other lithostratigraphical units, if only to emphasize that many Quaternary deposits lack conformable stratigraphical relations with one another. However, there are few examples of the formal use of the term, and there seems little additional value in the hierarchy of units (allogroup, alloformation, allomember) suggested by the North American Commission.

4.5 BIOSTRATIGRAPHY

Biostratigraphical units are bodies of sediment characterized by their fossilized animal or plant remains. Fossils derived from older deposits or intruding a deposit long after it was formed (e.g. mollusc borings) are not used to define such units. Boundaries of biostratigraphical units may or may not coincide with lithostratigraphical boundaries, and are often diachronous.

The fundamental unit in biostratigraphy is the biozone. This may be of any

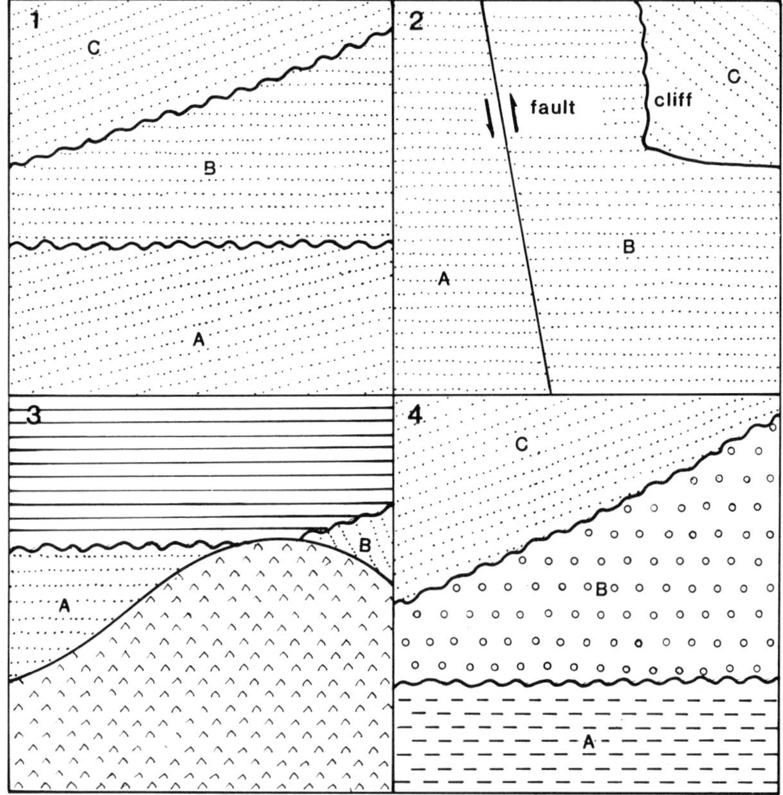

Fig. 4.3 — Possible relationships between allostratigraphical units (A, B, etc.) of similar lithology (1, 2 and 3) or different lithologies (4).

thickness or time duration. Seven types are distinguished (Fig. 4.4), though only the first is extensively used in Quaternary biostratigraphy:

(1) Assemblage biozone or cenozone. This consists of all beds characterized by a certain assemblage of a particular fossil group or groups, which can be distinguished from other assemblages of the same group or groups above and below. The ranges of individual members of the assemblage biozone outside the biozone in question are not considered. The assemblage should consist of at least three and preferably many more taxa; designation and differentiation of assemblage biozones are often aided by multivariate analysis methods.
(2) Concurrent range biozone or Oppel zone. This is an assemblage biozone which includes the strata deposited between the documented earliest occurrence of one or more taxa and the documented latest occurrence of one or more related taxa, the latter occurring higher in the succession than the former so that they overlap.
(3) Acme or abundance biozone. This is characterized by the exceptional abundance of a single taxon.

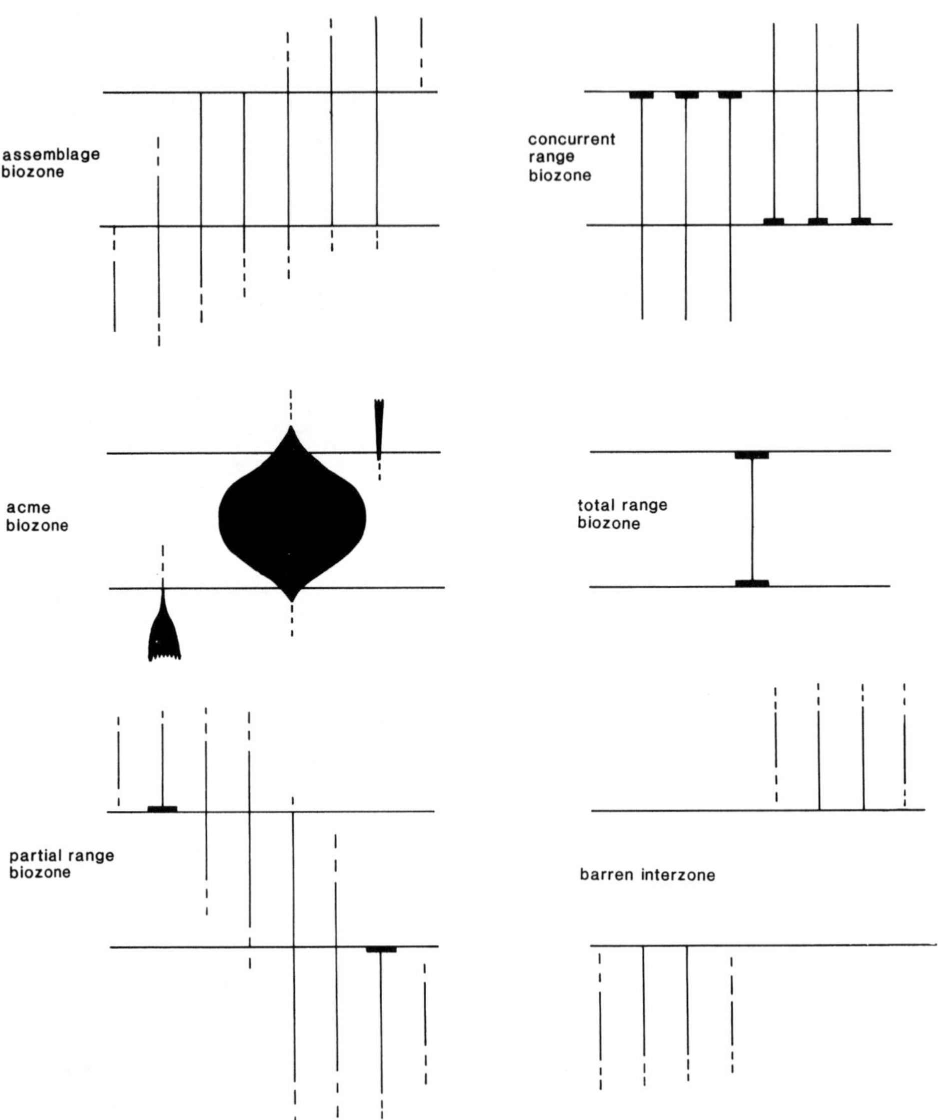

Fig. 4.4 — Types of biozone.

(4) Total-range biozone or taxon range zone. This consists of all strata, over the broadest possible area, deposited between the documented earliest and latest occurrences of a single specified taxon. Successive total-range biozones based on the earliest occurrences of related taxa forming part of an evolutionary lineage are termed lineage zones.

(5) Local-range biozone. This consists of strata deposited between the documented earliest and latest occurrences of a specified taxon, but only within a limited geographical area. Most range biozones are in fact of this type.
(6) Partial-range biozone. This consists of the strata lying between the last occurrence of one taxon and the earliest occurrence of another related taxon, the latter being later than the former so that the two do not overlap. It usually contains an assemblage of related taxa, which may be homogeneous or heterogeneous.
(7) Barren interzones. These consist of strata totally devoid of indigenous fossils between biozones of one or more types.

Biozones may be completely or partially divided into sub-biozones, and the latter into biohorizons, but there are no units larger than biozones.

4.6 MAGNETOSTRATIGRAPHY

Magnetostratigraphical units are bodies of rock characterized by certain remanent magnetic properties and distinct from units above and below which have different magnetic properties. Four palaeomagnetic properties can be inferred from measurements of remanent magnetism in rocks: polarity, field intensity, field pole position and the non-dipole component (secular variation). Polarity reversals are used widely in Quaternary geology for dating and correlation (see 5.10); they provide the boundaries between magnetostratigraphical units characterized by either normal (i.e. present day) or reversed polarity. Strictly these units are magnetopolarity units. Other palaeomagnetic properties are being used increasingly for dating Quaternary deposits (see Chapter 5), but as yet no further types of magnetostratigraphical unit have been formally proposed.

As polarity reversals occurred quite rapidly in terms of geological time, taking < 5000 years, they provide virtually synchronous surfaces which can be recognized worldwide. Many have been dated quite precisely by isotopic methods, so the recognition of one or more reversals in a sequence of Quaternary deposits whose approximate age is already known can provide exact dates for individual beds, either directly or by interpolation between known reversals. Magnetopolarity units can therefore be regarded as a type of chronostratigraphical unit.

The fundamental magnetopolarity unit is the polarity epoch or polarity chronozone. During the late Cenozoic these were approximately 10^6 years long, and have been named after pioneer workers in magnetostratigraphy. They are periods when the polarity was either mainly normal or mainly reversed, but most contain several short periods of the opposite polarity. These shorter magnetopolarity units, lasting 10^4–10^5 years, are known as polarity events or polarity sub-chronozones; usually only the events with opposite polarity to that of the epoch in which they occur have been given names, and these are based on type sites. Fig. 4.5 shows the epochs and events for the last 4 million years.

Even shorter magnetostratigraphical units, lasting 10^2–10^3 years and known as polarity excursions, are also named after localities. During excursions the geomag-

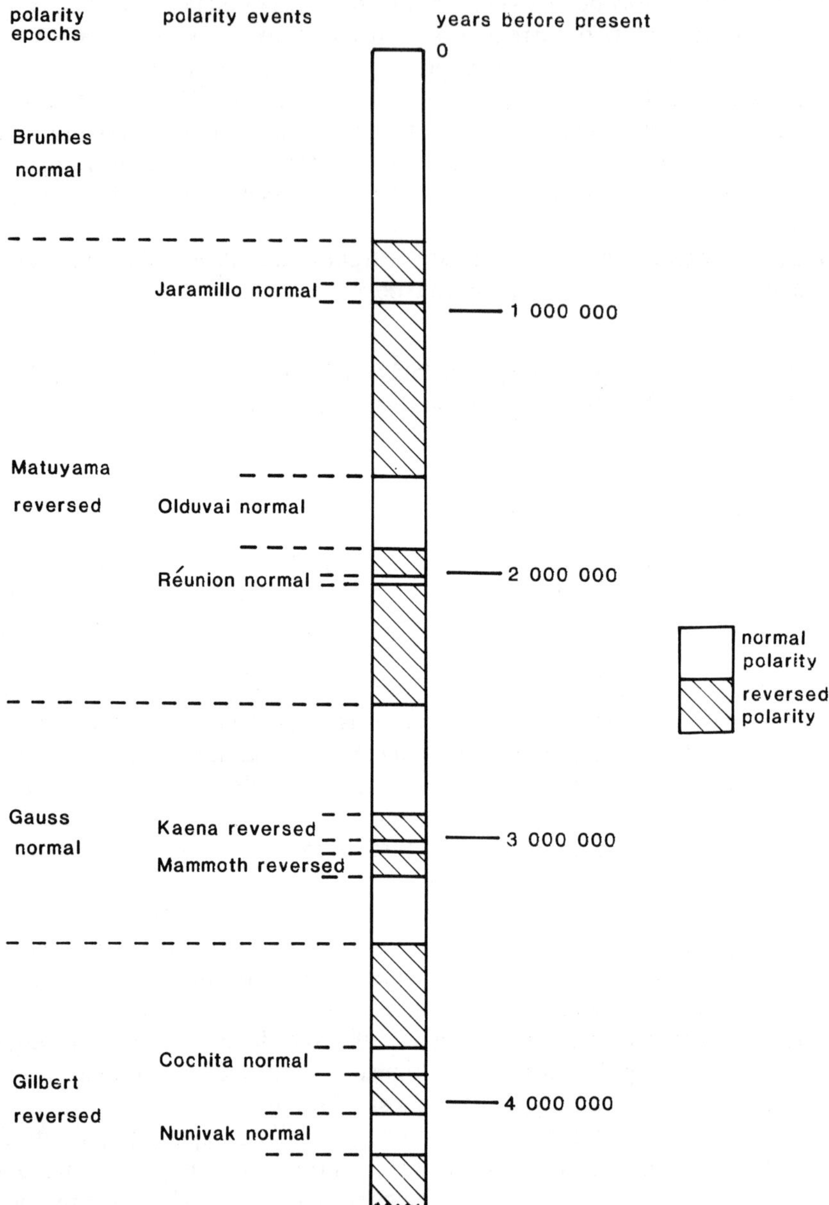

Fig. 4.5 — Magnetostratigraphical units for the last 4 million years (from Mankinen and Dalrymple 1979).

netic pole moved to intermediate latitudes and then returned. Some of the excursions recognized during the later part of the most recent (Brunhes normal) polarity epoch are given in Table 5.3, but few excursions are recognizable worldwide and some reported excursions are probably based on incorrect interpretations of the magnetic properties of sediments, and may never have existed.

4.7 PEDOSTRATIGRAPHY

Soils (see Chapter 3), whether buried or not, have a considerable stratigraphic significance, because they represent periods when there was a fairly stable land surface with little or no deposition or erosion. Buried soils often occur beneath unconformities, though this relationship may not always become clear until such soils have been traced laterally for some distance.

Because they may be formed on and transgress deposits and land forms of any earlier period, yet are distinct from younger deposits overlying them, and because they may extend through areas with different climates, faunas and floras, it is necessary to distinguish soils as stratigraphical units independent of lithostratigraphical, chronostratigraphical, biostratigraphical, morphostratigraphical and climatostratigraphical units. The American Commission on Stratigraphic Nomenclature (1961) originally used the term soil stratigraphic unit, but this was later changed to pedostratigraphic unit (North American Commission on Stratigraphic Nomenclature 1983). Several other less obvious terms with virtually the same meaning have also been proposed, including groundsurface (Butler 1959), pedolith (Crook and Coventry 1967), pedo–morpholith (Van Dijk *et al.* 1968), geosol (Morrison 1967) and pedoderm (Brewer *et al.* 1970). Geosol was adopted by the North American Commission on Stratigraphic Nomenclature (1983) as the fundamental and only unit in pedostratigraphical classification, but the meaning of the word is not immediately clear and its only advantage over the original term soil stratigraphic unit is brevity.

The soil stratigraphic unit was defined as ‘a soil with physical features and stratigraphic relations that permit its consistent recognition and mapping as a stratigraphic unit’ (American Commission on Stratigraphic Nomenclature 1961). This allowed the inclusion of non-buried soils, such as the relict equivalents of buried soils. But a retrograde step was taken by the North American Commission on Stratigraphic Nomenclature (1983) in defining the pedostratigraphic unit as ‘a buried traceable, three-dimensional body of rock that consists of one or more differentiated pedologic horizons’, thus deliberately excluding non-buried soils. Pedologic horizons were defined as ‘products of soil development which occurred subsequent to formation of the lithostratigraphic, allostratigraphic or lithodemic unit or units on which the buried soil was formed.... they are recognized in the field by diagnostic features such as color, soil structure, organic matter accumulation, texture, clay coatings, stains or concretions’.

To be useful in stratigraphy a soil stratigraphic unit should have a stated age range, beginning with the time it started to form and ending with the time it was buried, or the present in the case of a non-buried soil. The physical features of any soil change laterally of course, the different soil types being referred to as variants (Leamy *et al.* 1973) or soil facies (Morrison 1978), though they might better be described in terms of some suitable higher category of soil classification defined, for example, by the F.A.O. (1985a) or Soil Survey Staff (1975). Because of these lateral changes and the strong possibility that very similar (homotaxial) soils might have formed in the same region during different interglacials, interstadials or stadials, the internal physical features of a soil are unreliable as a basis for correlating soil stratigraphic units. Consequently the emphasis in recognition and correlation of units must be placed on consistent relations with other stratigraphical (e.g. lithostratigraphical) units and on direct dating. These aspects are discussed in Chapters 3 and 5 respectively.

4.8 MORPHOSTRATIGRAPHY

Morphostratigraphical units are geomorphological features resulting from single episodes of landscape development, mainly of depositional origin. Deposits are thus subdivided according to the land surface morphology of their outcrops. This concept is widely applied to morainic features on the surface of glacial sediments (mainly tills and glaciofluvial deposits), to river terraces, raised beaches, belts of aeolian dunes, major alluvial fans or gelifluction lobes. Except for some localized erosional extensions of depositional river terraces, the concept is not usually applied to landforms resulting from erosion, and in this way morphostratigraphical units differ from relief units and slope facets (see 6.3.1.1), which are often erosional in origin. The units are usually named after localities where they are clearly expressed or after the two localities marking the limits of elongated features. River terraces are sometimes merely numbered from the lowest (presumed youngest) upwards, as on maps of the British Geological Survey.

Many morphostratigraphical units include two or more lithostratigraphical units (e.g. moraines composed of till and glaciofluvial gravels), and many are diachronous. Some are suspected of having chronostratigraphical significance, but this is usually difficult to prove. The chronostratigraphical significance may be enhanced if there is a clear relationship between morphostratigraphical and pedostratigraphical units, such as soils of increasing depth, Harden Index (see 3.8.1), or decreasing $SiO_2/Al_2O_3+Fe_2O_3$ value occurring on moraines of increasing age (Fig. 4.6), assuming the

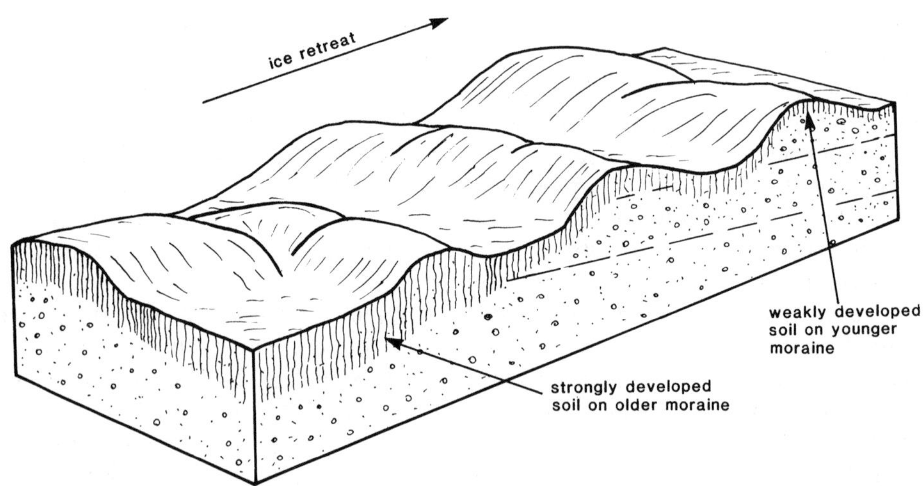

Fig. 4.6 — Soils with increasing degree of development on moraines of increasing age.

soils have not been eroded and were all developed under the same conditions of climate, organisms, relief and parent material.

The limitations of morphostratigraphical units in chronostratigraphy often result from doubts about their exact origin. For example, in lowland areas of glacial deposition, where ice lobes are virtually unconfined and can spread laterally (e.g. on the plains of mid-western USA), numerous low morainic ridges are often formed approximately parallel to the ice front. These are thought to mark successive ice margins formed either during stillstands in the progressive retreat of the ice front or by minor readvances of the front. However, where the relationship of these morphostratigraphical units to a lithostratigraphical sequence of tills dated by radiocarbon has been carefully investigated, as in Illinois (Willman and Frye 1970), the two types of units coincide only partially. Some ridges are composed of more than one till unit and some till units form two or more ridges, so the ridges may have formed in several different ways. This casts doubt on their value as chronostratigraphical units, despite the fact that there is a general decrease in the age of the units away from the outermost ice margin.

Because geomorphological features resulting from deposition are almost exclusively of Quaternary age, morphostratigraphical units are significant only in Quaternary geology. In this context their recognition and distinction from other types of stratigraphical units is very important, as major errors have arisen in the past through failure to recognize their chronostratigraphical limitations. It is therefore surprising that morphostratigraphy has been ignored by almost all the national and international committees on stratigraphy.

4.9 CLIMATOSTRATIGRAPHY

This aspect of stratigraphy, also vitally important in Quaternary studies, has similarly been ignored by most stratigraphy committees. Climatostratigraphical units are the basis for most regional subdivisions of the Quaternary (e.g. Table 1.2). The fundamental unit is the geologic-climate unit (American Commission on Stratigraphic Nomenclature 1961). These units include glacials, interglacials, stadials and interstadials. Unfortunately these were originally defined by the American Commission on Stratigraphic Nomenclature in terms that prevented their use beyond the areas repeatedly glaciated during the Quaternary. Glacials were defined as episodes when glaciers developed, reached a maximum and then receded, interglacials as times when the climate was incompatible with extension of glaciers, stadials as episodes within a glacial when glaciers were advancing, and interstadials as intraglacial episodes when glaciers were receding or at a standstill. However, the climatic fluctuations which caused glaciers to advance or retreat are strongly related to global insolation changes (see 1.3), and can be traced over a large proportion of the earth's surface using a wide range of proxy-climatic (sedimentological, palaeontological and palaeopedological) evidence. Therefore they are a very suitable basis for the subdivision of Quaternary time, provided decisions are made about where to draw boundaries between units on the continuously fluctuating curve of past temperatures, and also that the variable regional effects of the insolation changes on plants, animals, soils, the atmosphere, oceans and sedimentary processes are understood. As yet these decisions have not been made and there is limited information about the effects on plants, etc.; the value of climatostratigraphy is therefore limited and uncertain, but not negligible.

In many mid-latitude countries, such as Britain, the Netherlands and USA, where Quaternary climatic fluctuations had their strongest influence on plants, animals, soils, sediments and ice margins, glacials and interglacials have often been accorded the status of stages (see for example Mitchell *et al.* 1973). However, they are not stages in the chronostratigraphical sense of the word (Table 4.1) because, with the possible exception of the Holocene or Flandrian Stage of Mitchell *et al.* (10 000 years ago to the present), they are not bounded by synchronous surfaces. Even if their boundaries were placed at agreed points on the curve of past temperature fluctuations, they would be more or less diachronous because the various indicators of past climate often responded slowly to changes. For example, there is a considerable time lag between even a major temperature decrease and the arrival of an ice sheet in a lowland region, because ice takes a long while to accumulate and spread from upland areas. Likewise, woodland migrates only slowly from glacial refuges after a climatic improvement.

Another limitation of climatostratigraphy is that terrestrial deposits usually provide a very incomplete record of the Quaternary. It is therefore important to designate climatostratigraphical boundaries at type sites where sedimentation was continuous for as long as possible on either side of any boundary. Otherwise there will be unnecessary gaps in the sequence of units established for a region.

Despite these difficulties, which mean that climatostratigraphy is an unsuitable basis for worldwide subdivision of the Quaternary, units based on climatic change are often the most convenient way of correlating Quaternary sequences within mid-latitude regions. Over limited distances the effects of climatic change on a given fossil group, sedimentary process or soil-forming process are virtually synchronous, and therefore provide a suitable link between lithostratigraphy, biostratigraphy or pedostratigraphy and chronostratigraphy. The main problem with climatostratigraphy is knowing how far this link can be trusted, both in a geographical sense and in terms of the different types of proxy-climatic evidence available.

5

Dating Quaternary events

5.1 INTRODUCTION

The Quaternary was the shortest of all geological periods, but the changes of climate, sea level, faunas and floras which characterized it were numerous and rapid. Consequently these Quaternary events need to be dated much more precisely than is usually required in earlier geological periods. Some major climatic changes are now known to have occurred over periods of less than 1000 years. Accurate dating of such rapid changes is not too difficult if they occurred within the last 40 000 years or so, but dating of similar changes at, say, one million years ago requires very high precision indeed, and is not possible at present. This is the main reason why a full climatostratigraphic subdivision of the Quaternary has yet to emerge.

A wide range of dating methods is now available in Quaternary geology, based upon various physical, chemical and biological processes. Some are similar to those used for pre-Quaternary materials (e.g. potassium–argon dating), though they may be modified slightly to deal with the much younger Quaternary materials. However, Quaternary geologists have developed many other methods specifically for young materials, and these may be new to geologists who have not studied the Quaternary. Some of the methods have come from other disciplines, such as archaeology, botany or pedology. Indeed, the most useful advances in our understanding of many Quaternary problems, including dating and correlation, have arisen from multidisciplinary studies in which the needs of one discipline have been met by methods developed in another. Some dating techniques developed for Quaternary use (e.g. palynology) have also been profitably extended to pre-Quaternary materials.

Some previously popular Quaternary dating and correlation methods have been discredited. These include the 'count downwards from the top' method for glacial deposits, such as tills, and the idea that raised beaches, river terraces and erosion surfaces can be correlated over long distances by height. Such methods are excluded from this chapter, but conclusions based wholly or partly upon them are often repeated without qualification in current literature. A further problem is that strict application of stratigraphical procedures has often been ignored in Quaternary studies, mainly because of the difficulties involved in correlating deposits that are often unfossiliferous and change laterally in lithology more rapidly than typical pre-Quaternary marine deposits. These factors have led to considerable confusion over the dating of many Quaternary deposits, and it is important for the geologist to develop a critical faculty in reading Quaternary literature, and to try to distinguish reliable correlations from less reliable ones.

5.2 RADIOCARBON DATING

This method has now been used extensively for several decades for dating late Quaternary organic materials, such as wood, peat, seeds, leaves, bones, teeth, shells, soil humus, cloth and leather. Many universities have radiocarbon dating laboratories, and a service is offered by several commercial laboratories. The method depends upon measuring the very small amounts of ^{14}C relative to other carbon isotopes, as ^{14}C remains relatively constant during the life of an organism but decreases at a constant rate after death.

^{14}C is produced in the atmosphere by interaction between ^{14}N and neutrons produced when cosmic rays bombard various types of atoms in the stratosphere. It is oxidized to form CO_2, which then mixes with atmospheric CO_2 containing ^{12}C and ^{13}C; ^{12}C forms nearly 99% of this CO_2, ^{13}C just over 1%, and ^{14}C only one part in 10^{12}. From the atmosphere it is absorbed directly by land plants, or is dissolved in the sea and freshwaters and then absorbed by aquatic plants or animals; it is also taken up in turn by animals feeding on the land or aquatic plants. The ^{14}C in various living plants and animals thus reaches equilibrium with that in the atmospheric, oceanic and freshwater reservoirs of CO_2. But when these organisms die, exchange with these carbon reservoirs ceases, and the ^{14}C trapped within their fossilized bodies decays and eventually disappears. To determine the time elapsed since death, a decay rate based upon the originally calculated half-life of 5568 years (Libby 1952) is used, though more recently the half-life has been evaluated as 5730 ± 30 years. The oldest datable materials usually have ages equivalent to about seven half-lives (i.e. approximately 40 000 years).

Even in living organisms the amounts of ^{14}C are too small to measure by mass spectrometer, and have to be determined by counting the electrons emitted as the ^{14}C atoms disintegrate. In living organic material each gram of carbon gives about 13.8 disintegrations per minute. As this is much less than the amounts of background radiation from cosmic rays and gamma rays, the detector has to be protected from cosmic rays by a ring of geiger counters, which cancel their effect electronically, and from gamma radiation by a thick shield of iron or lead. However, a small background count within the detector must still be allowed for. The radiocarbon is introduced into the detector either as a gas (e.g. carbon dioxide, methane, acetylene) or in more modern equipment as a liquid hydrocarbon (usually benzene). In gas-proportional counting, the electrons discharged from ^{14}C atoms in the gas are attracted by a positively charged wire and counted electronically. In liquid-scintillation counting, the liquid is mixed with a scintillator, which flashes as each electron is emitted, and the flashes are then counted photoelectrically. The disintegrations happen at random, so each count over a short period is expressed with a statistical probability of deviation from a long-term mean. When the count and its standard error are converted to years, there is a 67% probability that the actual age lies within the ± range stated. The age is calculated from

$$\frac{T}{\log_e 2} \times \log_e \frac{(S-b)}{(S_o-b)}$$

where T is the half-life of ^{14}C, S is the count of the sample to be dated, b is the background count estimated by counting an equally sized sample of ancient carbon devoid of ^{14}C (e.g. coal), and S_o is the count from a sample of uncontaminated modern carbon, usually a standard oxalic acid (Mann 1983).

Originally it was assumed that the amount of ^{14}C in the atmosphere, and hence in living organisms did not differ in the past from present values, but variations of 1–2% were found over the last 1000 years by dating tree rings of known ages, and greater variations over the last 7000 years or so became apparent by dating annual rings from the extremely long-lived species *Pinus longaeva,* previously *P. aristata* (bristlecone pine) (Olsson 1970). Dating of Egyptian materials from 2000–3000 B.C. gave results up to 900 years too young (Berger 1970). These variations may result from changes in the cosmic ray flux related to sunspot cycles (Stuiver and Quay 1980) or changes in the earth's magnetic field (Bucha 1970). It is also possible that there are geographical changes in ^{14}C contents of living organisms so that dates from different continents are not exactly comparable. Because of these and other errors, radiocarbon dates are quoted in radiocarbon years before present (b.p.), present being taken as 1950 A.D. A conversion to sidereal years for the period 2500 B.C. to 1950 A.D. was agreed by the 12th International Radiocarbon Conference in 1985 (Stuiver and Pearson 1986, Pearson and Stuiver 1986), and various correction curves have been published for earlier periods (Stuiver 1982, Pearson and Baillie 1983, Pearson *et al.* 1983, Olsson 1986, Stuiver *et al.* 1986). A recent curve covering the last 7000 years is given in Fig. 5.1.

There are also several other possible sources of error in radiocarbon dating. Samples may be contaminated with younger carbon in humic compounds or recent plant roots, with older carbon in detrital constituents (e.g. coal or derived wood fragments), with ^{14}C from atomic bomb testing (this usually applies to exposed surface samples only), or with bicarbonate from percolating groundwater. Fig. 5.2 shows the errors resulting from various degrees of contamination with carbon of higher or lower activity than the dated sample.

Shells are especially prone to exchange with groundwater bicarbonate; specimens with a 'tight' matrix are usually selected (Mangerud 1972) and contaminated outer layers are usually removed with hydrochloric acid before dating, but the results are still rather unreliable. Bones are also unsuitable for dating, unless a collagen fraction can be extracted (Burleigh 1972). Aquatic plants may absorb bicarbonate from the surrounding water by photosynthesis; as the dissolved bicarbonate usually comes from old limestone bedrock, this 'hardwater error' results in an age greater than the true one (Deevey *et al.* 1954). Isotopic fractionation may also occur at various stages, such as during the mixing of surface ocean water with older ^{14}C-deficient water from below prior to absorption by marine organisms, during photosynthesis in certain plants, and during the processing of samples. This type of

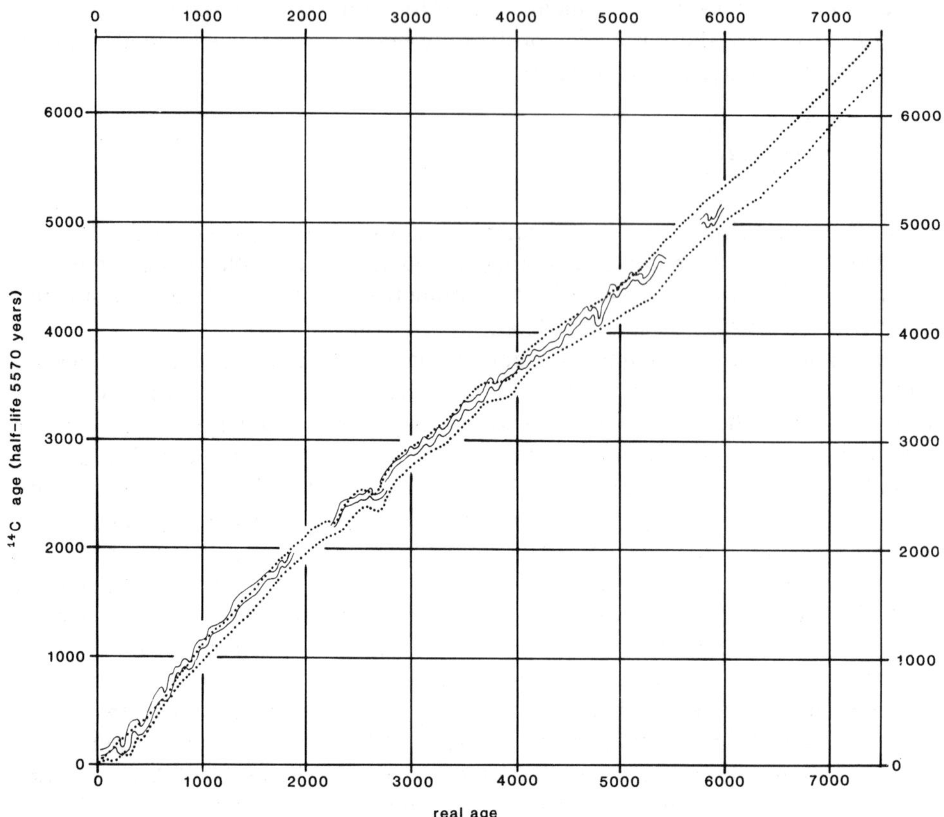

Fig. 5.1 — Calibration of ^{14}C ages by dendrochronology; the narrow band covers high precision ^{14}C measurements by Pearson and Baillie (1983) and Pearson *et al.* (1983), and the broader band (dotted lines) covers earlier dendrochronological samples (from Olsson 1986). Reproduced by permission of John Wiley & Sons Ltd.

error can often be corrected if the $^{13}C/^{12}C$ ratio is measured by mass spectrometry. Contamination by humic compounds is removed by sodium hydroxide extraction, and if these extracts are dated separately from the residue they usually give much more recent dates.

The size of sample required is normally enough to give 4–5 g carbon; this may mean several hundred grams of a weakly organic sediment or buried soil. Recently more sensitive methods have been developed by counting ^{14}C atoms directly (rather than disintegrations), using an accelerator or cyclotron as a high energy mass spectrometer (Hedges 1981, 1987, Farwell *et al.* 1984). The sample size can then be decreased approximately 1000-fold (i.e. to 1–5 milligrams of carbon), but the service is currently available in only a few laboratories, such as the Radiocarbon Accelerator Unit of Oxford University's Research Laboratory for Archaeology and History of Art (Batten *et al.* 1986).

The age limit of about 40 000 radiocarbon years has been extended by the Groningen laboratory (the Netherlands) using a thermal diffusion process of isotopic

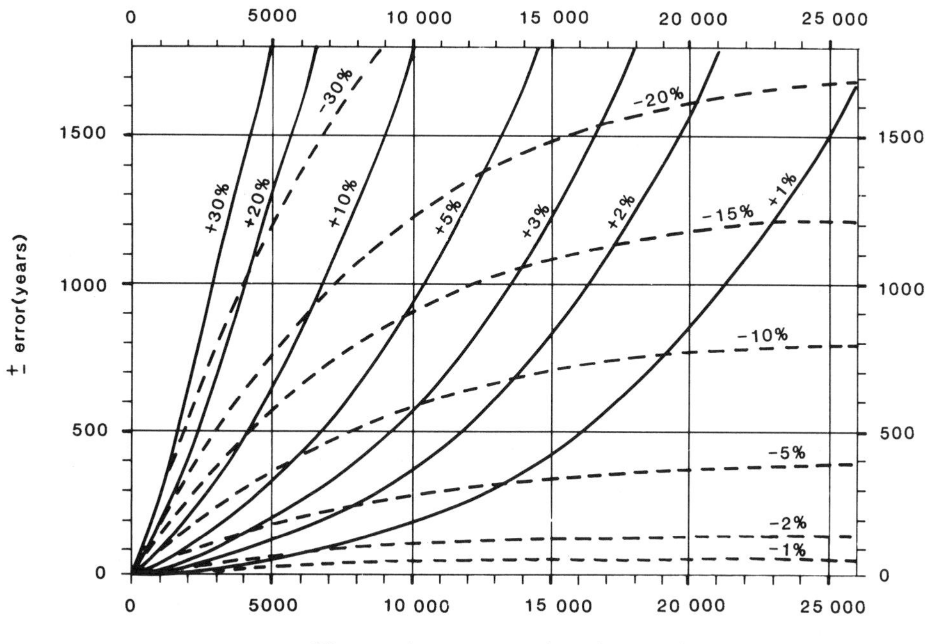

Fig. 5.2 — ^{14}C dating errors arising from various degrees of contamination with material having various higher activities (continuous curves) or lower activities (dashed curves) (from Olsson 1986).

enrichment (Haring *et al.* 1958). Dates as old as 74 000 radiocarbon years have been obtained by this method, but samples must be selected and treated with great care to avoid contamination with recent carbon. Accelerator mass spectrometry should double the effective range of ^{14}C dating to about 80 000 years, though this has yet to be realized, principally because of contamination with modern carbon (Hedges 1987).

5.3 URANIUM SERIES DISEQUILIBRIUM DATING

The two naturally occurring isotopes of uranium (^{235}U and ^{238}U) and a radioactive isotope of thorium (^{232}Th) decay through three different series of short-lived radioactive daughter isotopes (Figs 5.3–5.5) to the stable lead isotopes ^{207}Pb, ^{206}Pb and ^{208}Pb respectively. As the parent U and Th isotopes are much longer lived than the daughters, a state of secular radioactive equilibrium is established if a sample of the parent is left undisturbed in a closed system. When this equilibrium is reached, the stable end-member lead isotopes increase at the expense of the parent isotopes, but the proportions of intermediate daughter isotopes remain constant.

In many geological processes one or more of the daughter isotopes is either separated from its parent or co-deposited with the parent in amounts in excess of the secular equilibrium (Ku 1976). When these processes result in the deposition of

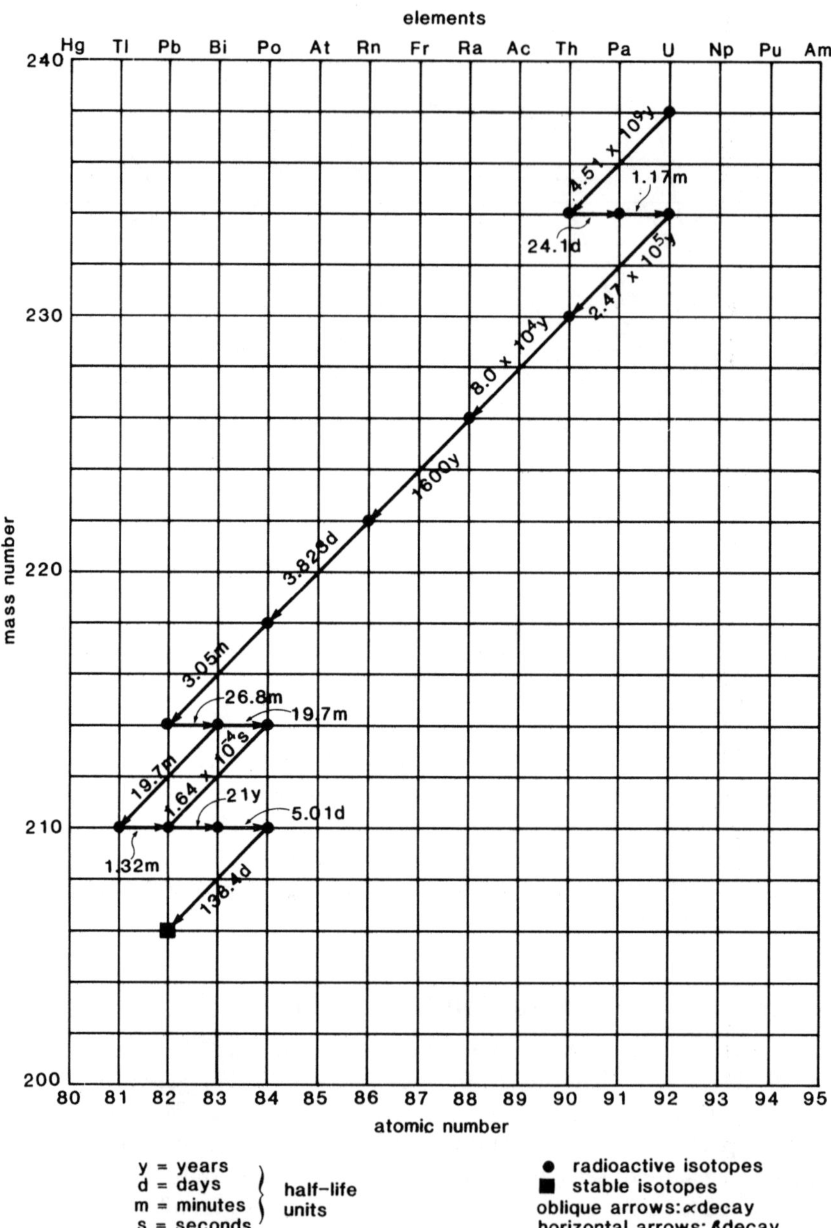

Fig. 5.3 — Scheme of ^{238}U decay series.

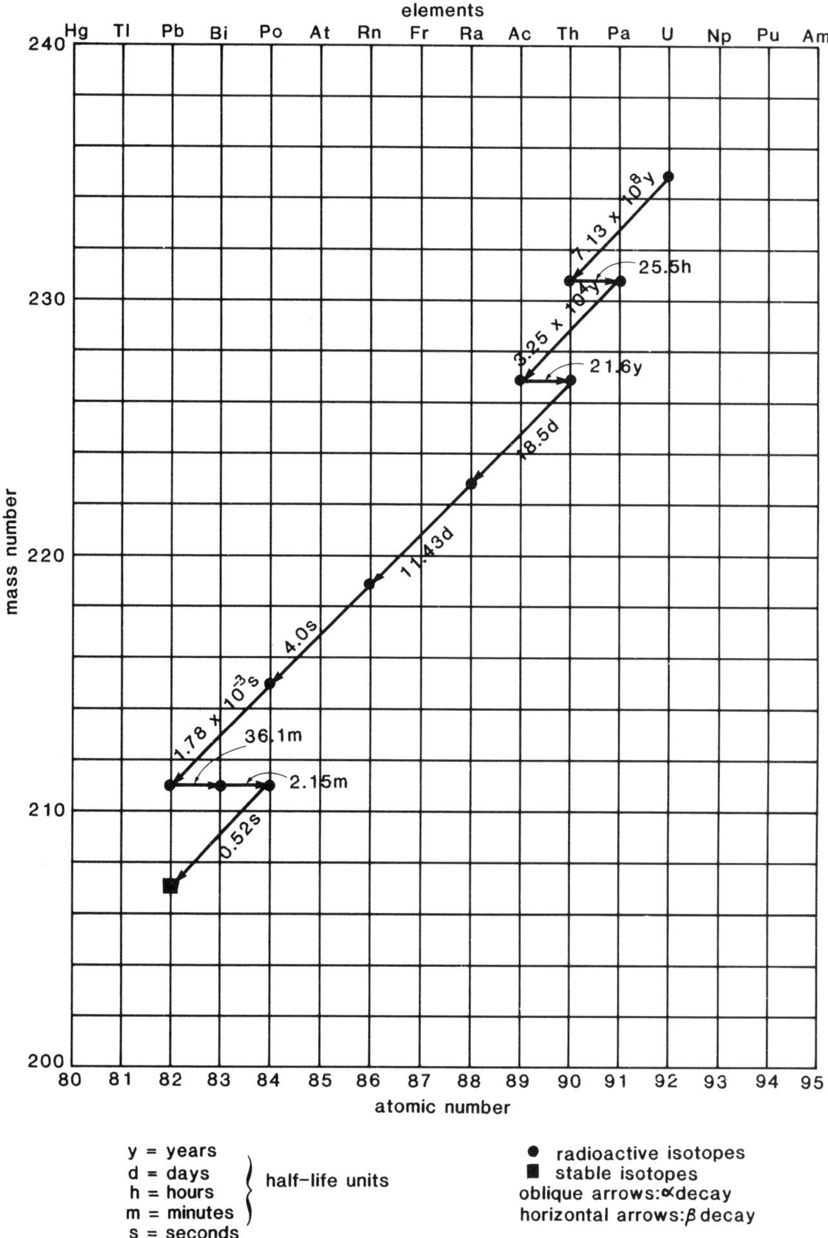

Fig. 5.4 — Scheme of ^{235}U decay series.

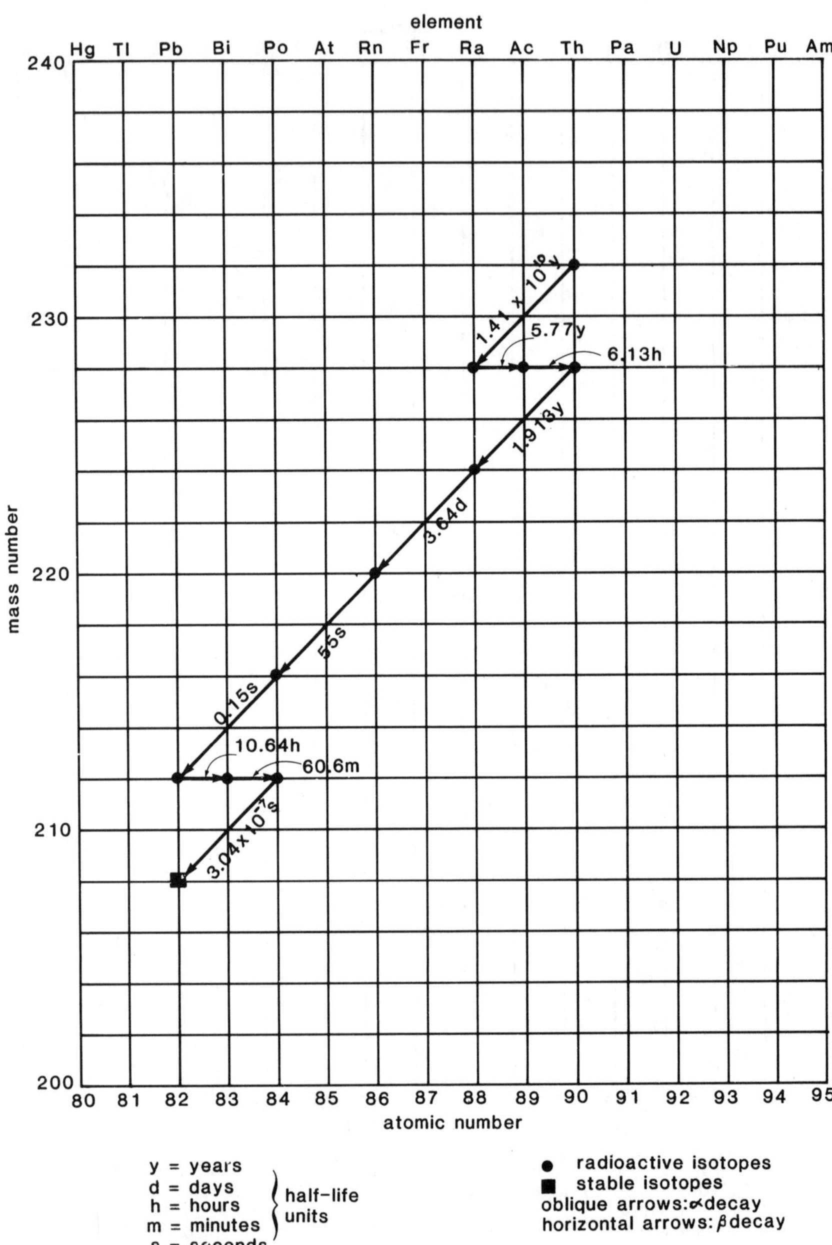

Fig. 5.5 — Scheme of ^{232}Th decay series.

sediment, crystallization of minerals or growth of shell or bone, the age of such materials may be determined by measuring the extent to which secular equilibrium has been re-established, assuming that the material has remained in a closed system since its formation. Separation of daughter isotopes from their parents may result from differences in their solubilities in various environments or their affinities for complexing agents such as clays or hydroxides.

Two types of secular disequilibrium exist. Daughter deficiency dating is based upon growth of an initially deficient daughter into equilibrium with its parent. Daughter excess dating depends on an initial excess of the daughter and its decrease towards equilibrium.

The commonest daughter deficiency methods rely upon the solubility of uranium as UO_2^{2+} ions in aerated water and the adsorption of daughter thorium and protoactinium isotopes by clays or their co-precipitation with hydroxides. The UO_2^{2+} ions are incorporated into carbonates precipitated from the water. Thus, providing no clays or hydroxides are incorporated into the carbonate, it initially contains U but no Th or Pa. Subsequently ^{230}Th forms from ^{234}U and ^{231}Pa from ^{235}U at constant rates, so that amounts appearing in the carbonate are proportional to the time since its crystallization. As ^{235}U is much less abundant in nature than ^{238}U, samples for ^{231}Pa/^{235}U dating should contain a total of at least 1 mg kg^{-1} uranium. The rate of decay of ^{234}U to ^{230}Th (half-life of 2.48×10^5 years) is such that the method cannot be used to date carbonates more than 350 000 years old. The ^{234}U/^{230}Th method also depends upon the initial absence of Th; this can be checked by looking for ^{232}Th in the sample, as any thorium originally in the sample would have contained some of this long-lived cosmogenic isotope. The ^{231}Pa/^{235}U method can be used only for dating samples less than 250 000 years old.

Daughter excess methods are used mainly for dating marine sediments. This is because the daughters of ^{238}U and ^{235}U produced in the sea are precipitated directly or adsorbed on clays or organic matter, so that immediately after deposition the sediment contains an excess of these isotopes, which then slowly decays. The initial concentration of the excess daughters is assumed to be the same as in modern sediments of similar clay and organic content. Where marine sedimentation has continued to the present day, it is possible to test that the daughter excess decreases regularly with depth below the sediment surface (i.e. with increasing age). Irregularities in the ^{230}Th or ^{231}Pa profile indicate either that the sediment accumulated at an irregular rate or that it has not behaved as a closed system.

Amounts of the daughter isotopes are determined by counting their disintegration rates, using either α or β counters following separation and purification of the elements by chemical methods. Artificial tracers such as ^{228}Th or ^{232}U are often added as standards to indicate the efficiency of the purification procedures. Ivanovich and Harmon (1982) gave further details of the methods used. Table 5.1 summarizes the applications and limitations of the main uranium and thorium series dating methods used in Quaternary studies. The materials which have been dated most successfully are corals (Neumann and Moore 1975, Harmon *et al.* 1981), cave speleothems (Gascoyne *et al.* 1981, 1983), manganese nodules and marine sediments (Ku 1976). Bones and teeth give unreliable dates because they often act as open systems; also there is often a long delay between the death of an animal and uptake of uranium by the bones (Szabo 1980). Molluscs generally do not give reliable dates

Table 5.1 — Uranium series dating methods

Method	Age range (10^3 yr)	Uses
(a) *Daughter deficiency methods*		
$^{230}Th/^{234}U$	5–350	Speleothems, travertines, caliche, corals, molluscs, bones, teeth, saline lake deposits, phosphorite, peat, manganese nodules
$^{231}Pa/^{235}U$	5–250	Speleothems, corals, molluscs
$^{228}Th/^{232}Th$	0.0001–0.015	Marine sediments, lake sediments
$^{227}Th/^{230}Th$	5-300	Speleothems, corals, molluscs
$^{4}He/^{234}U$	50-1500	Corals, groundwater
(b) *Daughter excess methods*		
^{230}Th	5–350	Marine sediments, manganese nodules
^{231}Pa	5–150	Marine sediments, manganese nodules
^{228}Ra	0.0001–0.03	Coral growth bands
^{210}Pb	0.001–0.4	Marine sediments, lake sediments, coral growth bands, snow, oil paintings, pewter, bronze

because they contain very little uranium initially and also act as open systems (Kaufman *et al.* 1971).

Speleothems are larger and more abundant in warm climates, and hardly form at all in glaciated or periglacial regions where there is little vegetation to raise the soil carbon dioxide content and dissolve carbonate. In several mid-latitude regions, speleothem dates are therefore concentrated to some extent during periods which correlate with warmer stages of the oceanic oxygen sequence (Harmon *et al.* 1978, Gascoyne *et al.* 1983).

5.4 POTASSIUM–ARGON DATING

This dating method, based upon the decay of radioactive ^{40}K to ^{40}A and ^{40}Ca (Dalrymple and Lanphere 1969), has been used mainly for pre-Quaternary deposits, because the half-life is very long (1310 million years). Indeed, Damon (1968) and others doubt its value for dating Quaternary materials, though it has been used to obtain ages as recent as 70 000 years on volcanic rocks (Richmond 1975).

As ^{40}Ca is indistinguishable from the calcium which is very abundant in most deposits, the method is based on determination of the stable daughter product ^{40}A, which is a gas. Consequently it can only be applied to potassium-containing minerals which have a lattice structure allowing retention of the ^{40}A produced. These include sanidine, anorthoclase, some plagioclase felspars, muscovite, biotite, hornblende, leucite and nepheline in volcanic rocks, and glauconite in marine sediments. The glauconite must be authigenic and not derived from an earlier sediment, and minerals which have been weathered or heated after crystallization are unsuitable because the ^{40}A has probably leaked from them, and the ages obtained are too young. Inherited argon, from older inclusions in rocks or absorbed from air in the sample, gives too old a date. For these reasons, it is important to obtain several dates on a deposit; single K/Ar dates are unreliable (Fitch 1972), especially for younger materials in which inherited argon may be very abundant in relation to radiogenic argon. However, Langley (1978) suggested a method for overcoming the problem of inherited argon in dating argillaceous sediments. Another modification, which may allow the errors associated with inherited argon to be evaluated, involves stepwise conversion of the ^{40}K into ^{39}A by neutron activation, and measurement of the $^{40}A/^{39}A$ ratio (Miller 1972).

In regions such as western USA, east Africa (Fitch *et al.* 1976), and the Rhine Valley (Frechen and Lippolt 1965), where volcanic deposits are interbedded with other Quaternary sediments, potassium–argon dating has proved very useful for clarifying the history of Quaternary events. Applications to non-volcanic Quaternary materials have been less successful.

5.5 THERMOLUMINESCENCE (TL) DATING

TL is the light emitted when crystalline or glassy minerals subjected to ionizing radiations are heated. The radiations, mainly α, β and γ rays from radioactive isotopes (^{40}K, U, Th, and other elements in the decay chains of the last two), produce defects in the minerals in which electrons are trapped. These are released by heating or by prolonged exposure to sunlight. The amounts emitted as light by heating can be measured with a photometer, and are proportional to the time elapsed since any trapped electrons were last released. This has been used to determine the time when pottery was fired (Fleming 1979) or burnt flints were last heated (Göksu and Fremlin 1972), the date of deposition of deep-sea sediments (Wintle and Huntley 1980), loess (Wintle 1981, 1987) and glaciolacustrine silts (Berger and Huntley 1982), and the date of burial of buried soils (Wintle and Catt 1985a).

The most sensitive natural minerals, responding to very small radiation doses, are fluorite and anhydrite. Quartz, feldspar and some other minerals are much less sensitive, but can be used to measure doses >1 gray. The range of total α, β and γ radiations in the ground is usually 1–10 grays $1000\,yr^{-1}$, so these less sensitive minerals can be used to determine doses acquired over about 100 years or more. The size of the TL signal given by a sample on heating depends on the radioactivity of the natural environment from which it was taken, the length of time it was in that environment, and the mean sensitivity of the minerals it contains. The past radiation dose is determined by comparing the natural TL signal of the sample with that induced in similar samples by different known laboratory doses of α, β and γ radiations. TL sensitivity of minerals is less for α than for β or γ radiations, and the effects of each must be determined separately. The total laboratory dose required to match the natural TL signal is often determined by three different methods (Wintle and Prószyńska 1983), and a weighted mean equivalent dose (ED) used to calculate age from

$$\mathrm{ED}=[(\beta+\gamma \text{ dose rate})+(k)(\alpha \text{ dose rate})\times \text{age}$$

where k is the ratio of TL sensitivity (TL per gray) for α radiation/sensitivity for β or γ radiation (usually 0.05–0.5).

The TL measurements are made on one of two grain sizes, fine sand (90–125 μm) and fine silt (usually 4-11 μm), separated from crushed or disaggregated samples by sieving and repeated settling under gravity or centrifugation. The fine silt particles are smaller than the mean range of α particles produced by the U and Th decay chains, and therefore contain TL resulting from past α, β and γ radiations. With fine silt fractions the measurements are made on the assemblage of minerals present (often mainly quartz and feldspar). However, with fine sands the measurements are made on quartz grains separated from other minerals by magnetic separation, flotation in bromoform and treatment with hydrofluoric acid. The acid dissolves feldspars and removes the outer skins of the quartz grains affected by α radiation entering the grains from their surroundings. As quartz contains very little U or Th, the internal α radiation is negligible, so the α dose rate can be ignored in the above equation.

The relevant dose rates in the age equation are determined from measurements of the U, Th and ^{40}K contents of the sample and its surroundings. The β dose rate from ^{40}K is determined from total K_2O content, assuming a constant ratio of isotopic abundances, and the α, β and γ contributions from U and Th decay chains are measured by neutron activation, γ spectrometry or α particle activity with a ZnS scintillation counter. The γ dose rate is affected by water content, as water partly absorbs the radiation energy; an allowance for this effect is usually based on the water content of the surrounding soil or sediment, but if this varies during the year (e.g. because of a fluctuating water-table), the annual dose can be measured by leaving a sensitive TL dosimeter such as fluorite in the place where the sample was taken, and measuring its TL signal after one year.

Other problems associated with the determination of dose rates result from disequilibria in the U and Th decay chains. The commonest of these effects results from diffusive losses of a gaseous member of the decay chains (^{222}Rn). To check whether Rn loss has occurred, the contributions from U and Th decay chains are measured twice, once unsealed to allow any Rn to escape and again in a sealed chamber to prevent losses.

The application of TL dating to sediments such as loess depends upon removal or 'bleaching' of the TL during deposition by exposure to sunlight. Since about 1965 the method has been used for dating various sediments in Russia (Dreimanis *et al.* 1978), Hungary, Poland and China, but different analytical methods were used, many of them ignoring problems such as the effect of water (Wintle and Huntley 1982), so most of the published dates, which range up to about 500 000 years, are unreliable. A major problem with sediments is that exposure to sunlight does not completely bleach them; the natural TL signal that they give on heating has a residual component in addition to that resulting from the radiation dose since deposition. Wintle and Huntley (1980) tried to distinguish these two components in oceanic sediments by measuring the decrease in TL when samples, which had been given various γ doses in addition to their natural dose, were exposed to a sunlamp for a fixed period. This gave dates in the range 7000–130 000 years which were within 20% of independent dates.

Because of the partial bleaching by exposure to sunlight, samples intended for TL dating should be stored in a light-proof box or bag, and sediment samples should be coherent and large enough to allow a generous surface layer to be pared off before analysis. The range of sediment types and ages suitable for dating is at present uncertain; in particular it is not clear which depositional processes effectively bleach particles of different sizes. Fine aeolian sediments such as loess seem to be the most promising, but fluvial, glaciofluvial, lacustrine, marine and colluvial deposits have also given fairly reliable dates in certain circumstances, and as the method is improved will probably be dated more readily. However, glacial deposits such as lodgement tills do not give realistic dates (Wintle and Catt 1985b).

Buried soils seem to give fairly reliable TL dates mainly because surface (A) horizons are continually exposed to sunlight by pedoturbation up to the time of burial. Wintle and Catt (1985a) suggested that the age obtained is slightly greater than the actual time of burial, though the error is no larger than the mean residence time error with ^{14}C dating of humus in buried soils. They also found that soil-forming processes such as decalcification and gleying decrease the TL signal obtained from subsurface soil horizons.

5.6 ELECTRON SPIN RESONANCE (ESR) DATING

Electrons generated by the α, β and γ radiation of radioactive elements and by cosmic rays produce defects in crystals and other solids bombarded by the radiations, and the extent of these defects, which is proportional to the geological age of the materials, can be measured with an ESR spectrometer (Ikeya 1978). To find the age of the material, or the time elapsed since the electrons were last released by heating (and the defects annealed), the total radiation dose received in the past must be divided by the annual radiation dose. The total or accumulated dose that a sample has received is usually determined by applying different additional γ-ray doses to similarly sized subsamples, measuring the increases in ESR intensity, and extrapolating to zero intensity the line joining the measured points. The annual dose is determined independently from knowledge of the amounts of various radioactive elements (mainly U, Th, K and their daughter products) in the sample and its surroundings, making allowances for disequilibria in the U decay series, sample size, variations in composition (e.g. zoning of crystals), accumulation of U by some materials (e.g. bones and teeth), and α-efficiency or the proportion of the α radiation producing damaging electrons. Total dose can usually be determined with a fairly small error ($<\pm5\%$), but the error in estimation of annual dose is at least $\pm10\%$, so the main uncertainty in an ESR date results from measurement of annual dose rates, which can vary greatly. The problems associated with the determination of total and annual doses were reviewed by Hennig and Grün (1983).

The range of materials datable by ESR is very wide, but there are many problems, not the least of which is the initial cost of the spectrometer. Datable materials include bones, teeth, mollusc shells, corals, foraminifera, apatite crystals, travertine, stalactites, lacustrine and marine precipitates of calcium carbonate, dolomite, volcanic glass and feldspar crystals, gypsum crystals and deformed quartz grains from fault zones (Ikeya 1985). The measurements can also be used to determine the temperature at which pottery or burnt flint was fired.

The main advantages of the method are the small size of sample required (usually about 0.25 g) and the wide age range of datable material (several million years), though routine measurements are limited to samples exposed to a minimum dose of a few hundred rads, which is equivalent to a minimum age of several thousand years at typical dose rates. Another advantage is that little sample preparation is required other than homogenization where possible. However, the dating of bones and teeth can cause problems because of their organic constituents, which are often difficult to remove completely (Driver 1979).

Although ESR dating has only become possible in the last decade, it is a very promising method, and the number of laboratories able to offer it has increased considerably in recent years. As the method is developed in the future, it will probably become applicable to a very wide range of materials, and span the time interval between the older limit of the ^{14}C method and younger limits of other well established isotopic techniques such as the K–Ar method.

ESR dating of shells from the Holsteinian marine interglacial deposits near Hamburg showed that this stage correlates with isotope stage 7 of the deep-sea succession (Linke *et al.* 1986), a date supported by amino acid studies (Miller and Mangerud 1985).

5.7 TEPHROCHRONOLOGY

Layers of tephra (mainly volcanic ash and pumice) are useful for dating and correlating Quaternary deposits in many countries, because they are deposited over quite large areas in very short periods of time (Einarsson 1986). However, some countries (e.g. Britain) are too far from any Quaternary volcanoes to have recognizable ash layers, and in regions subject to repeated ashfalls it is often difficult to distinguish different layers. Ash is often blown several thousand kilometres from the source, and is consequently one of the few deposits likely to be helpful in correlating terrestrial and oceanic successions.

The characteristics of tephra used for distinguishing and correlating separate falls include the refractive index (Hodder 1978), trace element composition (Izett 1981), microphenocryst content and vesicularity of glass fragments, and the composition and optical properties of phenocrysts such as ferromagnesian silicates (Mullineaux 1974) or iron–titanium oxides (Kohn 1979). Analyses of individual particles (e.g. by microprobe) are preferable to bulk analyses, which are often influenced by fractionation processes during transportation of the ash and post-depositional weathering.

Ash layers are usually dated by the K–Ar method, palaeomagnetic polarity measurements or the fission-track method (Westgate and Naeser 1985). The last method is based upon counting the number of fission tracks in glass fragments or zircon crystals from the ash, and calculating the age from the amount of ^{238}U present; this isotope produces fission tracks spontaneously at a constant rate and is the only commonly occurring natural isotope to produce significant numbers of tracks in periods of 10^5–10^7 years. The tracks are zones of damage caused by α particle bombardment, and can be accentuated by etching with hydrofluoric acid. For a piece of glass or a zircon grain with a given ^{238}U content, the number of tracks per unit area increases linearly with time. However, tracks can be annealed by heating; those in crystals are stable up to about 80°C, but tracks in glass can be removed by lower temperatures over long periods. Partial annealing can be detected and allowed for by measuring the diameter of tracks (Storzer and Wagner 1969), but any fission-track date determined on glass should be considered a minimum age. Apart from some U-rich zircons, all samples less than 100 000 years old give very imprecise results, because they contain too few tracks. However, many zircon grains are small and do not show many of the tracks formed by U atoms lying close to the crystal faces; the minimum dimension of datable zircons is about 75 μm. Also some basic tephras contain few or no zircons. Usually fission tracks are measured on 12 or more zircons or glass fragments per sample. This has the advantage that occasional zircons derived from older rocks or glass fragments from earlier ashes can be identified and eliminated from the age determination.

In some volcanic areas, such as Iceland and western USA, the systematic study of characteristic tephra layers from one or more centres, each layer dated from historical evidence or by radiometric or fission-track methods, has been developed to establish local tephrochronological systems. These are used for dating soils, archaeological features, deep-sea sediments, erosion surfaces, glacial and aeolian sediments, and glacier fluctuations. In N. America, fission-track dating showed that the Pearlette Ash, originally thought to be a single unit of Kansan age (Frye *et al.* 1947), includes at least three different tephras with ages of 0.6–2.0 million years (Table 5.2).

Table 5.2 — Dated widespread Quaternary tephra units in N. America (from Westgate and Naeser 1985); the Bishop and various Pearlette units were dated by the fission-track method

Tephra unit	Source	Age (yr)	Maximum known distance from source (km)
Bridge River	Meager Mountain, British Columbia	2600	550
Mount St. Helens (older set Y)	Mount St. Helens, Washington	4300	1150
Mazama	Crater Lake, Oregon	6600	1550
Glacier Peak	Glacier Peak, Washington	11 200	950
Pearlette 'O'	Yellowstone National Park, Wyoming	600 000	1200
Bishop	Long Valley, California	700 000	1850
Pearlette 'S'	Yellowstone, Wyoming	1 200 000	1200
Pearlette 'B'	Yellowstone, Wyoming	2 000 000	1200

This means that the stratigraphy based on the original assumption is largely incorrect (Boellstorff 1978).

5.8 DENDROCHRONOLOGY

Dendrochronology or tree-ring dating is based upon variations in thickness or density of the annual growth rings of trees. The rings vary in thickness mainly because of seasonal weather differences, which are uniform within limited areas, allowing correlation of timbers grown over the same period of time at different sites within that area. Rings are measured microscopically in slices or cores, usually of oak, which always grows a single ring per year. Curves showing the year-to-year changes in ring thickness are usually matched by eye or a scaling device (Pilcher 1973) against master curves based on dated sequences from living trees. However, the match is often uncertain, because the rings become thinner as the tree ages, and are also affected by environmental factors other than seasonal weather, such as soil, exposure, slope angle and aspect, and competition from surrounding trees. The match becomes poorer with increasing distance from the site of the master curve, leading to increased possibility of mismatching. It is therefore important to create master curves from averaged measurements on several timbers from each site, and use them for correlation over short distances only (<50 km). Tree-ring density is usually measured in thin section by an X-ray technique (Schweingrüber *et al.* 1978), and is probably more reliable than ring width as an indicator of climatic differences.

Dendrochronology has been used mainly for calibration of radiocarbon dating, using rings from the long-lived American tree, the bristlecone pine (*Pinus longaeva*). By cross-matching dead and living bristlecone pine wood, Ferguson (1970) produced a tree-ring chronology for eastern California covering the last 7500 years. It is also used in archaeology for dating timber from buildings, and in palaeoclimatology as an indicator of precisely dated climatic changes (Fritts 1976). For curve matching it is necessary to obtain long sequences of ring measurements, exceeding 100 years, but small pieces of timber rarely contain so many rings. At present dendrochronologies which can be used for precise archaeological dating over the last 1200 years in Britain are available for N. Ireland, S. Scotland and the east Midlands, but the areas over which these can be used effectively are probably quite small, and there is a need for the establishment of a larger number of local chronologies. Discontinuous records comprising floating chronologies not tied to historically dated wood have been established for much longer periods in some areas, for example the last 8000 years in north-east Ireland (Pilcher *et al.* 1977), but these have less value for high precision dating.

Errors in dendrochronological dating also arise from spurious matching of curves for timbers grown in quite different areas. This can happen, for example, if timbers were exported from one area for use in another.

5.9 VARVE CHRONOLOGY

Many lake sediments can be used for dating because their laminations result from annual cycles of climatic fluctuation. Each couplet consisting of a coarse, light (summer) layer and fine, dark (winter) layer represents a single year. This provides a precise chronology for the sediments themselves, where couplets can be counted downwards from the present sediment surface, and for dating the formation of the lake or of features associated with it.

Varved or annually laminated lake sediments were originally described from glacial lakes. They also occur in many temperate lakes as a result of seasonal changes in sedimentation, though these laminations are often disturbed by currents or bioturbation. The most useful laminated sediments form in fairly small, deep lakes with restricted inflow, such as kettle-hole lakes. The rate of sedimentation should be much greater than the rate of disturbance (Ludlam 1976), and this is typical of proglacial lakes, which freeze over in winter and have little fauna to disturb the sediment, yet receive large sediment influxes from summer melting of the glacier (see 2.2.6).

In temperate lakes, laminated sediments are best preserved where the benthos fauna is discouraged either by anaerobic bottom conditions or by lack of organic matter as food. The latter situation is usually found within deep enclosed basins on the floors of large lakes, as the slowly settling organic matter is decomposed before it reaches the bottom. Laminations in temperate lakes result from seasonal differences in production of diatoms or other phytoplankton (Simola 1977), in precipitation of calcium carbonate (Brunskill and Ludlam 1969, Peglar *et al.* 1984) or iron oxides (Anthony 1977), or in the relative proportions of detrital and various non-detrital constituents (Simola and Uimonen-Simola 1983).

Annual couplets range in thickness from <0.5 mm to 40 cm or more in some proglacial lakes. Differences in thickness may result from changes in influx of clastic sediment, production of organic constituents or precipitation of compounds from the lake water. These are influenced by local factors, such as soil cultivation and erosion, and regional factors, especially climatic changes. The effects of regional factors are perhaps best evaluated in large lakes, though avoiding the margins which are strongly influenced by local changes around the lake. Curve matching of thickness variation has been used to correlate sequences from site to site. In areas not influenced by human activities, such as recently deglaciated regions, this seems to be fairly successful. In Sweden, De Geer (1912, 1940) developed a varve chronology covering the last 17 000 years, though the reliability of its earlier parts has been questioned; it has been revised by Lundqvist (1975, 1980) and others, and used to date the northward retreat of the Scandinavian ice margin over this period (Mörner 1979).

The main problem with varve chronology is the difficulty of distinguishing annual from non-annual laminations. In glacial lakes, multiple couplets may form each year, and in temperate lakes, human activities and heavy rain or wind can produce laminations in periods both longer and shorter than a year (Simola and Tolonen 1981). It is therefore important to investigate the cause of laminations before using them for dating. The composition of laminae may be investigated microscopically in thin section or in grains adhering to transparent sticky tape pressed against a dried vertical surface of the sediments (Simola 1977). This will often show whether the laminations can be attributed to seasonal changes in the lake, such as differences in biological productivity or the accumulation of clay beneath a frozen surface in winter (see 2.2.6).

The laminations can be counted from a cut surface of a sediment core, from photographs of the core, or from X-ray radiographs, which often reveal laminations in apparently massive deposits (Saarnisto 1986). The fine structure of soft sediments beneath existing lakes is easily disturbed or destroyed by conventional coring and handling methods. This problem can be overcome by gently inserting a metal tube containing dry ice and ethanol into the soft sediment and freezing a 1–3 cm layer around the outside of the tube (Wright 1980). The frozen sediment is removed from the tube by replacing the freezing mixture with warm water. If the tube is inserted slowly, fine laminations are preserved even in the uppermost sediment layer, and there is no mixing or disturbance.

5.10 PALAEOMAGNETIC DATING

During the cooling of lava through the Curie Temperature (approximately 500°C), the cooling of baked pottery, the precipitation of iron minerals in sediments, or the deposition of fine-grained sediment in a fluid medium (water or air), small crystals of magnetic minerals such as magnetite are orientated parallel to the earth's magnetic field. As this magnetic field changed in the past in various ways, including reversals of the north and south geomagnetic poles, measurements of magnetic characteristics frozen into these materials can be used to date them relative to an established sequence of dated reversals and other changes.

The earth's magnetic field is thought to be produced by motions in the electrically conducting fluid core, which act as a self-exciting dynamo (Bullard 1972). The motions could be convection currents resulting from radioactive heating, and polar reversals may be related to catastrophic events, such as large meteorite impacts, or to random changes in the non-dipole magnetic field (Carrigan and Gubbins 1979). Transitions from the normal state of the field, in which its dipole direction wobbles several tens of degrees over the northern part of the earth's surface, to the reversed state (wobbling about a south polar direction) and vice versa take about 5000 years. This is a fairly rapid geological event, and is consequently a useful stratigraphic marker for dating and correlating worldwide (see 4.6). However, as there were numerous reversals during the last few million years, palaeomagnetic dating is useful only where measurements can be made on a fairly continuous sequence of lavas or deposits, or where an approximate indication of age has been obtained by another method.

Geomagnetic polarity epochs are time intervals during which the earth's field was mainly of one polarity, either normal or reversed (Fig. 4.5). Epochs dated over the last 4–5 million years have lasted 0.7–1.7 million years. Polarity events lasted about one tenth as long and exhibited opposite polarity to the epoch in which they occurred. The time scale for epochs and events given in Fig. 4.5 is based on measurements from lavas in various parts of the world dated by the potassium–argon method. Lavas provide the best record of the geomagnetic characteristics at the time of extrusion because they contain large amounts of magnetic minerals which actually crystallized under the influence of the magnetic field. Sediments give a much poorer record because they usually contain much smaller quantities of magnetic minerals and, as these were solid particles at the time of deposition, they were less influenced by the contemporary field. The best sediment samples are fine grained, unweathered and unaffected by secondary mineralization or lightning strikes, which can produce secondary magnetization. The resultant of the various magnetizations which have affected a sediment is known as the natural remanent magnetization (NRM). To obtain the detrital remanent magnetization (DRM) at the time of deposition, the (normally) less stable secondary magnetizations are usually removed by applying a magnetic field to the sample. As the applied field is intensified in steps, the secondary remanent magnetizations are unblocked. If the applied field is alternating and slowly decreased from its peak value at each step, the orientation of the unblocked grains is randomized, leaving the more stable magnetizations unaltered. The assumed DRM is obtained when the measured magnetic vector stops changing direction after further intensification of the applied field.

In addition to geomagnetic polarity epochs and events, there is evidence for short-term shifts in the position of the geomagnetic pole known as excursions. During excursions the pole may move over as much as 135° of latitude and back again at a rate of more than 5° per century (Verosub 1979). Many excursions during the Brunhes normal polarity epoch have been reported from various parts of the world (Table 5.3), but few can be correlated worldwide or even over quite short distances.

It is possible that some excursions can be detected only over small areas of the earth's surface (Harrison and Ramirez 1975), but equally likely that many spurious excursions have been based upon samples in which stable secondary magnetizations have been interpreted as the DRM.

As the earth's magnetic field is not just a simple dipole, but also has non-dipolar elements varying from place to place, it is possible to use well-dated master curves for secular variations in certain palaeomagnetic characteristics to date sedimentary sequences within limited areas. For example, in northern England, measurements on fine lacustrine deposits show fluctuations in magnetic declination and inclination with periodicities between 5×10^2 and 5×10^3 years over the last 15 000 years (Thompson 1977). The greatest fluctuations here are in declination, and measured changes in this, dated by ^{14}C and other methods, have been shown to be synchronous in several British lakes. Thompson and Turner (1979) established master curves for both declination and inclination (Fig. 5.6) from British lakes, and suggested that these might be used for relative dating throughout north-west Europe. However, they are different from Japanese and North American records for the same period (Turner and Thompson 1979), so the area over which they are applicable is uncertain at present.

The accuracy of such dating depends very much on how well new measurements fit the master curve for the region. Best-fitting curves are calculated as smoothed cubic splines (Thompson and Kelts 1975) and matched by eye. However, non-sequences and post-depositional disturbance of the sediment (e.g. by slumping) can cause problems with curve matching.

Measurements of secular variations in non-dipolar geomagnetic properties have been used successfully to date waterlain cave deposits (Gale *et al.* 1984) estuarine sediments (Suttill 1980) and oceanic deposits (Opdyke 1972) as well as lake sediments, but other types of deposits do not give curves which can easily be matched with known master curves. In lodgement tills, for example, the finest magnetic particles may preserve the contemporary geomagnetic field, but coarser particles are

Table 5.3 — Reported palaeomagnetic polarity excursions during the Brunhes Epoch

Excursion	Age (yr)	References
Laschamp	8000–20 000	Bonhommet and Zahringer (1969)
		Hall *et al.* (1979)
		Heller (1980)
Erieau	7600–14 000	Creer *et al.* (1976)
Lake Michigan	7500 and 13 000	Vitorello and Van der Voo (1977)
Gothenburg	12 350–12 400	Mörner *et al.* (1971)
		Mörner and Lanser (1974)
		Mörner (1977)
Maple Hurst Lake	12 500	Mott and Foster (1973)
Port Dover	13 300	Mörner (1976b)
Gulf of Mexico	15 000–18 000	Freed and Healy (1974)
Lake Biwa	18 000	Nakajima *et al.* (1973)
Rubjerg	23 000–40 000	Abrahamsen and Knudsen (1979)
Norre Lyngby	23 000–40 000	Abrahamsen and Readman (1980)
Kipp	24 000	Barendregt (1984)
Mono Lake	24 000	Denham (1974)
Lake Mungo	29 500	Barbetti and McElhinny (1976)
Gulf of Mexico	30 000–33 000	Clark and Kennet (1973)
Meadowcliff	30 500	Stupavsky *et al.* (1979)
Blake	105 000	Smith and Foster (1969)
		Denham (1976)
		Denham *et al.* (1977)
Lake Biwa	104 000–117 000	Yaskawa *et al.* (1973)

probably orientated by ice flow movements, shearing and deformation stresses (Barendregt 1985), giving mixed magnetic fabrics.

The usefulness of secular variations in correlation also varies from region to region. The geomagnetic anomalies in some areas persist for long periods, and consequently provide few changes than can be dated and used for correlation. In other areas, changes have often occurred quite rapidly, so that curves for variations in time of declination, inclination, pole position or other geomagnetic properties show numerous features useful for correlation by curve matching.

Within single depositional basins, especially lakes, variations in magnetic susceptibility (i.e. the intensity of magnetization or the extent to which samples are attracted to a magnet) can often be used for correlation of profiles. Susceptibility depends on the types and amounts of magnetic minerals present, and is likely to show synchronous changes throughout a lake because of changes in the source and type of sediment entering it (Oldfield *et al.* 1978). Such measurements of 'mineral magnetism' can be made quickly and easily, and often allow correlation of otherwise homogeneous sediment sequences, but only within a single basin and not between

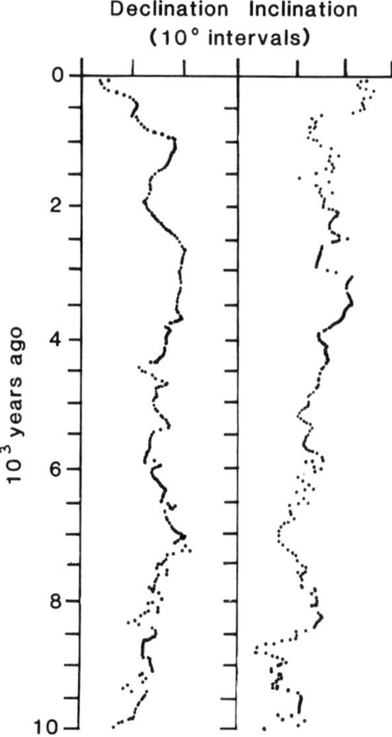

Fig. 5.6 — Master curves for geomagnetic declination and inclination for the last 10 000 years from Lake Windermere, England (from Thompson and Turner 1979). The records have been rotated so that the mean vector (average of the direction cosines) has zero declination and inclination.

different basins. Mineral magnetism is also useful in the recognition of kilns, hearths and habitation horizons, as burnt soil contains the strongly magnetic iron oxide maghemite.

5.11 AMINO ACID DATING

The analysis of amino acids has been developed over the past 20—30 years as a method for correlating and dating Quaternary deposits by various of the organic constituents they contain. It has been used for bones (Bada *et al.* 1979, Bada 1985), molluscs (Wehmiller 1982), corals (Wehmiller *et al.* 1976), foraminifera (King 1980), and wood (Rutter and Crawford 1984).

The proteins in organisms are composed mainly of about twenty amino acids. Most of these have molecules containing a single chiral or asymmetrical carbon atom (i.e. a tetrahedral carbon atom to which four different atoms or groups of atoms are attached), though the amino acid glycine has no chiral carbon atom, and threonine and isoleucine have two. Those containing one chiral carbon can exist in two stereoisomeric forms, which are mirror images of one another; one of these rotates polarized light to the left (laevorotatory) and the other to the right (dextrorotatory). The high molecular weight protein molecules of living organisms contain glycine and laevorotatory amino acids, but after death the laevorotatory or L-amino acids are slowly converted to dextrorotatory or D-amino acids until a 1:1 mixture of the two stereoisomers is attained. The L- to D-conversion (or racemization) occurs at a constant rate, provided temperature, Eh and pH remain constant, so the D/L ratio of a given amino acid may be used to determine the time since death of an organism. In cold climates, complete racemization takes several million years, but in tropical areas and hot deserts it may be achieved in 150 000 years, though different amino acids undergo racemization at different rates. Although both chiral carbon atoms in threonine and isoleucine may undergo conversion to produce four stereoisomers, only one additional isomer is usually produced during diagenesis. In isoleucine this is D-alloisoleucine, which is produced from one of two diastereomers (isomers that are not mirror images of one another) by the process known as epimerization.

Racemization and epimerization processes occur faster in wood than in shells, the rates in bones being intermediate. For relative dating it is therefore necessary to choose samples of similar materials, which have undergone similar diagenetic conditions of temperature, Eh, pH and moisture content, and to extract and measure the D/L ratio of the same amino acid from each. Rutter *et al.* (1985) summarized the methods for preparation and analysis of different types of samples. Because of the effect of temperature, measurements on Quaternary samples from cold climates are usually based on amino acids such as aspartic acid, which racemize quickly. In contrast, amino acids which racemize slowly, such as leucine, are used for samples from tropical areas.

One advantage of amino acid dating is that it is fairly cheap and quick, so that many samples can be analysed. This is useful if a deposit such as a till is to be dated from the derived shells, bones or wood fragments it contains. These could be of several ages prior to deposition of the till, and only the youngest of them will indicate the maximum age of the deposit. A single date could suggest that the till is much older than it is, but the youngest of several dates gives a much better indication of its age. However, when multiple samples which should all have the same age are analysed, the spread of results is often disconcertingly large (Fig. 5.7). This is probably because of unequal changes in the amino acids of different specimens of the same shell, bone or wood species during diagenesis.

5.12 ARCHAEOLOGICAL DATING

Many Quaternary deposits contain human artifacts, but they are useful for precise dating in some of the more recent periods only. Pottery, coins and other metal objects can provide quite precise dates for deposits up to about 2500 years old. However, to be useful in dating they should occur in abundance, because many artifacts are resistant, and an isolated coin or fragment of pottery could easily have been derived from an earlier deposit. Tools made in earlier periods from flint and other hard rocks are also often derived; in addition they are of limited use for dating

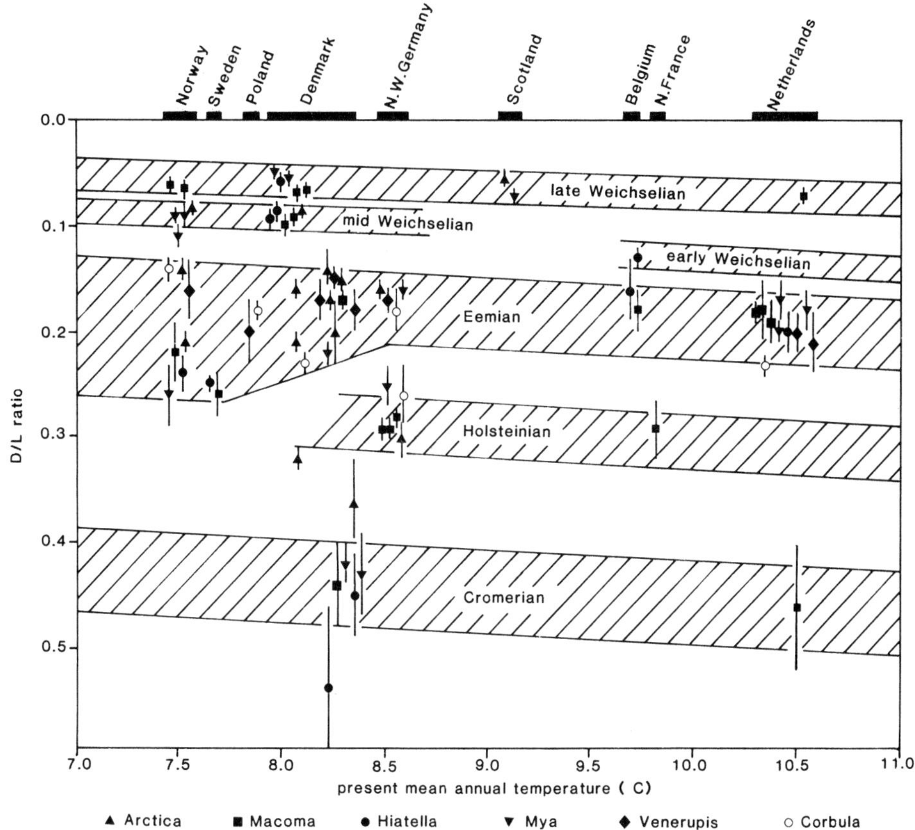

Fig. 5.7 — Mean D/L ratios for six molluscan genera from later European Quaternary stages plotted against current mean annual site temperature; the vertical bars indicate one standard deviation (from Miller and Mangerud 1985). Reproduced with permission from Quaternary Science Reviews, Volume 5, 1985, Copyright Pergamon Journals Ltd.

because their characteristics often do not change very rapidly with time, and changes are rarely concurrent in different parts of the world. At one time it was thought that the typology of stone artifacts could be used to date earlier Quaternary deposits in much the same way as evolutionary changes in various fossil groups can help date them. However, it is now known that the methods of toolmaking and the styles of different tool types migrated quite slowly from place to place, and some were introduced more than once to certain areas at quite different times. Also some cultures co-existed for long periods in some regions. At present it is therefore more appropriate to date the artifacts of stone age cultures using other dating methods than to expect the artifacts themselves to provide very precise dates.

Despite these problems, stone artifacts occurring *in situ* and fairly abundantly can give a very approximate indication of age, especially within isolated regions such as Britain. The earliest stone tools, found mainly in E. Africa, are pebbles partially flaked from one or more sides to make heavy tools for use as choppers (Fig. 5.8A). At the classic site of Olduvai Gorge in Tanzania, these unspecialized tools are identified as the Oldowan culture and are dated to about 1.6–1.8 million years ago. Similar industries are known from other parts of East Africa, South Africa, Pakistan, India, Burma, China, Java, Thailand and various parts of southern Europe (Wymer 1982). The nearest equivalent in Britain, from Clacton (Essex) and Swanscombe (Kent), is known as the Clactonian industry, but this is considerably younger, as it dates mainly from the Hoxnian interglacial and the later part of the Anglian cold stage, which were certainly less than 500 000 years ago.

About 1.4 million years ago in Africa the first handaxes appeared. At Olduvai these characterize the Developed Oldowan industry, but elsewhere they are more usually referred to as Acheulian. Typical handaxes are oval or pointed, and flaked bifacially to leave little or none of the original cortex of the pebble or nodule (Fig. 5.8B). In Africa, handaxe and chopper-core industries co-existed for a long period of time in the early and mid-Pleistocene, but the relationship between them is uncertain. Equally problematical is the exact purpose of handaxes; they could have been used as butchering knives, spearheads, spades or cleavers for chopping wood or bones. Many different types can be recognized, based on shape and size, but they do not seem to have much significance with respect to date of manufacture, except that long-pointed handaxes, those with a plano-convex cross-section, and others with a twisted long-section appeared only in the late Pleistocene. The oldest handaxes in Europe, from Abbeville in northern France (Bourdier 1969), various sites in Spain, and perhaps also Kents Cavern, near Torquay (south-west England), date from the Cromerian interglacial, which is probably equivalent to oceanic stage 13 (478 000–524 000 years ago). But most handaxe sites in Africa, Europe, India and the Near East are dated to a later warm stage (the Hoxnian in Britain), which is probably equivalent to oceanic stage 9 (303 000–339 000 years ago) or 11 (362 000–423 000 years ago).

Before the last (Eemian, Ipswichian) interglacial stage (=oceanic stage 5e, 116 000–128 000 years ago), handaxes had become less popular and were partly replaced by tools made from flakes like those discarded during the manufacture of handaxes. Flakes were probably sharper and therefore better for cutting meat or scraping skins than a handaxe, but were usually quite small. Larger flakes of various shapes were made by the Levallois technique. First an oval core was prepared by flaking a nodule around the edge on either side alternately with a heavy hammerstone; a flat striking platform was then prepared at one end, and a large flake detached from one side by a carefully directed blow on the platform with the hammerstone. The remainder of the core is called a 'tortoise core' from its resemblance to a tortoise shell (Fig. 5.8C). Because only one flake was produced from each nodule, the technique was wasteful and therefore used mainly at sites where larger amounts of flint were available, such as Baker's Hole, Northfleet, in the lower Thames valley, and the type site of Levallois near Paris. Most Levallois flakes were oval and characterized by a radial pattern of fractures on one (dorsal) side, a single conchoidal fracture on the other, and a striking platform with small facets at one end (Fig. 5.8D). However, many were secondarily worked around the edge, and some were elongate, blade-shaped flakes. The introduction of the Levallois tech-

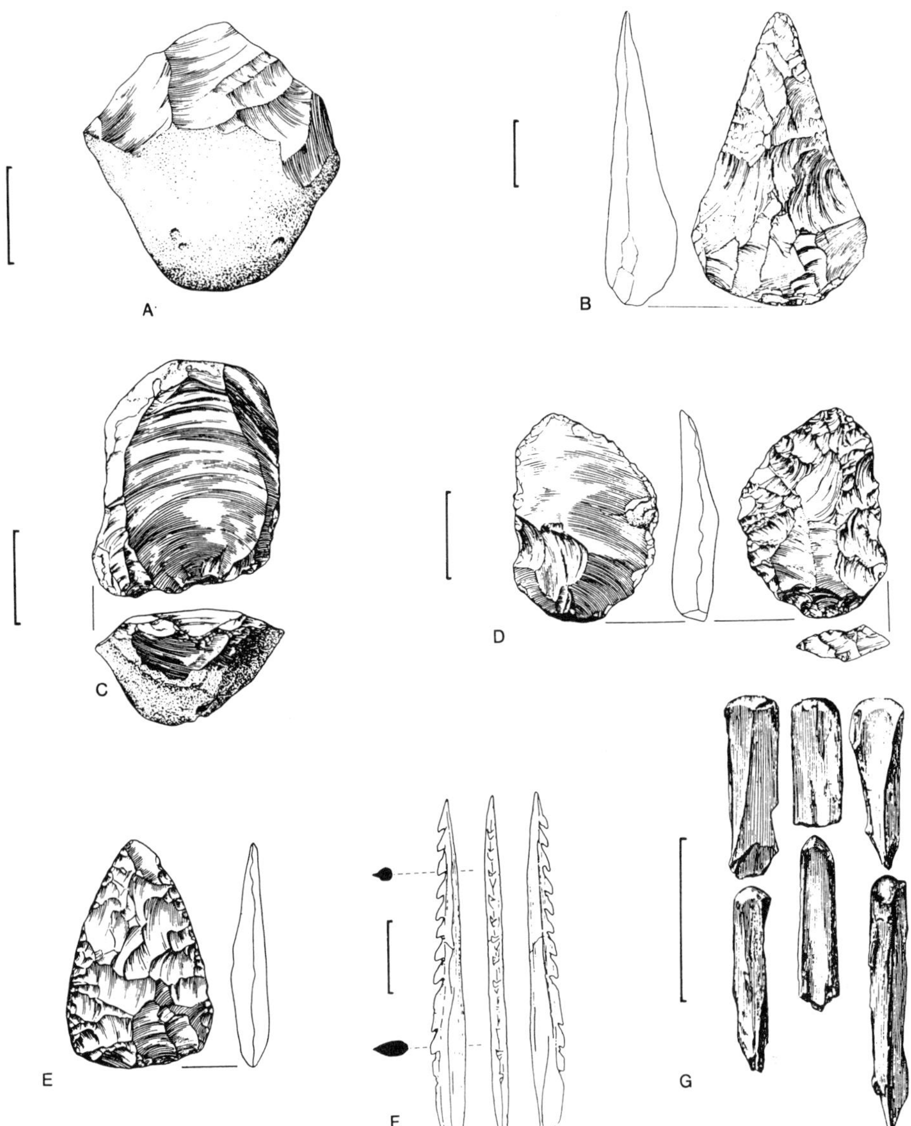

Fig. 5.8 — Tool types characteristic of various Quaternary periods in Europe: A, Chopper (Wimereux, France); >0.4 million years ago. B, Handaxe (Swanscombe, England); 0.1–1.4 million years ago. C, 'Tortoise core' (Brundon, Sudbury, England); 35 000–130 000 years ago. D, Levalloisian flake struck from 'tortoise core' (Brundon, Sudbury, England). E, Sub-triangular Mousterian handaxe (St. Jacques-sur-Darnetal, France); 35 000–80 000 years ago. F, Maglemosian bone point or harpoon (Skipsea, England); 7500–10 000 years ago. G, Obanian limpet scoop: 5000–7000 years ago. (A–E from Wymer 1982, F from Gilbertson 1984, and G from Lacaille 1954). (Each scale bar represents 5 cm).

nique occurred at approximately the same time as the fossil remains of man from various sites in Europe, Africa and the Near East show changes from the characteristics of *Homo erectus* (small skull with prominent brow ridges and large jaw) to those of *H. sapiens* (larger cranium with less prominent brow and smaller jaw). Although 'tortoise cores' first appear at or just before the 'last interglacial' (Eemian), they are also common in later periods, because they were an important preliminary stage in the manufacture of more advanced stone tools.

The early part of the last cold stage (Würm, Weichselian, Devensian) was the time of Neanderthal Man (*Homo sapiens neanderthalensis*) and of the Mousterian industry (Shackley 1980). Neanderthal Man had the large cranial capacity typical of modern man, but also some features inherited from *H. erectus*, such as a heavy face with brow ridges and large nasal apertures. His remains are more common than those of earlier periods, probably because deliberate burial of the dead was often practised. Mousterian implements include thin, small handaxes, often triangular (Fig. 5.8E), pointed or leaf-shaped (the last occurring mainly in eastern Europe where they were probably used as spearheads), Levallois flakes and blades. The blades were made by repeated blows with a hammerstone on a prepared striking platform, and differed from the Levallois blade-shaped flakes in having a few parallel fractures on one side instead of a crude radial pattern. Many were secondarily reworked at the margin to form scrapers or rudimentary knives.

By the later part of the last cold stage (after about 35 000 years ago) Neanderthal Man had been replaced by modern man (*Homo sapiens sapiens*) and Mousterian implements by the light, delicate (leptolithic) implements of the Upper Palaeolithic. The various Upper Palaeolithic industries are best developed in France. Long blades were removed from carefully prepared cores of flint or other fine-grained rock, and then fashioned into scrapers, awls, curved knives, points for boring, bifacial laurel-leaf-shaped points, etc. Bone was little used in the earliest (Perigordian) period, but later became popular for manufacture of fine points (Aurignacian and Solutrian), barbed speartips, fishing tridents and needles (Magdalenian and Azilian). The Perigordian and Aurignacian industries lasted till about 22 000 years ago. The Solutrian industry (22 000–19 000 years ago) was characterized initially by very refined pointed flint blades, such as the laurel-leaf points, and later by bone working including the earliest eyed needles. During the Magdalenian (17 000–11 500 years ago) there was an increasing use of bone and antler for fine harpoons, awls, needles, etc., and of flint for extremely small (microlithic) implements. The final industry of the French Upper Palaeolithic, the Azilian (11 500–11 000 years ago), was characterized by less refined small flint blades and flakes, and small but fairly crude bone and antler points and harpoons. Other artifacts of Upper Palaeolithic man include necklaces and bracelets of beads (made of bone, ivory, fossils, amber, fish vertebrae and stone), pendants, buttons and stylized statuettes of animals and women (venuses). Paintings and carvings on cave walls were also common, especially in the Magdalenian (Sieveking 1987).

Industries similar to the Upper Palaeolithic of France are known from northern Spain, Italy, Germany and other countries in central and eastern Europe. But in areas further north, such as Britain and the Netherlands, which were close to the greatly expanded Scandinavian ice sheet of the last glaciation, Upper Palaeolithic sites are much more sparse, and can be divided into an earlier series (probably

Aurignacian) before the time of glacial maximum (the Dimlington Stadial), and a later series dating from about 12 000 years ago (i.e. the middle of the Lake Windermere (=Allerød) Interstadial) onwards. A few of the later series are Magdalenian, but most of those in Britain are different from all the French Upper Palaeolithic industries, and are named Creswellian from the site of Creswell Crags in Nottinghamshire (Campbell 1977, Jenkinson 1984).

Other Upper Palaeolithic industries are known from northern and southern Africa, Iran, Iraq, Russia, Siberia, China, Japan, India, Java, Australia and North America (Wymer 1982). Those in Russia have some affinities with French and other European industries, but elsewhere they are quite different, suggesting little or no contact with European cultures. In the Far East, chopper-core industries persisted and leptolithic artifacts did not appear until very late in the last cold stage, though because of imprecise dating the first leptolithic industries in some areas (e.g. Kashmir) could even be Holocene. The same is true of Australia, which was first inhabited by aborigines about 40 000 years ago. As in New Guinea, the chopper-core industries of Australia include the unusually advanced tool type of ground-edged axes composed of fine volcanic or metamorphic rocks. The Palaeo-Indian artifacts of USA and Mexico are bifacially flaked leaf points similar to the earlier Upper Palaeolithic industries of Siberia, and it is likely that hunting communities originally migrated from Siberia into North America via what is now the Bering Straits about 25 000–20 000 years ago, when the sea level was low enough to provide a land bridge between the two continents but the bridge had not yet been closed by growth of the Keewatin glacier of Canada (Wymer 1982).

In Europe the transition from Upper Palaeolithic to Mesolithic cultures is drawn at the major climatic change at the beginning of the Holocene (10 000 years ago). The earliest industry was the Maglemosian, with sites dating from 10 000 to about 7500 years ago in lowland Britain (e.g. Star Carr, N. Yorkshire, Clark 1954) and various areas as far east as Estonia. Maglemosian artifacts include microliths, small flint blades, burins (engraving tools) and barbed harpoons made of bone and antler (Fig. 5.8F); bows and arrows (often with composite microlith heads) were used for hunting and flint axes for felling trees.

At several upland sites in England and Wales dating from about 8000 to 7000 years ago, a Mesolithic industry (Sauveterrian) dominated by flint microliths and lacking large axes often occurs beneath accumulations of peat. Charcoal is common at the same level as the microliths, suggesting that the early Holocene forest of the upland areas was often destroyed by burning in order to assist hunting activities. This resulted in degradation of the soil by loss of nutrients, and led either to waterlogging and accumulation of peat and blanket bog on low permeability deposits, or to development of heath on more permeable materials.

By the mid-Holocene, when the sea had risen eustatically to approximately its present level, groups of Mesolithic people known as 'Strandloopers' inhabited coastal areas, living mainly on seafish. In Britain they lived mainly in western Scotland (Obanian industry) and north-east Ireland (Larnian). These industries have few axes or microliths, and are characterized instead by flattish elongate artifacts (Fig. 5.8G) used for collecting shellfish (e.g. prising limpets from rock surfaces).

Mesolithic industries seem to have been confined to Europe. Elsewhere, Upper

Palaeolithic hunting industries persisted almost to the present day (e.g. in America, Australia and some subarctic areas), or were directly superseded by the farming industries of the Neolithic in areas where there was little or no forest development in the Holocene. The earliest farming communities arose in south-west Asia (e.g. Palestine and Iraq) almost 11 000 years ago, then spread slowly in various directions, reaching central Europe by 7000 years ago, and France, Britain and Scandinavia by 6000 years ago. In forested areas, the first work before land could be used for cereals or other crops was the removal of trees. Some woodland clearance was permanent (e.g. in East Anglia), but much of it was part of a shifting system, in which successive small areas were felled and burned, used for agriculture for a few years, and then abandoned when a new area was cleared. After abandonment the woodland regenerated in time. Temporary land use of this type is often known by the Danish term 'landnam'. The frequent felling required for repeated landnam episodes demanded high quality stone axes, which were made from various metamorphic and igneous rocks or from high quality fresh flint that was often mined from depths below the influence of Pleistocene frost-scattering, as at Grimes Graves, Norfolk (Clarke 1963, Sieveking *et al.* 1973). Other Neolithic artifacts include tools for soil cultivation (digging-sticks, hoes), harvesting (sickles) and grinding corn (querns), made from stone, antler, bone and wood.

Tools and weapons made of bronze were first used in Britain around 3800 years ago, and those of iron about 2500 years ago.

5.13 PALAEONTOLOGICAL EVIDENCE FOR THE AGE OF SEDIMENTS AND SOILS

Evolutionary changes in plants and animals are helpful in dating and correlating Quaternary deposits, but not to the same extent as in pre-Quaternary periods. This is because in most groups the rate of evolutionary change was slow compared with the short period of time involved. Quaternary faunas and floras did change rapidly with time, but mainly because of environmental factors related to the rapid climatic changes. These tend to mask the small evolutionary changes, except in regions such as the equatorial oceans which were influenced little by the climatic changes. Thus some evolutionary changes in foraminifera have helped date and correlate deep ocean sediments in tropical regions, but the same group is less useful with shallow marine sediments on or close to mid- and high-latitude land areas.

The dominant influence of climate on Quaternary faunas and floras led to the widespread adoption of climatostratigraphy for subdivision of Quaternary time. This is based partly on biostratigraphical subdivision of the fossiliferous Quaternary strata, using assemblage biozones rather than the range or other types of biozone by which pre-Quaternary successions are usually subdivided (see 4.5). Differences between assemblage biozones may result partly from evolutionary changes, but mainly they reflect changing environment. Consequently they are likely to be time-transgressive, and may be repeated at different times or in different places, so they are not really suitable for chronostratigraphical correlation.

The environmental factors influencing assemblage biozones are related to situations before, during and after deposition. Before deposition, the abundance of different plant and animal genera or species is influenced by factors such as water depth, salinity, temperature, pH and Eh in subaqueous environments, or by seasonal distribution of rainfall and air temperature, slope angle and aspect, and soil pH, Eh and drainage in terrestrial situations. During deposition, many fossil groups are subject to selective sorting by biological processes (e.g. feeding) and geological processes (e.g. irregular wind dispersal or sorting by water currents). After deposition, certain fossils may be selectively destroyed by weathering or diagenesis, or selectively translocated to sites away from the original place of deposition (e.g. illuviation of certain pollen grain types through well drained soil profiles).

Despite the various factors affecting the composition of assemblage biozones, their diachronous nature, and tendency to be repeated at different times, they have been used extensively in Quaternary geology for dating and correlation, often because no better method is available. Their obvious limitations for this purpose can be partly overcome if the numerous environmental factors determining their composition are well understood. This is because certain combinations of environmental characteristics may be diagnostic of particular periods within limited areas, and give rise to distinctive local assemblages of plants and animals. But even then the problem of long-distance correlation remains.

5.13.1 Plant remains as evidence of age

Because pollen grains are so abundant and widespread in Quaternary deposits, they have been used more than any other fossils for establishing assemblage biozones. Typical interglacial sequences in mid-latitude regions can be divided into four main assemblage biozones (Turner and West 1968) reflecting the climatic change from cold to temperate and back to cold (e.g. Fig. 1.7). In any given region the sequence of interglacial pollen zones is repeated in almost exactly the same form many times during the Quaternary. Successive interglacials in Europe have been tentatively distinguished (West 1977, pp. 354–379; 1980) by (a) the presence of certain thermophilous Tertiary relict trees (*Tsuga, Eucommia, Pterocarya,* etc.), which reappeared in several earlier Quaternary interglacials after having been banished southwards during the earliest cold stages, (b) the relative abundance of trees appearing at or soon after the climatic optimum of each interglacial (e.g. *Abies, Fagus, Tilia, Acer*), and (c) the abundance of *Corylus* and *Picea* pollen in different zones of each interglacial (Fig. 5.9). But as the exact reasons for these differences are poorly understood, they are probably of dubious value for dating and correlation, especially between Britain and the European mainland, because migration of certain genera may have been prevented in some interglacials by severance of the land connection.

Correlation of cold stage deposits by pollen assemblages is even less reliable, because they contain fewer genera and very little is known about their dependence upon environmental factors. In mid-latitude regions, plant fossil assemblages of cold periods may have no strict modern equivalents, and are therefore difficult to use for reconstructing environmental conditions or for dating and correlation.

A further problem with pollen assemblage biozones is that many grains can be identified only at generic level, whereas environmental interpretation is often different for different species within a genus. This can be overcome in part by the study of plant macroremains (leaves, seeds, etc.), which can often be identified at species level. Macroremains are also more representative of the local vegetation than

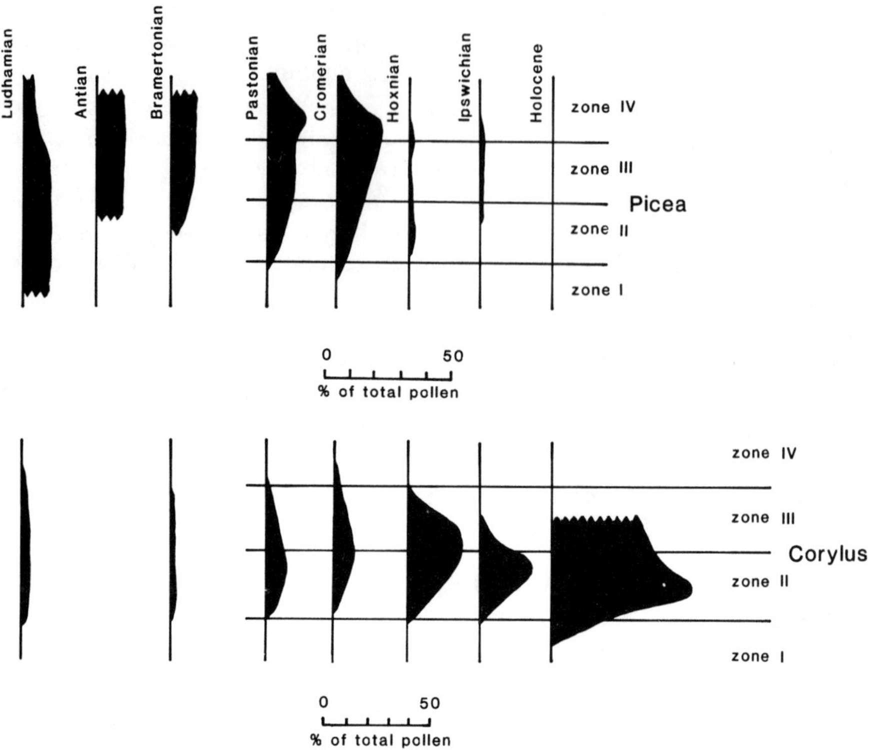

Fig. 5.9 — Schematic curves for changes in the amounts of *Picea* and *Corylus* pollen through various temperate Quaternary stages in East Anglia (from West 1980). Reproduced by permission of Cambridge University Press.

is pollen, but are rarely as abundant.

Preservation of pollen and plant macrofossils is best in anaerobic conditions, such as peat and waterlogged freshwater deposits. Plant remains are also well preserved in most marine sediments, but are usually derived from various environments on adjacent land areas, the pollen by wind transportation and macroremains by marine currents. Plant macrofossils are extracted by handpicking from samples broken along bedding planes, or by sieving samples dispersed in a dilute solution of sodium hydroxide or sodium hexametaphosphate (West 1977, Appendix 1). Pollen is extracted by centrifuging after similar dispersion, then oxidation, treatment with hydrofluoric acid to dissolve mineral constituents and acetolysis (Dimbleby 1961); also it may be separated from the sediment matrix by flotation in a heavy liquid such as a bromoform–alcohol mixture (Frenzel 1964). The separated grains are stained with safranin, and mounted for microscopic examination in glycerine jelly. Pollen grains and plant macrofossils are identified by morphological features, using reference collections of correctly identified modern material (e.g. Andrew 1984). Relative percentages are based on total counts of 600–1000 grains.

Absolute frequencies of pollen grains or other fossils, calculated as percentages of the total in a certain volume of sediment, allow the abundance of a particular taxon to be expressed independently of the abundances of others. In well-dated successions, absolute frequencies can be expressed as amounts per unit area per unit time (e.g. number of pollen grains per cm^2 per year), which enables the density of the original living community to be calculated (e.g. the number of trees of different genera per unit area). This gives a better idea of climatic and other environmental conditions at the time of deposition, which is more likely to help with correlation and dating than less quantitative results.

Pollen abundances are conventionally presented as histograms, the percentages or absolute frequencies being represented by bars of different lengths and at vertical intervals proportionate to distances between field samples. Changes in woodland composition (e.g. through an interglacial) are often shown by expressing pollen from tree genera as percentages of total arboreal pollen, but if non-tree pollen is abundant the pollen sum usually includes all types. With assemblages from environments other than closed forest, it is often difficult to differentiate between locally derived pollen, which usually indicates local environmental conditions (e.g. the presence of a stream, lake or bog), and far-travelled grains representative of the regional vegetation and therefore of the contemporary climate. However, useful information to help distinguish local and regional contributions may be obtained from associated plant macroremains, which come mainly from the local vegetation, or from features of the sediment indicating its conditions of deposition. Other factors that should be considered when interpreting pollen diagrams are discussed by West (1977, pp. 138–148).

5.13.2 Animal remains as evidence of age

Vertebrate remains, mainly bones and teeth, are often found in terrestrial Quaternary deposits, and probably have greater value for dating than plants and most other animal groups. This is because vertebrates evolved more rapidly than other groups during the Quaternary. The mammals are especially useful (Kurtén 1968, Stuart 1982, Sutcliffe 1985), though many remains are quite resistant and often derived from one deposit to another; single finds of bones or teeth in environments of high energy deposition must therefore be interpreted with caution. In some cave and fissure deposits, mammalian remains are preserved in abundance, because many animals die or leave the bones of their prey in caves, and the cave environment usually favours preservation. Remains of small mammals such as rodents (Sutcliffe and Kowalski 1976) are often extremely abundant. The different mammalian assemblages for individual stages of the British Quaternary (Table 5.4) result partly from evolutionary changes and partly from environmental factors (mainly climate, and connections with continental Europe controlled by sea-level changes). The most useful evolutionary changes are in the elephants, deer and voles. For example, among the voles, *Mimomys* occurs in earlier stages up to zone III of the Cromerian (Stuart 1977), and was then replaced by *Arvicola cantiana*, which lasted until the Hoxnian but was in turn replaced in later stages by *Arvicola terrestris*.

Another group of animals which have proved useful for dating, especially in the earlier parts of the Quaternary, are the molluscs. Their usefulness depends mainly upon the climatic indications they provide, though there were some evolutionary changes. In Britain a very generalized chronological sequence through the Quater-

Table 5.4 — Fossil vertebrate assemblages from various stages of the British Quaternary

Common name	Latin name	An	Ba	Br	Pp	Pa	Be	Cr	Ang	Ho	Wo	Il	Ip	De	Ho
Auvergne mastodon	*Anancus arvernensis*	X		X											
Southern elephant	*Archidiskodon meridionalis*	X		X		X		X							
Straight-tusked elephant	*Palaeoloxodon antiquus*									X		X	X		
Mammoth	*Mammuthus primigenius*										X	X	X	X	
Verticornis deer	*Premegaceros verticornis*	X						X		X		X	X		
Four-tined deer	*Euctenoceros tetraceros*	X		X		X									
Falconer's deer	*Euctenoceros falconeri*	X		X											
Fallow deer	*Dama nestii*	X		X		X									
Fallow deer	*Dama dama*							X		X			X		
Red deer	*Cervus elaphus*							X		X		X	X	X	X
Roe deer	*Capreolus capreolus*							X							X
Reindeer	*Rangifer tarandus*													X	
Gallic elk	*Libralces gallicus*	X		X		X									
Broad-fronted elk	*Libralces latifrons*							X							
European elk	*Alces alces*													X	X
Irish elk	*Megaceros giganteus*												X	X	
Bison	*Bison priscus*							X				X	X	X	
Narrow-nosed ox	*Leptobos*					X									
Musk ox	*Ovibos moschatus*											X		X	
Aurochs	*Bos primigenius*									X		X	X		X
Saiga antelope	*Saiga tatarica*													X	
Gazelle	*Gazella anglica*	X		X											
Wild boar	*Sus scrofa*							X					X		X
Hippopotamus	*Hippopotamus amphibius*							X					X		
European wild ass	*Equus hydruntinus*											X			
Horse	*Equus ferus*							X		X				X	
Horse	*Equus caballus*									X		X		X	
Steno's horse	*Equus stenonis*	X				X									
Etruscan rhinoceros	*Dicerorhinus etruscus*							X							
Merck's rhinoceros	*Dicerorhinus kirchbergensis*									X		X			
Narrow-nosed rhinoceros	*Didermocerus hemitoechus*									X		X	X		
Woolly rhinoceros	*Coelodonta antiquitatus*											X		X	
Spotted hyaena	*Crocuta crocuta*							X					X	X	
Short-faced hyaena	*Pachycrocuta brevirostris*					X		X							
Lion	*Panthera leo fossilis*									X		X	X		

Cave lion	*Panthera leo spelaea*													X	
Leopard	*Panthera pardoides*	X													
European jaguar	*Panthera gombaszoegensis*							X							
Sabre-toothed cat	*Homotherium sainzelli*	X						X							
Lynx	*Lynx issiodorensis*							X							
Wild cat	*Felis silvestris*												X		
Pannonian polecat	*Pannonictus pliocaenica*							X							
Reeve's otter	*Enhydriodon reevei*	X													
Wolverine	*Gulo gulo*							X						X	
Pine marten	*Martes martes*														X
Badger	*Meles meles*												X		
Wolf	*Canis lupus*	X						X		X		X	X	X	X
Red fox	*Vulpes vulpes*	X											X	X	X
Dhole	*Xenocyon lycanoides*							X				X			
Deninger's bear	*Ursus deningeri*							X							
Cave bear	*Ursus spelaeus*									X					
Brown bear	*Ursus arctos*											X	X	X	X
Beaver	*Castor fiber*	X		X				X					X		X
Giant beaver	*Trogontherium cuvieri*	X						X		X					
Ground squirrel	*Spermophilus primigenius*								X				X		
Siberian long-tailed suslik	*Spermophilus undulatus*								X				X		
Red-cheeked suslik	*Spermophilus major*													X	
Common hamster	*Cricetus cricetus*							X				X			
Dwarf hamster	*Phodopus songorus*										X				
Russian desman	*Desmana moschata*							X		X					
Rabbit	*Oryctolagus cuniculus*									X					
Hare	*Lepus timidus*										X		X	X	X
Norwegian lemming	*Lemmus lemmus*									X	X			X	
Collared lemming	*Dicrostonyx guglielmi*													X	
Tundra lemming	*Dicrostonyx torquatus*										X			X	X
Steppe lemming	*Lagurus lagurus*										X				
Vole	*Mimomys pliocaenicus*	X	X	X		X									
Vole	*Mimomys reidi*	X		X											
Vole	*Mimomys savini*							X							
Vole	*Mimomys newtoni*					X									
Vole	*Pitymys arvaloides*							X		X					
Vole	*Pitymys gregaloides*							X							
Vole	*Microtus ratticepoides*							X		X					

Table 5.4 — Continued

Common name	Latin name	An	Ba	Br	Pp	Pa	Be	Cr	Ang	Ho	Wo	Il	Ip	De	Ho
Northern vole	*Microtus oeconomus*												X	X	X
Tundra vole	*Microtus gregalis*													X	
Bank vole	*Clethrionomys glareolus*							X							
Vole	*Arvicola cantiana*							X		X					
Vole	*Arvicola terrestris*												X		X
Vole	*Pliomys episcopalis*							X							
Wood mouse	*Apodemus sylvaticus*							X							
Lesser white-toothed shrew	*Crocidura suaveolus*												X		
Macaque monkey	*Macaca sylvanus*							X		X					
Walrus		X													
Dolphin										X					
Whale		X													

An = Antian and earlier stages
Ba = Baventian
Br = Bramertonian
Pp = Pre-Pastonian
Pa = Pastonian
Be = Beestonian
Cr = Cromerian
Ang = Anglian
Ho = Hoxnian
Wo = Wolstonian
Il = Ilfordian
Ip = Ipswichian
De = Devensian
Ho = Holocene

nary was based upon the proportion of marine mollusc species still living in the surrounding seas (Harmer 1914–25), which increases upwards from 64% at the base of the Red Crag (probably late Pliocene) to 100% in the Holocene (Baden-Powell 1937). In the upper part of the Red Crag (Pre-Ludhamian cold stage) the percentage of species still extant is 87%, of which 10% are boreal or even arctic species (e.g. *Buccinum groenlandicum, Serripes groenlandicus, Neptunea despecta, N. contraria*) compared with only 2% at the base. In the Weybourne Crag (Baventian to Beestonian stages), 89% are still living, and 21% are northern or arctic species. Later deposits, interbedded with Anglian and later glacial sediments (e.g. Corton Beds in East Anglia, Bridlington Crag of Holderness), contain larger percentages of extant and arctic forms (Baden-Powell 1955). More detailed zonations based on marine mollusc assemblages have been attempted in the Netherlands (Spaink 1975) and for the preglacial Pleistocene deposits of East Anglia (Harmer 1914–25), but without much success. This is partly because marine mollusc assemblages seem to respond less to climatic changes than terrestrial animals and plants (Norton 1977).

In contrast, land and freshwater molluscs are effective indicators of climate; assemblages from glacial stages in Britain contain up to 34 arctic and ubiquitous species (Holyoak 1982), whereas interglacial assemblages often have more than 70 species representing various climatic zones (Kerney 1977); the present British fauna consists of about 200 species. Freshwater molluscs which help distinguish different interglacials in southern England, though only on the basis of a few known sites, are listed in Table 5.5. However, the assemblages from different cold stages in Britain

Table 5.5 — Occurrence of freshwater molluscs in later interglacials of southern England (from Kerney 1977)

	Cromerian	Hoxnian	Ipswichian	Holocene
Valvata goldfussiana	X			
Valvata naticina	X	X		
Sphaerium solidum	X			?
Sphaerium rivicola	X	X		X
Nematurella runtoniana	X			
Pisidium clessini	X	X	X	
Unio crassus	X	X		
Belgrandia marginata	X	X	X	
Bithynia inflata	X	X	X	
Marstoniopsis scholtzi	X		X	
Viviparus diluvianus		X		
Viviparus contectus			X	X
Theodoxus serratiliniformis	?	X		
Theodoxus fluviatilis				X
Potomida littoralis		X	X	
Margaritifera auricularia			X	
Corbicula fluminalis		X	X	

are very similar and do not help to distinguish these stages. Land molluscs are probably even more sensitive to environmental changes, and have been used extensively for palaeoenvironmental reconstructions of the late Devensian and Holocene (J.G. Evans 1972), especially in calcareous deposits and soils, which have poorly preserved pollen assemblages. They should be useful for distinguishing different interglacials, but interglacial faunas are still poorly known in Britain. Taken as a whole, the non-marine molluscs suggest that the Ipswichian climate was slightly warmer and more continental in southern England than either earlier interglacials or the Holocene (Kerney 1977). The eastern species *Bradybaena fruticum* is probably restricted to the Ipswichian in Britain.

Fossil Coleoptera (beetles) are common in many fine, organic Quaternary sediments, and seem to provide much detailed and reliable climatic and other palaeoenvironmental information. However, they showed almost no evolutionary changes during the Quaternary, and assemblages from different interglacials are often very similar, being determined mainly by similar climatic and local ecological conditions (Coope 1977). They confirm the molluscan evidence that the Ipswichian was slightly warmer than the Hoxnian and Holocene (average July temperature approximately 3°C warmer than that of southern England at the present), and also suggest that the Cromerian was a relatively warm interglacial. But it is likely that they are useful for correlation of deposits in warm or cold periods over only very short distances.

5.14 LICHENOMETRY

After a glacier has melted or retreated, the newly exposed morainic deposits or smoothed bedrock surfaces are initially colonized by lichens. Beschel (1950) suggested that the rate of lichen growth can be used to measure the time since a surface was exposed. Usually the maximum diameters of selected species of lichen (e.g. *Rhizocarpon geographicum*) are measured on surfaces whose ages are known from historical or other dating evidence, and the graph extrapolated to date surfaces of unknown age (Lock *et al.* 1980, Mottershead 1980). The method has been used for dating recent glacial retreat stages in arctic and alpine areas (Andrews and Webber 1964, Mottershead and White 1972, Benedict 1967), where lichen growth is not affected by atmospheric pollution.

5.15 DATING BY INTENSITY OF WEATHERING

Processes of physical and chemical weathering of rocks and sediments are fairly slow, and the intensity of their effects is roughly proportional to the time over which they have operated. This has often been used as a method of relative dating for later Quaternary sediments or erosion surfaces, especially those attributable to glaciations.

In Britain, Germany, northern USA and other areas subjected to more than one glaciation, a distinction has long been drawn between: (a) 'newer drift' areas with shallow, immature soils and well preserved features of glacial deposition (moraine ridges, eskers, kames, kettle holes, etc.), and (b) 'older drift' areas with deeper, more mature soils and a landscape smoothed by prolonged erosion. The period of landscape development between the two glaciations often resulted in considerable dissection of the earlier glacial deposits, so that they are now preserved as isolated patches at high levels (e.g. on major interfluves) in the present landscape (Bisat 1940). The 'newer drift' areas correlate well with those glaciated during the Devensian (Wisconsinan), but the 'older drift' is usually dated no more precisely than pre-Devensian, and may indeed be composite in age, related to two or more pre-Devensian glaciations. From the extent of dissection of glacial landscapes in N.W. Europe, Prestwich (1888) estimated that 8000–10 000 years have elapsed since the last glaciation; this is surprisingly close to modern estimates of the length of post-glacial (Holocene) time. Other estimates of the length of interglacials in Germany (Penck 1908) and USA (Kay 1931) based on relative depths of weathering were probably less accurate.

More refined methods of dating by intensity of weathering depend upon detailed observations of soil profile characteristics (see 3.7 and 3.8), thickness of weathering rinds on boulders or pebbles, and the extent of preservation of small-scale glacial erosion features on hard bedrock. Differences in the thickness of weathered rinds on boulders or the ratio of weathered to fresh boulders have been used to determine the relative ages of bouldery moraines, especially in upland areas where lithological similarity of the original moraines can be assumed (Birman 1964, Sharp 1969, Miller 1973, Porter 1975, Colman and Pierce 1981). As with soil profile characteristics, rates of weathering of boulders depend on various factors, such as particle size distribution of the fine matrix around the boulders, mean annual temperature and rainfall, site slope and drainage, and vegetation, so it is important to compare rind thicknesses and ratios of weathered to fresh boulders sampled in strictly similar situations. Scales of weathering of boulders were devised by Boyer and Pheasant (1974) and Dyke (1979). A special type of weathering rind, which has been used to date archaeological sites and deposits from 10^2 to 10^6 years old, is the hydration rind (perlite) on obsidian fragments (Friedman and Long 1976, Friedman and Trembour 1978); the thickness of the rind (usually $<20\ \mu m$) is measured with a microscope, and depends on the length of exposure, the silica content of the obsidian, and the temperature during exposure. Andrews and Miller (1980) suggest that the uncertainty in estimating age by this method is often 20–30%.

Small-scale glacial erosion features, such as striae on bedrock surfaces, are progressively erased by weathering after disappearance of the glacier responsible, or after exposure of the surface from beneath a till cover. This has been used for relative dating by Dahl (1967) and Dyke (1979).

Exposed limestone surfaces, such as limestone pavements, are lowered by dissolution and weathering at fairly constant rates, whereas surfaces protected beneath impermeable cappings undergo negligible lowering. If the rate at which the exposed surfaces can be independently estimated, the mean difference in height between exposed and protected surfaces gives a rough estimate of the time when the protective capping was deposited. For example, Sweeting (1965) calculated that the pavements of Carboniferous Limestone in northern England are lowered by about 0.04 mm per year, and as surfaces protected from weathering beneath the large Silurian gritstone erratics of Norber (Fig. 5.10) are about 40 cm above the surrounding pavement, this gives a round figure of 10 000 years since the erratics were

Fig. 5.10 — 'Perched erratics' of Silurian gritstone on pavement of Carboniferous Limestone, Norber, near Austwick, North Yorkshire, England.

emplaced. This indicates at least that they resulted from the most recent (late Devensian) glaciation of the area rather than an earlier ice advance.

5.16 COSMOGENIC BERYLLIUM DATING

The unstable isotope of beryllium, ^{10}Be, is produced mainly in the atmosphere by the interaction of cosmic rays and nitrogen and oxygen atoms. It is subsequently deposited on the earth's surface in rain or snow, and is adsorbed by clay minerals and organic matter in soils and sediments (Brown 1987). Assuming that the soil is derived from a non-sedimentary parent material devoid of ^{10}Be, and that there have been negligible losses by erosion or dissolution during weathering, the amount in the soil profile is proportional to the length of the soil development period. To calculate this, allowance must be made for the radioactive decay of ^{10}Be to ^{10}B, which has a half-life of 1.5 million years. Pavich *et al.* (1986) used this technique to determine the age of soils derived from granitic alluvium on terraces of the Merced River in California.

As in ^{14}C dating, the recent development of accelerator mass spectrometry has greatly improved the sensitivity and precision of ^{10}Be determination. Other uses of ^{10}Be determinations by this method include measuring past solar, geomagnetic and climatic modulations of cosmogenic isotope production from ^{10}Be profiles in ice cores (Oeschger *et al.* 1987), and as a sediment tracer in studies of soil erosion, basin transport, and subduction of lithospheric plates (Brown 1987).

6

Maps of Quaternary features

6.1 INTRODUCTION

Because Quaternary studies necessarily involve several different disciplines, there are many classes of feature which need to be portrayed on maps. They can be divided into three groups:

(1) Direct observations of natural features, such as:
  - (a) the lithology of sediments occurring at the surface
  - (b) the relief and geomorphological features associated with these sediments
  - (c) the characteristics of soils developed on them
  - (d) geophysical properties and borehole data indicating the nature and extent of subsurface deposits
  - (e) the nature and extent of any buried soils
  - (f) the location of archaeological, interglacial and other special sites.

(2) Scientific interpretations of these observations, including:
  - (a) ages of land surfaces
  - (b) palaeogeography (previous distribution of land, sea, rivers, lakes, glaciers, permafrost)
  - (c) palaeoclimates (past precipitation, temperature, wind directions)
  - (d) palaeoecology (past vegetation types, animal life)

(3) Economic or other applied interpretations, such as:
  - (a) gravel or groundwater reserves
  - (b) occurrence of placer deposits with valuable minerals
  - (c) suitability of land for agriculture or forestry
  - (d) stability of land (evidence for landslips or neotectonic activity)
  - (e) likelihood of problems occurring during or after construction of buildings, roads, canals, bridges, dams, airports, etc.

These features can be shown at various scales. Maps may be divided according to scale as follows:

(a) plans (up to 1:10 000)
(b) large-scale maps (1:10 000 to 1:100 000)
(c) medium-scale maps (1:100 000 to 1:500 000)
(d) small-scale maps (1:500 000 to 1:1 000 000)
(e) maps of countries (1:1 000 000 to 1:5 000 000)
(f) maps of continents (1:5 000 000 to 1:30 000 000)
(g) maps of the world (smaller than 1:30 000 000)

To obtain a comprehensive view of the effects of Quaternary processes on an area, it is necessary to examine evidence recorded in several ways, principally as lithological, geomorphological, and soil maps. No way has yet been devised of portraying all Quaternary features on a single map at any scale. Some countries produce 'Quaternary' maps, but they show only the remnants of extensive Quaternary deposits and the location of special sites such as fossiliferous interglacial deposits. They do not show the effects of various processes of Quaternary erosion or soil formation.

6.2 QUATERNARY LITHOLOGICAL MAPS

Maps showing the lithology of Quaternary deposits occurring at the present land surface are based primarily on field observations, though these may be supplemented by interpretation of aerial photographs and other remotely sensed data. As in all fieldwork, codes of practice such as those published by the Geologists' Association (1974) and Institution of Geologists (1985) should be strictly observed, not only for the safety of all involved but also to work efficiently and professionally, and to avoid giving offence to landowners, quarry managers and others. Careful preparation for fieldwork is also important; for example, it is sensible to wear clothes and footwear suitable for the weather and ground conditions likely to be encountered, to have suitable topographic base maps or aerial photographs of the study area, and to carry all the equipment likely to be required.

In addition to the usual field equipment carried by most geologists — such as a compass, clinometer, measuring tape, hammer, hand lens, notebook, map-case, map-scale, protractor, pencils, eraser, penknife, acid-bottle, and perhaps also a camera, photographic scale, pocket stereoscope for viewing aerial photographs, aneroid barometer, Abney, Alidade or Dumpy level and staff, polythene bags and labels — Quaternary scientists often carry a spade, bricklayer's trowel or large knife for cleaning and smoothing sections in soft sediments. This helps to display the bedding and other sedimentary structures.

6.2.1 Use of aerial photographs

Aerial photographs often reveal geological structures which are not obvious on the ground, and in the absence of a topographic base map may be used for plotting positions of exposures. However, an accurate base map cannot be traced directly from aerial photographs because of the distortions of scale, both horizontally away from the centre (or principal point) of each photograph, and vertically, because high ground was closer to the camera than low ground. In addition, few aerial photographs are taken with the optical axis of the camera exactly vertical. Corrections for all these distortions must be made if the photographs are to be used for the preparation of an accurate base map (Miller 1961).

As well as providing complete and up-to-date patterns of roads, railways, buildings, coastlines, drainage networks and patches of vegetation, aerial photographs can also be used to trace Quaternary geological boundaries. The edges of screes, gelifluction lobes or alluvium, and the positions of landslides and faults are usually easy to identify. Other Quaternary and pre-Quaternary lithological boundaries may also be identified, but it is often difficult to infer the rock or sediment types involved; these must usually be determined in the field. Differences of tone or texture indicating vegetation changes often result from soil differences, which may in turn reflect changes in surface geology, though this needs to be verified in the field. Lineaments, such as master joints, faults and other geological contacts, or drumlins and fluted moraines in glaciated areas, may be emphasized by drainage patterns. When examining aerial photographs, features which cannot immediately be matched with any on the ground should also be recorded, as their significance may be discovered subsequently.

Various types of aerial photograph are now available, providing slightly different forms of information relevant to the mapping of Quaternary deposits. The commonest type in use is the black and white panchromatic photograph, which has been used, for example, to locate granular deposits as aggregate for construction purposes (Mollard and Dishaw 1958, Dowling and Williams 1964, Mountain 1967). In addition, black and white film which is sensitive to near-infrared wavelengths (0.7–1.0 μm), if used with a near-infrared filter to eliminate the visible wavelengths (<0.7 μm), can show differences of soil moisture content (Curran 1981); it may therefore indicate boundaries between deposits with different water retaining properties (Hunter and Bird 1970) or archaeological features which affect moisture content (e.g. ditches infilled with organic silt). With narrow-band filters the same film has been used to map other lithological boundaries (Gilbertson and Longshaw 1975). Colour aerial photographs are generally regarded as superior to black and white prints for mapping lithological boundaries (Fischer 1962, Chaves and Schuster 1964) and archaeological features (Strandberg 1967), and colour film which is sensitive to near-infrared wavelengths has been used for mapping recent intertidal features (Wallace 1981). This last type, known as false-colour near-infrared film, shows infrared radiation as red, red objects as green, green objects as blue, and blue objects as black. The use of multispectral imagery obtained from aircraft or from space in mapping Quaternary features is considered further in 6.3.1.2.

6.2.2 Field mapping of Quaternary deposits

Quaternary deposits may be examined and recorded in permanent exposures (sea, lake and river cliffs), excavations (quarries, road and railway cuttings, and foundations for buildings), and temporary natural exposures (uprooted trees, animal burrows, landslip scars), by digging trenches and trial pits, or by drilling. Various types of drilling equipment are suited to soft Quaternary sediments. Hand augers such as the Jarrett or Dutch soil augers, rotary drills, and shell and auger percussion drills are used for inorganic sediments, including tills, sands, loess and gelifluction deposits. More specialized borers are used for organic sediments such as soft peat and gyttja; the best of these is the Russian-pattern peat borer (Jowsey 1966), especially the modified version described by Barber (1984). In addition to the type of deposit to be penetrated, the choice of drill also depends on the depth to be reached and the accessibility of the borehole site. For example, hand augers are fairly light and portable, but are difficult to use in stony deposits and cannot penetrate deeper than 7–10 m at the most.

Positions of exposures and boreholes should be marked on a base map with a precision of <1 mm (i.e. to within 10 m on a 1:10 000 map), either by reference to topographic features marked on the map or by measuring from known points along a compass bearing. Distances in the field can be estimated fairly accurately by pacing, provided the length of an average pace has previously been estimated over a fairly long known distance, though it should be remembered that paces shorten on moderate or steep slopes. Heights of exposed boundaries between lithostratigraphical units should be levelled from mean sea level or a nearby benchmark, or may be measured approximately with an aneroid altimeter. If a suitable topographic base map is not available, one may be prepared either from corrected aerial photographs or by plane table surveying; the techniques are described in detail by Moffitt (1959), Ray (1960), Miller (1961), Compton (1962) and Reedman (1979). Simultaneous preparation of topographic and lithological maps, especially as large-scale plans, has the advantage that minor geomorphological features related to lithology, such as changes of slope, can be shown, whereas they may not be evident from a published topographic map or from contours interpolated between spot heights.

If a topographic base map is already available, exposures are marked initially along traverses. It is often best to direct these along river valleys, which contain most of the exposures in many terrains, and because of meanders often allow precise location of sites. In areas of simple geology, such as gently dipping strata of uniform thickness, boundaries between lithostratigraphical units can be interpolated with some certainty between widely-spaced parallel traverses orientated parallel to the dip. However, many Quaternary deposits do not have such a simple structure, and traverses for detailed mapping must then be closely spaced so as to locate all available exposures. They should be based on straight lines along compass bearings, distances being measured by tape, pacing or pedometer; the same techniques can be used to plot positions of exposures or boreholes lying close to but not actually on the traverses. Because location errors increase along misaligned traverses, it is important to run traverses between known points or in closed loops; any closing errors are then distributed along the whole traverse.

To clarify complex stratigraphical relationships within a single exposure (e.g. a cliff or quarry face), it is often necessary to produce extremely detailed plans. An effective technique in this job is to cover the exposure with a square grid using string and pegs or stones, and then plot the details within each square individually on squared paper.

6.2.3 Description of deposits

Lithostratigraphical and soil stratigraphical units distinguished in each exposure should be described as far as possible in the field, using a field notebook and marking the position of the exposure on one of the field slips (the topographical base map cut into pieces of manageable size). To ensure that descriptions are comprehensive, uniform in style, and can be understood in detail by other workers, a standard field handbook such as Hodgson (1976) should be used at all times, and the Munsell chart should be used for colour notations. In addition the topography, vegetation, soil type (or soil catena) and land-use associated with outcropping formations should be recorded.

Formations are named provisionally from suitable type sites (see 4.1). A complete succession for a region is then built up from all described exposures, though this may be difficult or impossible if several lithostratigraphical units have to be recognized as allostratigraphical units bounded by discontinuities. The units should be identified as far as possible in terms of sedimentary facies indicating mode of deposition. This involves making observations of fossils, bedding structures, non-detrital mineral constituents (e.g. glauconite, vivianite, pyrite), and the nature of boundaries between units. Photographs are a useful supplement to field descriptions of sections, especially those with complex bedding or glaciotectonic structures. Photographs should be logged in the field notebook so that their significance is not forgotten. Sketches of the views seen through the camera viewfinder are often the best way of recording the significance of photographs taken in the field.

6.2.4 Sampling deposits

Representative samples of units are usually taken for specific laboratory studies, such as microfossil analysis, particle size distribution, thin section study, mineralogical or chemical analyses. These serve to confirm or quantify differences between units, and may assist correlation of units from site to site. It is easy to underestimate the time required for most of these laboratory studies, and also their cost. This can lead to over-sampling, though collecting too many samples is probably better than taking too few, as it may be expensive or impossible to return for resampling. Nevertheless, time spent in the field deciding which samples to take for the various laboratory studies is never wasted. It is in fact an integral part of the field description and interpretation of individual deposits or sequences of deposits.

While completing a comprehensive field description of deposits and interpretation of facies, problems arise which demand information that cannot be obtained in the field. At that point, samples designed to shed light on each problem are selected. The intended method of analysis and its purpose determine the size and type of sample taken. For example, samples for particle size and mineralogical analyses of <2 mm fractions may be disturbed samples no larger than 100 g, but for thin sections, undisturbed samples in Kubiena tins are required (Murphy 1986).

6.2.5 Economic aspects

While making field descriptions of sections, the economic value of individual deposits should be noted. This might include the suitability of certain deposits for aggregate, brickmaking, pottery, roadstone or other purposes (Bates 1969), any observed or suspected content of valuable minerals (e.g. placer deposits in alluvial sequences), or the occurrence of water resources (e.g. springs as evidence of groundwater). In glaciated regions, vertical and horizontal changes in the abundance of ore fragments in till can often be used to locate the ore body in the underlying bedrock (see 7.2.4).

6.2.6 Geophysical investigations

Most Quaternary lithological maps show only the distribution of units occurring on the present land surface, which can be determined fairly readily from small exposures, shallow drilling or augering. Information on the nature of subsurface Quaternary deposits, their thickness, and the height of the buried bedrock surface is more difficult to obtain. Deep excavations, boreholes and high river, lake, or sea cliffs provide localized (point or linear) evidence of subsurface Quaternary deposits, but interpolation between these sites is much less reliable than with regularly stratified pre-Quaternary deposits. Examination of any linear exposure of glacial, fluvial, or slope deposits shows that they are indeed very variable and impersistent.

Various geophysical methods can be used to infer positions of subsurface lithological boundaries and to trace them laterally, though it is only recently that they have been used extensively with Quaternary deposits. Most of the techniques can only locate boundaries between units of markedly different lithology, such as clay and sand, and even with these, groundwater can cause problems. Less distinctive deposits are often difficult or impossible to differentiate and this limits the use of most geophysical methods in detailed mapping of subsurface Quaternary sediments.

However, geophysical methods have the important advantage of cheapness compared with other subsurface exploration techniques. Waitland (1953) estimated that as a means of obtaining subsurface information suitable for civil engineering interpretation, test drilling costs approximately seven times as much as geophysics. He found that the average error in locating the bedrock surface by seismic methods was 10%. Since then, geophysical methods have become more precise and probably also cheaper relative to drilling.

6.2.6.1 Seismic surveys

Seismic reflection and seismic refraction techniques have been applied to Quaternary deposits on land, though often with limited success. The main problem with the reflection method is retaining the high frequency component to obtain good resolution in the uppermost 200 m of the ground. For best results it is important to have suitable surface conditions, such as the unweathered clays of the intertidal mud flats investigated by Doornenbal and Helbig (1983), and also to use high frequency (>100 Hz) geophones. Units thinner than about half a wavelength (perhaps several metres) cannot be resolved, but the reflections from bedding planes allow unconformities to be recognized and depositional environments to be inferred from bedding structures such as dunes.

Seismic refraction surveys (Sjögren 1984) can be made quickly and cheaply using the hammer and plate method to locate velocity interfaces within 20–30 m of the ground surface. Deeper penetration is obtained by the more expensive method of detonating charges in boreholes. Clays show greater velocities than sand or gravel

(Table 6.1), a difference used for example by Masson Smith (1968) to assess gravel resources lying between till or alluvium and the London Clay in parts of Essex, E. England. The presence of a water-table can increase the velocity in gravel to 1.7–2.0 km sec^{-1} (Hollyer and Allender 1982), similar to that in clay; however, the two can still be distinguished if transverse as well as longitudinal waves are measured, because the speed of transverse waves is not influenced by water content. Conversely, if enough is known about the geology from other sources, sudden velocity increases can be used to locate the water-table and thus evaluate a groundwater resource. Seismic refraction can also be used to measure the depth to hard, compact bedrock along a traverse, to locate fractured or weathered bedrock zones (which may be important as sources of groundwater, or may cause difficulties in engineering), and to delimit actual or potential landslide areas (Geological Society Engineering Group Working Party 1988). Apart from the problem of distinguishing water-saturated layers from compact sediments or rocks with similar velocities, problems of interpretation also arise if layers close to the ground surface have higher velocities than those below. For example, a clay horizon within gravel can lead to the total thickness of gravel being underestimated.

Seismic methods provide the best approach to the problem of mapping Quaternary deposits offshore (Garrard and Dobson 1974, Boulton *et al.* 1981, Balson and Cameron 1985). They have recently been used, for example, to map Quaternary formations on the continental shelf around Britain by the the Marine Geology Unit of the British Geological Survey. Formations are defined according to characteristic seismic velocities and large-scale bedding structures indicated by seismic reflections, though reflections are sometimes obscured by pockets of gas; formations defined in this way may not coincide with lithostratigraphical formations. Typical energy sources at sea are (a) sparkers of 500–4000 J strength or air guns, which provide general information based on penetration to 800–1000 metres below the sea bed, and (b) pingers or boomers, which give better definition of near-surface seismic reflectors, such as bedding planes in fine sediments. Figs 6.1–6.3 show typical sparker and air gun profiles from parts of the North Sea off the east coast of England. They allow features such as the bedrock surface and the shapes of deep buried tunnel valleys to be drawn. Fig. 6.4 shows a typical pinger profile, giving more detail of sedimentary structures close to the sea floor. The strongest seismic reflection is usually from the sea floor itself, and profiles obtained in this way (acoustic reflection profiles) are often useful for mapping characteristic Quaternary landforms offshore, (Flint and Gebert 1976, Healy 1981, Landmesser *et al.* 1982, Wingfield 1987).

6.2.6.2 Gravity surveys

In areas where there is a large density difference between Quaternary sediments and bedrock, gravity surveys are useful for tracing changes in the depth to bedrock. Differences between Quaternary deposits are rarely large enough to produce detectable anomalies. In Britain, gravity surveys have been used successfully to determine the thickness of the till filling tunnel valleys cut into chalk bedrock (Barker and Harker 1984). The maximum difference in density between chalk and boulder clay reported by these workers was 0.27 Mg m^{-3}, but the contrast between chalk and gravel was less, with the result that there was no anomaly over parts of a deep tunnel valley filled mainly with sand and gravel, and a large raft of chalk within

Table 6.1 — Typical seismic velocities of Quaternary deposits and other near-surface materials (from Soiltest Inc. 1977)

Material	Velocity (km sec^{-1})
Dry sands and gravels	0.25–0.50
Moist sands, silts, and gravels	0.50–0.9
Fractured bedrock	0.60–2.45
Clays, some shales	1.50±
Saturated sands and other granular materials below the groundwater table	1.50–2.45
Hard, unfractured bedrock	2.45+

gravel could not be detected. Assuming that the proportion of till to sand and gravel decreased eastwards along the valley, it was possible to use gravity profiles to construct cross-profiles of the bedrock surface (Fig. 6.5).

Many of the small gravity anomalies that result from differences in the lithology and thickness of Quaternary deposits are easily confused with, or overshadowed by, those resulting from bedrock features, such as igneous intrusions or irregularities in the surface of dense pre-Mesozoic basement rocks. However, basement features may be significant because sometimes they influence the deposition of Quaternary strata. For example, in East Anglia the basins in which the early Pleistocene marine 'crag' was deposited were probably determined partly by faults in the underlying Chalk (Cornwell 1985), and many of the faults produce detectable anomalies because they originated by posthumous movement along deep-seated structures in the pre-Mesozoic basement.

6.2.6.3 Resistivity surveys

In many areas of interbedded Quaternary clays and sands, measurements of electrical conductivity (or its reciprocal, resistivity) often provide the best means of rapidly locating shallow boundaries between deposits (Clarke 1983, Mathers and Zalasiewicz 1985a, Cornwell 1985, Zalasiewicz *et al.* 1985). Clays generally have much lower resistivities than sands and gravels (Table 6.2). However, the resistivity of coarse deposits is decreased if they occur below the water-table, especially if the water is saline. This may mean that such deposits cannot be distinguished from clay-rich horizons (Mathers and Zalasiewicz 1985b).

Resistivity may be measured remotely by induction or directly with ground electrodes. The depth of exploration with hand-held inductive electromagnetic conductivity measuring equipment, such as that currently used by the British Geological Survey (Cornwell 1985), depends mainly on the distance between the transmitter and receiver coils. Equipment with a separation of 3.7 m (the EM 31 model of Geonics Ltd) responds to conductivity changes in the uppermost 6 m, and can be used to map, for example, the thickness of a thin till sheet over gravel (Fig. 6.6). The larger EM 34 model has a 40 m separation and 30 m depth of exploration, but must be operated by two persons. Using both sizes of equipment, Cornwell (1985) mapped deep till-filled tunnel valleys cut in the Chalk of Suffolk, eastern

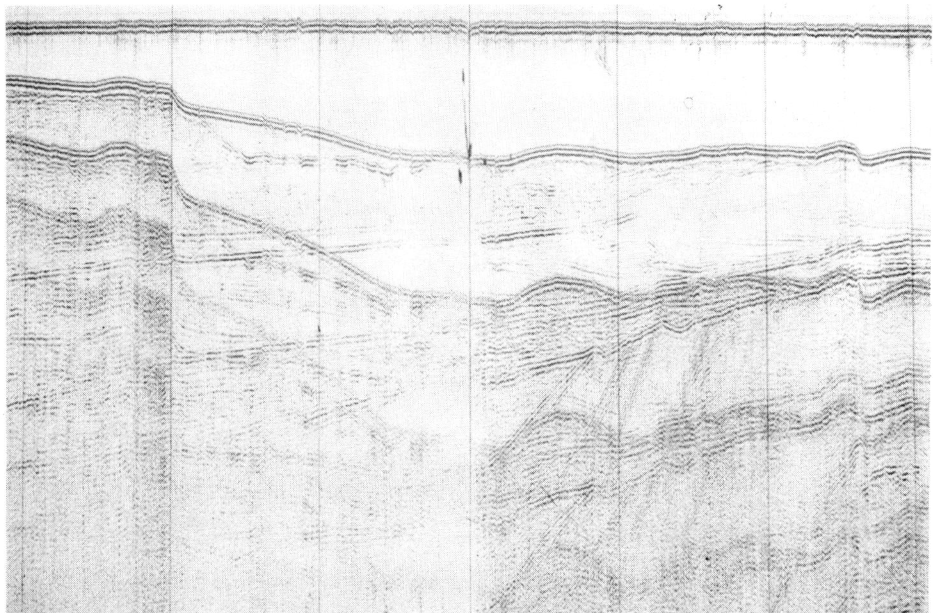

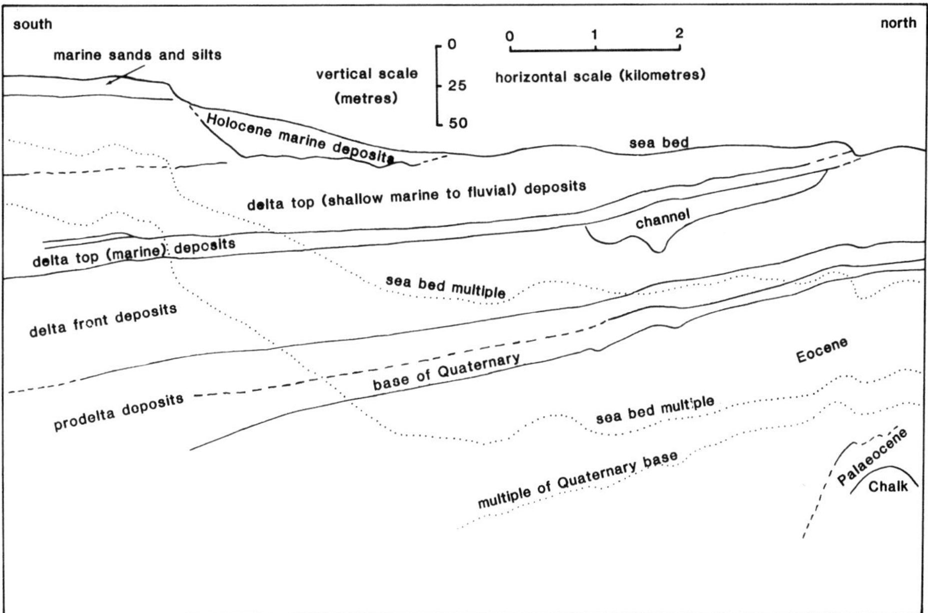

Fig. 6.1 — Sparker profile across part of the Outer Silver Pit, southern North Sea, showing Lower-Middle Pleistocene deltaic deposits capped by Upper Pleistocene marine sands/silts and Holocene marine deposits. Note the sub-parallel reflectors in the prodelta deposits and delta-top (marine) deposits, the bundles of oblique sigmoidal internal reflectors in the delta front deposits, and the irregular discontinuous reflectors within the shallow marine to fluvial delta top deposits, the last representing a complex architecture of channels and their fills. Interpretation by Dennis H. Jeffery (British Geological Survey). Reproduced by permission of the Director, British Geological Survey: NERC copyright reserved.

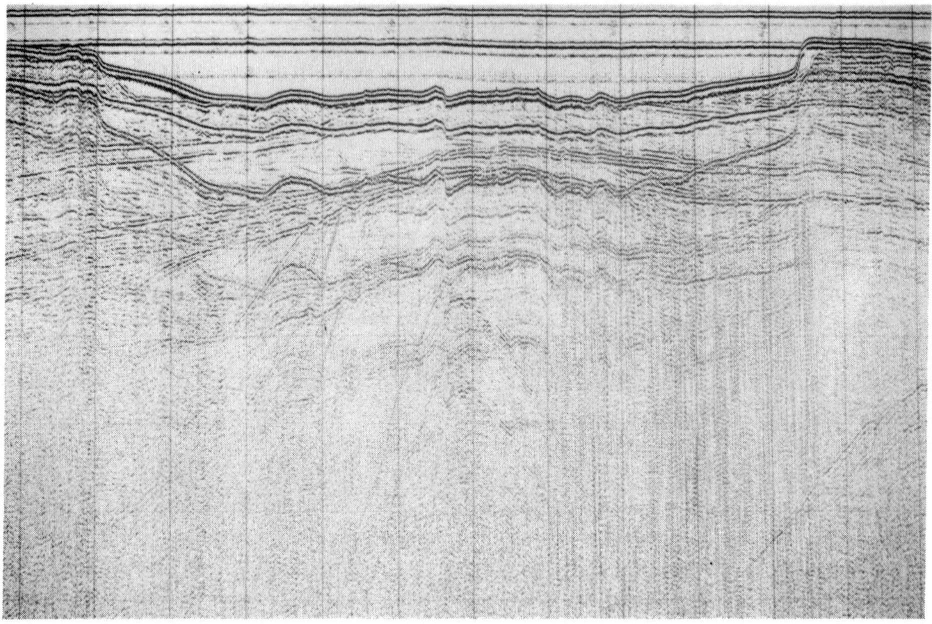

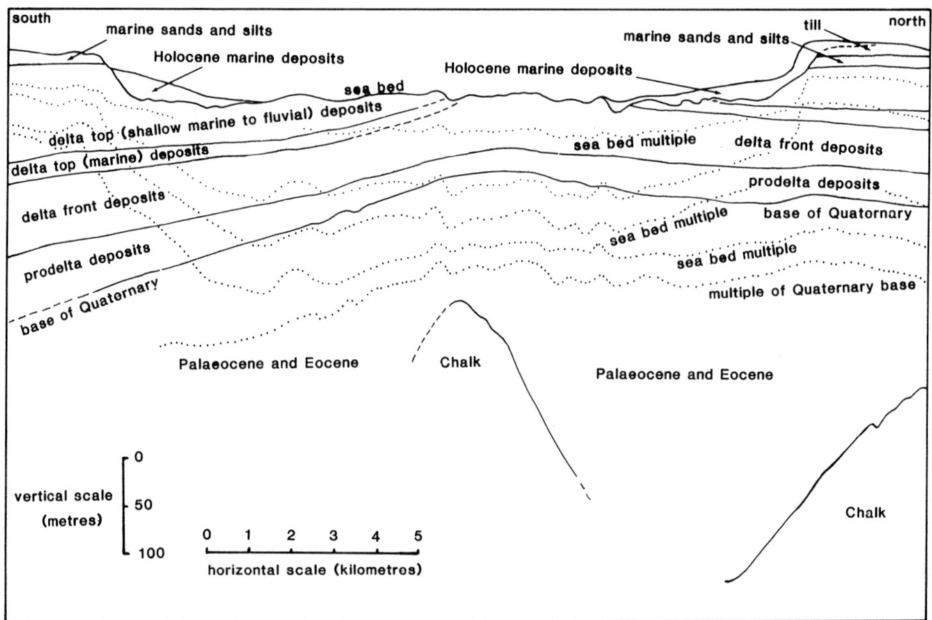

Fig. 6.2 — Airgun profile along the same line across the Outer Silver Pit as the sparker profile shown in Fig. 6.1. Note the different scale from Fig. 6.1. The deformation of the pre-Quaternary Chalk and Tertiary deposits results from salt diapirs at depth; note that the movement has slightly affected the Lower-Middle Pleistocene deltaic deposits. Interpretation by Dennis H. Jeffery (British Geological Survey). Reproduced by permission of the Director, British Geological Survey: NERC copyright reserved.

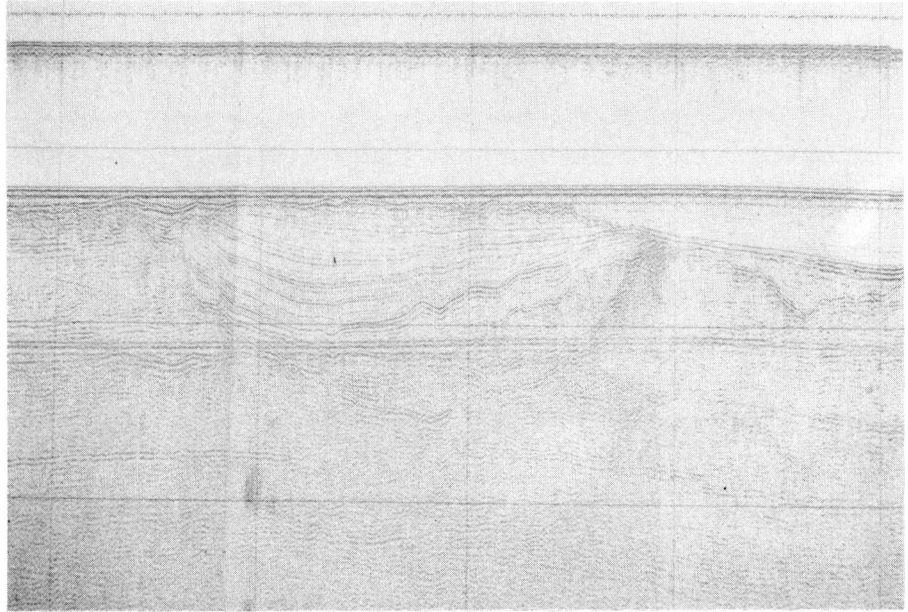

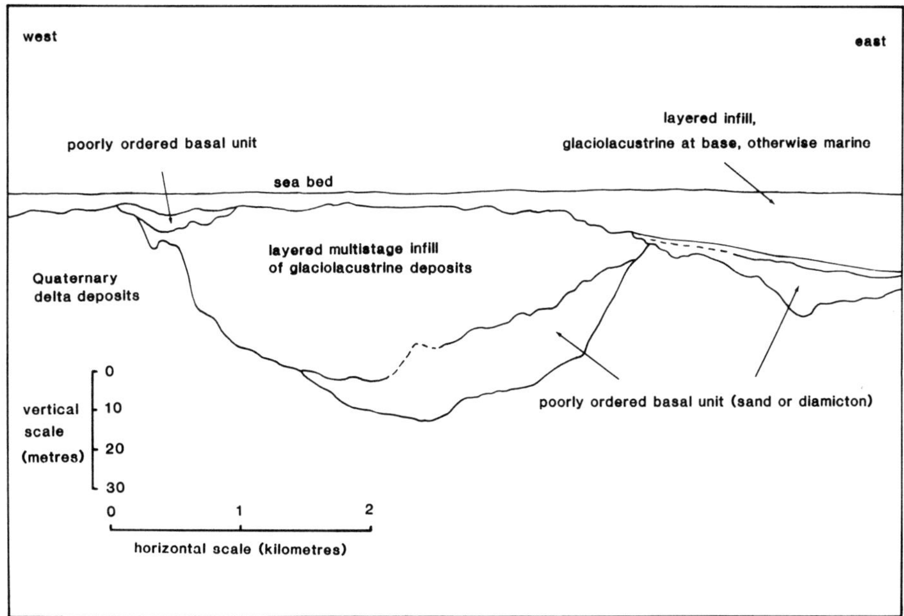

Fig. 6.3 — Sparker profile across the Outer Silver Pit, southern North Sea, showing two generations (Anglian and Devensian) of sub-glacially cut tunnel valleys. The infills are penecontemporaneous with the valleys; subsequent erosion has removed the upper layers of the Anglian infill. Interpretation by Dennis H. Jeffery (British Geological Survey). Reproduced by permission of the Director, British Geological Survey: NERC copyright reserved.

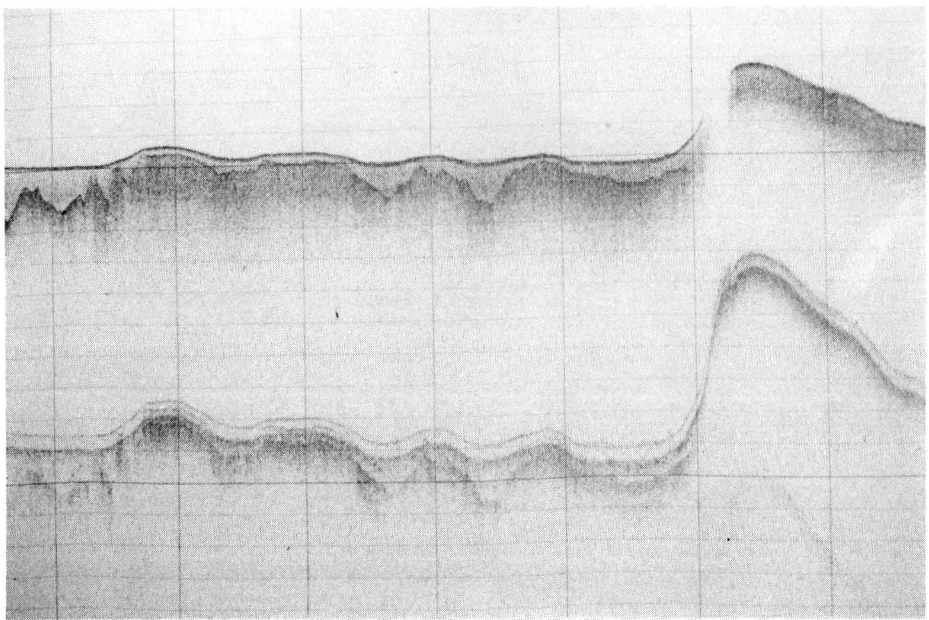

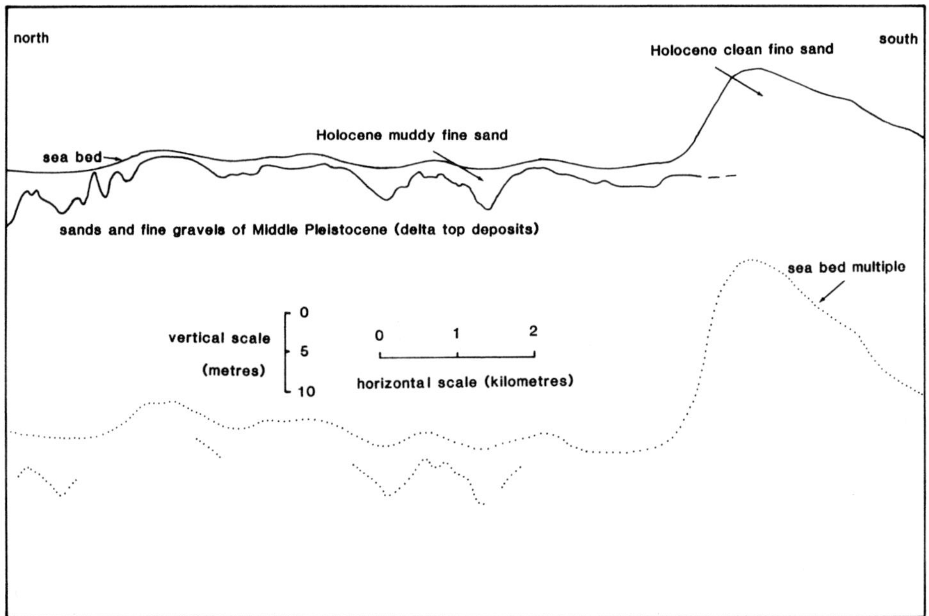

Fig. 6.4 — Pinger profile illustrating variations in the thickness of Holocene marine sediments at the eastern end of the Outer Silver Pit, southern North Sea. The sand bank is migrating slowly northwards. Note how the sea bottom here generally reflects the sub-Holocene topography. Interpretation by Dennis H. Jeffery (British Geological Survey). Reproduced by permission of the Director, British Geological Survey: NERC copyright reserved.

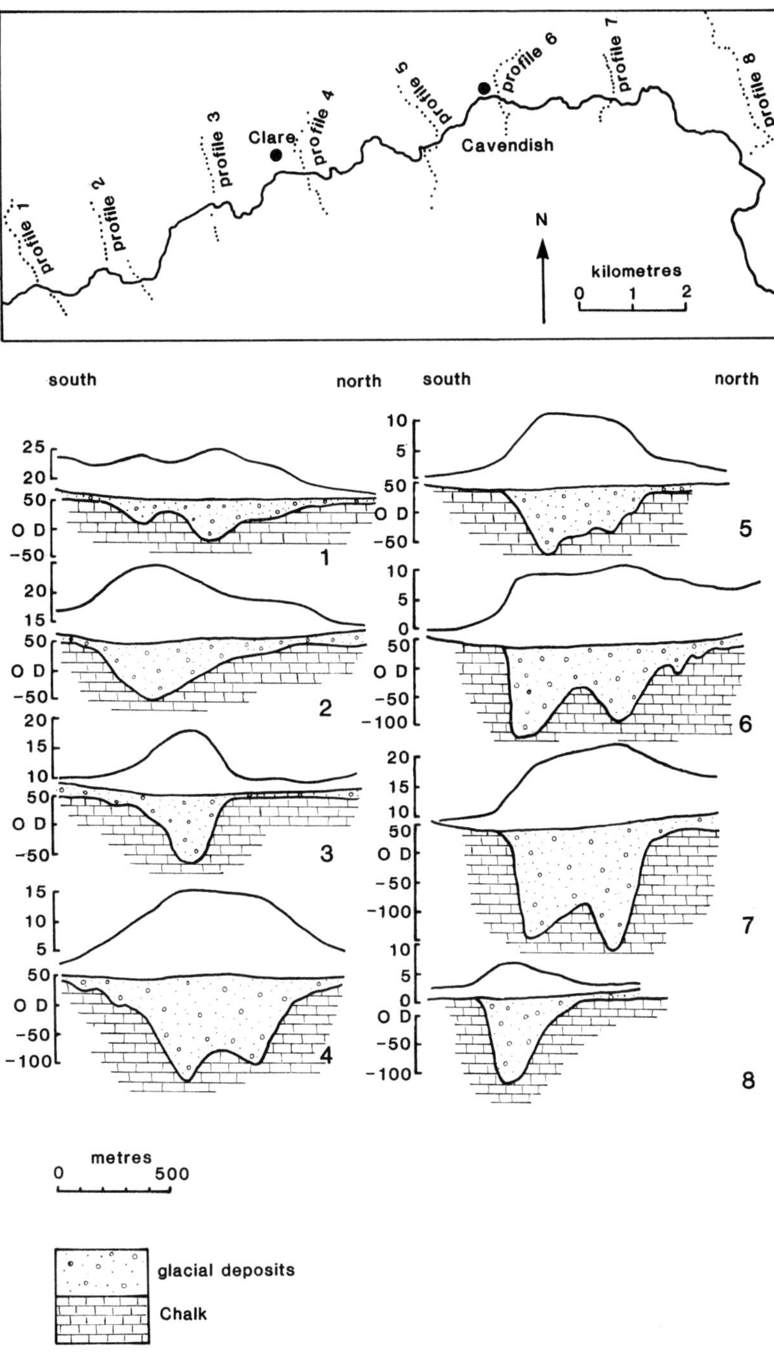

Fig. 6.5 — Location of gravity profiles across the Stour buried tunnel valley, Essex, England (top), and interpretation of anomalies along each profile (bottom). Gravity stations along each profile are indicated by dots; the gravity profiles (Bouguer anomalies) are calibrated in gu, and the vertical scales of the geological sections are in metres O.D. (from Barker and Harker 1984).

Table 6.2 — Typical resistivity values for Quaternary and other materials (from Soiltest Inc. 1977)

Material	Resistivity (ohm cm^{-1})
Moist clays	1000 –3000
Moist silts	3000 –15 000
Dry silts and sands	15 000 –75 000
Fractured bedrock	30 000 –100 000
Sand or gravel with finer matrix	100 000±
Slightly fractured bedrock	100 000–300 000
Massive hard bedrock, coarse dry gravels	300 000+

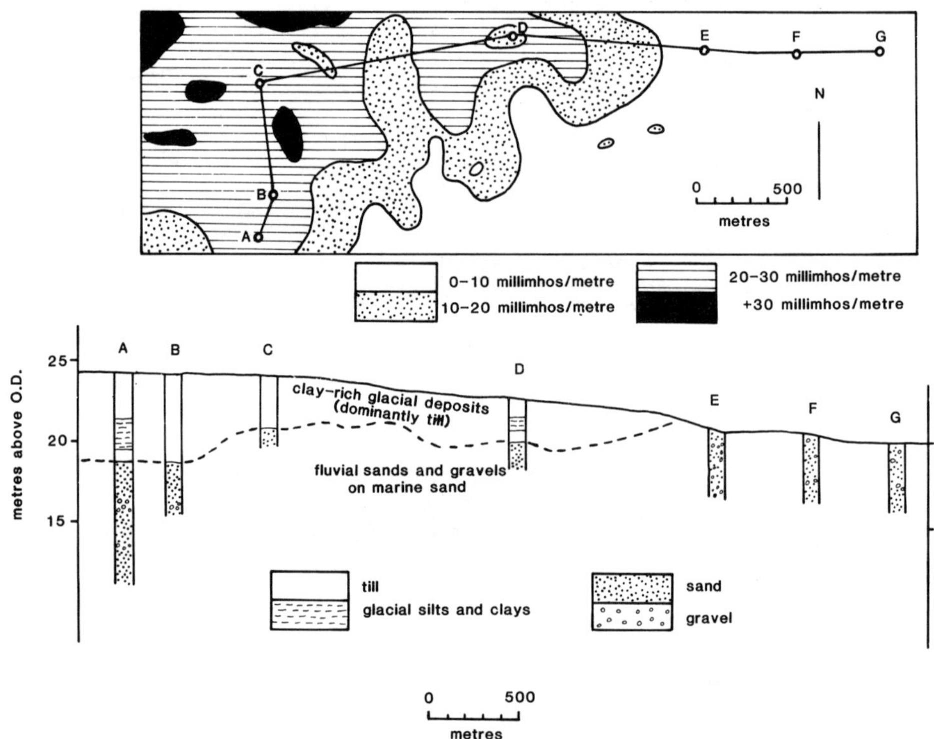

Fig. 6.6 — Contoured conductivity map of an area near Tunstall, Suffolk, E. England (top), and section across the area based on boreholes A–G (bottom) (from Zalasiewicz and Mathers 1985).

England; Fig. 6.7 shows the changes in conductivity along a traverse across one of the tunnel valleys east of Stowlangtoft, Suffolk. Shallow resistivity data can often be obtained more rapidly using a multi-electrode array such as the Offset-Wenner system with multicore cable (Barker 1981); Clarke (1983) found this method quicker and more reliable for evaluating thin, patchy sand and gravel resources in glaciated terrain.

Resistivity measurements have also been used to detect underground cavities in karst regions (Smith and Randazzo 1975, 1986, Denahan and Smith 1984, Ballard *et al.* 1983), the presence of disseminated conducting minerals eroded from an ore body buried beneath a glacial overburden (Phillips *et al.* 1984), and areas where buried pipes or other steel structures will become corroded (Field 1979).

In addition to ground-based surveys, airborne inductive conductivity surveys have been used fairly successfully in sand and gravel prospecting (Culley 1973).

6.2.6.4 Downhole gamma logs

Various geophysical measurements made down open boreholes can be used to infer lithological boundaries and make lithostratigraphical correlations between boreholes. This is often cheaper than extracting cores for visual inspection. In addition to the methods already discussed, a useful technique is gamma ray counting, which effectively distinguishes clayey from sandy sediments. Most clays have greater gamma radioactivity (usually 20 or more counts sec^{-1}) than sand, though the pattern may be reversed if the clay is kaolinitic or the sand strongly micaceous.

6.2.6.5 Ground-probing radar

Subsurface interface radar (or ground-probing radar) sends long wavelength electromagnetic pulses into the ground from a transmitting antenna, and collects with a receiving antenna the reflections from objects or interfaces between deposits. The signals are then amplified and processed to provide a profile which can reach to 20 m depth under ideal conditions, though the usual prospecting depth is much less, especially in clay. The skin depth (Janza 1975), at which the wave amplitude is decreased to 37% of its value at the ground surface, is greatest at low angles of incidence, longer wavelengths and greater resistivity or lower moisture contents (Ulaby *et al.* 1981, 1982). The technique has been used for various applications in lithological mapping (Leggo 1982, Bjelm *et al.* 1983), for measuring the thickness of permafrost (Annan and Davis 1976), sea and freshwater ice (Campbell and Orange 1974), for geotechnical site assessment (Benson and Glaccum 1979), for locating archaeological remains such as buried foundations, burial mounds or underground watercourses (Imai *et al.* 1987), for studying the internal structure of morainic landforms (Sutinen 1985), and for investigating lateral variability of soils (Johnson *et al.* 1980, Olson and Doolittle 1985, Collins and Doolittle 1987).

6.2.6.6 Radioglaciology

Electromagnetic radiation of even longer (radio) wavelengths can penetrate ice, and has recently been used to measure the thickness and rate of movement of glaciers (Whillans 1976), to map the subglacial topography (Morgan and Budd 1975, Robin *et al.* 1977), to locate subglacial lakes, to determine the condition of the glacier base (wet or frozen), and to identify till or layering within the ice (Bogorodsky *et al.* 1985).

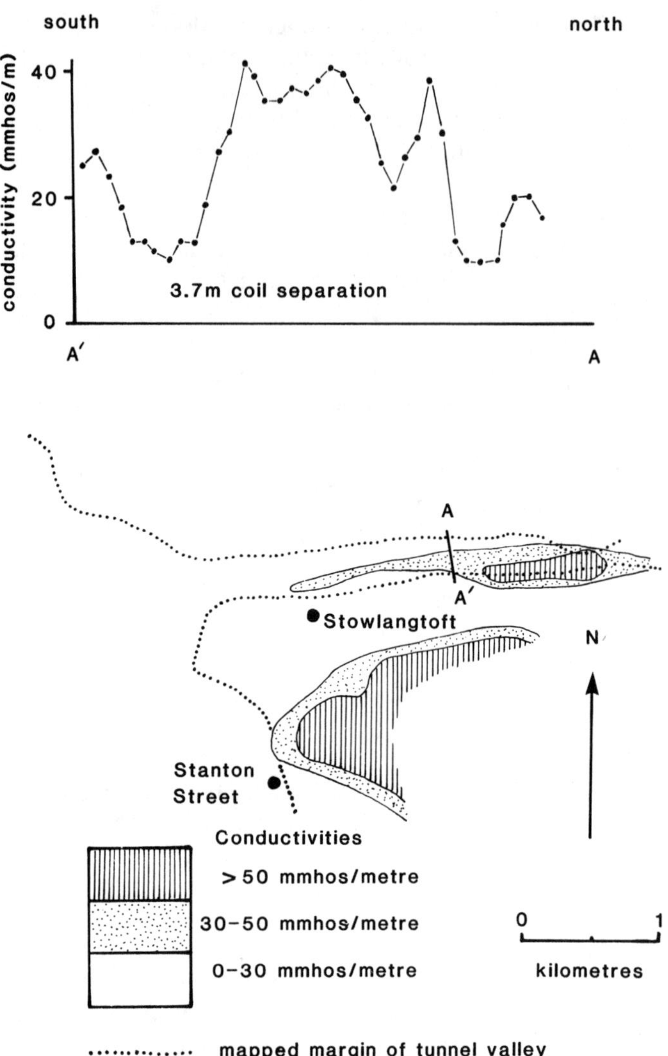

Fig. 6.7 — Conductivity traverse across a buried tunnel valley near Stowlangtoft, Suffolk, E. England; location of traverse A–A′ shown on contoured conductivity map below (from Cornwell 1985).

6.2.6.7 Geothermics

Precise measurements of ground temperature at depths of 20–100 cm can be used to locate underground cavities, both man-made (tunnels, mines, etc.) and natural (karstic). Soil temperature anomalies of up to 1°C have been measured at 20 cm depth over cavities (Mościcki 1987), and can be used to supplement other geophysical measurements (gravity or resistivity) for location of cavities.

6.2.7 Availability of Quaternary lithological maps

The official maps published by most national geological survey organizations at 1:25 000 to 1:100 000 scales are of the 'solid and drift' type, that is Quaternary and pre-Quaternary deposits are shown in approximately the same detail. Examples are the 1:63 360, 1:50 000 and 1:25 000 maps of the British Geological Survey (Plate 13), the 1:50 000 maps of the Bureau de Recherches Géologiques et Minières in France, the 1:50 000 maps of Spain and Portugal, the excellent 1:25 000 maps of Switzerland, and the current 1:50 000 maps of Italy. Most of these are issued with short (30–100 pp.) explanatory memoirs, usually giving brief descriptions of the Quaternary deposits; the British memoirs provide more detail, but are often issued many years after publication of the maps to which they relate.

Solid and drift maps are inevitably a compromise, showing Quaternary deposits at the expense of the underlying solid formations, and usually also portraying a limited range of Quaternary features, such as only those deposits exceeding a certain minimum thickness. Despite this, few countries have published Quaternary or 'drift only' maps at these scales, though many produce 'solid only' sheets shorn of all Quaternary features. In Europe the only countries with any significant large-scale coverage of pure Quaternary mapping are Sweden and Finland. The Swedish Ae series (1:50 000) covers about 30% of that country, and the Finnish Quaternary maps (1:100 000) provide about 20% coverage, mainly in southern parts of the country. Both have English translations of the map legends, and extended summaries in English of the accompanying memoirs, which give detailed descriptions of the Quaternary deposits and their composition, origin, age and economic value (suitability for aggregate, brickmaking or fuel, groundwater reserves, etc.). A few of the recent southern Finland maps are printed at 1:20 000 scale, but so far only one of these has an explanatory memoir. Both the Finnish and Swedish Quaternary maps show all exposed pre-Quaternary bedrock in red. The French BRGM organization has also published a limited number of Quaternary maps at 1:50 000 scale with full explanatory memoirs (e.g. Vincent and Cavelier 1968).

For the age and origin of European Quaternary deposits, the most comprehensive coverage (and in many areas the most detailed) is offered by the International Quaternary Map of Europe. This was compiled by the International Union for Quaternary Research (INQUA), and was published between 1967 and 1980 in sixteen sheets at 1:2 500 000 scale by UNESCO and Bundesanstalt für Bodenforschung in West Germany. Advantages of this map are that it gives more indication of the age of deposits and a more unified treatment than the different national maps, but the legend (1967) is now somewhat dated and of course the scale precludes detailed local interpretation.

Several geological survey organizations have published small-scale national synoptic Quaternary maps, which are useful mainly for obtaining a countrywide picture of the distribution of different deposits. For example, in 1977 the British Geological Survey published a Quaternary map of Britain in two sheets at 1:625 000 scale. This shows the distribution of the most widespread deposits, such as boulder clay, glacial gravel, raised beaches, river terrace gravels, Holocene alluvium, lake deposits, peat, clay-with-flints (see 3.4), brickearth (mainly loess) and aeolian sands. It also shows selected archaeological and other dated sites, and major areas of landslipping, drumlin fields and periglacial patterned ground. However, it does not give the ages of deposits, except to show the southern limit of the Devensian glaciation. Some deposits on the floors of surrounding seas are shown, but in this respect the map is superseded by the 1:250000 maps of the United Kingdom continental shelf published by the British Geological Survey and based mainly on recent geophysical surveys. Each of these sheets covers an area of 2° of longitude by 1° of latitude, and is issued in five forms: Quaternary, Sea-bed sediments, Solid geology, Aeromagnetic and Gravity. However, some show both Quaternary deposits and sea-bed sediments. About fifteen of the Quaternary sheets are currently available, and the remainder (covering most of the area between 14°W and 4°E and from 48° to 63°N) are in preparation.

To obtain information about current availability of Quaternary maps, it is best to approach directly the geological survey organization of the country concerned. In Britain the British Geological Survey have sales desks at the following addresses: British Geological Survey, Keyworth, Nottinghamshire NG12 5GG; British Geological Survey, Murchison House, West Mains Road, Edinburgh EH9 3LA; Geological Museum, Exhibition Road, London SW7 2DE.

6.3 GEOMORPHOLOGICAL MAPS

Whereas topographic maps portray the shape of the land surface (or the ocean floor) by a uniform and usually continuous set of symbols, such as contour lines, geomorphological maps subdivide the topography into landscape units (e.g. areas of uniform slope), define the spatial relationships and regional distribution of these units, and interpret them in terms of age, origin and significance for practical applications. Various types of geomorphological maps may be recognized (Demek 1972):

(1) General geomorphological maps, depicting the shape, origin and age of the relief.
(2) Partial geomorphological maps, depicting a certain limited range of landscape units.
(3) Basic geomorphological maps (general and partial), designed for geomorphological research purposes.
(4) Applied geomorphological maps (general and partial), which emphasize certain properties of relief for practical applications, as in land-use planning and economic development.
(5) Special geomorphological maps for use in other scientific disciplines, such as geology, hydrogeology or ecology.

Two types of processes produce relief features. Exogenic processes result from solar energy input and the effects this has on the atmosphere, biosphere and hydrosphere, including fluvial, glacial, glaciofluvial, marine, lacustrine, aeolian, periglacial and slope erosion and deposition, karst processes, accumulation of peat, and anthropogenic erosion and deposition. Endogenic processes are driven by energy from within the earth, and include tectonic and volcanic processes, and deposition by hot springs. Most landforms produced by exogenic processes are small and are often superimposed on larger forms created by endogenic processes. Further distinctions between relief features are based upon processes of erosion and accumulation.

Early geomorphological maps were constructed by various techniques and used various sets of symbols. As a result, the International Geomorphological Congress held at Stockholm in 1960 established a Subcommission on Geomorphological Mapping, which later published manuals (Demek 1972, Demek and Embleton 1978) to unify the content of geomorphological maps and encourage their production and use worldwide. Tables 6.3 and 6.4 show the main symbols recommended by the subcommission for endogenic and exogenic landforms respectively. Figure 6.8 illustrates the use of some symbols. The full legend includes different symbols according to the sediment types of which the landforms are composed. This may seem to result in overlap with lithological maps, but lithological data may be significant for the development of certain landforms, such as cuestas, monadnocks or tors, and for depositional processes resulting in other characteristic forms (e.g. aeolian dunes).The mode of origin of forms is often distinguished by colour: red for endogenic; green for fluvial and glaciofluvial depositional landforms; brown for fluvial, glaciofluvial and karst erosional landforms; pink for glacial and nival depositional forms; violet for glacial, nival and thermokarst erosional forms; yellow for aeolian landforms; deep blue for marine forms; black for biogenic and anthropogenic forms. Lighter tints are often used for older forms, darker for younger. Slope classes (Table 6.6) are distinguished by intensity of grey shading; present water surfaces, glaciers, snow and firn are shown in pale blue.

Techniques in geomorphological mapping were discussed in detail by Crofts (1974, 1981).

6.3.1 Preliminary aspects of geomorphological mapping

At the planning stage of producing a geomorphological map, existing data are evaluated by examination of existing topographic maps of the defined area, of aerial photographs or satellite imagery, and of previous descriptions of the landforms. The topographic maps give initial impressions of major landforms and their distribution, the drainage patterns, and features such as settlements, road and rail networks significant for access to the area.

6.3.1.1 Use of aerial photographs

Vertical aerial photographs provide further information on the drainage network and also allow detailed mapping of many landforms, such as subaerial dunes (Davis and Neal 1963), glacial forms (Welch and Howarth 1968, Karlén 1973, Hjort 1979, Gordon 1981) and coastal features (Welsted 1979). Most endogenic forms (fault scarps, folds and recent volcanic features) and some exogenic constructional and erosional landforms may be identified from aerial photographs, and their relative ages can often be inferred from cross-cutting relationships. Sequential sets of photographs taken at different times may show landscape changes which indicate current geomorphological processes, such as neotectonic uplift or subsidence, river channel migration, movement of sand dunes, or coast erosion. As they allow rates of change to be measured, they are very useful for predictive purposes in civil engineering.

Many aerial photographs show few or no characteristic landforms, but by use of a stereoscope the land surface can be divided into morphological units bounded by abrupt breaks of slope or more gradual changes of slope. Slope facets are the smallest

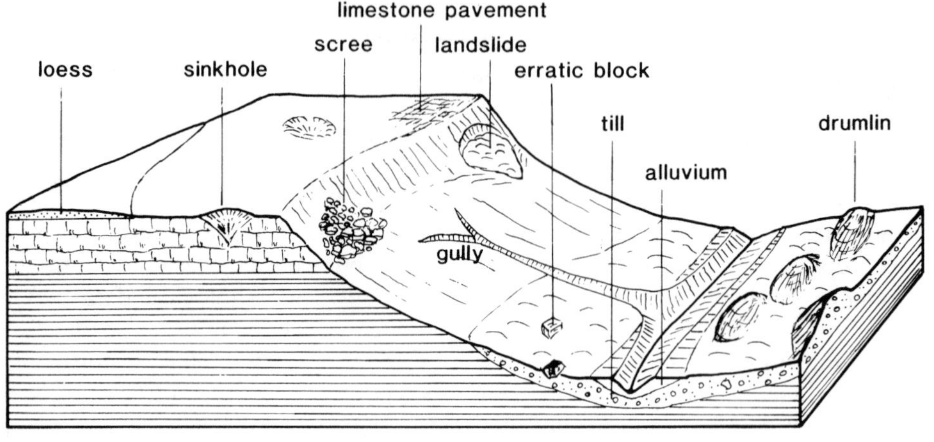

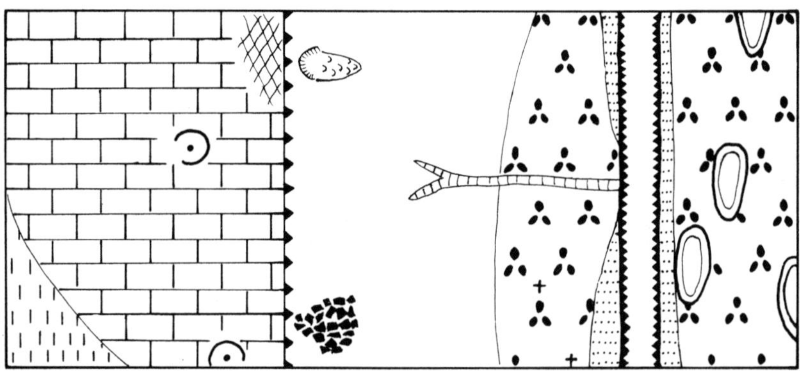

Fig. 6.8 — Geomorphological map (below) of area illustrated in block diagram (above), to demonstrate use of symbols for geomorphological maps.

homogeneous units (usually <500 m across) that can be distinguished on aerial photographs; they may be described as flat, rectilinear (sloping at a given angle), concave or convex. Slope facets are grouped into relief units (e.g. a river floodplain, a peneplain or a glacial morainic ridge) which show repeating patterns of facets. These range widely in size and degree of homogeneity, and consequently may be impossible to delimit and difficult to identify in a single photograph. They are described in terms of the range of slope angles, drainage pattern, types of slope profile, relative relief, plan form, orientation and relative proportions of highland and lowland (Young 1976). Recognition of certain types of relief unit often allows the nature of surface deposits or soil patterns and characteristics to be predicted directly from the aerial photograph.

Table 6.3 — Symbols recommended for endogenic landforms

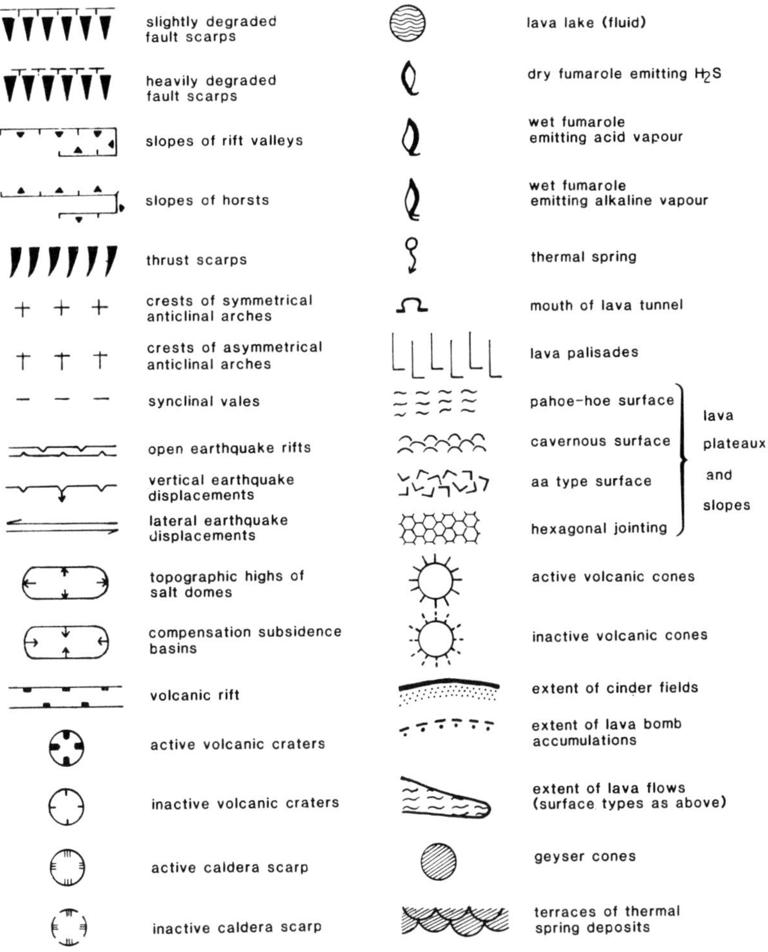

6.3.1.2 Multispectral imagery

Multispectral imagery obtained from aircraft or earth satellites can be used in various ways for identifying and mapping geomorphological features. It includes imagery based on visible light (wavelength 0.4–0.7 μm), near-infrared (0.7–1.4 μm) and middle-infrared (1.4–3.0 μm) radiation reflected from the earth's surface, middle- and thermal-infrared (3–50 μm) radiation emitted by the earth's surface, and back-scattering of man-made microwave radiation or radar (Curran 1985). Although satellite imagery has a lower resolution than most aerial photographs, it has the advantage of suffering less distortion.

The first generation of earth resources satellites, the American Landsat 1, 2 and 3 launched between 1972 and 1978, carried four-waveband multispectral scanning

Table 6.4 — Symbols recommended for exogenic landforms

sandstone dipslopes

limestone dipslopes

extrusive rock dipslopes

pediments

exhumed planation surfaces

ridges formed by intersection of valley sides

hog-back ridges
(sandstone)
(limestone)
(extrusive rocks)
(crystalline rocks)

monoclinal ridges
(sandstone)
(limestone)
(extrusive rocks)

sharp rocky summits (horn)

rounded summits

cols

edges of mesas
(sandstone)
(limestone)
(extrusive rock)

edges of cuestas
(sandstone)
(limestone)

residual hills
(sandstone)
(limestone)
(extrusive rocks)
(volcanic necks)

edges of outliers

natural arches

earth pillars

rocking stones

erratic boulders

scars of rock falls

scars of rock slides

scars of landslides

screes

talus cones and alluvial fans

landslide tongues

colluvial fans

tropical solifluction planes

playas,sabkhas

rock-cut perennial stream

rock-cut seasonal stream

fill-cut perennial stream

fill-cut seasonal stream

ox-bows in solid rock
(fresh and holding water)
(old and dry)

ox-bows cut in alluvium
(fresh and holding water)
(old and dry)

rapids in river bed

waterfalls

Table 6.4 — *continued*

plunge pools
river gorges
river terrace scarps
river-cut plains
river-built plains
(blocks)
(gravel and sand)
(mud)
delta plains
delta levées
river levées
wind gaps
severed spurs
gullies
loess canyons
asymmetric valleys
sides of valleys cut by proglacial streams
sides of ice-marginal valleys cut by meltwater
edges of sandur
ice-marginal meltwater channels (abandoned)
erosional residuals of till
sandur plains
glaciolacustrine plains
ice-contact slopes
kame ridges (gravel)
esker ridges

subglacial channels
moulins
limestone pavement
sinkholes
(active)
(inactive)
dolines
uvalas
caves
natural bridges
karst gorges
hums
travertine cascades
sea caves
roches moutonnées
ice-smoothed bedrock surfaces
glacial striae
upper edges of glacial troughs and corries
glacially-eroded valleys and hanging valleys
drumlins
till plains
end moraine ridges
push moraine ridges
blocky moraine ridges

Table 6.4 — *continued*

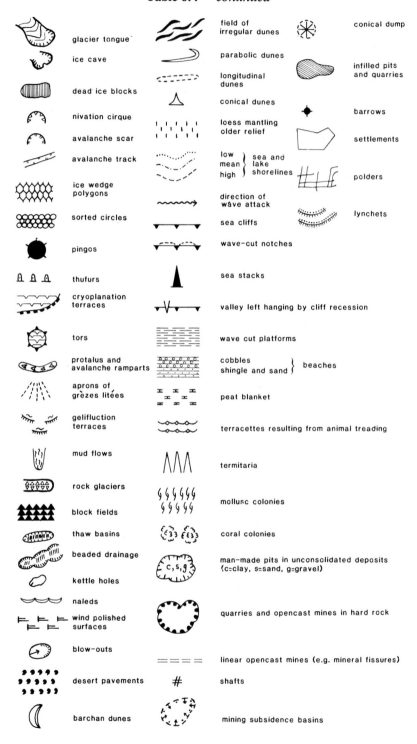

glacier tongue
ice cave
dead ice blocks
nivation cirque
avalanche scar
avalanche track
ice wedge polygons
sorted circles
pingos
thufurs
cryoplanation terraces
tors
protalus and avalanche ramparts
aprons of grèzes litées
gelifluction terraces
mud flows
rock glaciers
block fields
thaw basins
beaded drainage
kettle holes
naleds
wind polished surfaces
blow-outs
desert pavements
barchan dunes

field of irregular dunes
parabolic dunes
longitudinal dunes
conical dunes
loess mantling older relief
low, mean, high } sea and lake shorelines
direction of wave attack
sea cliffs
wave-cut notches
sea stacks
valley left hanging by cliff recession
wave cut platforms
cobbles, shingle and sand } beaches
peat blanket
terracettes resulting from animal treading
termitaria
mollusc colonies
coral colonies
man-made pits in unconsolidated deposits (c=clay, s=sand, g=gravel)
quarries and opencast mines in hard rock
linear opencast mines (e.g. mineral fissures)
shafts
mining subsidence basins

conical dump
infilled pits and quarries
barrows
settlements
polders
lynchets

systems (MSS) measuring reflectance in green (0.5–0.6 μm), red (0.6–0.7 μm) and two near-infrared wavelengths (0.7–0.8 and 0.8–1.0 μm) with a resolution of 80 metres. This information has been used for mineral exploration (Missallati *et al.* 1979), for mapping geological structures (Iranpanah and Esfaniari 1980) and locating road construction materials such as calcrete (Beaumont 1979), for identifying landslides (Sauchyn and Trench 1978) and other geomorphological features (Verstappen 1977, Kayan and Klemas 1978, Robinove *et al.* 1981), for soil mapping (Westin and Frazee 1976, Imhuff *et al.* 1982), and many other purposes (Lulla 1983).

Apart from man-made objects, such as buildings, roads and airfields, the three materials visible on the earth's surface from the air or from space are soil, vegetation and water. These have different responses to the various wavebands, but all three can provide information useful in geomorphological mapping.

The reflectance properties of soil in the visible, near-infrared and middle-infrared wavelengths are dependent on the following factors in order of importance: moisture content, particle size distribution, structure and iron oxide content (Stoner and Baumgardner 1981). The increased moisture content of fine (e.g. clay-rich) soils decreases their reflectance in visible, near-infrared and middle-infrared wavelengths (Jensen and Hodgson 1983). Increasing organic matter content up to approximately 5% of the soil also decreases visible reflectance, but larger amounts do not increase soil blackness. Increasing iron oxide content causes an increase in the reflectance of red light (0.6–0.7 μm wavelength) and a decrease in the reflectance of green light (0.5–0.6 μm); this can be used to map ferruginous materials, such as iron ore deposits (Vincent 1973) and strongly weathered rubefied soils, especially oxisols.

The thermal infrared radiation of soil is determined mainly by moisture content; wet soils are cooler during the day but warmer at night than dry soils. This characteristic can be used to distinguish areas of clayey and sandy deposits, which retain different amounts of moisture, or to map areas with a high groundwater table.

After it was realized that diagnostic absorption bands for clays and other minerals occur in the middle- and thermal-infrared wavelengths (Abrams *et al.* 1977), instruments were developed with additional infrared spectral channels, partly with the intention of mapping soils and surface deposits of different mineralogical compositions from space. Initially the Thematic Mapper (TM), added to Landsat 4 in 1982, included channels at 1.55–1.75 μm (a moisture-sensitive band), 2.08–2.35 μm for spectral features of carbonates, sulphates and hydroxyl-containing minerals, and 10.4–12.5 μm to detect the fundamental molecular vibrations of silicates. Later the Shuttle Multispectral Infrared Radiometer (SMIRR) had ten bands in the 0.5–2.5 μm solar reflection range to extend the identification of carbonate and hydroxyl minerals (Rowan *et al.* 1987). This allows distinction of muscovite, smectite, illite and kaolinite clays — all of which have Al–OH absorption bands — from chlorite, biotite and amphiboles — which have Mg–OH absorption bands. More recent instruments can offer 128 channels in the 2.0–2.5 μm region and 256 channels in the 0.4–2.5 μm range, using imaging spectroscopy (Vane *et al.* 1983). The limited number of spectral bands provided by earlier systems can easily be displayed visually by different colours, but this is more difficult with large numbers of wavebands, so that the emphasis now is on specific narrow bands or combinations of bands which indicate certain minerals in surface layers (e.g. Marrs and Paylor 1987).

The French satellite Système Probatoire de l'Observation de la Terre (SPOT), launched in 1986, has two multispectral solid state linear arrays instead of a scanner for multispectral sensing. This system has several advantages, such as smaller size, less weight, no moving parts, lower power requirements, longer life and greater reliability, but cannot sense middle or thermal infrared (Thompson 1979). It can be used to record in either panchromatic mode (resolution 10 m) or multispectral mode (resolution 20 m) (Begni 1982). The multispectral wavebands are 0.50–0.59 μm (green), 0.61–0.69 μm (red), and 0.79-89 μm (near infrared). Uses are discussed by Chevrel *et al.* (1981).

Much of the earth's surface is covered by more or less dense vegetation, so that little or no soil is visible from the air or from space. However, some characteristics of the vegetation canopy can provide useful information about the nature of soils, their parent materials, and the geomorphological history of the land surface. A healthy grass cover has weak blue and red reflectance, moderate green, and strong near-infrared and middle-infrared reflectance; certain variations in these reflectance properties result from water stress in periods of drought, which appears sooner on sandy soils than on more water-retentive loamy or clayey soils. Also in cereal crops the premature senescence resulting from water shortage on sandy soil or a shallow soil over hard compact bedrock is indicated by increased reflection of red and blue wavelengths. However, canopy reflectance properties at these wavelengths are also influenced by (a) the density of the vegetation and angle of elevation of the sensor, which determine the amount of soil visible through some canopies, (b) the solar elevation angle and solar and sensor azimuth, which determine the amount of shadow within the vegetation (Curran 1983), and (c) seasonal changes even in non-deciduous canopies. As a result, the interpretation of differences in reflectance recorded by space or airborne sensors often requires information that can only be obtained at ground level, though certain emergent patterns, such as ice wedge polygons, may be sufficiently characteristic to allow useful inferences to be drawn without recourse to ground-based measurements.

At present the interpretation of differences in thermal-infrared radiation and radar returns from vegetated surfaces are even more complex. However, thermal-infrared linescanning can be used to detect water stress in crops (Bartholic *et al.* 1972), which is often related to soil particle size distribution, and to locate frost hollows (Sutherland *et al.* 1981), volcanic centres (Friedman *et al.* 1981), hot springs (Dean *et al.* 1982) and underground fires (Hirsch *et al.* 1971). Some changes in the radar return from a crop can also be related to variation in soil moisture content and therefore to particle size distribution (de Loor *et al.* 1974; Ulaby *et al.* 1979).

Clear water bodies, such as lakes, are easily recognized in airborne or space imagery because they reflect and absorb very little light of visible wavelengths (most is transmitted), but strongly absorb near- and middle-infrared radiation, and usually reflect microwave radiation (radar) strongly away from the receiving antenna. However, waves on the water surface increase the reflectance of all wavelengths except thermal infrared, and suspended silt or clay (e.g. from river or glacial meltwater inflows) increases the reflectance in visible wavelengths. The decomposing organic (humic) constituents in lake waters increase the red and decrease the blue reflectance; the chlorophyll in living plants (e.g. algal blooms) increases green reflectance and decreases red and blue reflectance.

Sideways-looking airborne radar (SLAR) is perhaps the most useful remote sensing technique in geomorphological mapping. As with other radar techniques, it has the advantages of good spatial resolution, especially in the form termed synthetic aperture radar or SAR (Lodge 1981), and the ability to penetrate cloud. In addition it gives a good impression of relief and enhances microtopography (Lewis and Waite 1973), though the large shadows can obscure some important details. Small-scale radar images often show very clearly any regional glacial lineations, such as drumlin orientations parallel to ice movement directions, and concentric end moraine ridges. Stereo pairs of SLAR images, produced by imaging an area at two different altitudes, are very useful for topographic mapping (McCoy and Lewis 1976, Leberl 1979), for the study of drainage patterns (Koopmans 1973, Tricart 1975, Parry *et al.* 1980), for the identification of subaerial dunes (Blom and Elachi 1981), and for mapping granular deposits suitable for highway construction (Barr and Miles 1969). Calibrated SAR has also been used to estimate the moisture content and particle size distribution of surface soils (Dobson and Ulaby 1981, Bernard *et al.* 1982), to identify crops (Ulaby *et al.* 1980), to measure thicknesses of ice on rivers, lakes and reservoirs (Chizhov *et al.* 1978), and to locate archaeological features (Adams *et al.* 1981). As yet only one earth resource satellite, the American Seasat, has carried SAR; this was launched in 1978 but failed after about four months. Another may be launched by Canada in 1989.

6.3.1.3 Calculation of morphometric indices

Existing topographic maps and aerial photographs are used in the early stages of geomorphological mapping to calculate various relief indices, such as slope angles, relief amplitude, and valley density. As well as quantifying the surface morphology, these factors often suggest aspects of the recent Quaternary history (e.g. neotectonic uplift), indicate how accessible a previously little known region might be, how susceptible it is to landslipping or soil erosion, and how suitable it is for construction of roads, railways, towns, airports, dams, reservoirs, etc.

Slope angles are measured from contoured maps or directly from aerial photographs, and areas with certain ranges of slope angle are delimited on a base map, using dividers to measure distances between contours. Slope angles may be expressed in degrees, gradients or percentages (Table 6.5). Table 6.6 gives a general-purpose classification of slope angles; different class boundaries might be used in areas with a limited range of slope angles. The identification of many geomorphological features (e.g. asymmetric valleys) is easier from maps showing slope classes differentiated by colours or screens of increasing density than from contoured maps.

Maps of relief amplitude are useful for comparing the degrees of dissection in different areas. They are constructed by determining the maximum height difference for each square in a fine grid over the area (e.g. 1 km^2 at 1:25 000 scale), grouping the values into suitable classes, and shading or colouring the map accordingly. Table 6.7 gives a general-purpose classification of relief amplitude; other classes may be devised for use in regions of more limited amplitude.

Other useful morphometric indices include valley depth (differences in height between watershed and valley floor), which is useful for comparing intensities of

Table 6.5 — Relationship between commonly used measures of slope (from Demek 1972)

Degrees	Percentage	Gradient 1:	Percentage	Degrees/ minutes	Gradient 1:	Gradient 1:	Degrees/ minutes	Percentage
1	1.75	57	1	0° 34′	100	1	45° 00′	100
2	3.49	29	2	1° 09′	50	2	26° 34′	50
3	5.24	19	3	1° 43′	33.3	3	18° 26′	33.3
4	7.0	14.3	4	2° 18′	25	4	14° 02′	25
5	8.75	11.4	5	2° 52′	20	5	11° 19′	20
6	10.5	9.5	6	3° 26′	16.7	6	9° 28′	16.7
8	14.0	7.1	8	4° 35′	12.5	8	7° 07′	12.5
10	17.6	5.7	10	5° 43′	10.0	10	5° 43′	10.0
12	21.3	4.7	12	6° 51′	8.3	15	3° 49′	6.7
15	26.8	3.7	15	8° 32′	6.7	20	2° 52′	5.0
20	36.4	2.75	20	11° 20′	5.0	30	1° 54′	3.3
25	46.6	2.14	25	14° 02′	4.0	50	1° 10′	2.0
30	57.7	1.73	30	16° 41′	3.3	75	0° 46′	1.33
40	84.0	1.19	40	21°48 ′	2.5	100	0° 34′	1.00
45	100	1.00	50	26° 34′	2.0	150	0° 23′	0.67
50	119	0.84	75	36° 52′	1.3	200	0° 17′	0.50
60	173	0.58	100	45° 00′	1.0	250	0° 14′	0.40
70	257	0.36	200	63° 27′	0.5	300	0° 11′	0.33
80	567	0.18	500	78° 42′	0.2	500	0° 7′	0.20
90	Infinite	0.00	1000	84° 18′	0.1	1000	0° 3′	0.10

Table 6.6 — Slope angle classes and some characteristics (from Demek 1972)

Slope category	Description	Likely origins	Processes	Limitations
0°–0° 30′	Plain	River floodplains, river terraces planation surfaces, sandar	No sheetwash, no landslips, little gelifluction	No obstacle to walking, road, railway, airport, town construction, agriculture forestry
0°30–2°	Slightly sloping	Till plains, pediments, watershed areas, gentle valley slopes	Weak sheetwash, rare gullying, slight gelifluction, some mudflows	No obstacle to walking, roads, towns; railways and airports may require earth moving
2°–5°	Gently inclined	Older moraines, eskers, kames, drumlins, dunes, valley-side foot slopes	Strong sheetwash, some gullying, strong gelifluction, occasional landslips	No obstacle to walking but becoming difficult for wheeled vehicles; irrigation difficult and cultivation along contours advisable
5°–15°	Strongly inclined	Steeper slopes of young moraines, terrace steps, gentler valley sides in mountain areas	Strong sheet and rill erosion, landslips and other mass movements becoming common	Limit for wheeled traffic and town construction; soil cultivation impossible without terracing
15°–35°	Steep	Inactive coastal cliffs, dry alluvial cones, fault scarps, valley sides in mountain areas	Intensive denudation processes, landslips common	Walking exhausting, transport with special vehicles only, no building, suited only to pasture or forest
35°–55°	Precipitous	Glacial troughs, canyons, undercut slopes of valleys in mountain areas	Rapid denudation, discontinuous cover of soil and unconsolidated deposits	Walking difficult, limit of forest
>55°	Vertical	Cliffs, upper mountain slopes	Rock falls	Walking very difficult, economic use impossible

Table 6.7 — Classes of relief amplitude (from Demek 1972)

Relief amplitude (m)	Description
0– 30	Plain
30– 75	Gently undulating hilly land
75–150	Dissected hilly land
150–200	Gently undulating highlands
200–300	Dissected highlands
300–450	Gently undulating mountains
>450	Dissected mountains

current fluvial incision, slope curvature (rectilinear, concave, convex), and the distribution of various microrelief forms (e.g. thúfurs, sinkholes), which often indicate the nature of surface deposits or the recent Quaternary history of the land surface.

6.3.2 Field mapping of geomorphological features

After the analysis of existing topographic and other maps, aerial photographs, satellite imagery, etc., fieldwork is usually necessary to help delineate landforms and clarify their age, origin, and significance for the purpose for which the geomorphological map is being made. At the same time, current geomorphological processes can be observed,and critical levels such as the heights of river terraces or raised beaches can be measured with an aneroid barometer or surveying equipment. Fieldwork is best done at a time of the year when crops and other vegetation are sparse; very often a partial cover of melting snow clearly reveals features that are difficult to see at other times.

There are two types of approach to the field mapping of geomorphological features. In the traversing method, parallel traverses are walked across the main landforms, and breaks of slope along each traverse are marked on a base map; the breaks are then traced between the traverses. Alternatively boundaries of landforms are traced individually, following each break of slope, and starting on the valley floors, then working up the valley sides to the interfluve crests. In either method, microforms between continuous breaks of slope are also noted; these may indicate incipient disintegration of larger landforms (e.g. landslides, erosion rills), neotectonic activity (e.g. earthquake rifts), soil faunal activity (e.g. termite mounds), or soil disturbance by formation and decay of ground ice (e.g. pingos).

Fieldwork also presents an opportunity to accumulate evidence for the age and origin of both major and minor landforms. This may be based upon samples taken for isotopic or other dating methods, for palaeontological studies or for sedimentological analyses, upon studies of soil profile development as an indication of the age of the land surface, or upon observations of contemporary processes. Relative ages of some features may be established from cross-cutting relationships, or from the relative extents of landform degradation. All this information is then built into a local model of landscape development, which must be continually tested against accumulating field and laboratory evidence. Local models may also be tested according to the extent to which they fit into a regional model of landscape development. However, any model is no more than a working hypothesis based upon the current body of established facts.

Contemporary processes of landform development may be observed directly or sometimes inferred from vegetation characteristics. For example, on slopes prone to mass movement, trees may have bent trunks, or lean up-slope if there has been very recent movement. Neotectonic activity is indicated by abrupt fault scarps, angular facets on spurs, sharply incised V-shaped canyons extending down to the base of a fault scarp, often with increasing gradient towards the scarp, poor correlation between topographic forms and rock resistance, a history of frequent earthquakes, warped terraces and other displacements of older topographic surfaces, and parallel drainage with off-setting of stream courses.

Another important aspect of fieldwork is the recording of data likely to be relevant specifically to the ultimate use of the map. A common application of geomorphological maps is in highway and other branches of civil engineering (Cooke and Doornkamp 1974; Brunsden *et al.* 1975a, 1975b; Coates 1978, Doornkamp *et al.* 1979), in which case special attention might be paid to ground conditions such as site drainage, the existence of inactive landslides, which could be reactivated by earth-moving, areas prone to flooding, dust storms or invasion by mobile sand dunes, or areas of usable aggregate. As well as predicting how site conditions will affect any engineering, it is also important to envisage the effects of engineering on the landscape. This aspect of fieldwork is especially important in areas where dense vegetation obscures the land surface from the air.

Geomorphological mapping based on field observations is useful also in areas where drilling equipment cannot be used to investigate subsurface conditions, either because of unstable ground, or through environmental sensitivity as in a nature reserve (Pitts 1979).

6.3.3 Predictive geomorphological maps

Accumulated geomorphological information can be used to produce various types of applied geomorphological maps predicting future changes in the landscape (Demek and Embleton 1978). Those predicting effects of completely natural processes, such as fluvial erosion and the future positions of river courses, are based on extrapolation of past rates measured over as long a period as possible. A second type attempts to predict when natural geomorphological processes will be interrupted, especially by human influences, such as slope erosion following forest clearance; these are mainly based on evidence from analogous situations. A third type tries to predict catastrophic events, such as landslides, and is based upon knowledge of similar events and the factors causing them in the past.

There are several problems in predicting by extrapolation from measured rates. Measurements made over a short period are rarely sufficient for prediction over a much longer period because of fluctuations in rates of change. The extent to which these fluctuations are resolved and understood depends upon the frequency of measurements as well as the length of time over which they are made. Some geomorphological processes are slower than others, and each has its own minimum characteristic prediction time. This influences the interval between observations used as the basis for prediction; too frequent observations may create difficulties by detecting minor fluctuations irrelevant to the prediction (i.e. noise). However, if the frequency is matched to a specific prediction time, it may preclude interpolation for shorter-term prediction.

Prediction from the evidence of analogous situations is also problematical, because no two areas or problems are exactly alike. The evidence obtained from analogues must therefore be modified. The type and extent of modification required for prediction in any situation becomes clearer as the number of analogues studied increases. This is another example of modelling in geomorphology. The roles played by geomorphological processes in producing new landforms are repeatedly re-estimated as new situations are studied. As this research progresses a particular model either persists or gives way to another which is in better agreement with existing knowledge. Expressed as far as possible in mathematical terms, models provide a starting point for predictions, and often highlight deficiencies which can be remedied by new measurements. For important predictions in geomorphology, several forecasts may be prepared by independent methods or different experts. Disagreements between independent estimates are then resolved as far as possible by discussion.

6.3.4 Availability of geomorphological maps

Very few geomorphological maps have yet been published by any official national organization. A few are available in Italy, such as the Subiaco sheet published in 1981, and West Germany has started to produce a series at 1:25 000 scale, such as the Bad Sooden-Allendorf sheet discussed by Moller and Stablein (1986). However, many other areas have been surveyed privately for research purposes or development contracts. Although some of these are published in research papers, most remain unpublished.

6.4 MAPS OF SURFACE SOILS

The distribution of soil types on the present land surface is the result of several different factors. First, it depends on processes of deposition and erosion during the Quaternary, and to a lesser extent in earlier periods; these determined the distribution of parent materials. Second, it depends upon relief (geomorphological features), which influences internal drainage and the lateral movement of materials in solution and suspension. These two factors are shown by, or may be inferred from, the types of maps discussed in 6.2 and 6.3, but lithological and geomorphological maps are not adequate substitutes for a soil map, either individually or together. This is because other factors are also involved in determining soil characteristics, such as the length of time the land surface has remained stable or virtually so (i.e. the length of the soil-forming period), the climate and vegetation during this period, and the effects of man and animals over the same period (see 3.1).

In theory the legend of a soil map could be constructed to allow all these factors to be inferred, i.e. a soil map could serve as a combined map cf the Quaternary and pre-Quaternary surface lithology, of geomorphological features, present climatic factors, natural vegetation and the effects of animals and man. However, this is never fully achieved, because the effects of many of these factors on soil characteristics are still imperfectly understood. Indeed, some soil maps virtually ignore all formative factors; these are the special-purpose soil maps (Dent and Young 1981), which show measured variation of a limited number of (often ephemeral) properties relevant to soil usage (e.g. pH or nitrogen content for crop fertility interpretation, or compressive strength for shallow engineering works). As described in 3.3, most maps published by national and international soil survey organizations are general-purpose maps portraying variation in more permanent profile properties (e.g. particle size distribution) thought to be useful for a range of practical purposes. But as there is no universally agreed general-purpose soil classification system, such maps have variable value for interpretation of soil-forming factors. Their value for this purpose is also limited by the fact that boundaries on soil maps are often drawn from geomorphological features, such as breaks of slope, or even copied from boundaries on geological or vegetation maps, without the surveyor checking that these do cause changes in soil profile characteristics. Comparisons of independently produced soil and geomorphological maps for the same area of land (e.g. Bridges and Doornkamp 1963) have shown that soil boundaries coincide with geomorphological features in some areas but elsewhere are poorly correlated with them.

6.4.1 Preliminary aspects of soil mapping

As in lithological and geomorphological mapping, there is much preparatory work for a soil survey that is normally done before fieldwork commences. For example, assuming that a general-purpose survey is to be made, existing data on topography and any previous surveys of climate, geomorphology, geology, vegetation, animal life and the history of human activities are all worth appraising. For a special-purpose survey, both the aim of the work and the area to be mapped will be precisely defined, and only a small part of the pre-existing data will be relevant. Indeed, the more clearly the aims of a soil map are defined, the easier it is to design a programme of work for achieving them, and the more quickly and cheaply is it accomplished. In contrast, general-purpose surveys are often slow and expensive, though they are used more widely and have a longer-lasting value.

The classification system to be used for a planned soil map is decided before mapping begins. For a general-purpose survey it is usually best to employ the system already used in the country concerned, as this facilitates comparison with neighbouring regions, and also allows interpretations to be based on the research and practical experience already accumulated in nearby areas. However, it is also important to relate the units used to a more widely known system (e.g. F.A.O. 1974a, Soil Survey Staff 1975) (see Chapter 3), as this allows even wider correlation and transfer of technical knowledge.

Further details of the planning and preparation of soil surveys, especially for commercial contracts, are considered by Stobbs (1970), Young (1973), Western (1978), Dent and Young (1981) and Soil Survey Staff (1951, 1981).

6.4.1.1 Use of aerial photographs

Black and white panchromatic aerial photographs have been used in soil mapping for at least thirty years, both as a substitute for topographic base maps and as a source of information about soil properties and boundaries between soil types (Soil Survey Staff 1966, Goosen 1967, R. Evans 1972, Carroll *et al.* 1977, White 1977). They have also been used to identify areas subject to soil erosion (Stephens *et al.* 1982), to choose suitable sites for detailed investigation of representative profiles, and to choose characteristic catenary transects. Black and white film which is sensitive to near infrared can provide useful supplementary information for soil erosion and conservation studies (Stephens *et al.* 1981, Garland 1982), and for recognition of poorly drained areas.

Colour aerial photographs have also been used in soil mapping (Simakova 1964, American Society of Photogrammetry 1968) and for the recognition of patterns of runoff and overland flow (Wallace 1973), but they have poorer resolution and the additional information on soils that they provide is usually slight, except perhaps in desert areas. Colour film which is sensitive to near infrared (false-colour infrared film) is more useful, because it distinguishes healthy vegetation (showing as bright red) from vegetation that is diseased (yellow to black), or suffering moisture stress because the soil is shallow or coarse-textured (dark red). Also whereas the bare surface of well-drained soil appears blue–green on this film, poorly drained soils are darker because water absorbs much of the infrared. It has therefore been used for mapping soils of different moisture contents (Curran 1979), for showing crop marks resulting from archaeological features (Curran 1980), and for mapping flooded areas such as wetlands (Steward *et al.* 1980).

The most useful aerial photographs for soil surveying have scales of 1:5 000 to 1:50 000. Although large-scale photographs show more detail than those of smaller scale, much of this information may be superfluous and large-scale photographs usually have disadvantages in terms of cost and time spent in interpretation. It is therefore wise to choose the smallest scale giving the detail required for the eventual soil map; this is usually 2–3 times the map scale.

Soil boundaries are provisionally inferred from aerial photographs using geomorphological features (e.g. breaks and changes of slope), vegetational changes where the soil surface is obscured, or differences in reflectance of bare soil resulting from differences of organic content, particle size or moisture. Soil reflectance is very useful in certain areas, such as dark peatlands with pale sand- or silt-filled river channels (Seale 1975), and vegetation is useful in flat terrain with few visible geomorphological features, or in semi-arid regions little influenced by agriculture. But where there has been appreciable human activity (deforestation, burning, grazing, arable farming, earthworks), this usually obscures any natural relationships between soil and vegetation, and produces new vegetation patterns, which are often quite prominent in aerial photographs but are unrelated to soil differences. The response of natural vegetation to differences of groundwater level, soil salinity, pH or particle size distribution in flat areas of recent deposition (e.g. river floodplains) can often be used to map soil boundaries very rapidly and precisely from large-scale photographs (Dent 1980).

After a preliminary rapid stereoscopic examination of all the aerial photographs available for an area, to note major landform features, vegetation patterns and differences of soil reflectance, a detailed interpretation of each photograph is attempted. Boundaries are drawn initially around the most conspicuous features (e.g. along sharp breaks of slope); then areas between are examined more carefully to identify the less obvious boundaries. At this stage all possible boundaries should be marked, unless they result in units too small to show at the final map scale. If one map unit grades into another without a clear boundary, an arbitrary line is drawn between the two, and is marked for special attention at the later stage of field survey.

Many major breaks in slope and some of the more gradual changes of slope coincide with sharp soil boundaries, but most gradual changes of slope are associated either with a gradual change in soil properties or with no change. All the boundaries drawn on the aerial photographs must therefore be checked in the field; sites for checking are, however, best chosen from the photographs themselves, bearing in mind boundaries which are (a) typical, (b) problematic and (c) accessible.

6.4.1.2 Multispectral and satellite imagery

Specific uses of multispectral imagery from aircraft or space satellites in mapping soil characteristics such as moisture retention are summarized in 6.3.1.2. Imagery from an airborne scanner is expensive to obtain and has few advantages over panchromatic and infrared air photography, so it has been used very little for soil mapping. The main advantages of satellite imagery, such as Landsat, over aerial photography are cheapness, ready availability (see Curran 1985, pp. 227–229), and coverage of large areas at a uniform quality. It has therefore been used for rapid production of small-scale soil maps (Mitchell and Howard 1978), for preliminary interpretation before examining large-scale aerial photographs, and for planning where to take new aerial photographs. However, Landsat imagery has two strong disadvantages — poor resolution and little or no relief effect — which mean it has limited value in large- and medium-scale soil mapping. Its infrared wavebands are useful mainly for distinguishing different types of vegetation. Different crops can often be distinguished by their spectral signatures (various wavebands combined to form false-colour composite images), but the spectral signatures of bare soil surfaces are rarely characteristic of particular soil types in general-purpose classifications, because many subsurface properties are used as diagnostic criteria (see 3.3).

More recent satellite imagery only partly overcomes the deficiencies of Landsat for large-scale soil mapping. TM and SMIRR imagery (see 6.3.1.2) have the additional infrared wavebands useful for distinguishing some soil minerals, which can often help identify different soil types, but do not give improved resolution. SPOT imagery has considerably better resolution, but includes only one near-infrared waveband (0.79–0.89 μm).

6.4.2 Field mapping of surface soils

In most soil surveys, fieldwork is used primarily to investigate the character of units suggested by aerial photographs and to verify the provisional boundaries between these units. These two aspects are part of a research operation akin to modelling in geomorphological mapping (see 6.3.3), in which relationships are progressively established between soil profile characteristics (which cannot easily be observed) and ground surface features (which can). This is done either in a purely mechanistic way, by studying soil profile characteristics and surface features (e.g. slope position) at a sufficient number of sites to establish significant correlations between the two, or more theoretically by dividing the landscape into areas within which soil-forming factors (parent material, climate, relief, organisms, and time) are regarded as sufficiently uniform to produce single soil types. The latter approach is usually quicker, but it relies to a greater extent on the experience and expertise of the soil surveyor, and its precision is less easily measured. Either method is developed in one or more small areas of the region to be mapped, which are selected from the aerial photographs as being representative of the whole. This type of approach is often known as free soil surveying.

A development of the mechanistic approach is grid surveying, in which the soil profile is examined at the intersections of a square grid of lines laid down over the whole area; boundaries between map units are then drawn between grid points on different soil types. Provided the grid is fine enough, this produces more reliable boundaries, and also has the advantage that percentage areas of each soil type can be expressed with a known degree of confidence (e.g. Soil Survey of England and Wales 1983). But it is a slower and more expensive procedure because the number of observation points is much greater than in free survey, and many of them are really unnecessary in large areas of uniform ground. It is most appropriate for large-scale surveys, especially where no aerial photographs or topographic base maps are available, where dense vegetation limits the usefulness of aerial photographs, or where the soil pattern is complex and not related to surface features. Often a compromise between grid and free surveying is appropriate, such as a widely spaced grid to provide statistical information combined with some additional sites chosen by the surveyor to develop a model of soil distribution in relation to geomorphological and vegetation features.

6.4.2.1 Developing a map legend

Once the soil classification system to be used has been decided, a provisional map legend based on it is formulated for use during the fieldwork stage of map preparation. This legend is usually based on preliminary surveys of small representative areas selected from the aerial photographs. It may be enlarged and modified as mapping progresses, though excessive change should be avoided. The legend attempts to define all the soils present, list their characteristics, and show their known relationships to geomorphological features, geology, vegetation and other soil-forming factors. Many soil types are constant in character over quite large areas and thus form pure, extensive map units. Others are so intricately mixed that the patterns either cannot be resolved without excessively detailed field investigation or cannot be portrayed at the final map scale. These must be incorporated into compound map units (e.g. soil associations), the composition of which should be defined in the legend.

As mapping progresses, additional types of soil which do not fit existing units may be discovered. If these are extensive and distinctly different from existing units, they are described, defined and added to the legend, though some may be accommodated by redefining existing units. Differences between map units should be larger than the errors which might normally be made in measuring the diagnostic properties. Once mapping is completed the legend is correlated with other units already proposed in the classification system used.

In addition to the usual political and cultural boundaries, as defined for example by the Ordnance Survey in Great Britain and the U.S. Geological Survey in the USA, soil maps also show built-up areas and patches of disturbed ground (e.g. quarries and landfill sites) separately from the virgin land to which the legend applies.

6.4.2.2 Soil site and profile descriptions

In addition to the equipment mentioned in 6.2, fieldwork for soil survey usually requires an auger (Dutch or screw type), soil colour charts, field pH kit, Kubiena tins (for undisturbed samples for thin sectioning) (Murphy 1986), a supply of plastic balls for bulk density measurements (Hodgson 1976, Appendix II), a core sampler for water retention measurements (Dagg and Hosegood 1962), and possibly an electrical conductivity meter. The format, terminology and techniques for describing soil profiles, their site characteristics, and environmental setting are now almost standardized internationally, and are given in the field handbooks of various soil survey organizations (Soil Survey Staff 1951, 1981, Hodgson 1976, Taylor and Pohlen 1970, Maignien 1969, F.A.O. 1977, Dumanski 1978). The site descriptions (climate, vegetation, land use, drainage, elevation, local and regional relief, condition of the soil surface, occurrence of nearby rock outcrops, and evidence for current erosion or deposition) provide information on factors of soil formation, the likely lateral extent of the soil type described, and its possible relationships to other soils in a catena.

The profile description can be made at various levels of detail. Profiles representing all the map units are described fully from large (at least 1 m wide and 1.5–2 m deep), specially dug pits, and at the same time samples are taken for supporting laboratory analyses, including thin-section studies. These representative profiles are often chosen according to the central concept for each soil type in the area, and this should be borne in mind when selecting the site if the unit is known to be rather variable. Less detailed descriptions are made from auger borings and other exposures for the purpose of identifying soil types. These usually include at least the thickness, colour, particle size distribution and structure of each horizon, and brief assessments of some site characteristics, especially vegetation, drainage, and relief. Brief descriptions of this type are used when checking the existence of boundaries originally suggested by the examination of aerial photographs.

Field observations are usually transferred from field notebooks to specially designed record cards on which the details of each profile are noted, often in coded form. This allows the profile descriptions to be filed according to soil type (series or some higher unit), district, or whatever system is required. If data are to be stored on computer, it is quicker to record field information directly in numerical code; a suitable system is given by Hodgson (1976).

6.4.2.3 Sampling and laboratory analyses

For special-purpose soil surveys, the sampling technique is usually decided in advance and dictated by the purpose of the survey. Very often a square grid pattern offers advantages over irregular sampling when results are to be analysed statistically, for example in constructing isopleths. The distance between sampling sites is decided according to the number of samples that can be transported and analysed, and the precision required in locating isopleths.

Sampling strategies for a general-purpose soil survey are much less definite, however. Very often samples are taken from all horizons of the representative profiles at the time full descriptions are made. The location of samples can then be recorded on a sketch of the profile. In addition, samples may be taken from other sites, to give a measure of the variability of each soil type recognized. However, this can quickly lead to a very lengthy and expensive programme of analyses, as there are many possible types of soil chemical, physical and mineralogical analyses (Jackson 1969, Hesse 1971, Soil Conservation Service 1972, Avery and Bascomb 1974, Hall *et al.* 1977, Head 1980, 1982, 1986, Ministry of Agriculture, Fisheries and Food 1982, 1986, Jarrett 1983, Blakemore *et al.* 1987). Consequently it is important to decide at an early stage what purposes the analyses will serve. Some may be required to place soil types within the classification system being used; numerous analyses are required to place soils in the American soil taxonomy, for example. Others may be required for subsequent interpretation of the soil map in agriculture, forestry, irrigation, road-building or some other land-use application. In either situation it will probably be unnecessary to perform all analyses on all samples collected. Decisions about the analyses required are best made in the field (e.g. during description of the profile); samples of the required size and type can then be taken and stored in the most suitable way.

Most soil samples can safely be stored moist for short periods in polythene bags, preferably double-bagged for protection, with the sample label between the two bags. If a long period (more than 2–3 weeks) is likely to intervene between sampling and analysis, the samples should be air-dried and gently crushed before storage. However, samples of waterlogged horizons must be kept in an anaerobic condition by squeezing air from the bag before sealing it, and pyritic samples should be frozen as soon as possible to prevent oxidation and formation of sulphuric acid. Freezing is also important if samples are to be analysed for nitrate, though it is less critical if total nitrogen content is required.

Particle size analysis provides a good example of the range of problems that require consideration when selecting samples for laboratory analysis. As it influences so many fundamental, permanent soil properties (see 7.5.1), particle size distribution is probably the single most important soil characteristic to be measured. It also provides some evidence for the nature of the soil parent material and for certain soil-forming processes (e.g. clay illuviation), and is therefore often indispensable for classifying soils. Numerous laboratory methods of particle size analysis are available (Allen 1981), but only a few can be used routinely with soils because of the very large range of particle sizes most soils contain (Catt 1985). However, using the technique of field texturing (McRae 1988), it is possible to determine relative amounts of sand (>63 μm), silt (2–63 μm) and clay (<2 μm) fairly precisely without spending any time in the laboratory (Hodgson *et al.* 1976).

In a special-purpose survey for the planning of an irrigation scheme, which would require detailed information on soil permeability across a site, rapid field texturing of successive soil horizons at a large number of points, perhaps on a grid basis, would be more useful than a few precise laboratory measurements on profiles representing the taxonomic units recognized. In contrast, in a general-purpose survey it may be important for taxonomic reasons to know whether the B horizon of a certain unit is a clay-enriched argillic horizon or not, in which case it will be necessary to take samples through one or more representative profiles and determine amounts of fine (<0.2 μm in the English system) as well as total (<2 μm) clay, and also make thin sections to facilitate recognition of illuvial clay bodies (argillans). If there is a suspicion that differences of clay content through the profile arose from inhomogeneity of parent material, then this might be evaluated by very detailed particle size analyses at 0.5 or 0.25 ϕ intervals ($\phi = -\log_2$ mm), using sieves and the pipette sampling technique (Catt and Weir 1976), a Coulter Counter (Pennington and Lewis 1979), or a Sedigraph (Welch *et al.* 1979).

Proper and efficient use of supporting laboratory facilities in a soil survey depends mainly upon the field surveyor knowing the methods available, their relative costs, limitations, and suitability in relation to the purposes of the survey. In a general-purpose survey, the decisions are sometimes made by the requirements of the soil classification system being used. If not, they can be difficult to make, because several possible uses of the survey may be envisaged. In such circumstances experienced surveyors usually opt for a fairly limited range of inexpensive analyses, which have proved to be of some value for several purposes; these often include sand, silt and clay percentages, organic carbon content, calcium carbonate percentage, pH, cation exchange capacity, exchangeable cations, and moisture contents after (a) draining under gravity, and (b) at the approximate suction exerted by plant roots (usually 15 bar). But this type of compromise rarely satisfies more than a small proportion of potential map users. As additional information relating to the Quaternary history of the landscape, it is usually of limited value, though this is partly because there is still little known about the relationships between soil properties and soil-forming factors, especially chronofunctions, climofunctions, and biofunctions.

6.4.3 Availability of soil maps

For very general soil information of any part of the world, the F.A.O.–UNESCO soil map of the world, published in eighteen sheets between 1970 and 1980, is usually the best starting point. However, the small scale (1:5 000 000) and lack of detailed primary soil information in some regions are major problems for localized interpretation. The F.A.O. in Rome maintain an updated version, incorporating subsequent surveys, and can also provide information of the current state of mapping in most parts of the world.

For information about medium- and large-scale soil maps, the bibliographies of the F.A.O. (1972), Orvedal (1975–81), the Commonwealth Bureau of Soils (address: CAB International, Wallingford, Oxfordshire, OX10 8DE, UK) and the Land Resources Development Centre (Tolworth Tower, Surbiton, Surrey KT6 7DY, UK) give details of earlier coverage in most countries. The F.A.O. (1972) also refers to some geological and geomorphological maps. For more comprehensive and up-to-date information, enquiries should be directed to the soil survey organization in the country concerned. For England and Wales this is now Soil Survey and Land Research Centre, Silsoe Campus, Silsoe, Bedford MK45 4DT; this organization also holds a computerized national soil database which includes unpublished and recent information. Its published large-scale maps mainly 1:63 360 and 1:25 000 (Plate 14), with a few recently completed at 1:50 000, cover about 25% of England and Wales, though there is also complete coverage at 1:250 000 (Soil Survey of England and Wales 1983). Scottish maps (mainly 1:63 360) are available from the Soil Survey of Scotland, Macaulay Institute for Soil Research, Craigiebuckler, Aberdeen AB9 2QJ. In the USA most large-scale soil maps are published on aerial photographic bases at scales of 1:15 840 to 1:31 680 (mostly at 1:20 000 or 1:24 000), and are available from Information Division, Soil Conservation Service, Department of Agriculture, Washington DC. Most west European countries have fairly complete large-scale coverage of soil maps; for example, Belgium has complete coverage at 1:20000.

6.5 PALAEOGEOGRAPHICAL MAPS OF THE QUATERNARY

Using evidence assembled from various sources, it is possible to construct different types of Quaternary palaeogeographical maps. These might show the distribution of land and sea at certain times based upon evidence of raised beaches, submerged forests and peat beds, or submerged cliff-lines. Others might show the land surface topography and soil types of a past period, using evidence from buried soils, lake deposits, and peat beds. Yet others may take evidence from the distribution of Quaternary fluvial deposits and buried or unburied terrace remnants to suggest earlier courses of rivers (the so-called proto-courses), or use a combination of lithological and geomorphological evidence to reconstruct ice margins at different times during a cold stage.

Most palaeogeographical maps are interpretations of research findings rather than a direct record of observations. Many of them are rather speculative, because they are based upon a few isolated pieces of evidence, and dating difficulties often place doubt on the equivalence in time of all the pieces of evidence. Despite these weaknesses, palaeogeographical maps are very useful because they identify areas where inconsistencies occur or where new types of evidence might be found. In these respects they act as models for the various aspects of Quaternary stratigraphy, in that palaeogeographical maps for successive periods should differ only in ways which can logically be explained by known Quaternary processes. However, they are continually in need of revision, and should never be regarded as final.

Palaeogeographical maps are based on (a) facies characteristics of precisely dated sediments and analysis of the environment in which they were deposited, (b) properties of buried and relict soils and their significance for past climate, vegetation, and relief, and (c) the recognition of erosional features. Important sedimentary facies characteristics include: (a) the presence of fossils and of authigenic minerals indicating, for example, marine deposition, (b) particle size distribution, (c) grain shape and roundness, (d) sedimentary structures such as different types of cross-bedding, pebble imbrication, or graded bedding, (e) post-depositional structures such as load-casts, mud-cracks and raindrop prints, (f) vertical variation in sequences, such as the occurrence of cyclothems, (g) lateral variation in thickness and particle size of sedimentary units. Interpretation of observations is assisted by experimental studies (e.g. use of flume tanks to interpret fluvial bedforms and sedimentary structures formed at different depths and flow rates), by statistical analysis (e.g. trend surface or other methods of spatial analysis), and by production of computer simulation models. Environmental analysis depends mainly upon strict comparisons with modern analogues, though some of these are still imperfectly documented (e.g. the subglacial and periglacial aeolian environments).

6.6 QUATERNARY PALAEOECOLOGICAL MAPS

These maps portray past distributions of plants and/or animals. Like palaeogeographical maps, they express research results rather than direct field observations, and are usually based on palaeontological studies. For example, the commonest type uses pollen analyses of deposits dated to certain periods to reconstruct lateral variations in past vegetation communities. This often demands use of correction factors (e.g. Bradshaw 1981) to convert fossil pollen counts into percentage areas occupied by the various taxa, so as to make allowance for unequal production, dispersal, and preservation of different pollen types. Such maps are helpful in archaeology to infer environments of human habitation or the effects of man on vegetation, and are used in palaeoclimatology to reconstruct climatic gradients. Comparison of palaeoecological maps for successive periods has been used to establish past rates of vegetational changes in response to changing climate; this information helps predict vegetation responses to future climatic change.

6.7 APPLIED QUATERNARY MAPS

Various types of maps portray selected Quaternary features, often in combination with some aspects of pre-Quaternary geology, for economic applications. Most are special-purpose maps often drawn under private contract, and are never published, though some are available on open file from geological survey organizations. They include maps showing the distribution and quality of mineral reserves, such as aggregate, placer minerals, diatomite, brick-clay or water, and maps showing suitability of ground for specific construction purposes. No set procedures for production of these maps are laid down; the way the information is portrayed is best left to the ingenuity of the Quaternary scientist responsible. A British example is provided by the numerous mineral assessment maps at 1:25 000 and 1:50 000 scales produced by the British Geological Survey. These cover about 25% of the country, and are mainly maps of Quaternary sand and gravel resources. They are issued with reports giving details of the quality of the deposits and the borehole records upon which the resource assessments were based.

Two types of applied Quaternary maps have less specific purposes. The first of these, known as engineering geology maps, are intended for a fairly wide range of interpretations in civil engineering, and their use for any specific geotechnical application usually depends upon the expertise of an experienced engineering geologist. UNESCO published a guide to engineering geology maps (Dearman 1976), which covers the principles, objectives and techniques of map production. As these maps are most useful for building work in urban areas, published examples are mainly plans of large cities. Many are presented as several sheets, showing:

(1) Lithology of bedrock or Quaternary deposits occurring within 1–2 metres of the ground surface.
(2) Isopachytes of unconsolidated deposits overlying hard bedrock.
(3) Hydrogeological features, including depth to the water-table, direction of groundwater movement, and chemical characteristics of the groundwater.
(4) Sites where detailed subsurface information is available (e.g. boreholes).
(5) More specific interpretations, such as earthquake susceptibility or geothermal gradients.

In Britain, engineering geology maps of certain urban areas (e.g. Belfast, S.E.

Essex, Forth Estuary) and areas subject to landslipping (e.g. W. Dorset, S. Wales) have been published by British Geological Survey (BGS); maps of other special study areas are also available on open file from BGS.

The second type of general-purpose applied map based partly on Quaternary features is the land capability map. This portrays the potential of land for production of arable crops or livestock, for forestry, horticulture, wildlife conservation or recreational uses, and is based principally on mapping and interpretation of surface soils (Mackney 1974), though information on other natural resources, vegetation, climate and geomorphology is usually also required. Land capability maps were originally produced in the USA for farm planning (Klingebiel and Montgomery 1961), and similar, agriculturally orientated maps have since been introduced in Britain (Bibby and Mackney 1969, Bibby *et al.* 1982) and many other countries (F.A.O. 1974b). They grade land into one of seven (UK) or eight (USA) classes, according to the effects its physical properties have on limitations to the number of crops which can be consistently produced with a favourable ratio of yield to inputs. As an example, Table 6.8 gives the characteristics of the seven classes of land currently recognized in Britain.

Capability subclasses were originally recognized according to the type of agricultural limitation involved: e=erosion hazard, w=excess water, c=climatic limitations to plant growth, s=soil limitations (principally rooting depth). Subsequently additional subclasses have been recognized, especially in relation to other soil limitations to crop growth, such as stoniness, high water-table, droughtiness, workability, susceptibility to structural damage, and salinity, and to gradient (subclass g) as a limitation to cultivation by machinery. Rankings within some classes have also been introduced in some national classifications to provide further detail; for example in Britain, two divisions are recognized in classes 3 and 4 according to increasing restrictions to arable cropping; class 5 is divided into three, based on potential for reclamation; and class 6 is divided into three according to the grazing value of existing vegetation (Bibby *et al.* 1982).

The boundaries between classes and divisions in terms of climatic, gradient, soil and vegetational limitations are based for a given country or region upon the accumulated experience of local soil surveyors, farmers and advisers. Examples of some boundaries used in Britain are given in Fig. 6.9 and Tables 6.9 and 6.10; full details are given by Bibby *et al.* (1982, pp. 21–65).

Limiting factors in agricultural capability classifications often differ from country to country or region to region. This is because (a) crops grown in different regions have different climatic or soil requirements, (b) what is considered the best (i.e. class 1) land in one country may be distinctly poorer than the best in another, and (c) some land characteristics are more important in one region than in another. The F.A.O. (1976) attempted to standardize the previously variable procedures and terminology in land evaluation, and emphasized that different gradings are required for different types of proposed land use, even for different arable crops or farming methods. Each mapping unit in the F.A.O. system is therefore classed according to its suitability for fairly specific purposes; examples are: (a) rainfed annual cropping of groundnuts with subsistence maize using cattle-drawn farm implements, (b) commercial wheat production on large freehold farms with high capital input but low labour intensity, (c) softwood plantations operated by a government forestry

Table 6.8 — Agricultural land capability classes in Britain (from Bibby *et al.* 1982)

Class	Cropping characteristics	Soil characteristics	Site characteristics
1	Very flexible, including exacting crops, such as winter-harvested vegetables, consistently high yields	Deep, well-drained loams, good moisture reserves, well structured	Level or gently sloping, favourable climate
2	Flexible, but yields less consistently high, and some winter harvesting of vegetables may be difficult	Minor problems of wetness or workability, slightly unfavourable particle size or structure	Minor climatic or slope problems
3	Good yields of a narrow range of crops (mainly cereals), moderate but variable yields of some other crops	Problems of wetness, restricted rooting depth, unfavourable particle size or structure	Greater climatic problems, steeper slopes may cause erosion
4	Suited primarily to grass with short arable breaks (barley, oats, forage crops), good grass yields but other crops very variable	Severe wetness, occasional floods, shallow or very stony soils	Moderate climatic problems and/or moderately steep gradients, erosion common
5	Restricted to grass, but yields are variable, much improvement of grassland possible	Severe wetness, frequent floods, shallow or very stony soils	Severe climatic problems, steep slopes, strong erosion risk
6	Range of grazing qualities giving >5 months grazing per year; some improvement possible, but most is rough grazing	Very severe wetness or other limitations, preventing extensive use of machinery for land improvement	Very severe climatic or slope problems, some areas affected by severe industrial pollution
7	Very limited agricultural value, limitations cannot be rectified	Extremely severe wetness, extremely stony, bare rock, scree, beach deposits	Extremely severe climate, extremely steep, areas of toxic waste tips

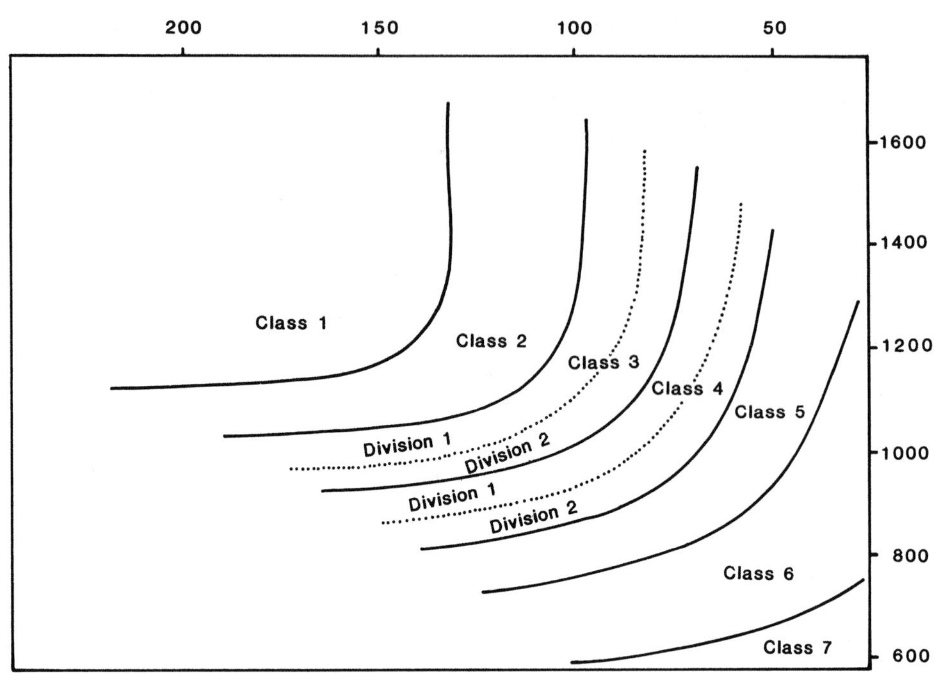

Fig. 6.9 — Climatic boundaries for land capability classes in Britain (from Bibby *et al.* 1982). The vertical axis is the lower quartile value of accumulated day-degrees above 0°C for January — June (inclusive), and the horizontal axis is the median value of annual maximum potential soils moisture deficits.

department, and (d) national parks for recreation and tourism. Land is assessed as suitable (S) or not suitable (N); suitable land can sustain without damage the use under consideration, and should yield benefits which justify the inputs, whereas land which is not suitable has one or more qualities which preclude sustained use of the type considered. Three classes of suitability are distinguished:

S1 (high suitable): land with no limitations to sustained use for the purpose considered, or with limitations so minor that they will neither raise inputs nor decrease productivity or benefits significantly.
S2 (moderately suitable): land with limitations which will increase inputs or decrease productivity, but not to the extent that the overall advantage gained from use will be appreciably inferior to that expected on S1 land.
S3 (marginally suitable): land having limitations which will decrease benefits to such a level that use is only marginally justified.

Two classes are distinguished in the 'not suitable' order:

N1 (currently not suitable): land having limitations which preclude sustained use and cannot be corrected at present at an acceptable cost, but which may be surmountable in the future.

Table 6.9 — Limits of some factors affecting land capability classes in Britain (from Bibby *et al.* 1982)

Class and division	Slope limits (°)	Soil depth (cm)	Flood risk
1	< 3	>60	Negligible
2	< 7	>45	Negligible
3.1	< 7	>45	Non-damaging short winter floods, rare summer floods
3.2	<11	>20	
4.1	<11	>20	Damaging floods 1 year in 5, some risk of summer flooding
4.2	<15	>20	
5.1	<11	—	Damaging floods 1 year in 3, or more frequently provided resulting erosion is negligible
5.2	<15	—	
5.3	<25	—	
6.1	—	—	Damaging floods in most years, often causing erosion
6.2	—	—	
6.3	—	—	
7	—	—	

Table 6.10 — Size and abundance of stones as limiting factors for land capability classes in Britain (from Bibby *et al.* 1982)

		Capability class if stones are:		
	Volume % stones	Very small and small (0.2–2 cm)	Medium and large (2–20 cm)	Very large (>20 cm)
Stoneless	<1	1	1	1
Very slightly stony	1–5	1	2–3	2–3
Slightly stony	6–15	1–2	3–4	4
Moderately stony	16–35	3	4–5	4–5
Very stony	36–70	4	5	5
Extremely stony	>70	5	5	5

N2 (permanently not suitable): land having limitations which seem permanently to preclude sustained use for the purpose considered.

Suitability subclasses are indicated by lower case letters following the class symbol, and indicate reasons for limitations, such as e for erosion (e.g. S3e). Further subdivision is necessary if two or more otherwise similar subclasses on a map differ in terms of management requirements. For example, two S3e units would be distinguished as S3e-1 and S3e-2 if one could be best managed by terracing, and the other by planting a fast-growing second crop to cover the ground at a time when it would otherwise be exposed to heavy seasonal rain.

Further details of land suitability evaluation are given by Dent and Young (1981), and guidelines relating to land evaluation for rainfed and irrigated agriculture are given by F.A.O. (1984) and F.A.O. (1985b) respectively. Climate, soil and water requirements of individual crops are summarized from various sources by Dent and Young (1981, Table 10.9).

Much less effort has been put into evaluating soil and other characteristics determining suitability of land for non-agricultural uses. However, soil factors influencing suitability of land for civil engineering, pipe-laying, playing fields, golf courses, camping, and wildlife conservation in Britain are discussed by various contributions in Jarvis and Mackney (1979).

7

Economic significance of Quaternary studies

7.1 INTRODUCTION

The economic importance of Quaternary deposits, mainly in terms of their influence on the character of agricultural soils, was originally recognized a century and a half ago. In Britain, for example, special 'drift' editions of the 1:63 360 maps were introduced following the pioneering work of J. Trimmer in Norfolk in 1844–46 (Bailey 1952). These showed the distribution of a few broad groups of Quaternary deposits (mainly boulder clay, sand and gravel, brickearth and clay-with-flints), but they were difficult to produce, especially when fieldwork was done at the 1:63 360 scale, because in most areas the distribution of Quaternary deposits is more random and unpredictable than that of the older ('solid') bedrock formations. As a result they were little used, even after they were improved by the use of 1:10 560 field sheets. In other countries, such as USA, Germany, Switzerland, the Netherlands and Scandinavia, Quaternary mapping started later, but the maps have proved more useful because the deposits themselves are often thicker and more extensive, and frequently cause major problems in civil engineering, such as landslides.

Because the Quaternary is the most recent period of geological time, and in effect embraces the present, it impinges more or less strongly on most human activities and interests. Many applied aspects of Quaternary studies are more cultural than economic, such as understanding the environment and evolution of early man. Despite their importance, these will not be discussed in this chapter, which is concerned principally with selected applications in industries such as mineral exploration, civil engineering and agriculture.

7.2 QUATERNARY MINERAL RESOURCES

In many parts of the world, Quaternary deposits are quarried for use in bulk as sand, gravel, brickearth (mainly loess) and materials with special properties (e.g. diatomite for manufacture of dynamite). Locally they are also worked for concentrations of valuable minerals (e.g. placer deposits).

7.2.1 Quaternary sources of aggregate

In Britain, production of aggregate (rock particles which are used in a bound or unbound condition to form part or all of an engineering or building structure) is the largest single non-fuel mineral industry in both volume and value. In 1983 it was about 30% of British non-fuel mineral production in value terms. Quaternary gravels from sites on land provided over 50% of British aggregate before 1967, but as many of the available deposits became exhausted and planning constraints were imposed on others, increasing amounts have come from pre-Quaternary crushed hard rock sources and from sea-bed gravels (Lewis 1969, Collis and Fox 1985), though these are often more expensive than aggregate from terrestrial Quaternary deposits. The main Quaternary deposits suitable for aggregate production are glaciofluvial gravels, river terrace and channel deposits, raised beaches and screes, gelifluction and other slope deposits. The reserves, ease of extraction, and suitability for aggregate of these deposits all depend on the Quaternary history of the area in which they occur.

Glaciofluvial gravels occur mainly as fairly small bodies (eskers, kames, valley trains within confined valleys), which often thin out rapidly and unpredictably, and may contain lenses or rafts of till; many eskers and kames also have a useless overburden of till, which is likely to vary in thickness quite unpredictably. Other glaciofluvial gravels form proglacial outwash plains (sandar), which are often very extensive and become progressively thinner and finer away from the ice margin; these gravels may contain small till rafts or mudballs close to the ice margin, but the main bodies of fine sediment not suitable for aggregate are infills of kettle holes, especially in Devensian sandar. Depending on the rocks traversed by the parent glacier, glaciofluvial gravels may contain almost any mixture of rock types among the larger clasts, and many may make the deposit unsuitable for aggregate. Soft clasts (shale, soft sandstone, chalk, weathered crystalline rocks) and those likely to react unfavourably with cement in making concrete (e.g. pyritic sediments) are more likely to occur in gravels transported short distances in the ice and meltwater stream; long-distance transport helps remove such clasts from gravel grades by crushing and abrading them into sand and finer particles. Otherwise it is possible to remove them by heavy media separation (Haynes and Wyman 1962).

River terrace gravels are usually well suited to aggregate production. They often form fairly extensive and quite thick layers along valley sides, usually in well-drained positions above the present water-table and with little or no overburden. However, much gravel is dredged from the bed of the Rhine and other European rivers. Soft clasts may occur, especially in areas of soft bedrock, but because of the considerable age of many terraces these unsuitable components have often been removed by weathering to a considerable depth. For example in mid-Pleistocene terraces of the River Thames in southern England, chalk clasts have been removed by weathering, often to depths exceeding 10 m, leaving gravels composed mainly of extremely hard and inert fragments of siliceous flint nodules. However, weathering also often increases the content of fine material such as clay and iron oxides, which lowers the quality of the aggregate. In contrast, point-bar or channel-bar gravels in the present river channel are usually unweathered and more likely to contain unsuitable clasts; also they may present extraction problems, such as a high groundwater table, the necessity for diversion of the river's course, or removal of an overburden of fine overbank deposits, and may contain channels filled with fine silty or clayey sediment.

Raised beach gravels are also variable in composition, depending on the nature of the cliff and wave-cut platform beneath. Some contain only the most resistant clasts, but others are rich in soft weatherable rocks. They are usually quite thin and laterally restricted, often forming a narrow (<100 m wide) band parallel to the cliff, though some beaches are several kilometres wide (Hodgson 1964). They usually become finer in a seaward direction, because the equilibrium between onshore wave transport and seaward movement down the beach under gravity or backwash approaches the shore as the mass of particles increases. Many raised beaches are deeply buried beneath an overburden of glacial, aeolian or periglacial slope deposits; these often reach a maximum thickness close to the buried cliff, where the beach deposits are also thickest.

Slope deposits rarely provide large reserves of good quality aggregate. Screes beneath steep, high slopes often contain quite coarse blocks, which need crushing before use. They are rarely very extensive and may change laterally in composition if the bedrock outcrops above are variable. Many of the constituent clasts may have been softened by frost action during or after deposition, and problems arise in quarrying because the loose deposits are on steep slopes and may become unstable. Gelifluction deposits also vary in composition according to the nature of the source rocks up-slope, and are often too strongly contaminated with clay to provide useful aggregate.

Sea-floor gravels were often originally non-marine, having accumulated as fluvial, glaciofluvial or shallow-water (beach or deltaic) deposits in cold stages when the sea level was lowered eustatically. However, many were partly reworked and redistributed during the subsequent rise of sea level, so their occurrence is even less predictable than similar deposits on land. Vibrocore sampling, seismic profiling and sidescan sonar are used as exploration techniques, but exploitation may cause problems because clean gravels are often the best spawning grounds for fish.

7.2.2 Other Quaternary mineral resources

Other Quaternary sediments quarried in bulk for industrial purposes include (a) diatomites from certain lake deposits, which are used as filtering agents, as abrasives or for absorbing nitroglycerin to make dynamite, and (b) sands for glass-making, building or refractory purposes. Pure diatomites of Quaternary age were formed mainly in interglacial or Holocene lakes, though some older (Tertiary) workable diatomites are from marine sites on continental margins. Diatomites are usually white, cream or pale grey, but other lacustrine deposits (e.g. *Chara* marls) may be similar in colour, and simple chemical or microscopic analysis is required to distinguish them.

The best Quaternary glass-making sands are periglacial coversands, especially those from which iron oxide and clay grain-coatings have been naturally removed by Holocene podzolization, as in upper horizons of the Shirdley Hill Sands of south-west Lancashire, England (Hall and Folland 1967, p. 43). Coversands and shallow marine sands are also very suitable as building and refractory moulding sands, but fluvial and other sands are usually less well sorted and often require screening. Sand used for concrete should be virtually free of most constituents other than quartz; even feldspar in more than trace amounts can cause hair-cracks in concrete.

The organic decomposition products in some anaerobic non-calcareous lake muds are able to fix and concentrate uranium from solution (Petersen 1979). At present, useful concentrations of uranium are known only from sandstones associated with pre-Quaternary lake muds, but exploration in similar deposits of more recent lakes may also be profitable.

7.2.3 Placer deposits

In many parts of the world, Quaternary fluvial and beach sediments contain valuable minerals (gold, tin, titanium, diamonds), and are worked as placer deposits. Such deposits account for over half of the world production of gold, tin and titanium and almost half the world's diamond production. Previously placers were thought to occur almost randomly, but better knowledge of how Quaternary climatic changes affected sea level and processes of fluvial erosion and deposition has recently improved exploration techniques for these valuable mineral deposits (Sutherland 1985). In many humid tropical regions, the intense weathering of rocks during long pre-Quaternary periods of stable climatic conditions resulted in a considerable concentration of insoluble residual elements in the soils. During the Quaternary, alternating arid and humid climatic conditions favoured placer development in many areas. In arid periods, erosion of the enriched residues was widespread because there was less vegetation to stabilize the soil. In subsequent humid periods, greater soil stability decreased sediment influx and encouraged reworking of the previously introduced fluvial sediments; this led to further concentration of heavy minerals such as native gold, diamonds, and tin and titanium oxides in alluvial channel sediments. The placer minerals are therefore sought in alluvial deposits of certain humid periods, which are located using conventional stratigraphic and dating methods.

One of the clearest examples of the value of Quaternary stratigraphy in the location of placer deposits is provided by the study of Hall *et al.* (1985) of the Birim diamond placer in Ghana. The ultimate source of the diamonds here is a series of steeply dipping breccias and greywackes in the Lower Birimian metasediments of Proterozoic age (Fig. 7.1). Weathering of these rocks has produced a mantle at least 27 m thick, which is bimodal, being composed of silty clay with about 5% gravel-sized clasts derived mainly from quartz veins. The diamondiferous floodplain deposits of the River Birim were investigated in numerous boreholes between Oda and Akwatia (Fig. 7.1). They are up to 10 m thick and comprise an upward-fining sequence of channel gravels, followed by discontinuous beds of sand, then clayey silts and silty sands. Radiocarbon dating of leaves and wood allowed three chronostratigraphic units to be defined, which were deposited at 13 000–11 000 b.p., 9000–7500 b.p. and from 2100 b.p. to the present. These periods correlate well with episodes of increased lake levels and alluvial deposition in other parts of West Africa, so that they probably reflect major environmental changes affecting the whole region (Pastouret *et al.* 1978). The following sequence of changes was inferred:

Pre-21 000 b.p. Formation of low terraces.

21 000–13 500 b.p. Ogolian arid period (Kolla *et al.* 1979), during which the northern arid belt expanded southwards so that the rain forest in southern Ghana was replaced by savanna grassland; fluvial activity was at a minimum.

13 500–10 500 b.p. Return to wetter conditions with increased discharge and floods

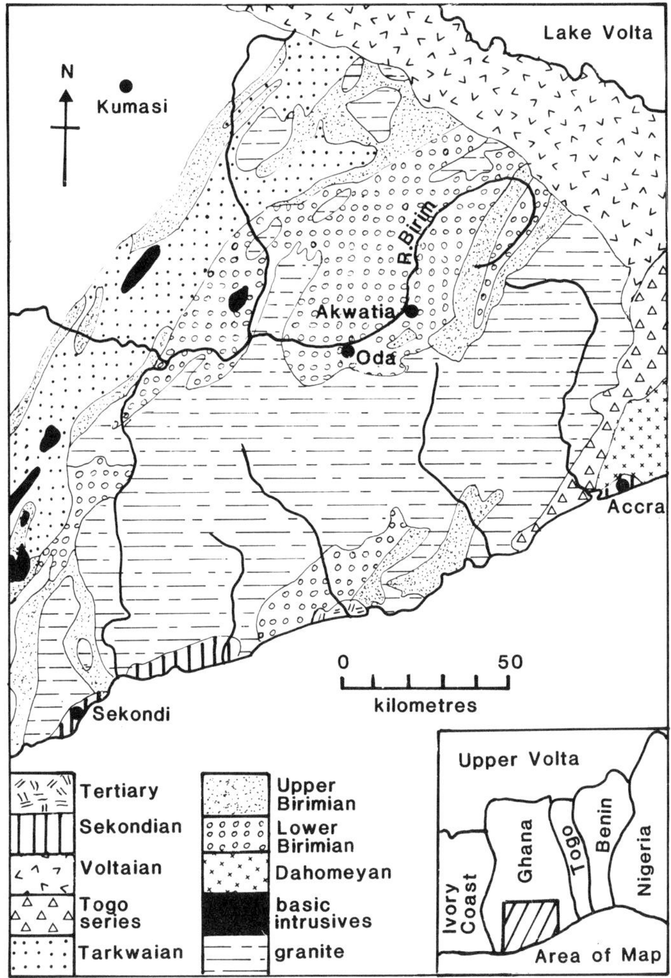

Fig. 7. 1 — Geological map of southern Ghana showing location of Birim catchment with alluvial placer deposits (from Hall *et al.* 1985). Reproduced by permission of the Geological Society from *Journal of the Geological Society*, Volume 142 (1985).

resulting from storms over a non-forested catchment; extensive erosion of pre-existing sediments and deposition of the oldest layer of floodplain alluvium.

10 500–7000 b.p. Forest was gradually re-established but discharges remained high, leading to aggradation of the coarse gravels in the middle floodplain unit.

7000–4500 b.p. Decreased discharge and slight reworking of the middle floodplain unit.

4500–3000 b.p. Mid-Holocene arid episode (Talbot 1981) with minimal fluvial activity.

3000 b.p. to present. Increased discharge led to deposition of the youngest alluvial unit of the floodplain.

The boreholes showed that diamonds occur mainly in the coarse gravels, the richest concentrations of large gems being associated with the oldest unit of floodplain alluvium (deposited 13 500–10 500 years ago), intermediate concentrations occurring in the two later Holocene alluvial units, and the smallest amounts in the low terraces formed before 21 000 b.p. (Table 7.1 and Fig. 7.2).

Table 7.1 — Mean concentration of diamonds in alluvial placer deposits of three ages from the Birim drainage basin, Ghana

Grade of deposits (carats m^{-3})	Older floodplain alluvium (13 500–10 500 b.p.)	Later floodplain alluvium 10 500–7000 b.p. and <3000 b.p.)	Low terrace deposits (>21 000 b.p.)
<0.01	6.0	16.0	43.3
0.01–0.76	74.3	74.0	48.3
0.76–2.29	16.0	11.3	7.6
2.29–3.92	1.0	0.3	0.0
>3.92	2.6	0.6	0.6

The circumstances leading to diamond concentration in the richest horizons were probably (a) rapid slope erosion from the strongly weathered soils on hillslopes, (b) flushing of colluvial deposits which had accumulated in small tributary valleys during the Ogolian dry period, (c) scouring to form discontinuous bedrock channels, and (d) deposition and frequent partial reworking of coarse channel gravels. Most of the diamonds in the gravels were of medium to coarse sand size, suggesting that they were trapped at times of moderate flow in the voids between previously deposited gravel clasts; penetration into the gravels was perhaps assisted by 'jiggling' of the surface gravel on the stream bed under high shear stress (Beschta and Jackson 1979).

7.2.4 Quaternary deposits and the location of bedrock ore bodies

Where Quaternary deposits obscure ore bodies in the underlying bedrock, petrographic or geochemical analyses are often used to help locate the ores. Successful interpretation of these analytical results depends upon identification of the depositional processes responsible for the Quaternary cover and the processes by which the ore was incorporated into it. A common approach is to analyse samples from surface or immediate subsurface soil horizons for an element or mineral characteristic of the ore, and then look for the ore body approximately beneath the point of maximum concentration. This is less successful where soils are derived from transported sediments, as in glaciated terrains, than where the soils are residual in origin (Govett 1973).

As described in 2.2.2, material eroded from a subglacial source such as a mineral vein is incorporated first into the basal layers of the ice sheet, then rises into

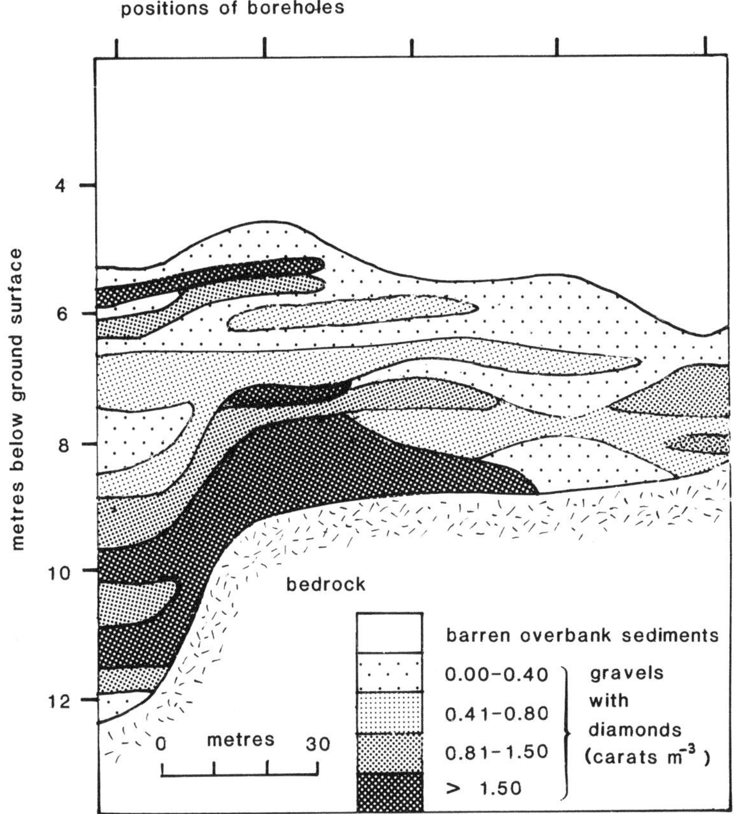

Fig. 7.2 — Variation in diamond concentration within floodplain gravels of River Birim, Ghana (from Hall *et al.* 1985). Reproduced by permission of the Geological Society from *Journal of the Geological Society,* Volume 142 (1985).

progressively higher layers away from the source in the direction of glacier movement. The zone of incorporation also broadens and becomes more diffuse down-glacier, to form a 'plume' rather like the smoke blown down-wind from a chimney (Drake 1983). Consequently any anomaly appearing at the surface is some distance down-glacier from the subcrop. The distance between the maximum surface concentration and the nearest up-glacier outcrop or subcrop is designated K (Lee 1965). The value of K increases with increasing thickness of the glacier, and therefore very approximately with increasing thickness of the lodgement till deposited by the glacier, but multiple till sequences and multiple ice advances from different directions may complicate the pattern. Additional complications arise from redeposition by streams, marine or lacustrine wave action, and gelifluction or other slope movements.

Some mapped distributions of glacial erratics show two or more surface concentrations in the till down-glacier from the source (Fig. 7.3); these may result from repeated glacial erosion of the ore body or glacial recycling of till deposited earlier by

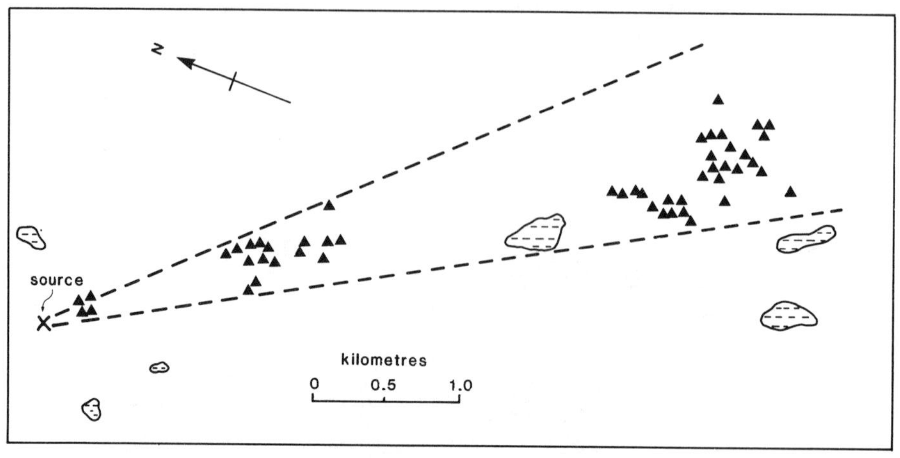

Fig. 7.3 — Distribution of glacially transported molybdenum ore boulders at Souvaara, Finland (from Hyvärinen *et al.* 1973).

the same ice sheet (Drake 1983). The width of surface anomalies in till sheets is very variable, presumably depending on local ice dynamics; some are narrow ribbons (Shilts 1976), but others spread as widely as 65° (Flint 1971, p. 179). Some are curved around large topographic irregularities in the bedrock surface.

Fluvial erosion and transportation of material from an outcropping ore body result in anomalies of various types and at various distances downstream, depending on (a) the stream flow velocity and discharge, (b) the solubility of the ore, (c) how easily it is disrupted by corrasion or evorsion, (d) how easily particles are entrained by the stream flow, and (e) processes of redeposition. If the ore is insoluble, sediment samples must be analysed, but the relative positions of the ore body and its maximum concentration in the alluvium are difficult to predict, because the latter depends upon the density and peak size of the transported ore particles, the flow rate of the river, which may be very variable, and other factors. Fine particles are usually carried further than coarser or denser particles at a given flow rate before they are deposited. However, particle shape is also important, especially with very dense materials (Shumilov and Shumovskiy 1975); soft minerals such as gold may change shape fairly rapidly through repeated impacts during transportation, and this can either hasten or delay deposition (Hallbauer and Utter 1977). Deposition of dense ore particles, transported as part of the rolling or saltating bed-load, often results from entrapment in pores between coarser particles on the stream bed, as proposed by Hall *et al.* (1985) for accumulation of diamonds in the Birim placer (see 7.2.3). It also occurs preferentially in the wake of large obstacles which separate the stream flow (Fig. 7.4), in the mixing zone downstream of a confluence (Mosley and Schumm 1977), and on the downstream side of channel bars or point bars close to meanders (Smith and Beukes 1983). Repeated erosion and redeposition of alluvium during floods may move heavy mineral concentrations progressively downstream. It is therefore

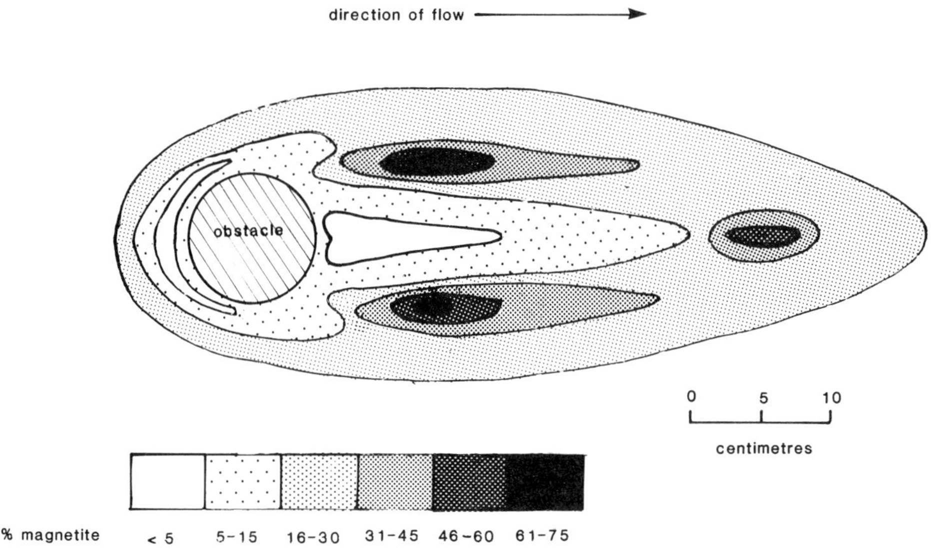

Fig. 7.4 — Concentration of magnetite around an isolated obstacle, as recorded in a flume experiment (from Best and Brayshaw 1985). Reproduced by permission of the Geological Society from *Journal of the Geological Society,* Volume 142 (1985).

impossible at present to generalize about the relationship between alluvial anomalies and bedrock ore bodies. However, many of the factors mentioned are also important as sedimentological controls on the distribution of alluvial and beach placers (Reid and Frostick 1985), so further research on transportation and concentration of heavy minerals in aqueous media would serve a dual purpose.

7.3 THE USE OF PALYNOLOGICAL TECHNIQUES IN PETROLEUM EXPLORATION

Several methods developed by Quaternary palynologists have recently been adopted by the petroleum industry to help date and correlate pre-Quaternary sediments, to reconstruct depositional environments as an aid to predicting the distribution of potential reservoir and source rocks, and for sedimentological modelling of field development projects. As pollen grains are very small ($<10\ \mu m$), they can survive the drilling process and may be extracted in larger numbers than most other fossils from the small rock fragments (cuttings) recovered. They are also very widely distributed in different environments and are consequently the only common fossils which can be used to correlate marine and non-marine sediments.

Detailed knowledge of the stratigraphy of an area is essential for understanding the temporal relationships between source rocks, reservoir rocks, the timing of hydrocarbon generation, and the formation of structures suitable as hydrocarbon traps. However, in areas of rapid deposition, such as the offshore deltas of large rivers, evolutionary changes (appearances and extinctions) in most fossil groups occurred too slowly to provide enough information for precise stratigraphic control. In these circumstances various methods of quantitative palynology, such as subdivision into pollen assemblage biozones, can be used to enhance stratigraphic resolution and establish correlations.

Together with other fossil groups, such as marine microplankton, pollen assemblages from cuttings have also been used to reconstruct depositional environments. This helps to predict the distribution of potential reservoir or source rocks, and assists small-scale sedimentological modelling for field development projects. Palaeoenvironmental gradients identified in this way are also useful in the search for stratigraphic hydrocarbon traps. Interpretation of this type depends upon detailed knowledge of the ways in which pollen is transferred from plants to sediments, and the effects of transport and other processes in removing or preferentially concentrating certain types. Studies of pollen distribution in the modern environment, such as the investigation by Tinsley and Smith (1974) of the progressive decline of pollen of different tree species away from a woodland margin, which were originally made to help interpret Quaternary fossil pollen assemblages, are basic to this type of work in petroleum exploration.

A further aspect of petroleum palynology is the characterization of source rocks by investigation of their total organic composition and its maturity level. After they are buried, sediments are affected by heat and pressure, and the colour and reflectivity of the organic matter is irreversibly changed. The extent of change indicates whether the source rocks have been altered enough to release hydrocarbons, and this can be assessed from the state of preservation of pollen and spores. Studies of organic constituents in the source rock can also indicate the most likely types of hydrocarbons (oil, gas or condensate) that were generated during diagenesis.

7.4 QUATERNARY FEATURES IN CIVIL ENGINEERING

Early British engineers concerned with building canals or railways and improving roads appreciated the importance of geological features, but in the early twentieth century the development of rigorous methods of measurement and interpretation in soil mechanics led many to believe that geology has little real value in civil engineering. However, most rock materials are inherently variable, and laboratory measurements on a restricted number of samples often have a limited value in assessing the geotechnical features of a site. This is especially true of sites influenced by Quaternary processes of deposition, ground disturbance or weathering, which usually show greater variability than areas of undisturbed pre-Quaternary bedrock. As Quaternary processes have extensively affected most mid- and high-latitude areas such as Britain, it follows that a full appreciation of at least the more recent Quaternary history is usually essential for correct geotechnical assessment of sites in these areas.

Following several failures in the construction of motorways, housing estates, bridges and reservoirs, which were expensive to rectify yet could have been avoided if gelifluction deposits or other Quaternary features had been recognized, collaboration between civil engineers and Quaternary scientists is now more common in Britain and many other countries, but it could usefully be extended and developed further. Legget and Karrow (1983) described many expensive errors directly attributable to this lack of collaboration or to the failure of civil engineers to recognize Quaternary features and their significance. These included structural failures arising from foundations built upon large glacial erratics (McIldowie 1936) or a thin cemented hardpan (Jacobi and Davis 1925, p. 385), both mistaken for bedrock in exploratory boreholes; and the bankruptcy, defaulting and claims for extra payments of many millions of dollars that arose from difficulties in excavating part of the St. Lawrence Seaway in 1956–7, because the degree of compaction of basal till (the Malone Till) and the stickiness and instability of the overlying glaciomarine quick clay (the Leda Clay) were ignored (Cleaves 1963). Such avoidable problems are fortunately now less frequent, but do still occur.

7.4.1 Landslips

Many landslips on quite gentle slopes result from reactivation of old gelifluction sheets and periglacial mudflows. These originated in the more recent cold periods of the Quaternary, especially the final cold episode of the Devensian (the Loch Lomond Stadial in Britain), and were stabilized early in the Holocene when the climate improved and forest developed on the slopes. Beneath escarpments and on valley sides, slopes are often covered by thin periglacial deposits separated from pre-Quaternary clay formations beneath by one or more slip planes almost parallel to the land surface (Weeks 1969); locally a humic soil of the Windermere Interstadial occurs beneath the gelifluction or mudflow deposits (Fig. 7.5). The natural slope

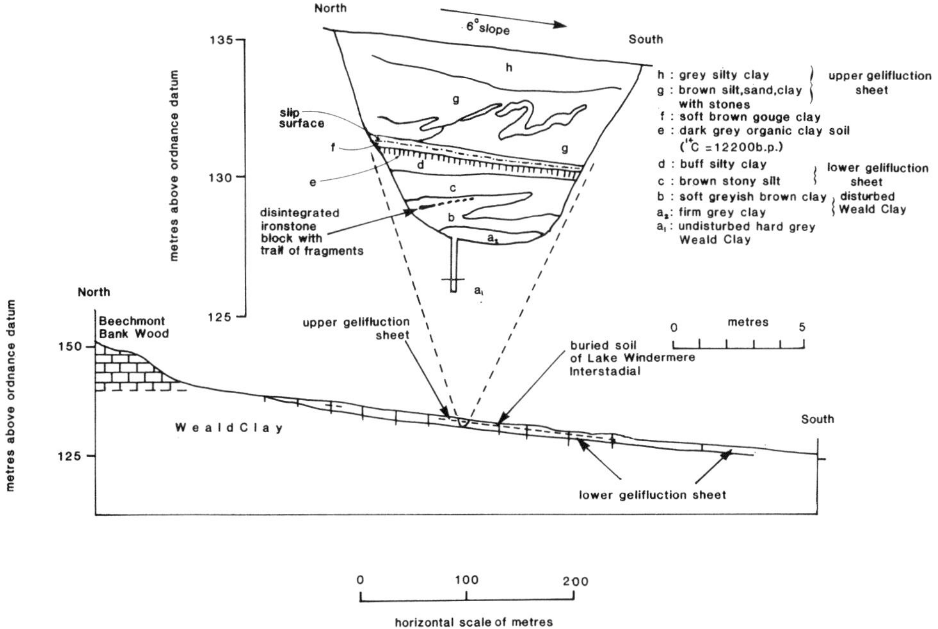

Fig. 7.5 — Section of gelifluction deposits with buried soil on Lower Cretaceous Weald Clay slope below scarp of Hythe Beds limestone, near Sevenoaks, S.E. England (from Skempton and Weeks 1976). Reproduced by permission of the Royal Society, London.

angles (usually up to approximately 8°) were clearly determined by the movement of material on the slopes under periglacial conditions. Deforestation in the later Holocene has left the periglacial deposits prone to renewed movement; this usually occurs when the toe of the gelifluction sheet or mudflow is removed, either naturally by stream erosion or artificially during construction of foundations for a road or building (Hutchinson *et al.* 1973, Skempton and Weeks 1976, Biczysko 1981). Unusually heavy precipitation or diversion of drainage water (Conway 1979), leading to increases of porewater pressure in the slope deposits to levels approaching those of periglacial conditions, may also provoke reactivation.

The irregular lobate margins of gelifluction sheets and mudflows on clay slopes can often indicate the likelihood of this type of landslip. But in some areas there is no geomorphological evidence of previous movement (Biczysko 1981), either because the deposits are older than the latest Devensian cold episode and are therefore more degraded, or because the telltale surface features have been obscured by recent cultivation and colluviation.

It is only quite recently that the extent of periglacial activity in Britain and many other mid-latitude countries has been recognized; many clay-rich slope deposits have been ignored in the past because they are difficult to distinguish from *in situ* weathered clay bedrock. As Jones and Derbyshire (1983) commented, "the relatively late realization of the true nature and extent of periglacial earths in lowland Britain has led to unexpected difficulties being encountered in a number of engineering operations". Indeed, examples of clay slope failures are sufficiently numerous in Britain, and remedial measures are sufficiently costly, for it to be cheaper to assume that all extensive clay slopes steeper than about 5° are prone to slipping by reactivation of periglacial movements, and are to be avoided when siting housing estates, new roads, reservoirs, etc.

In upland regions which were glaciated repeatedly during the Quaternary, many valley slopes were steepened by glacial erosion. This often leads to landslipping, either when patches of glacial deposits left on the valley sides are undermined, overloaded or saturated with water, or when melting of the glacier leads to release of lateral pressure then fracturing and collapse of the bedrock along dilation joints parallel to the slope.

Oversteepening of valley slopes by glacial erosion in areas of gently dipping, interbedded hard and soft bedrock may also lead to cambering and landslipping by rotation of blocks between gulls (Kellaway *et al.* 1971). Gulls and similar open rock fractures resulting from glacial and periglacial processes may create other engineering problems, such as leakage from reservoirs (Knill 1971); they often involve an additional expense in construction work, because they demand greater excavation of bedrock than was originally expected (Knill 1968) or necessitate reinforcement of foundations for buildings. Provided no further movement is expected, gulls can be arched over in foundations, or buildings positioned so that any gull is beneath the central third of a concrete foundation raft (Hawkins and Privett 1981).

Because many Quaternary deposits are soft and easily eroded, river valleys are often deeply incised into thick Quaternary sequences, especially where land has risen rapidly by glacio-isostatic rebound since the last glaciation. The steep sides of such valleys are often prone to landslipping because some Quaternary deposits are less permeable than others. Landslips in saturated lacustrine and deltaic sands overlying

Fig. 7.6 — View of Sevenoaks By-pass traversing late Devensian gelifluction deposits overlying slopes of Weald Clay beneath Hythe Beds Scarp, Kent, England.

impermeable till, which affected the road approach to a ferry over the Saskatchewan River in Canada, were described by Lidgren and Sauer (1982).

7.4.2 Bearing capacity and settlement of Quaternary deposits

Quaternary deposits have a wide range of bearing capacities, permeabilities and settlement characteristics. Glacial deposits in particular are very variable (Marsland 1977), and Boulton and Paul (1976) have suggested that processes operating during transport in the glacier, during deposition and after deposition can all influence the geotechnical properties of tills. Lodgement and other basal tills, which have often been compacted by a considerable thickness of glacial ice, behave like other pre-Quaternary overconsolidated clays, though they often contain larger amounts of weatherable minerals and weathering may modify their geotechnical properties to some considerable depth below the ground surface (Eyles and Sladen 1981). Other till types are usually less dense but more permeable and compressible (McGown and Derbyshire 1977), as also are many Holocene fluvial, lacustrine and estuarine deposits. Even quite deeply buried strata of weak Quaternary sediments (e.g. interglacial or interstadial peats) can cause serious settlement of large structures (Mohr 1937), especially if the weight is transferred to deeper subsurface deposits through piles. Uneven settlement of road surfaces or embankments in areas underlain by soft Quaternary deposits can present problems which are often expensive to rectify, though they are less problematic with railways because the track can simply be re-levelled cheaply with ballast. Problems associated with the flow of loose, poorly consolidated till after heavy rain were described by Eden (1976a).

Settlement on very soft deposits is often minimized by preloading sites such as bridge foundations to consolidate the sediment before building commences.

Among the least stable of Quaternary deposits are the so-called quick clays, which have been the cause of many landslips in eastern Canada (Tavenas *et al.* 1971, Eden 1976b, Penner and Burn 1978), Norway, and other heavily glaciated terrains. Quick clays were deposited in glaciomarine conditions and are composed mainly of non-swelling minerals derived by glacial erosion and crushing of crystalline rocks. Dating of shells suggests that the rate of sedimentation was extremely high (Gadd 1986). Because of isostatic rebound following deglaciation, quick clays have often been uplifted above present sea level and have therefore lost soluble salts by leaching. This allows repulsive forces to disperse and reorientate the clay particles, decreasing grain-to-grain contacts; the moisture content is therefore abnormally high. Remoulding of the leached clay decreases the initial strength by as much as 99% (Rosenqvist 1977), so that deposits which have been disturbed may flow freely on slopes as gentle as 0.25°. For the same reason, pile driving for foundations in quick clays should be avoided. Stability can often be restored by mixing potassium chloride with the clay to reflocculate it and increase contact between particles.

Some fine glaciolacustrine silts behave in a similar way to quick clays, being fairly cohesive and retaining a large proportion of water in their natural state, but becoming completely structureless and fluid if disturbed or remoulded. The best-known deposit of this type is the so-called "bull's liver", which was deposited in glacial Lake Flushing and has caused many foundation problems in the New York city area (Parsons 1976).

Dispersion and collapse of the clay bridges between silt particles when loess is saturated have considerable geotechnical significance (Krinitzsky and Turnbull 1967, Sheeler 1968, Krayev 1969), in that improperly drained foundations of buildings (Hardy 1950) and unsealed canal or reservoir walls in loess are liable to collapse. The settlement is large in loess with a dry bulk density <1.28 but small or zero if the density exceeds 1.44 (Clevenger 1956); also the lower the void ratio (Audric and Bouquier 1976) and the greater the clay content (Handy 1973), the less likely is a loess to collapse. Lehr (1967) showed that if the porosity of loess is decreased to $<40\%$ by compaction, any further collapse on saturation is small, so a common practice is to flood and roll a loess site before starting construction work (Lobdell 1981). Deep road cuttings in loess are often terraced with risers of 4–5 m to avoid serious slumping (Gwynne 1950). Because of its high porosity, loess is also subject to frost-heave by formation of ice lenticles; this is mainly a problem with roads in loess areas, especially where the deposit is thin over a less permeable horizon.

A further problem with thick loess is the sudden collapse of subsurface pipes, caverns and fissures formed where water flows through the highly permeable sediment disaggregating and removing silt particles (Landes 1933); the collapse produces surface depressions and gullies which increase the length by headwall erosion (Fookes and Knill 1969, Bradford *et al.* 1978).

Many Quaternary clays of non-glacial origin contain layer silicate minerals, such as smectite, which contract appreciably on drying. The shrinkage resulting from this process in dry weather can cause foundation problems leading, for example, to cracks in the walls of buildings, or irregularities of pavements (Kassif *et al.* 1970). Nearby trees are the main cause of problems with buildings (Skempton 1954,

Bozozuk and Burn 1960, Hammer and Thomson 1966), because they extract large amounts of water through their roots. The worst trees in this respect are those which normally live in poorly drained soils, such as alder, aspen, willow, poplar and elm (Legget and Crawford 1965).

Peat deposits often have water contents of 75–98% and are extremely compressible, though this property (constrained deformation) varies with the structure and morphology of the plant remains present and the extent of humification (Hobbs 1986). The distribution of water content between pores of different sizes influences the consolidation behaviour. Laboratory testing, however, provides little indication of how a peat will perform when loaded, as for example in the construction of an embankment over a mire. This is partly because, as a result of rapid horizontal drainage, many peats are more permeable and compressible in the field than measurements on small test specimens in the laboratory suggest. For important engineering works in mires, large-scale field trials are therefore considered essential, though it is usually better to replace the peat with imported firmer sediment. Organic deposits are more common in high latitudes (e.g. the Canadian muskeg) than low, because they decompose less rapidly in cold conditions.

In limestone and other karst regions, Quaternary solution features may lead to foundation problems. General surface lowering is too slow to constitute a hazard, and collapse of a bedrock roof into a cavern is probably a very rare event (Culshaw and Waltham 1987). However, the subsidence of an unconsolidated cover into subsurface cavities is fairly common, and often occurs rapidly with no warning, especially if the cover is a cohesive clay which can temporarily bridge the developing cavity until it is quite large (Lamoreaux and Newton 1986). According to Kleywegt and Enslin (1975), rapid dropouts of this type are most likely to occur where there is a fluctuating perched water-table in the cover, or where the rockhead is sharply pinnacled. Lowering of the ground water-table by excessive pumping has also caused sudden karstic subsidence in the USA (Foose 1953) and South Africa. The main foundation problems with infilled dolines are differential settlement of buildings because of the very variable thickness of soft sediment over hard bedrock, and road subsidence (Geyer and Socolow 1979).

Because of the potential disasters resulting from unheralded collapse into solution cavities or unrecorded mines, various attempts have been made to detect such features by geophysical methods (Kennedy 1968, Grainger *et al.* 1973, Creedy and Freeman 1974, McDowell 1975, Darracott and Lake 1981). McCann *et al.* (1987) concluded that it is only possible to detect cavities whose depth of burial is less than twice their effective diameter (the cavity plus a surrounding zone in which the rock properties are influenced by the cavity). Some subsurface collapse features are also visible in aerial photographs (Norman 1969), even if they are not evident from ground level.

Major irregularities in a buried bedrock surface beneath soft Quaternary sediments can arise through various Quaternary processes, and are often likely to present engineering problems through the need to excavate more deeply than originally anticipated, through ingress of groundwater, or through rectification of differential subsidence. In addition to the solution cavities in karst regions and concealed mine workings, erosion hollows and channels are common in bedrock surfaces beneath river valleys (Berry 1979) and glacial deposits; they also occur on cambered slopes (Jones and Derbyshire 1983), even where these have a smooth appearance suggesting stability, because some Quaternary deposits are flexible enough to conceal rockhead movements. Bedrock surfaces modified by subglacial erosion are often extremely irregular; in addition to roches moutonnées and the small-scale p-forms (potholes and irregular troughs up to 20 m deep and wide), much larger buried valleys or tunnel valleys can occur. These are often cut by subglacial meltwater streams under a considerable hydrostatic head and may therefore be very steep-sided and deep, perhaps extending well below the base level of nearby rivers (Woodland 1970). Their infills are usually glaciofluvial sands and glaciolacustrine silts with irregular patches of basal gravel and subglacial melt-out till. The longitudinal profile is often much less regular than that of a subaerial river valley, and fracturing of adjacent bedrock is often important in water supply, because the improved transmissivity results in greatly increased yields from wells (Lloyd *et al.* 1981). The same property often causes leakage from reservoirs (Mackin 1941) or flooding of tunnels cut mainly in bedrock but intersecting the base of a buried valley (Legget and Karrow 1983). The siting of dams in valleys which have been overdeepened by glacial erosion and partially filled with gravel is extremely critical. If the dam is not founded completely on bedrock, leakage may occur through gravel beneath the dam; in contrast, rock bars extending across the valley may make a very suitable base for a dam, as for example in the case of the Vyrnwy Reservoir dam in Wales (Deacon 1896). The largest tunnel valleys are those formed during the Elsterian glaciation in areas south of the Baltic Sea (Ehlers *et al.* 1984); these extend to a maximum depth of 434 m below sea level in areas of soft Tertiary bedrock, and many are several kilometres wide.

Because of glacial reversal of drainage, the bedrock surface beneath a river valley may slope in the opposite direction to the present land surface. Philbrick (1976) described an example of this, which led to advantageous resiting of the Kinzua Dam on the Allegheny River in north-west Pennsylvania, USA. Another problem with dams resulting from glaciation is the smoothing of bedrock surfaces by ice erosion. A concrete dam will often require special bonding to such a surface, either by roughening of the rock or by anchoring with rock bolts; otherwise the concrete may slide over the surface.

When digging open excavations, cost considerations demand that the minimum material is removed, and this means cutting side slopes as steeply as possible consistent with safety. Known angles of repose for different materials have often been relied upon too closely in these circumstances, leading to later collapse of some cut slopes or unnecessary removal of material from others. With clayey deposits especially, the extent of compaction, natural moisture content, particle size distribution and mineralogical composition are all critical, and may be measured in the laboratory. However, heterogeneity and discontinuities, such as laminae of different composition, old slip planes or fissures produced by various periglacial disturbances (Morgan 1971), can override these factors in determining slope stability. Many of these features result from Quaternary processes and can be identified if an experienced Quaternary geologist examines the freshly cut slope. For example, uniform compact clayey lodgement till is stable, even on a fairly steep slope, provided its original moisture content is maintained, but thin layers of waterlain sediments, extensive erratic rafts of soft preglacial sediment, sand wedge casts or gently inclined shear planes can all become slip surfaces down which the sides of an excavation may slump. Another interesting example is the slip surfaces in Clay-with-flints, the paleo-argillic 'residual soil' formed in a thin veneer of basal Tertiary sediment overlying the Chalk of southern England (see 3.4). These surfaces have formed in the weathered clay either by deep periglacial disturbance (cryoturbation) or by earlier subsurface slumping into solution hollows formed in the chalk beneath; their presence is usually quite obvious because the normally reddish-brown clay is gleyed and pale grey adjacent to the fissure, and the surface itself is slickensided and shiny with clay oriented either by stress during movement or by illuvial deposition from water percolating down the fissure.

Civil engineering operations offshore, such as the siting of drilling rigs, laying of pipelines, erection of barrages or digging of tunnels, also require information about the distribution and geotechnical properties of Quaternary deposits. In many shallow seas the Quaternary succession is similar to that on adjacent land areas, because sea level was depressed eustatically at the time of deposition and what is now sea floor was then an extension of the land. However, such successions may have been truncated or reworked by marine erosion during the subsequent rise of sea level, and are often covered by a variable thickness of recent marine sediments. Also, compared with equivalent deposits on land, the compressibility of Quaternary sediments beneath the sea floor is often high, especially where biogenic gas is present. In deeper water, soft glaciomarine sediments often predominate; when disturbed, these are prone to slip on the steep slopes at the edge of the continental shelf. Various geophysical methods (see 6.2.6) can be used to map the distribution of major units on the sea floor, though samples from boreholes are usually required to determine the precise nature and geotechnical properties of the deposits. As biogenic gas strongly affects the velocity of seismic P waves but hardly influences S waves, the ratio of the two seismic velocities can be used to estimate the amount of gas present (Smith 1987).

7.4.3 Influence of Quaternary features on siting of roads, railways and airports

The most suitable routes for roads and railways and the best sites for airports are often determined by Quaternary features. This may have greater importance in large or underdeveloped countries than in small, densely populated countries such as Britain, where the choice of routes or sites for new engineering work is often constrained by existing settlements and lines of communication, or by the ownership of land. But even here an appreciation of Quaternary events can often help the civil engineer make minor modifications to routes, sites or the design of structures, which will save unnecessary expenditure and avoid problems in subsequent use.

In many glaciated areas (e.g. Canada), roads and railways are often best routed along gravel ridges such as eskers (Legget and Karrow 1983). These are usually better drained than intervening land underlain by muskeg (peat) or impermeable clays, and also provide a ready supply of aggregate for surfacing, manufacture of concrete or railway ballast. Other areas to be avoided if possible in choosing routes for roads and railways include active sand dunes, river floodplains, avalanche scars, landslips, debris flows, karst and terrain close to wet-based glaciers, the last mainly because of jökulhlaups. However, some problems can be overcome by engineering ingenuity, such as the former Steffenbach Bridge on the Furke–Oberalp railway in Switzerland, which crossed a prominent alpine avalanche scar, and in winter could be folded out of the way of the frequent avalanches.

Airfields require large, flat, well-drained areas close to the cities they are to serve. The best sites are often till plains (e.g. Mirabel Airport, Montreal) or extensive river terraces (e.g. Heathrow Airport, London), though many other landscape types can be made suitable by a small amount of levelling and the installation of an efficient drainage system to carry away the large amounts of runoff from runways and other extensive covered areas. Often the civil engineer can use Quaternary features to advantage; for example, at Bowling Green Airport in Kentucky, USA, the surface is efficiently drained by disposal of runoff into the underlying limestone through natural sinkholes.

7.5 INFLUENCE OF QUATERNARY EVENTS ON AGRICULTURE AND FORESTRY

To grow successfully and profitably, agricultural crops and trees require a climate providing adequate warmth and moisture, and an adequate depth of soil suitable for root penetration, which provides both physical support and supplies of water and nutrients. Climatic influences are best discussed in terms of the prediction of future trends of climatic change (see 7.8). Soil properties influencing plant growth often result from past Quaternary events, including processes of deposition, erosion and soil disturbance *in situ*, though many have been modified by human activities such as soil cultivation and application of natural or artificial fertilizers.

7.5.1 Influence of the Quaternary on soil properties

As explained in 3.3 and 6.4, for the production of general-purpose maps useful in agriculture, silviculture and other applied fields, soils are usually classified on the basis of profile characteristics. These characteristics are usually some combination of properties inherited from the parent material or materials and imposed by pedological processes (weathering, leaching, illuviation, gleying) acting in various environmental conditions and for various lengths of time in the geologically recent past. Because of the widespread occurrence of Quaternary deposits on present land surfaces and the relative stability of large parts of such surfaces for much of the Quaternary, both of these groups of soil-determining factors reflect Quaternary history. Even in areas where the soil parent material is purely pre-Quaternary, Quaternary history is important because the pedological processes have usually been influenced by environmental changes related directly or indirectly to Quaternary climatic changes, and the very absence of Quaternary deposits is probably the result of Quaternary erosion processes.

The depth of soil that can be exploited by plant roots may be limited by the occurrence of hard, poorly fissured bedrock close to the surface or by soil horizons (e.g. ironpans or fragipans) made compact and impenetrable by pedological processes. In many mid- and high-latitude upland areas, where there was little weathering of bedrock even during warmer and wetter Quaternary periods and glacial or slope erosion was widespread, the depth of exploitable soil equates almost exactly with the depth of Quaternary deposits. However, some of the most compact Quaternary deposits, such as lodgement tills and gelifluction deposits, can be difficult for roots to penetrate. Soil pans formed by frost action (Cx horizons) or cementation with redeposited iron, alumina, silica, carbonate or humus (Cm horizons) are often totally impenetrable, and are frequently a cause of poor growth or wind-throw in forest plantations. However, deeper root penetration can be encouraged by deep cultivation techniques (subsoiling).

Particle size distribution is the most important individual soil property, because it determines the retention and release of water and plant nutrients, and the strength, trafficability and ease of cultivation of the soil. Outside the tropics, pedological processes such as weathering and clay illuviation usually have only a small effect on particle size distribution, and in most profiles it is determined principally by the nature and sequence of Quaternary deposits. Clay-rich deposits, such as boulder clays, lacustrine and fine alluvial sediments, give soils which are waterlogged in wet seasons, and therefore prone to compaction, structural deterioration, plough-pan formation and lack of aeration if cultivated with heavy machinery. Also, as water drains away slowly, timing of cultivations is difficult because the periods when soil moisture content is low enough are much shorter than with better drained soils. In contrast, sandy soils formed on glaciofluvial deposits, coversands or other coarse Quaternary sediments are easy to cultivate and do not suffer from waterlogging and an anaerobic root environment (unless they are subject to a high groundwater table), but are instead prone to drought conditions in dry seasons, loss of nitrogen and other soluble plant nutrients by leaching, disaggregation leading to formation of a hard surface capping which prevents growth of seedlings, and erosion by wind and water (see 2.4.1).

Loamy soils, such as the silty horizons derived wholly or mainly from loess, possess the good aspects of sandy soils (good drainage and aeration, ease of cultivation) and have an ideal particle size distribution and structure for retention of water against gravity, easy root penetration into as well as between aggregates (peds), and uptake of water and nutrients. Crops in loess and other silty soils thus grow better, respond more readily to applied fertilizers, and survive drought better. Loess soils are regarded as the most fertile soils in many parts of the world (Chesworth 1982); for example, in Britain they give greater yields of winter wheat than any other soil types (Fig. 7.7). However, loess soils often suffer from structural breakdown under heavy rain, and this can lead to formation of a surface capping and to severe erosion by runoff (Boardman and Hazelden 1986). In many areas (e.g. Guernsey, Channel Islands) the problems of surface capping and erosion of loess soils are avoided by extensive cultivation under glass.

Even soils in thin loess (30–100 cm) over hard rock, sand or clay are known to perform slightly better in agriculture and horticulture than soils in the same substrata but without a loess cover. This has led to the suggestion that it may be profitable to remove loess from areas where thick deposits are about to be sterilized by industrial development, airports, etc., and spread it thinly over nearby loess-free farmland or reclaimed land (Catt 1978). In Iowa, USA, Drake and Ririe (1981) showed that opencast coal mine sites can be profitably reclaimed for corn-growing by spreading loess in this way.

The accumulation of illuvial clay as argillans filling or partially filling the voids in

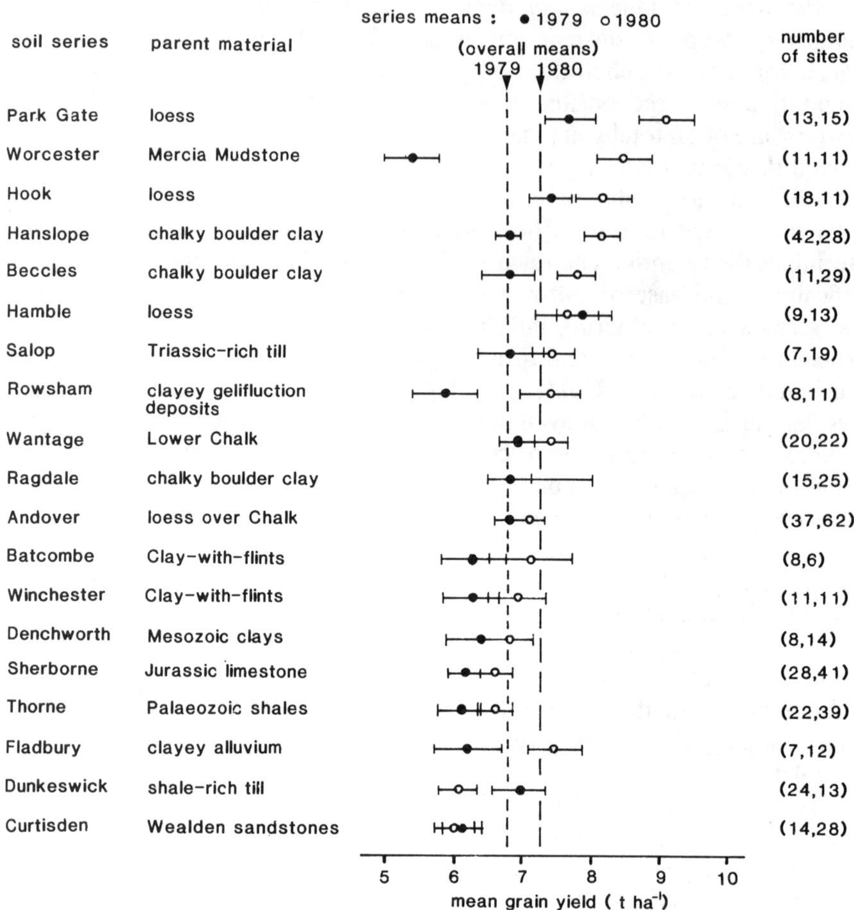

Fig. 7.7 — British yields of winter wheat for 1979 and 1980 in relation to soil parent materials (from Weir *et al.* 1984).

argillic (Bt) horizons can restrict root penetration and impede profile drainage, though not as drastically as an ironpan or fragipan. In many mid-latitude regions the effect of argillic horizons on plant growth is scarcely detectable, however. This is probably because the most extensive argillans, formed in interglacial periods, were subsequently disrupted, especially by cryoturbation in cold periods, thus conferring a fresh structure and better drainage on the B horizon.

Many soils formed in glacial and periglacial deposits have significantly larger natural reserves of mineral nutrients (K, Ca, Mg and many trace elements) than soils in pre-Quaternary sediments. This is because the glacial and periglacial sediments contain much material derived directly from crystalline igneous and metamorphic rocks, which were weathered physically, often to form very fine particles, but were not weathered chemically. Most pre-Quaternary sediments are composed instead of minerals derived from soils which were chemically weathered and leached for long periods in generally warmer conditions than prevailed for most of the Quaternary.

By dispersing fresh, unweathered minerals in the form of glacial deposits and periglacial loess, Quaternary cold periods had an important rejuvenating effect on soils, especially in mid-latitude regions. Further soil rejuvenation resulted from wholesale removal of strongly weathered mantles by glacial erosion, gelifluction, etc., and from extensive mixing of less weathered subsoil material with surface horizons by cryoturbation. The possible effects of this rejuvenation on evolution of plants and animals (perhaps including man) are interesting if somewhat speculative. For example, Russell (1973) suggested that it could account for the different pH requirements of typical temperate and tropical crops; most temperate crops yield best at soil pH values >6.5 because their wild ancestors had adapted to the rejuvenated, base-rich, neutral or alkaline Quaternary soils of mid-latitude regions, whereas tropical crops yield best in the slightly acid residual soils (pH 5.0–5.5) that have persisted in low latitudes for long periods, often since the mid-Tertiary.

Patterns of short-range soil variation (e.g. within a single field) can result from several Quaternary processes, and often cause considerable variation in crop yield (Evans and Catt 1987). A good farmer can usually modify soil and crop management techniques to obtain optimum production from different soil types, but only if the individual soils form areas larger than a single field. If the different soil types occupy small, intricately-shaped areas within a field, differential management is difficult or impossible with existing machinery; the farmer then has the choice of (a) management that is suited to only one of the two or more soils present, or (b) treatment that is a compromise between them. Either can result in significant loss of yield and inefficient use of land. Short-range soil variation leading to this type of problem in agriculture and forestry can result from periglacial soil disturbance (e.g. relict ice wedge polygons, Fig. 2.50), karstic disturbance, irregular deposition of colluvium, alluvium, various types of glacial sediment or coversand (e.g. in dunes), and archaeological features (e.g. ditches or foundations of old buildings). The extent of yield limitation depends on the type and density of the soil variation pattern; cyclic patterns, such as polygons or stripes, have a more predictable effect on crop yield than non-cyclic variation, such as kettle holes, dolines, gulls, burial mounds and lynchets (Catt 1986, p. 230).

7.6 HYDROGEOLOGICAL FEATURES OF THE QUATERNARY

Quaternary strata are utilized extensively as aquifers in many parts of the world (USA, Canada, Australia, Scandinavia, the Netherlands), but in Britain they are now quite unimportant. This difference reflects the availability of suitable bedrock aquifers and the greater possibility of pollution of near-surface groundwater, especially in unconfined aquifers, in densely populated or industrialized areas. In Britain, for example, numerous small private water supplies were previously drawn from Quaternary deposits such as river terrace gravels, but many have become progressively more polluted, and as a result the public supplies are now taken either from surface reservoirs or from the larger and deeper bedrock aquifers in southeastern parts of the country. Countries strongly dependent upon Quaternary sources of groundwater usually have bedrock supplies which are small or difficult to extract (e.g. in hard crystalline bedrock of low porosity), or they are sparsely populated and have little industrial or agricultural pollution.

In the USA more groundwater used to be extracted from coarse Quaternary strata than all other aquifers combined (Johnson 1966), but as in Britain the proportion has recently declined because of surface pollution. In the Netherlands almost all the groundwater is extracted from the Quaternary deposits, which are very thick because of continuing subsidence of the North Sea basin throughout the Quaternary; however, increasing care is necessary again to avoid pollution from the surface, and also to avoid over-pumping near the coast, which can lead to saline intrusion.

Where Quaternary aquifers are in use, knowledge of Quaternary stratigraphy and geological history is often important for assessing the size and likely quality of groundwater resources (Meneley 1970, Sauer and Beckie 1975). The lithology and geometry of aquifers and intervening aquicludes or aquitards indicate the approximate volume of each groundwater resource and the magnitude and direction of groundwater flows. Both glacial and fluvial deposits are important aquifers in many parts of the world, but their variability of particle size distribution causes great heterogeneity in hydraulic properties, such as porosity and hydraulic conductivity. For example, the architecture of alluvium deposited by single-channel streams, with fine-grained channel-fill and overbank deposits, may lead to variations of 2–3 orders of magnitude in hydraulic conductivity. In such deposits horizontal conductivity often exceeds vertical conductivity by 2–10 times because the beds are laterally continuous but there are many rapid vertical changes in composition. In contrast, aeolian deposits are usually more homogeneous and also more porous and permeable. Aeolian sands commonly have porosities of 30–45% and hydraulic conductivities as high as 10^{-4} m s^{-1}. Loess has a lower conductivity (10^{-5} to 10^{-7} m s^{-1}, or even less in clayey loess), but the buried soils that commonly occur in thick loess sequences are often zones of secondarily increased vertical permeability (McGary and Lambert 1962).

Many tills are aquitards rather than aquicludes because of fissures and pockets or lenses of glaciofluvial sediment. Their resistance to flow (e.g. from an aquifer above the till to another below) depends upon the abundance of these features and the total thickness of the till unit, which are in turn dependent upon the depositional regime of the parent glacier and the post-depositional history of the till (e.g. depth of weathering). Whereas unweathered clay-rich lodgement tills have hydraulic conductivities of 10^{-10} to 10^{-12} m s^{-1}, those of weathered, fissured tills may be as large as 10^{-7} m s^{-1} (Williams and Farvolden 1969, Grisak and Cherry 1975). The largest Quaternary groundwater resources are often from buried valleys, such as the large gravel-filled tunnel valleys (Freeze and Cherry 1979).

Apart from the strong possibility of surface pollution, the main problem with the quality of shallow groundwater from unconfined Quaternary aquifers is the presence of iron and manganese in solution. These are derived from soil horizons where acidity and strongly reducing conditions resulting from the presence of organic matter cause both elements to dissolve. On exposure to the atmosphere they are oxidized to insoluble compounds, often assisted by filamentous bacteria such as *Leptothrix, Crenothrix, Clonothrix* and *Gallionella*. The resulting precipitates discolour the water and may encrust well screens or block pipes and taps.

The removal of undesirable constituents, such as nitrate, chloride and bacteria,

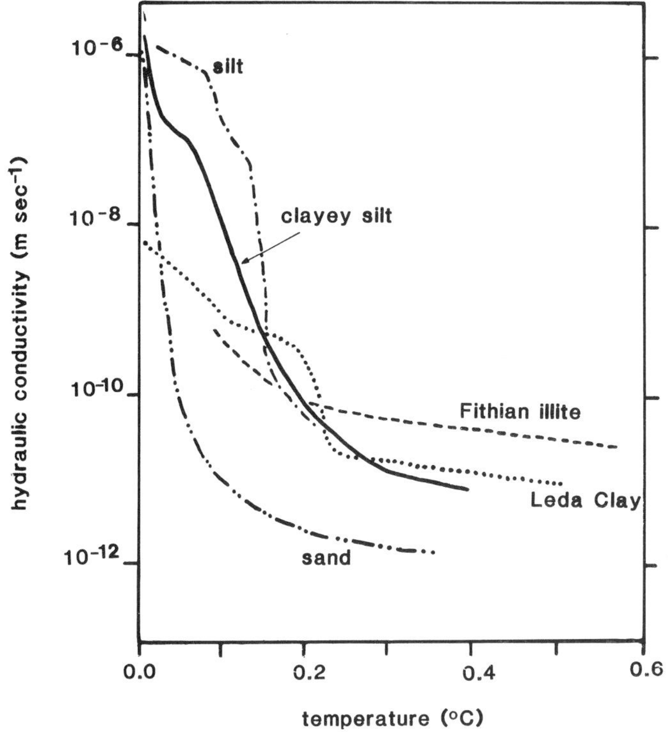

Fig. 7.8 — Relationship between hydraulic conductivity and temperature in frozen sediments of various particle size distributions (from Burt and Williams 1976). Reproduced by permission of J. Wiley & Sons.

from groundwater depends upon slow percolation through the unsaturated zone. Even rapidly permeable Quaternary deposits are effective in removing these constituents, but groundwater in karst regions often remains contaminated by sewage, fertilizer or runoff from farmyards because of rapid flow through large solution cavities (Driscoll 1986).

As many glacial sediments contain easily weathered minerals or even soluble salts derived perhaps from evaporite deposits up-glacier, groundwater from glacial aquifers may be saline (Spears and Reeves 1975), especially if the stratigraphy and structure of the deposits result in long groundwater flowpaths. The more soluble constituents are likely to be concentrated in tills rather than waterlain deposits such as glaciofluvial gravels, but as groundwater is drawn from an intertill or subtill gravel, recharge may occur by downward flow through the overlying till aquitard, and lead to an increase in salinity as pumping continues. In North America natural groundwaters from glacial deposits are placed in one of the following three categories of composition (Freeze and Cherry 1979, pp. 284–286:

(1) Slightly acidic, soft, fresh water (<100 mg l^{-1} total dissolved solids), in which Na, Ca and Mg are dominant cations and HCO_3 is the main anion.
(2) Slightly alkaline, hard, fairly fresh water (<1000 mg l^{-1} total dissolved solids), in which Ca, Mg and HCO_3 are the main ions.

(3) Slightly alkaline, brackish water (1000–10 000 mg l^{-1} total dissolved solids), in which Na, Mg, Ca, HCO_3 and SO_4 are all abundant, though SO_4 is often the dominant anion.

The first type occurs mainly in glacial deposits derived from igneous and metamorphic rocks, and the second in calcareous glacial deposits subject to carbonate dissolution; both are suitable for human consumption or agricultural use (e.g. irrigation). Type (3) groundwaters are produced by dissolution of carbonates, gypsum (often originating from oxidation of sulphides such as pyrite, and reaction of the resulting sulphuric acid with calcium carbonate), anhydrite and halite, followed by exchange of Ca^{2+} for Na^+ and Mg^{2+} on smectitic clays in the tills. They are often unsuitable for either consumption or irrigation. Examples are known mainly from the Great Plains of Saskatchewan and Manitoba in Canada (Cherry 1972, Grisak *et al.* 1976).

Many high permeability deposits are transformed into aquitards or even aquicludes with very low hydraulic conductivities when they are influenced by permafrost. The effect is greatest in coarse deposits such as sand, which show a rapid decrease in hydraulic conductivity at only a few tenths of a degree below 0°C. In contrast, some clays show only a small change on freezing, and may even remain more permeable than frozen sand (Fig. 7.8). In regions of discontinuous permafrost, low-permeability permafrost zones are often restricted to areas such as valley floors where the water-table is fairly close to the ground surface. Unfrozen aquifers beneath the permafrost may be recharged by flow through unsaturated deposits on the valley sides, and because of confinement by the permafrost are often under pressure, so that the water in wells penetrating the permafrost rises to or even above the ground surface (Williams 1970).

7.7 SEA-LEVEL CHANGES

Although the eustatic rise of sea level resulting from melting of the Devensian ice sheets had virtually ceased before about 3500 years ago, slow changes still occur in many areas as a result of glacio-isostatic rebound, tectonic movements in the earth's crust, climatic fluctuations, changes in the geoid, and other factors (see 2.10). The effects of these are economically important mainly in densely populated areas close to sea level, where flooding can cause extensive damage and loss of life. Because several different factors are involved in determining sea level at any particular place, accurate prediction of future trends even over the next few decades is impossible. Decisions relating to coast protection works are usually based on extrapolation from past trends, derived either from tidal records during the last century or so, or from geological evidence for changes over the last few thousand years, but both methods are unlikely to give very accurate predictions. The geological approach depends upon dating peat beds, shell banks, archaeological and other organic remains by ^{14}C assay, and estimating their height above or below sea level at the time of deposition (Tooley 1978). However, there are various difficulties involved in calculating mean sea level at any particular time, even if the dating is completely satisfactory (Kidson 1982). Perhaps the most important factor likely to influence future sea-level trends is the increase in atmospheric CO_2, which may cause a rapid eustatic rise by warming polar regions and accelerating the melting of polar ice caps (see 7.8).

Fig. 7.9 — The Thames Barrier, looking upstream towards central London with gates open: flood defence embankment seen to left.

A typical area in which prediction of future sea-level changes is very important is the Thames Estuary, because 116 km^2 of central London with a population of 700 000 and about 250 000 buildings now lie below the highest water level recently reached by the river, and the cost of flooding was estimated in 1984 to be between £3000 and £4000 million (Horner 1984). The main danger of flooding arises from storm surges in the North Sea. These are associated with occasional Atlantic depressions which take a more southerly course than usual. The decreased air pressure in a depression allows the sea surface to rise by 10 mm for every millibar drop in pressure. The maximum height of this water hump is about 300 mm, though it can increase if the centre of the depression passes over shallow water. The hump associated with a depression passing south of the usual course between Iceland and Scandinavia is driven by northerly winds into the funnel-shaped confines of the southern North Sea. The Straits of Dover are too shallow to allow much of this water to pass, and the Coriolis effect forces it westwards onto the English coast. If this coincides with high tide, it can raise the predicted water level at Southend, near the mouth of the Thames Estuary, by 4 m; at London Bridge the increase in water level is approximately 2.5 m.

Measured tide levels at Southend and London Bridge have recently risen by mean values of 340 mm and 700 mm per century respectively (Rossiter 1972). These changes are attributed mainly to irregular tectonic subsidence of the southern North Sea region, and agree approximately with geological estimates of the rate of subsidence of the Thames Estuary over much longer periods (Devoy 1979, Greensmith and Tucker 1980). In addition, much of the Thames floodplain beneath London is sinking by small but irregular amounts through peat wastage and desiccation of clayey alluvium. To protect the low-lying parts of the city in the light of these adverse trends, a mobile barrier was built across the river at Woolwich Reach (Fig. 7.9) and 110 kilometres of flood defences were constructed downstream. The work, completed in 1982, was designed to withstand a 1000-year return period high water up to the year 2030 A.D. When closed, the gates of the barrier, 31 m and 61 m wide, can support a water-level difference of 9.9 m. Geological evidence of Holocene sea-level changes in the area provided valuable background information for decisions relating to the construction of these sea defences.

7.8 FUTURE CLIMATIC CHANGES

In recent years a growing body of evidence from both land and the ocean depths has shown that the history of climatic change during the last few million years was extremely complex. In addition to the numerous major cold and warm stages indicated by the oceanic oxygen isotope record, palaeontological and palaeopedological studies at numerous land-based sites have shown that subsidiary but still quite large oscillations of temperature and humidity were superimposed on the curve of major changes. During major cold stages the subsidiary oscillations gave rise to colder stadials and warmer interstadials, either of which may have lasted from a few centuries to many thousands of years. The climatic record of warm interglacial stages usually seems more stable, but the details for the present interglacial (the Holocene) resolved in terrestrial successions suggest that even interglacial climatic stability is something of an illusion. This becomes even more clear when various lines of historical evidence for climatic change are considered (Lamb 1977). Meteorological records, variations in glacier margins and lake levels, and much documentary evidence of past weather conditions all indicate that significant climatic changes have occurred over the last 1000 years or so. In particular, the period 1550–1850 A.D. (the 'Little Ice Age') was distinctly colder than either preceding centuries or the period since.

There is every reason to suppose that climatic changes on all these time scales (10^2–10^5 approximately) will continue in the future, but the question of when changes will occur is usually difficult to decide. As the major changes leading to the cold and warm stages recognized in deep ocean sediments have been to a large extent forced by the orbital cycles (Hays *et al.* 1976), their future occurrence can be predicted with some certainty from astronomical constants. This indicates that declining radiation will bring cooler conditions leading to a temperature minimum possibly as soon as 4000 years hence (Kukla 1975), though the severity of this episode is uncertain. However, long-term prediction of this type is probably more of academic interest than practical value.

The factors controlling shorter-term climatic changes such as the 'Little Ice Age' are less certain (see 1.3), though it would be very useful to know when these changes might occur, because they could have devastating economic effects. For example, the fall in mean annual air temperature of 1–2°C during the 'Little Ice Age' probably shortened the crop growing season in central England by as much as one month compared with the present (Lamb 1977); this led to manifold increases in the price of wheat and frequent famines, especially between A.D. 1550 and 1600–50. Manley (1957) calculated the accumulated month-degrees below 13.4°C each year since A.D. 1698 for central England, to indicate changes in fuel demand for indoor heating; the increase in annual demand was approximately 100% between the coldest and warmest years, and the demand of the coldest-decade in this period was 20% greater than that of the warmest. This suggests that a return to Little Ice Age conditions would increase the cost of heating modern buildings in Britain by approximately £1 000 000 000 per year at present prices. However, according to Bray (1971), the next cold period equivalent to the 'Little Ice Age' will not reach its climax until about A.D. 3500. Lamb (1977) suggested that "the present tendency of the natural climate is towards a further, but fluctuating, cooling and no likely recovery of the temperature levels prevailing in 1930–55 until around 2100 A.D". From a consideration of the past effects of the 18.6-year lunar nodal tide cycle and the 11-year solar sunspot cycle on droughts and floods in the history of China and other areas. Currie and Fairbridge (1985) suggested that the interior of N. America will experience a prolonged drought in late A.D. 1991 and that north-east China will have a drought in early A.D. 2001.

As we are now approaching the end of an interglacial, some Quaternary geologists have sought to draw a parallel with the close of the last interglacial (oceanic stage 5e). This warm stage lasted about as long as the Holocene has already, and seems to have passed very rapidly into the next cold stage (5d) recognizable in the deep-sea cores (Kukla 1980). According to Woillard (1979), the 5e/5d transition in the sequence at Grand Pile peat bog in the Vosges Mountains, where sampling across this boundary was more detailed than elsewhere, took only 150±75 yr. This rapid change was questioned by Holyoak (1986), but the transition was apparently as rapid (<100 yr) in a marine sequence at Skaerumhede, Denmark (Bahnson *et al.* 1973), and almost as quick in the loess record of central Europe (Kukla and Kocí 1972). Also most warm stages in the oceanic sequence seem to have ended very abruptly (the 'terminations' of Broecker and Van Donk 1970). So it is possible that when the Holocene 'interglacial' does end, very cold tundra-like conditions far worse than the 'Little Ice Age' could appear within a few decades.

In view of the known decreases in atmospheric carbon dioxide during cold stages of the Quaternary, and the increases at the beginning of the last interglacial and of the Holocene (see 1.3), many scientists now believe that climatic change over the next few decades will be influenced mainly by the presently increasing levels of atmospheric carbon dioxide. The carbon dioxide increase has resulted mainly from the burning of increasing amounts of wood and fossil fuels, but in addition the destruction of forest for timber and creation of agricultural land, especially in tropical areas, has decreased the rate at which CO_2 is removed from the atmosphere to form plant tissue by photosynthesis. Further warming may also arise from increases in other trace gases in the atmosphere, including methane, produced in the increasingly extensive anaerobic soils of rice paddies, nitrous oxide from car exhausts, and chlorofluorocarbons released from aerosol cans, refrigerators and polystyrene products. All these compound gases warm the atmosphere by absorbing more infrared radiation than elemental gases such as nitrogen and oxygen.

During the last two main cold stages of the Quaternary, the carbon dioxide content of the atmosphere, as indicated by analysis of air bubbles in ice cores (see 1.3), was between 190 and 210 parts per million (ppm) by volume. It had increased to a maximum of 296 ppm by the beginning of the last interglacial and to approximately 260 ppm in the early Holocene (Barnola *et al.* 1987). The concentration today is

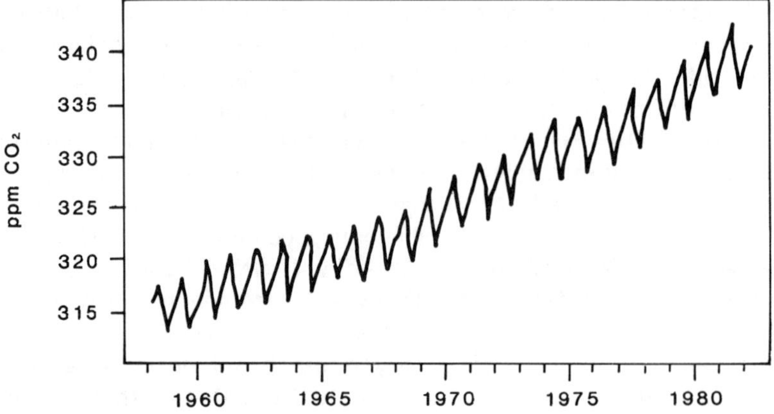

Fig. 7.10 — Concentration of atmospheric carbon dioxide at Mauna Loa Observatory, Hawaii, 1958–1982 (from Keeling *et al.* 1982). The annual variation results from seasonal changes in photosynthesis.

340–350 ppm, having increased from a pre-industrial (early nineteenth century) level of 260–280 ppm (Chen and Drake 1986); the average yearly increment between 1958 and 1982 at Mauna Loa in Hawaii was 1.14 ppm (Keeling *et al.* 1982) (Fig. 7.10). Continuation of this rate of increase will lead to doubling of the pre-industrial level by some time between A.D. 2050 and 2100.

The effects of this magnitude of carbon dioxide increase have been predicted by various mathematical climate models (Schlesinger 1983). All of these suffer from uncertainties, such as the rate at which the oceans remove carbon dioxide from the atmosphere and the response of biota to increased atmospheric carbon dioxide, but most agree that a doubling will lead to a mean increase of approximately 4°C in worldwide temperatures. This would be little less than the warming at the end of the last glaciation (5–6°C), though that was over a much longer period (at least 400 years). However, the predicted temperature increase will not be geographically uniform: according to some models, it will be as much as 10°C in high latitudes but less than 1°C in the tropics, and warming will be greatest in winter, except perhaps in Antarctica. Flohn (1981) suggested that this type of warming would lead initially to disappearance of the thin arctic sea-ice cover, which is more sensitive to climatic change than the large Antarctic ice sheet, and that the resulting unipolar glacial condition would shift the climatic zones considerable distances, to produce warm dry regions around latitudes 10°S and 40°N but increased precipitation between 10 and 20°N and north of 50°N. However, changes in the distribution of rainfall are more difficult to predict than changes of temperature.

Seidel and Keyes (1983) examined the effects of various suggested energy policies for delaying the warming that will probably result from a doubling of atmospheric carbon dioxide. They concluded that a worldwide ban on coal burning by A.D. 2000 would delay a 2°C increase until A.D. 2055 and a 3.5°C increase until A.D. 2100, but recognized that such a ban is economically and politically impossible. Other measures would have smaller effects, delaying the temperature rise by only a decade or so. Most of the uncertainties in their assessment arose from the unknown effects of other trace gases in the atmosphere, especially chlorofluorocarbon compounds, though it is unlikely that a ban on their use will have much delaying effect because they persist in the atmosphere for at least 100 years. Other possible methods of decreasing atmospheric carbon dioxide, such as scrubbing emissions, have been discussed by Marchetti (1977), Hoffert *et al.* (1979), Baes *et al.* (1980), Feely and Chen (1982), and Horn and Steinberg (1982), but all such proposals seem to be difficult, ineffective or prohibitively expensive.

Mercer (1978) suggested that the warming resulting from a doubling of atmospheric carbon dioxide content would melt much of the West Antarctic ice sheet as well as the arctic sea-ice cover. This would raise sea level by 4–6 metres (Kellogg 1979, Hansen *et al.* 1981), though Bentley (1983) suggested that disintegration of the ice sheet would take at least 500 years. A sea-level rise of this magnitude would flood many densely inhabited low-lying regions, such as the Netherlands, parts of south-eastern USA, and several major cities alongside estuaries, though centres of population could probably be moved gradually to higher ground if the rate of rise were slow.

Changes in the distribution of rainfall as a result of the increased global temperature in the twenty-first century could lead to further social and economic problems, because important agricultural regions, such as northern USA, would become too arid to support their present levels of crop production. Also rivers in regions receiving increased rainfall, such as the Brahmaputra, Mekong, Niger, Volta and Blue Nile, would be subject to disastrous floods (Revelle 1982). Although the climatic changes will probably come gradually, natural variations could lead to major floods or crop losses in certain years early in the twenty-first century, and these may create economic problems for some nations. Recent desertification in parts of Africa may even be the first result of twentieth century increases in atmospheric trace gases.

To some extent the increased carbon dioxide content of the atmosphere may stimulate photosynthesis and thus increase yields of some crops in areas receiving sufficient rain. Wheat and rice would probably respond more strongly in this way than maize and other crops, because of the different types of photosynthetic processes involved. Higher carbon dioxide levels may also decrease transpiration by some species, allowing them to survive the summer dryness better than others. However, some crops may be less nutritious because they may contain less protein, and others may be stunted by the competition from increased growth of weeds. Breeding of new varieties by genetic engineering may enable crops to adapt to changes in both rainfall and atmospheric composition, but the effect on wildlife which has less capacity to adapt, could be much greater.

At present the various predictions for future climate are based on fairly crude assumptions, and consequently do not give a clear coherent picture; in particular, the effect of increased trace gases in the atmosphere is likely to oppose the longer-term cooling related to orbital perturbations. However, many important industries (agriculture, forestry, fuel and power, fisheries, civil engineering, water supply, waste disposal, tourism and insurance) have a considerable interest in the timing and magnitude of future climatic changes. The impact of changes could also be intensely political, because national and international order depends upon many of the economic factors that would be affected. A clearer picture will undoubtedly emerge from continuing efforts to understand and model the dynamics of atmosphere–ocean interactions and the effects of atmospheric pollution. But it is also important to reconstruct past changes in more detail, starting with those based on instrumental records of the last few centuries, and then moving back in time to changes inferred from historical, archaeological, geological, palaeontological and palaeopedological features. These provide evidence for the pattern of natural climatic changes that would have occurred in the future without atmospheric pollution (i.e. the moving baseline against which to judge the effects of pollution). Also, if past changes of a type comparable to those expected in the next century or so can be identified, they may indicate the likely effects of the future changes on wildlife. This is probably the best economic justification for continuing research aimed at increasingly precise reconstruction and dating of past events during the Quaternary.

References

Aario, R. 1977. Classification and terminology of morainic landforms in Finland. *Boreas* **6**, 87–100.

Abrahamsen, N. and Knudsen, K. L. 1979. Indications of a geomagnetic low-inclination excursion in supposed middle Weichselian interstadial marine clay at Rubjerg, Denmark. *Phys. Earth Planet. Inter.* **18**, 238–246.

Abrahamsen, N. and Readman, P. W. 1980. Geomagnetic variations recorded in older (≥23 000 b.p.) and younger Yoldia Clay (~14 000 b.p.) at Norre Lyngby, Denmark. *Geophys. J. Roy. Astron. Soc.* **62**, 345–366.

Abrams, M. J., Ashley, R. P., Rowan, L. C., Goetz, A. F. H. and Kahle, A. B. 1977. Mapping of hydrothermal alteration in the Cuprite mining district, Nevada, using aircraft scanner images for the spectral region 0.46 to 2.36 μm. *Geology* **5**, 713–718.

Adams, G. F. (ed.) 1975. *Planation surfaces, peneplains, pediplains and etchplains.* Dowden, Hutchinson and Ross, Stroudsburg.

Adams, R. E. W., Brown, W. E. and Culbert, J. P. 1981. Radar mapping, archaeology and ancient Maya land use. *Science* **213**, 1457–1463.

Aguirre, E. and Pasini, G. 1985. The Plio–Pleistocene boundary. *Episodes* **8**, 116–120.

Ahlmann, H. W. 1948. Glaciological research on the north Atlantic coasts. *Roy. Geogr. Soc. Res. Ser.* **1**, 1–83.

Åhman, R. 1976. The structure and morphology of minerogenic palsas in northern Norway. *Biul. Perygl.* **26**, 25–31.

Alexander, R. W., Coxon, P. and Thorn, R. H. 1986. A bog flow at Straduff Townland, County Sligo. *Proc. Roy. Irish Acad.* **B86**, 107–119.

Allen, J. R. L. 1965. A review of the origin and characteristics of recent alluvial sediments. *Sedimentology* **5**, 89–191.

Allen, J. R. L. 1970. *Physical processes in sedimentation.* George Allen and Unwin, London.

Allen, J. R. L. 1978. Studies in fluviatile sedimentation: an exploratory quantitative model for the architecture of avulsion controlled alluvial suites. *Sedim. Geol.* **21**, 129–147.

Allen, J. R. L. 1983. River bedforms: progress and problems, pp. 19–33 in: *Modern and ancient fluvial systems* (eds. J. D. Collinson and J. Lewin). International Association of Sedimentologists Special Publication 6. Blackwell, Oxford.

Allen, P. A. and Collinson, J. D. 1986. Lakes, pp. 63–94 in: *Sedimentary environments and facies* (ed. H. G. Reading), 2nd edition. Blackwell, Oxford.

Allen, T. 1981. *Particle size measurement.* 3rd edition. Chapman and Hall, London.

American Commission on Stratigraphic Nomenclature 1961. Code of stratigraphic nomenclature. *Bull. Amer. Assoc. Petrol. Geol.* **45**, 645–665.

American Commission on Stratigraphic Nomenclature 1970. *Code of stratigraphic nomenclature.* 2nd edition. American Association of Petroleum Geologists, Tulsa.

American Society of Photogrammetry 1968. *Manual of colour aerial photography.* American Society of Photogrammetry, Falls Church.

Andersen, S. T. 1966. Interglacial vegetational succession and lake development in Denmark. *Palaeobotanist* **15**, 117–127.

Andersen, S. T. 1979. Brown earth and podzol: soil genesis illuminated by microfossil analysis. *Boreas* **8**, 59–73.

Anderson, R. Y. 1984. Orbital forcing of evaporite sedimentation, pp. 147–162 in: *Milankovitch and climate Part 1* (eds. A. Berger, J. Imbrie, J. Hays, G. Kukla and B. Saltzman). NATO ASI Series C126. Reidel, Dordrecht.

Andersson, J. G. 1906. Solifluction, a component of subaerial denudation. *J. Geol.* **14**, 91–112.

Andrew, R. 1984. A practical pollen guide to the British flora. *Quat. Res. Assoc. Tech. Guide* **1**. Quaternary Research Association, Cambridge.

Andrews, J. T. 1971. Techniques of till fabric analysis. *Brit. Geomorph. Res. Grp Tech. Bull.* **6**, 1–43.

Andrews, J. T. and Miller, G. H. 1980. Dating Quaternary deposits more than 10 000 years old, pp. 263–287 in: *Timescales in geomorphology* (eds. R. A. Cullingford, D. A. Davidson and J. Lewin). Wiley, Chichester.

Andrews, J. T. and Smith, D. I. 1970. Statistical analysis of till fabric: methodology, local and regional variability. *Quart. J. Geol. Soc. Lond.* **125**, 503–542.

Andrews, J. T. and Webber, P. J. 1964. A lichenometrical study of the northwestern margin of the Barnes Ice Cap: a geomorphological technique. *Geogr. Bull.* **22**, 80–104.

Annan, A. P. and Davis, J. L. 1976. Impulse radar sounding in permafrost. *Radio Sci.* **11**, 383–394.

Anthony, R. S. 1977. Iron-rich rhythmically laminated sediments in Lake of the Clouds, northeastern Minnesota. *Limnol. Oceanogr.* **22**, 45–54.

Arrhenius, S. 1896. On the influence of carbonic acid in the air upon the temperature of the ground. *Lond. Edinb. Dubl. Phil. Mag. J. Sci.* Ser. 5, **41**, 237–276.

Arulanandan, K., Loganathan, P. and Krone, R.B. 1975. Pore and eroding fluid influences on the surface erosion of a soil. *J. Geotech. Engng Div. ASCE* **101**, 53–66.

Ashley, G. M. 1975. Rhythmic sedimentation in glacial Lake Hitchcock, Massachusetts–Connecticut, pp. 304–320 in: *Glaciofluvial and glaciolacustrine sedimentation* (eds. A.V. Jopling and B.C. MacDonald). Society of Economic Palaeontologists and Mineralogists Special Publication **23**.

Audric, T. and Bouquier, L. 1976. Collapsing behaviour of some loess soils from Normandy. *Quart. J. Engng Geol.* **9**, 265–277.

Avery, B. W. 1980. Soil classification for England and Wales (higher categories). *Soil Surv. Tech. Monogr.* **14**. Soil Survey of England and Wales, Harpenden.

Avery, B. W. and Bascomb, C. L. (eds.) 1974. Soil survey laboratory methods. *Soil Surv. Tech. Monogr.* **6**. Soil Survey of England and Wales, Harpenden.

Babel, U. 1975. Micromorphology of soil organic matter, pp. 369–473 in: *Soil components. Volume 1. Organic components* (ed. J. E. Gieseking). Springer, New York.

Bada, J. L. 1985. Amino acid racemization dating of fossil bones. *Ann. Rev. Earth Planet. Sci.* **13**, 241–268.

Bada, J. L., Masters, P. M., Hooper, E., Daling, D., Berger, R. and Suess, H. E. 1979. The dating of fossil bones using amino acid racemization. *Proc. 9th Int. Conf. Radiocarbon Dating* **9**, 740–756.

Baden Powell, D. F. W. 1937. On a marine Holocene fauna in north-western Scotland. *J. Anim. Ecol.* **6**, 273–283.

Baden Powell, D. F. W. 1955. The correlation of the Pliocene and Pleistocene marine beds of Britain and the Mediterranean. *Proc. Geol. Assoc.* **66**, 271–292.

Baes, C. F., Beal, S. E., Lee, D. W. and Marland, G. 1980. Options for the collection and disposal of carbon dioxide. *Rept ORNL-5657 Oak Ridge Nat. Lab., Tennessee.*

Bagnold, R. A. 1941. *The physics of blown sand and desert dunes.* Methuen, London.

Bahnson, H., Petersen, K.S., Konradi, P.B. and Knudsen, K.L. 1973. Stratigraphy of Quaternary deposits in the Skaerumhede II boring: lithology, molluscs and foraminifera. *Geol. Surv. Denmark Yearbook* 1973, pp. 27–62.

Bailey, E. 1952. *Geological survey of Great Britain.* Murby, London.

Ballantyne, C. K. 1978. The hydrologic significance of nivation features in permafrost areas. *Biul. Perygl.* **27**, 5–10.

Ballantyne, C. K. 1987. The present-day periglaciation of upland Britain, pp. 113–126 in: *Periglacial processes and landforms in Britain and Ireland* (ed. J. Boardman). Cambridge University Press.

Ballantyne, C. K. and Whittington, G. 1987. Niveo-aeolian sand deposits on An Teallach, Wester Ross, Scotland. *Trans. Roy. Soc. Edinb.* **78**, 51–63.

Ballard, R. F., Cuenod, Y. and Jenni, J. P. 1983. Detection of karst cavities by geophysical methods. *Bull. Int. Assoc. Engng Geol.* **26–27**, 153–157.

Balson, P. S. and Cameron, T. D. J. 1985. Quaternary mapping offshore East Anglia. *Modern Geol.* **9**, 221–239.

Banerjee, I. 1973. Sedimentology of Pleistocene glacial varves in Ontario, Canada. *Geol. Surv. Can. Bull.* **226**.

Barber, K. 1984. A large-capacity Russian-pattern sediment sampler. *Quat. Newsl.* **44**, 28–31.

Barbetti, M. F. and McElhinny, M. W. 1976. The Lake Mungo geomagnetic excursion. *Phil. Trans. Roy. Soc. Lond.* **A281**, 515–542.

Barendregt, R. W. 1984. Correlation of Quaternary chronologies using paleomagnetism — examples from southern Alberta and Saskatchewan, pp. 120–136 in: *Correlation of Quaternary chronologies* (ed. W. C. Mahaney). Geobooks, Norwich.

Barendregt, R. W. 1985. Dating methods of Pleistocene deposits and their problems: VI. Paleomagnetism, pp. 39–51 in: *Dating methods of Pleistocene deposits and their problems* (ed. N. W. Rutter). Geoscience Canada Reprint Series 2. Geological Association of Canada, Toronto.

Bariss, N. and Bronger, A. 1981. Natürliche und anthropogene Owragbildung in verschiedenen Klimazonen. Ein Beitrag zur Morphodynamik in Lössgebieten. *Zeitschr. Geomorph.* N.F. **25**, 180–202.

Barker, R. D. 1981. The offset system of electrical resistivity sounding and its use with a multicore cable. *Geophys. Prospecting* **29**, 128–143.

Barker, R. D. and Harker, D. 1984. The location of the Stour buried tunnel-valley using geophysical techniques. *Quart. J. Engng Geol.* **17**, 103–115.

Barnes, P. W., Asbury, J. L., Rearic, D. M. and Ross, C. R. 1987. Ice erosion of a sea-floor knickpoint at the inner edge of the stamukhi zone, Beaufort Sea, Alaska. *Marine Geol.* **76**, 207–222.

Barnola, J. M., Raynaud, D., Korotkevich, Y. S. and Lorius, C. 1987. Vostok ice core provides 160 000-year record of atmospheric CO_2. *Nature* **329**, 408–414.

Barr, D. J. and Miles, R. D. 1969. Techniques for utilising side-looking airborne radar (SLAR) imagery in regional highway planning, pp. 49–56 in: *Remote sensing and its application to highway engineering*. Special Reports of the Highways Research Board **102**.

Barshad, I. 1966. The effect of a variation in precipitation on the nature of clay mineral formation in soils from acid and basic igneous rocks. *Proc. Int. Clay Conf. Jerusalem* **1**, 167–173.

Bartholic, J. F., Namken, L. N. and Wiegand, C. L. 1972. Aerial thermal scanner to determine temperatures of soils and crop canopies differing in water stress. *Agron. J.* **64**, 603–608.

Bascomb, C. L. 1974. Physical and chemical analyses of <2 mm samples, pp. 14–41 in: *Soil survey laboratory methods* (eds. B. W. Avery and C. L. Bascomb). *Soil Surv. Tech. Monogr.* **6**. Soil Survey of England and Wales, Harpenden.

Bateman, R. M. and Catt, J. A. 1985. Modification of heavy mineral assemblages in English coversands by acid pedochemical weathering. *Catena* **12**, 1–21.

Bates, R. L. 1969. *The geology of the industrial rocks and minerals*. Dover, New York.

Batten, R. J., Cronk, C. R., Gillespie, R., Gowlett, J. A. J., Hedges, R. E. M. and Perry, C. 1986. A review of the operation of the Oxford Radiocarbon Accelerator Unit. *Radiocarbon* **28**, 2A, 177–185.

Baulig, H. 1956. Pénéplaines et pédiplaines. *Bull. Soc. Belge Etudes Géogr.* **25**, 25–58.

Beaumont, T. E. 1979. Remote sensing for the location and mapping of engineering construction materials in developing countries. *Quart. J. Engng Geol.* **12**, 147–158.

Begni, G. 1982. Selection of the optimum spectral bands for the SPOT satellite. *Photogramm. Engng Remote Sensing* **48**, 1613-1620.

Behling, R. E. 1972. Calculated dates of selected glacial events in Wright Valley. *Antarct. J. U.S.* **7**, 247–248.

Bell, M. 1983. Valley sediments as evidence of prehistoric land use on the South Downs. *Proc. Prehist. Soc.* **49**, 119–150.

Benedict, J. B. 1967. Recent glacial history of an alpine area in the Colorado Front Range, U.S.A. I. Establishing a lichen growth curve. *J. Glaciol.* **6**, 817–832.

Benedict, J. B. 1976. Frost creep and gelifluction features: a review. *Quat. Res.* **6**, 55–76.

Benson, R. C. and Glaccum, R. A. 1979. Radar surveys for geotechnical site assessment. *Amer. Soc. Civil Engrs Reprint* 3794B.

Bentley, C. R. 1983. The west Antarctic ice sheet: diagnosis and prognosis, pp. IV.3–IV.50 in: *Proc. Carbon Dioxide Res. Conf., Berkeley Springs 1982*.

Berger, G. W. and Huntley, D. J. 1982. Thermoluminescence dating of terrigenous sediments. *PACT (Journal of the European study group on physical, chemical and mathematical techniques applied to archaeology)* **6**, 495–504.

Berger, R. 1970. Ancient Egyptian radiocarbon chronology. *Phil. Trans. Roy. Soc. Lond.* **A269**, 23–36.

Berger, W. H. 1982. Increase in carbon dioxide in the atmosphere during deglaciation: the coral reef hypothesis. *Naturwissenschaften* **69**, 87–88.

Berger, W. H. and Keir, R. S. 1984. Glacial-Holocene changes in atmospheric CO_2 and the deep-sea record, pp. 337–351 in: *Climate processes and climate sensitivity* (eds. J. E. Hansen and T. Takahashi). *Geophysical Monograph* **29**. American Geophysical Union, Washington.

Berger, W. H. and Killingley, J. S. 1982. The Worthington Effect and the origin of the Younger Dryas. *J. Marine Res. Suppl.* **40**, 27–38.

Berggren, W. A. and Van Couvering, J. A. 1974. The late Neogene. Biostratigraphy, geochronology and paleoclimatology of the last 15 million years in marine and continental sequences. *Palaeogeogr. Palaeoclim. Palaeoecol.* **16**, 1–216.

Bernard, H. A. and Major, C. F. 1963. Recent meander belt deposits of the Brazos River: an alluvial 'sand' model. *Bull. Amer. Assoc. Petrol. Geol.* **47**, 350.

Bernard, R., Martin, P. H., Thony, J. L., Vauchlin, M. and Vidal-Madjar, D. 1982. C band radar for determining surface soil moisture. *Remote Sensing Env.* **12**, 189–200.

Berry, F. G. 1979. Late Quaternary scour-hollows and related features in central London. *Quart. J. Engng Geol.* **12**, 9–29.

Beschel, R. 1950. Flechten als Altersmasstab rezenter Moränen. *Zeitschr. Gletscherk.* **1**, 152–161.

Beschta, R. L. and Jackson, W. L. 1979. The intrusion of fine sediments into a stable gravel bed. *J. Fisheries Res. Bd Can.* **36**, 204–210.

Best, J. L. and Brayshaw, A. C. 1985. Flow separation — a physical process for the concentration of heavy minerals within alluvial channels. *J. Geol. Soc. Lond.* **142**, 747–755.

Bibby, J. S. and Mackney, D. 1969. Land use capability classification. *Soil Surv. Tech. Monogr.* **1**. Soil Survey of England and Wales, Harpenden; Soil Survey of Scotland, Aberdeen.

Bibby, J. S., Douglas, H. A., Thomasson, A. J. and Robertson, J. S. 1982. *Land capability classification for agriculture*. Soil Survey of Scotland, Aberdeen.

Biczysko, S. J. 1981. Relic landslip in west Northamptonshire. *Quart. J. Engng Geol.* **14**, 169–174.

Birkeland, P. W. 1969. Quaternary paleoclimatic implications of soil clay mineral distribution in a Sierra Nevada–Great Basin transect. *J. Geol.* **77**, 289–302.

Birkeland, P. W. 1984. *Soils and geomorphology*. Oxford University Press, New York.

Birkeland, P. W. and Janda, R. J. 1971. Clay mineralogy of soils developed from Quaternary deposits of the eastern Sierra Nevada, California. *Bull. Geol. Soc. Amer.* **82**, 2495–2514.

Birkeland, P. W. and Shroba, R. R. 1974. The status of the concept of Quaternary soil-forming intervals in the western United States, pp. 241–276 in: *Quaternary environments: proceedings of a symposium* (ed. W. C. Mahaney). York University Toronto Geographical Monograph **5**.

Birman, J. H. 1964. Glacial geology across the crest of the Sierra Nevada, California. *Geol. Soc. Amer. Spec. Paper* **75**.

Bisat, W. S. 1940. Older and newer drift in East Yorkshire. *Proc. Yorks. Geol. Soc.* **24**, 137–151.

Bjelm, L., Follin, S. G. W. and Svensson, C. 1983. A radar in geological subsurface investigation. *Bull. Int. Assoc. Engng Geol.* **26–27**, 10–14.

Black, R. F. 1974. Ice-wedge polygons of northern Alaska, pp. 247–275 in: *Glacial geomorphology* (ed. D. R. Coates). New York State University, Binghamton.

Black, R. F. 1976. Periglacial features indicative of permafrost: ice and soil wedges. *Quat. Res.* **6**, 3–26.

Blakemore, L. C., Searle, P. L. and Daly, B. K. 1987. Methods for chemical analysis of soils. *New Zealand Soil Bur. Sci. Rept* **80**. D.S.I.R., Lower Hutt.

Blom, R. and Elachi, C. 1981. Spaceborne and airborne imaging radar observations of sand dunes. *J. Geophys. Res.* **86**, 3061–3073.

Bloom, A. L. 1967. Pleistocene shorelines: a new test of isostasy. *Bull. Geol. Soc. Amer.* **78**, 1477–1493.

Bloomfield, C., Brown, G. and Catt, J. A. 1970. The distribution of sulphur in the mud of Lake Victoria. *Plant and Soil* **33**, 479–481.

Bluck, B. J. 1974. Structure and directional properties of some valley sand deposits in southern Iceland. *Sedimentology* **21**, 533–554.

Bluck, B. J. 1979. Structure of coarse grained braided stream alluvium. *Trans. Roy. Soc. Edinb.* **70**, 181–221.

Boardman, J. and Hazelden, J. 1986. Examples of erosion on brickearth soils in east Kent. *Soil Use Managem.* **2**, 105–108.

Bockheim, J. G. 1980. Solution and use of chronofunctions in studying soil development. *Geoderma* **24**, 71–85.

Bockheim, J. G. 1982. Properties of a chronosequence of ultraxerous soils in the Trans-Antarctic Mountains. *Geoderma* **28**, 239–255.

Boellstorff, J. 1978. North American Pleistocene stages reconsidered in light of probable Pliocene–Pleistocene continental glaciation. *Science* **202**, 305–307.

Bogorodsky, V. V., Bentley, C. R. and Gurmandsen, P. E. 1985. *Radioglaciology*. Reidel, Dordrecht.

Bonhommet, N. and Zahringer, J. 1969. Paleomagnetism and potassium–argon date determinations of the Laschamp geomagnetic polarity event. *Earth Planet. Sci. Lett.* **6**, 43–46.

Bonneau, M. and Souchier, B. 1982. *Constituents and properties of soils* (trans. V. C. Farmer). Academic Press, London.

Boothroyd, J. C. and Ashley, G. M. 1975. Process, bar morphology and sedimentary structures on braided outwash fans, north-eastern Gulf of Alaska, pp. 193–222 in: *Glaciofluvial and glaciolacustrine sedimentation* (eds. A. V. Jopling and B. C. McDonald). Society of Economic Paleontologists and Mineralogists Special Publication **23**.

Boulton, G. S. 1968. Flow tills and related deposits on some Vestspitsbergen glaciers. *J. Glaciol.* **7**, 391–412.

Boulton, G. S. 1970. On the deposition of subglacial and melt-out tills at the margins of certain Svalbard glaciers. *J. Glaciol.* **9**, 231–245.

Boulton, G. S. 1972. Modern arctic glaciers as depositional models for former ice-sheets. *J. Geol. Soc. Lond.* **128**, 361–393.

Boulton, G. S. 1979. Processes of glacier erosion on different substrata. *J. Glaciol.* **23**, 15–38.

Boulton, G. S. and Paul, M. A. 1976. The influence of genetic processes on some geotechnical properties of glacial tills. *Quart. J. Engng Geol.* **9**, 159–194.

Boulton, G. S., Chroston, P. N. and Jarvis, J. 1981. A marine seismic study of late Quaternary sedimentation and inferred glacier fluctuations along western Inverness-shire, Scotland. *Boreas* **10**, 39–51.

Boulton, G. S., Jones, A. S., Clayton, K. M. and Kenning, M. J. 1977. A British ice-sheet model and patterns of glacial erosion and deposition in Britain, pp. 231–246 in: *British Quaternary studies recent advances* (ed. F. W. Shotton). Clarendon Press, Oxford.

Bourdier, F. 1969. Etude comparée des dépôts Quaternaires des bassins de la Seine et de la Somme. *Bull. Inf. Géolog. Bassin Paris* **21**, 169–220.

Bowen, D. Q. 1978. *Quaternary geology. A stratigraphic framework for multidisciplinary work*. Pergamon, Oxford.

Bowler, J. M. 1973. Clay dunes: their occurrence, formation and environmental significance. *Earth Sci. Rev.* **9**, 315–338.

Boyer, S. J. and Pheasant, D. R. 1974. Weathering zones and former ice limits in eastern Baffin Island, N.W.T., Canada. *Bull. Geol. Soc. Amer.* **85**, 805–810.

Boylan, P. J. 1981. The role of William Buckland (1784–1856) in the recognition of glaciation in Great Britain, pp. 1–8 in: *The Quaternary in Britain* (eds. J. Neale and J. Flenley). Pergamon, Oxford.

Bozozuk, M. and Burn, K. N. 1960. Vertical ground movement near elm trees. *Géotechnique* **10**, 19–32.

Bradford, J. M., Piest, R. F. and Spomer, R. G. 1978. Failure sequence of gully headwalls in Western Iowa. *Soil Sci. Soc. Amer. J.* **42**, 323–328.

Bradshaw, R. H. W. 1981. Modern pollen representation factors for woods in south-east England. *J. Ecol.* **69**, 45–70.

Bray, J. R. 1971. Solar–climate relationships in the post-Pleistocene. *Science* **171**, 1242–1243.

Brewer, R., Crook, K. A. W. and Speight, J. G. 1970. Proposal for soil stratigraphic units in the Australian stratigraphic code. Report by the subcommittee for soil-stratigraphic nomenclature. *J. Geol. Soc. Australia* **17**, 103–111.

Brice, J. C. 1964. Channel patterns and terraces of the Loup River in Nebraska. *U.S. Geol. Surv. Prof. Paper* **422-D**, 1–41.

Bridges, E. M. and Doornkamp, J. C. 1963. Morphological mapping and the study of soil patterns. *Geography* **48**, 175–181.

Bridgland, D. R. 1985. Uniclinal shifting: a speculative reappraisal based on terrace distribution in the London Basin. *Quat. Newsl.* **47**, 26–33.

Briggs, D. 1977. *Sediments*. Butterworth, London.

Broecker, W. S. 1982. Ocean chemistry during glacial time. *Geochim. Cosmochim. Acta* **46**, 1689–1705.

Broecker, W. S. and Peng, T.H. 1986. Carbon cycle: 1985. Glacial to interglacial changes in the operation of the global carbon cycle. *Radiocarbon* **28**, 2A, 309–327.

Broecker, W. S. and Van Donk, J. 1970. Insolation changes, ice volumes and the O^{18} record in deep-sea sediments. *Rev. Geophys. Space Phys.* **8**, 169–198.

Broscoe, A. J. 1959. Quantitative analysis of longitudinal stream profiles of small watersheds. *Office of Naval Research, Geography Branch, Project NR 389–42, Technical Report* **18**.

Brown, L. 1987. ^{10}Be: recent applications in earth sciences. *Phil. Trans. Roy. Soc. Lond.* **A323**, 75–86.

Bruins, H. J. and Yaalon, D. H. 1981. Stratigraphy of the Netivot section in the desert loess of the Negev (Israel). *Acta Geol. Acad. Sci. Hung.* **22** (1979), 161–169.

Brunsden, D., Doornkamp, J. C., Fookes, P. G., Jones, D. K. C. and Kelly, J. H. M. 1975a. The use of geomorphological mapping techniques in highway engineering. *J. Highw. Engng* **22**, 35–41.

Brunsden, D., Fookes, P. G., Jones, D. K. C. and Kelly, J. H. M. 1975b. Large scale geomorphological mapping and highway engineering design. *Quart. J. Engng Geol.* **8**, 227–253.

Brunskill, G. J. and Ludlam, S. D. 1969. Fayetteville Green Lake, New York: I. Physical and chemical limnology. *Limnol. Oceanogr.* **14**, 817–829.

Bryan, R. B. 1968. The development, use and efficiency of indices of soil erodibility. *Geoderma* **2**, 5–26.

Bucha, V. 1970. Evidence for changes in the earth's magnetic field intensity. *Phil. Trans. Roy. Soc. Lond.* **A269**, 47–55.

Bull, W. B. 1964. Geomorphology of segmented alluvial fans in western Fresno County, California. *Prof. Paper U.S. Geol. Surv.* **352-E**, 89–129.

Bull, W. B. 1972. Recognition of alluvial-fan deposits in the stratigraphic record, pp. 68–83 in: *Recognition of ancient sedimentary environments* (eds. K. J. Rigby and W. K. Hamblin). Society of Economic Paleontologists and Mineralogists Special Publication **16**.

Bullard, E. 1972. Geomagnetic dynamos, pp. 232–244 in: *Nature of the solid earth* (ed. E. C. Robertson). McGraw-Hill, New York.

Bullock, P., Federoff, N., Jongerius, A., Stoops, G., Tursina, T. and Babel, U. 1985. *Handbook for soil thin section description*. Waine Research Publications, Wolverhampton.

Burleigh, R. 1972. Carbon-14 dating, with application to dating of remains from caves. *Stud. Speleol.* **2**, 176–190.

Burt, T. P. and Williams, P. J. 1976. Hydraulic conductivity in frozen soils. *Earth Surf. Processes* **1**, 249–360.

Butler, B. E. 1959. Periodic phenomena in landscapes as a basis for soil studies. *C.S.I.R.O. Soil Publ.* **14**.

Campbell, J. B. 1977. *The Upper Palaeolithic of Britain.* Oxford University Press, Oxford.

Campbell, K. J. and Orange, A. S. 1974. A continuous profile of sea ice and freshwater ice thickness by impulse radar. *Polar Record* **17**, 31–41.

Canada Soil Survey Committee 1978. The Canadian system of soil classification. *Canada Dept Agric. Publ.* **1646**.

Carol, H. 1947. The formation of roches moutonnées. *J. Glaciol.* **1**, 57–59.

Carrigan, C. R. and Gubbins, D. 1979. The source of the earth's magnetic field. *Sci. Amer.* **240**, 118–130.

Carroll, D. M., Evans, R. and Bendelow, V. C. 1977. Air photo-interpretation for soil mapping. *Soil Surv. Tech. Monogr.* **8**. Soil Survey of England and Wales, Harpenden.

Catt, J. A. 1978. The contribution of loess to soils in lowland Britain, pp. 12–20 in: *The effect of man on the landscape: the lowland zone* (eds. S. Limbrey and J. G. Evans). Council for British Archaeology Research Report **21**.

Catt, J. A. 1985. Soil particle size distribution and mineralogy as indicators of pedogenic and geomorphic history: examples from the loessial soils of England and Wales, pp. 202–218 in: *Geomorphology and soils* (eds. K. S. Richards, R. R. Arnett and S. Ellis). George Allen and Unwin, London.

Catt, J. A. 1986. *Soils and Quaternary geology*. Clarendon Press, Oxford.

Catt, J. A. 1987. Effects of the Devensian cold stage on soil characteristics and distribution in eastern England, pp. 145–152 in: *Periglacial processes and landforms in Britain and Ireland* (ed. J. Boardman). Cambridge University Press.

Catt, J. A. and Hodgson, J. M. 1976. Soils and geomorphology of the Chalk in south-east England. *Earth Surf. Processes* **1**, 181–193.

Catt, J. A. and Weir, A. H. 1976. The study of archaeologically important sediments by petrographic techniques, pp. 65–91 in: *Geoarchaeology* (eds. D. A. Davidson and M. L. Shackley). Duckworth, London.

Catt, J. A., Green, M. and Arnold, N. J. 1982. Naleds in a Wessex downland valley. *Proc. Dorset Nat. Hist. Archaeol. Soc.* **104**, 69–75.

Catt, J. A., Weir, A. H. and Madgett, P. A. 1974. The loess of eastern Yorkshire and Lincolnshire. *Proc. Yorks. Geol. Soc.* **40**, 23–39.

Cegla, J. 1969. Influence of capillary ground moisture on eolian accumulation of loess. *Bull. Acad. Polonaise Sci. Ser. Sci. Géol. Géogr.* **17**, 25–27.

Chappell, J. and Shackleton, N. J. 1986. Oxygen isotopes and sea level. *Nature* **324**, 137–140.

Charlesworth, J. K. 1959. *The Quaternary Era* (2 volumes). Edward Arnold, London.

Chaves, J. R. and Schuster, R. L. 1964. Use of aerial colour photography in materials surveys. *Highw. Res. Rec.* **63**, 1–9.

Chen, C. T. A. and Drake, E. T. 1986. Carbon dioxide increase in the atmosphere and oceans and possible effects on climate. *Ann. Rev. Earth Planet. Sci.* **14**, 201–235.

Chepil, W. S. 1945. Dynamics of wind erosion. III. Transport capacity of the wind. *Soil Sci.* **60**, 475–480.

Chepil, W. S. 1956. Influence of moisture on credibility of soil by wind. *Soil Sci. Soc. Amer. Proc.* **20**, 288–292.

Chepil, W. S., Siddoway, F. H. and Armbrust, D. 1963. Climatic index of wind erosion conditions in the Great Plains. *Soil Sci. Soc. Amer. Proc.* **27**, 449–451.

Cherry, J. A. 1972. Geochemical processes in shallow groundwater flow systems in five areas in southern Manitoba, Canada. *Proc. 24th Int. Geol. Congr. Montreal*, Section 11, 208–211.

Chesworth, W. 1982. Late Cenozoic geology and the second oldest profession. *Geoscience Canada* **9**, 54–61.

Chevrel, M., Courtois, M. and Weill, G. 1981. The SPOT satellite remote sensing mission. *Photogramm. Engng Remote Sensing* **47**, 1163–1171.

Chizhov, A. N., Glushnev, V. G., Slutsker, B. D. and Borodulin, V. V. 1978. The use of radar to measure ice thicknesses in rivers, lakes and reservoirs. *Soviet Hydrology: Selected Papers* **17**, 116–127.

Chorley, R. J., Malm, D. E. G. and Pogorzelski, H. A. 1957. A new standard for estimating drainage basin shape. *Amer. J. Sci.* **255**, 138–141.

Clark, H. C. and Kennet, J. P. 1973. Paleomagnetic excursion recorded in latest Pleistocene deep-sea sediments, Gulf of Mexico. *Earth Planet. Sci. Lett.* **19**, 267–274.

Clark, J. A., Farrell, W. E. and Pelter, W. R. 1978. Global changes in post-glacial sea level: a numerical calculation. *Quat. Res.* **9**, 265–287.

Clark, J. G. D. 1954. *Excavations at Starr Carr.* Cambridge University Press, London.

Clark, P. U. 1987. Subglacial sediment dispersal and till composition. *J. Geol.* **95**, 527–541.

Clarke, M. R. 1983. Geophysical evaluation of scattered occurrences of sand and gravel in drift deposits, pp. 157-169 in: *Prospecting and evaluation of non-metallic rocks and minerals* (eds. K. Atkinson and R. Brassington). Institution of Geologists, London.

Clarke, R. R. 1963. *The Grime's Grave flint mine.* H.M.S.O., London.

Clayden, B. and Hollis, J. M. 1984. Criteria for differentiating soil series. *Soil Surv. Tech. Monogr.* **17**. Soil Survey of England and Wales, Harpenden.

Clayton, K. M. 1977. River terraces, pp. 153–167 in: *British Quaternary studies recent advances* (ed. F. W. Shotton). Clarendon Press, Oxford.

Cleaves, A. B. 1963. Engineering geology characteristics of a basal till: St. Lawrence Seaway Project. *Geol. Soc. Amer. Case History Series* **4**.

Clevenger, W. A. 1956. Experience with loess as foundation material. *Proc. Amer. Soc. Civil Engrs* **82** (SM3), Paper 1025, 1–26.

Coates, D. R. 1978. Geomorphic engineering, pp. 3–21 in: *Geomorphology and engineering* (ed. D. R. Coates). Dowden, Hutchinson and Ross, New York.

Collins, M. E. and Doolittle, J. A. 1987. Using ground-penetrating radar to study soil microvariability. *Soil Sci. Soc. Amer. J.* **51**, 491–493.

Collinson, J. D. 1978. Vertical sequence and sand body shape in alluvial sequences, pp. 577–586 in: *Fluvial sedimentology* (ed. A. D. Miall). Canadian Society of Petroleum Geologists Memoir **5**.

Collinson, J. D. 1986. Alluvial sediments, pp. 20–62 in: *Sedimentary environments and facies* (ed. H. G. Reading). Blackwell, Oxford.

Collis, L. and Fox, R. A. (eds.) 1985. *Aggregates: sand, gravel and crushed rock aggregates for construction purposes*. Geological Society of London Engineering Geology Special Publication **1**.

Collomb, E. 1847. Sur les anciens glaciers des Vosges. Résultats sommaires d'une exploration faite avec la Société Géologique de France. *Arch. Sci. Phys. Nat. Genève* (Ser. 4) **6**, 199–214.

Colman, S. M. and Pierce, K. L. 1981. Weathering rinds on andesitic and basaltic stones as a Quaternary age indicator, western United States. *U.S. Geol. Surv. Prof. Paper* **1210**.

Committee on stratigraphic nomenclature 1933. Classification and nomenclature of rock units. *Bull. Geol. Soc. Amer.* **44**, 423–459.

Compton, R. R. 1962. *Manual of field geology*. Wiley, New York.

Conway, B. W. 1979. The contribution made to cliff instability by head deposits in the west Dorset coastal area. *Quart. J. Engng Geol.* **12**, 267–275.

Cooke, R. U. 1970. Stone pavements in deserts. *Ann. Assoc. Amer. Geogr.* **60**, 560–577.

Cooke, R. U. and Doornkamp, J. C. 1974. *Geomorphology in environmental management*. Clarendon Press, Oxford.

Coope, G. R. 1977. Quaternary Coleoptera as aids in the interpretation of environmental history, pp. 55–68 in: *British Quaternary studies recent advances* (ed. F. W. Shotton). Clarendon Press, Oxford.

Corbel, J. 1959. Vitesse de l'erosion. *Zeitschr. Geomorph.* **3**, 1–28.

Cornwell, J. D. 1985. Applications of geophysical methods to mapping unconsolidated sediments in East Anglia. *Modern Geol.* **9**, 187–206.

Coxon, P. 1978. The first record of a fossil naled in Britain. *Quat. Newsl.* **24**, 9–11.

Craig, N. and Halais, P. 1934. The influence of maturity and rainfall on the properties of lateritic soils in Mauritius. *Emp. J. Exp. Agric.* **2**, 349–358.

Creedy, D. P. and Freeman, J. 1974. Some preliminary observations relating to the use of earth resistivity measurements for cave detection. *Trans. Brit. Cave Res. Assoc.* **1**, 215–222.

Creer, K. M., Anderson, T. W. and Lewis, C. F. M. 1976. Late Quaternary geomagnetic stratigraphy recorded in Lake Erie sediments. *Earth Planet. Sci. Lett.* **31**, 37–47.

Cremaschi, M. 1987. *Paleosols and vetusols in the central Po Plain (northern Italy): a study in Quaternary geology and soil development*. Proefschrift Universiteit van Amsterdam, Fysisch Geografisch en Bodemkundig Laboratorium, Universiteit van Amsterdam.

Crickmay, C. H. 1933. The later stages of the cycle of erosion. *Geol. Mag.* **70**, 337–347.

Crocker, R. L. 1952. Soil genesis and the pedogenic factors. *Quart. Rev. Biol.* **27**, 139–168.

Crofts, R. S. 1974. Detailed geomorphological mapping and land evaluation in highland Scotland, pp. 231–251 in: *Progress in geomorphology* (eds. E. H. Brown and R. S. Waters). Institute of British Geographers Special Publication **7**.

Crofts, R. S. 1981. Mapping techniques in geomorphology, pp. 66–75 in: *Geomorphological techniques* (ed. A. S. Goudie). George Allen and Unwin, London.

Croll, J. 1864. On the physical cause of the change of climate during geological epochs. *Phil. Mag.* (Ser. 4) **28**, 121–137.

Croll, J. 1867. On the eccentricity of the earth's orbit, and its physical relations to the glacial epoch. *Phil. Mag.* (Ser. 4) **33**, 119–131.

Crook, K. A. W. and Coventry, R. J. 1967. Climatically controlled Quaternary sedimentation and soils in Ryans Creek Valley, N.S.W. *Australia New Zealand Assoc. Adv. Sci.*, Section C Abstracts of Proceedings, T9–11.

Crowther, E. M. 1931. The relationship of climatic and geological factors to the composition of soil clay and the distribution of soil types. *Proc. Roy. Soc. Lond.* **B107**, 1–30.

Culley, R. W. 1973. Use of airborne resistivity surveys for gravel location. *Bull. Can. Inst. Min. Metall.* May 1973, 1–5.

Culshaw, M. G. and Waltham, A. C. 1987. Natural and artificial cavities as ground engineering hazards. *Quart. J. Engng Geol.* **20**, 139–150.

Curran, P. J. 1979. The use of polarised panchromatic and false colour infrared film in the monitoring of soil surface moisture. *Remote Sensing Env.* **8**, 249–266.

Curran, P. J. 1980. The Bussex rhyne. *Proc. Somerset Arch. Nat. Hist. Soc.* **124**, 167–169.

Curran, P. J. 1981. The estimation of the surface moisture of a vegetated soil using aerial infrared photography. *Int. J. Remote Sensing* **2**, 369–378.

Curran, P. J. 1983. Multispectral remote sensing for the estimation of green leaf area index. *Phil. Trans. Roy. Soc. Lond.* **A309**, 257–270.

Curran, P. J. 1985. *Principles of remote sensing*. Longman, London.

Currey, D. R. 1964. A preliminary study of valley asymmetry in the Ogotoruk Creek area, north-western Alaska. *Arctic J. Arctic Inst. N. Amer.* **17**, 85–98.

Currie, R. G. 1979. Distribution of solar cycle signal in surface air temperature over North America. *J. Geophys. Res.* **84**, 753–761.

Currie, R. G. 1981a. Evidence for 18.6-year M_N signal in temperature and drought condition in North America since A.D. 1800. *J. Geophys. Res.* C11, 11055–11064.

Currie, R. G. 1981b. Solar cycle signal in air temperature in North America: amplitude, gradient, phase and distribution. *J. Atmos. Sci.* **38**, 808–818.

Currie, R. G. 1984. Evidence for 18.6-year lunar nodal drought in western North America during the past millenium. *J. Geophys. Res.* **89**, 1295–1308.

Currie, R. G. and Fairbridge, R. W. 1985. Periodic 18.6-year and cyclic 11-year induced drought and flood in northeastern China and some global implications. *Quat. Sci. Rev.* **4**, 109–134.

Curry, D., Adams, C. G., Boulter, M. C., Dilley, F. C., Eames, F. E., Funnell, B. M. and Wells, M. K. 1978. A correlation of Tertiary rocks in the British Isles. *Geol. Soc. Lond. Spec. Rept* **12**.

Cvijic, J. 1893. *Die Karstphenomen.* Penks Geographischen Abhandlungen **5**.

Dagg, M. and Hosegood, P. H. 1962. Details of a hand sampling tool for taking undisturbed soil cores. *E. Afric. Agric. For. J.* Supplement to special issue, 129–131.

Dahl, R. 1965. Plastically sculptured detail forms on rock surfaces in northern Nordland, Norway. *Geogr. Ann.* **A47**, 83–140.

Dahl, R. 1967. Post-glacial microweathering of bedrock surfaces in the Narvik district of Norway. *Geogr. Ann.* **A49**, 155–166.

Dalrymple, G. B. and Lanphere, M. A. 1969. *Potassium argon dating: principles, techniques and applications to geochronology*. Freeman, San Francisco.

Damon, P. E. 1968. Radioactive dating of Quaternary tephra. *Proc. 8th INQUA Congr. USA 1965,* 195–206.

Dan, J., Yaalon, D. H. and Koyumdjisky, H. 1968. Catenary soil relationships in Israel. I. The Netanya catena on coastal dunes of the Sharon. *Geoderma* **2**, 95–120.

Dan, J., Yaalon, D. H., Moshe, R. and Nissim, S. 1982. Evolution of Reg soils in southern Israel and Sinai. *Geoderma* **28**, 173–202.

Dansgaard, W., Johnsen, S. J., Møller, J. and Langway, C. C. 1969. One thousand centuries of climatic record from Camp Century on the Greenland ice sheet. *Science* **166**, 377–381.

Dansgaard, W., Johnsen, S. J., Reeh, N., Gundestrup, N., Clausen, H. B. and Hammer, C.U. 1975. Climatic changes, Norsemen and modern man. *Nature* **255**, 24–28.

Dare-Edwards, A. J. 1984. Aeolian clay deposits of southeastern Australia: parna or loessic clay. *Trans. Inst. Brit. Geogr.* (New Ser. **9**, 337–344.

Darracott, B. W. and Lake, M. I. 1981. An initial appraisal of ground probing radar for site investigation in Britain. *Ground Engng* **14**, 14–18.

Davis, C. K. and Neal, J. T. 1963. Descriptions and airphoto characteristics of desert landforms. *Photogramm. Engng* **29**, 621–631.

Dawson, A. G. 1980. Shore erosion by frost: an example from the Scottish late glacial, pp. 45–53 in: *Studies in the lateglacial of north-west Europe* (eds. J. J. Lowe, J. M. Gray and J. E. Robinson). Pergamon, Oxford.

Dawson, A. G., Matthews, J. A. and Shakesby, R. A. 1987. Rock platform erosion on periglacial shores: a modern analogue for Pleistocene rock platforms in Britain, pp. 173–182 in: *Periglacial processes and landforms in Britain and Ireland* (ed. J. Boardman). Cambridge University Press.

Deacon, G. F. 1896. The Vyrnwy works for the water-supply of Liverpool. *Minutes Proc. Inst. Civil Engrs* **126**, 24–125.

Dean, K. G., Forbes, R. B., Turner, D. L., Eaton, F. D. and Sullivan, K. D. 1982. Radar and infrared remote sensing of geothermal features of Pilgrim Springs, Alaska. *Remote Sensing Env.* **12**, 391–405.

Dearman, W. R. (ed.) 1976. *Engineering geological maps: a guide to their preparation*. UNESCO Earth Science Publication **15**.

Deevey, E. S., Gross, M. S., Hutchinson, G. E. and Kraybill, H. L. 1954. The natural ^{14}C contents of materials from hard-water lakes. *Proc. Nat. Acad. Sci.* **40**, 285–288.

De Geer, G. 1912. A chronology of the last 12000 years. *XIth Int. Geol. Congr. Stockholm* **1**, 241–253.

De Geer, G. 1940. Geochronologica Suecica principles. *K. Sven. Vetenskapsakad. Handl.* (Ser. 3), **18**, No. 6.

De Kimpe, C. R. and Martel, Y. A. 1976. Effects of vegetation on the distribution of carbon, iron and aluminium in the B horizons of northern Appalachian spodosols. *Soil Sci. Soc. Amer. J.* **40**, 77–80.

De Loor, G. P., Jurriëns, A. A. and Gravesteijn, H. 1974. The radar backscatter from selected agricultural crops. *Inst. Electr. Electron. Engrs Trans. Geosci. Remote Sensing* **12**, 70–74.

Demek, J. (ed.) 1972. *Manual of detailed geomorphological mapping*. Academia, Prague.

Demek, J. and Embleton, C. (eds.) 1978. *Guide to medium-scale geomorphological mapping*. E. Schweizerbart'sche Verlagsbuchhandlung, Stuttgart.

Denahan, B. J. and Smith, D. L. 1984. Electrical resistivity investigation of potential cavities underlying a proposed ash disposal area. *Env. Geol.* **6**, 45–49.

Denham, C. R. 1974. Counter-clockwise motion of paleomagnetic directions 24 000 years ago at Mono Lake, California. *J. Geomagn. Geoelect.* **26**, 487–498.

Denham, C. R. 1976. Blake polarity episode in two cores from the Greater Antilles outer ridge. *Earth Planet. Sci. Lett.* **29**, 422–434.

Denham, C. R., Anderson, R. F. and Bacon, M. P. 1977. Paleomagnetism and radiochemical age estimates for late Brunhes polarity episodes. *Earth Planet. Sci. Lett.* **35**, 384–397.

Denny, C. S. 1967. Fans and pediments. *Amer. J. Sci.* **265**, 81–105.

Dent, D. 1980. Acid sulphate soils: morphology and prediction. *J. Soil Sci.* **31**, 87–100.

Dent, D. and Young, A. 1981. *Soil survey and land evaluation*. George Allen and Unwin, London.

Denton, G. H. and Hughes, T. J. 1981. *The last great ice sheets.* Wiley, New York.

Derbyshire, E. and Mellors, T. W. 1986. Loess, pp. 237–246 in: *A handbook of engineering geomorphology* (eds. P. G. Fookes and P. Vaughan). Surrey University Press, Guildford.

Derbyshire, E., Gregory, K. J. and Hails, J. R. 1979. *Geomorphological processes.* Butterworth, London.

Devoy, R. J. N. 1979. Flandrian sea level changes and vegetational history of the lower Thames. *Phil. Trans. Roy. Soc. Lond.* **B285**, 355–407.

Devoy, R. J. N. 1982. Analyses of the geological evidence for Holocene sea-level movements in southeast England. *Proc. Geol. Assoc.* **93**, 65–90.

Dimbleby, G. W. 1961. Soil pollen analysis. *J. Soil Sci.* **12**, 1–11.

Dimbleby, G. W. 1985. *The palynology of archaeological sites.* Academic Press, London.

Dobson, M. C. and Ulaby, F. T. 1981. Microwave backscatter dependence on surface roughness, soil moisture and soil texture. Part III — soil tension. *Inst. Electr. Electron. Engrs Trans. Geosci. Remote Sensing* **19**, 51–61.

Dodonov, A. E. 1981. Stratigraphy of the Upper Pliocene–Quaternary deposits of Tajikstan (Soviet Central Asia). *Acta Geol. Acad. Sci. Hung.* **22** (1979), 63–73.

Dodonov, A. E. 1984. Stratigraphy and correlation of Upper Pliocene — Quaternary deposits of central Asia, pp. 201–211 in: *Lithology and stratigraphy of loess and paleosols* (ed. M. Pécsi). Geographical Research Institute, Hungarian Academy of Sciences, Budapest.

Doeglas, D. J. 1962. The structure of sedimentary deposits of braided rivers. *Sedimentology* **1**, 167–190.

Donner, J. J. and West, R. G. 1956. The Quaternary geology of Braganeset, Nordaustlandet, Spitsbergen. *Skr. Norsk Polarinst.* **109**, 1–29.

Doornenbal, J. C. and Helbig, K. 1983. High-resolution reflection seismics on a tidal flat in the Dutch Delta — acquisition, processing and interpretation. *First Break* May 1983, 9–20.

Doornkamp, J. C. and King, C. A. M. 1971. *Numerical analysis in geomorphology: an introduction*. Edward Arnold, London.

Doornkamp, J. C., Brunsden, D., Jones, D. K. C., Cooke, R. U. and Bush, P. R. 1979. Rapid geomorphological assessments for engineering. *Quart. J. Engng Geol.* **12**, 189–204.

Dormaar, J. F. and Lutwick, L. E. 1966. A biosequence of soils of the rough fescue prairie–poplar transition in southwestern Alberta. *Can. J. Earth Sci.* **3**, 457–471.

Dormaar, J. F. and Lutwick, L. E. 1969. Infrared spectra of humic acids and opal phytoliths as indicators of paleosols. *Can. J. Soil Sci.* **49**, 29–37.

Dowling, J. W. F. and Williams, F. H. P. 1964. The use of aerial photographs in materials surveys and classification of landforms, pp. 209–236 in: *Proceedings of a conference on civil engineering problems overseas.* Institution of Civil Engineers, London.

Drake, L. D. 1983. Ore plumes in till. *J. Geol.* **91**, 707–713.

Drake, L. D. and Ririe, G. T. 1981. A low-cost method of reclaiming strip-mined land in Iowa to agriculture. *Env. Geol.* **3**, 267–279.

Dreimanis, A., Hütt, G., Raukas, S. and Whippey, P. W. 1978. Dating methods of Pleistocene deposits and their problems. I. Thermoluminescence dating. *Geosci. Can.* **5**, 55–60.

Driscoll, F. G. 1986. *Groundwater and Wells. 2nd edition*. Johnson Division, St. Paul, Minnesota.

Driver, H. S. T. 1979. The preparation of thin slices of shell and bone for thermoluminescence. *PACT (Journal of the European study group on physical, chemical and mathematical techniques applied to archaeology)* **3**, 290–297.

D'Souza, V. P. C. and Morgan, R. P. C. 1976. A laboratory study of the effect of slope steepness and curvature on soil erosion. *J. Agric. Engng Res.* **21**, 21–31.

Duchaufour, P. 1982. *Pedology, pedogenesis and classification* (trans. T. R. Paton). George Allen and Unwin, London.

Dumanski, J. (ed.) 1978. *Manual for describing soils in the field.* Agriculture Canada, Ottawa.

Dyke, A. S. 1979. Glacial and sea-level history, southwestern Cumberland Peninsula, Baffin Island, Canada. *Arct. Alp. Res.* **11**, 179–202.

Dylik, J. 1951. Some periglacial structures in Pleistocene deposits of middle Poland. *Bull. Soc. Sci. Lett. Lodz, Sci. Math. Nat. Classe* **3**, 1–6.

Eberl, B. 1930. *Die Eiszeitenfolge im nordlichen Alpenvorlande.* Filser, Augsburg.

Eden, W. J. 1976a. Construction difficulties with loose tills on Labrador Plateau, pp. 391–400 in: *Glacial till* (ed. R. F. Legget). Royal Society of Canada Special Publication **12**.

Eden, W. J. 1976b. Mechanism of landslides in Leda Clay with special reference to the Ottawa area, pp. 159–171 in: *Fourth Guelph symposium on geomorphology* (eds. E. Yatsu, A. J. Ward and F. Adams). GeoAbstracts, Norwich.

Edmonds, C. N. 1983. Towards the prediction of subsidence risk upon the Chalk outcrop. *Quart. J. Engng Geol.* **16**, 261–266.

Edwards, M. 1986. Glacial environments. pp. 445–470 in: *Sedimentary environments and facies* (2nd edition) (ed. H. G. Reading). Blackwell, Oxford.

Edwards, M. B. 1979. Late Precambrian glacial loessites from north Norway and Svalbard. *J. Sedim. Petrol.* **49**, 85–92.

Ehlers, J., Meyer, K. D. and Stephan, H. J. 1984. The pre-Weichselian glaciations of north-west Europe. *Quat. Sci. Rev.* **3**, 1–40.

Einarsson, T. 1986. Tephrochronology, pp. 329–342 in: *Handbook of Holocene Palaeoecology and Palaeohydrology* (ed. B. E. Berglund). Wiley, Chichester.

Ellis, S. 1983. Micromorphological aspects of arctic-alpine pedogenesis in the Okstindan Mountains, Norway. *Catena* **10**, 133–147.

Embleton, C. and King, C. A. M. 1975. *Glacial geomorphology*. Edward Arnold, London.

Emiliani, C. 1955. Pleistocene temperatures. *J. Geol.* **63**, 538–578.

Emiliani, C. 1966. Paleotemperature analysis of Caribbean cores P 6304–8 and P 6304–9 and a generalized temperature curve for the past 425 000 years. *J. Geol.* **74**, 109–126.

Evans, J. G. 1972. *Land snails in archaeology with special reference to the British Isles*. Seminar Press, London.

Evans, R. 1972. Air photographs for soil survey in lowland England: soil patterns. *Photogramm. Rec.* **7**, 302–322.

Evans, R. 1980. Mechanics of water erosion and their spatial and temporal controls: an empirical viewpoint, pp. 109–128 in: *Soil erosion* (eds. M. J. Kirkby and R. P. C. Morgan). Wiley, Chichester.

Evans, R. and Catt, J. A. 1987. Causes of crop patterns in eastern England. *J. Soil Sci.* **38**, 309–324.

Evenson, E. B. 1971. The relationship of macro- and microfabric of till and the genesis of glacial landforms in Jefferson County, Wisconsin, pp. 345–364 in: *Till: a symposium* (eds. R. P. Goldthwait, J. L. Forsyth, D. L. Gross and F. Pessl). Ohio State University Press, Columbus.

Eyles, C. H. and Eyles, N. 1984. Glaciomarine sediments of the Isle of Man as a key to late Pleistocene stratigraphic investigations in the Irish Sea basin. *Geology* **12**, 359–364.

Eyles, N. 1985. Glacial geology: a landsystems approach, pp. 1–18 in: *Glacial geology: an introduction for engineers and earth scientists* (ed. N. Eyles). 2nd edition. Pergamon, Oxford.

Eyles, N. and Sladen, J. A. 1981. Stratigraphy and geotechnical properties of weathered lodgement till in Northumberland, England. *Quart. J. Engng Geol.* **14**, 129–141.

Eyles, N., Eyles, C. H. and Miall, A. D. 1983. Lithofacies types and vertical profile models; an alternative approach to the description and environmental interpretation of glacial diamict and diamictite sequences. *Sedimentology* **30**, 393–410.

Fairbridge, R. 1977. Rates of sea-ice erosion of Quaternary littoral platforms. *Studia Geol. Polon.* **52**, 135–142.

Farres, P. 1978. The role of time and aggregate size in the crusting process. *Earth Surf. Processes* **3**, 243–254.

Farwell, G. W., Grootes, P. M., Leach, D. D. and Schmidt, F. H. 1984. The accelerator mass spectrometry facility at the University of Washington: current status and an application to the ^{14}C profile of a tree ring. *Nuclear Instr. Methods* **233**, B5, 2, 144–149.

Feely, R. A. and Chen, C. T. A. 1982. The effect of excess CO_2 on the calculated calcite and aragonite saturation horizons in the northeast Pacific. *Geophys. Res. Lett.* **9**, 1294–1297.

Ferguson, C. W. 1970. Dendrochronology of bristlecone pine, *Pinus aristata*: establishment of a 7484-year chronology in the White Mountains of eastern California, pp. 237–259 in: *Radiocarbon variations and absolute chronology* (ed. I. U. Olsson). Wiley, New York.

Ferrians, O. J., Kachadoorian, R. and Greene, G. W. 1969. Permafrost and related engineering problems in Alaska. *U.S. Geol. Surv. Prof. Paper* **678**.

Field, E. G. 1979. Corrosion control in the water industry. *Water Services* **83**, 609–616.

Finkl, C. W. and Gilkes, R. J. 1976. Relationships between micromorphological soil features and known stratigraphic layers in Western Australia. *Geoderma* **15**, 179–208.

Fischer, W. A. 1962. Colour aerial photography in geologic investigations. *Photogramm. Engng* **28**, 133–139.

Fisher, D. A. 1979. Comparison of 10^5 years of oxygen isotope and insoluble impurity profiles from the Devon Island and Camp Century ice cores. *Quat. Res.* **11**, 299–305.

Fitch, F. J. 1972. Selection of suitable material for dating and the assessment of geological error in potassium–argon dating, pp. 77–91 in: *Calibration of hominoid evolution* (eds. W. W. Bishop and J. A. Miller). Scottish Academic Press, Edinburgh.

Fitch, F. J., Hooker, P. J. and Miller, J. A. 1976. Argon 40/argon 39 dating of the KBS tuff in Koobi Fora Formation, East Rudolph, Kenya. *Nature* **263**, 740–744.

Fleming, S. J. 1979. *Thermoluminescence techniques in archaeology.* Clarendon Press, Oxford.

Flint, R. F. 1971. *Glacial and Quaternary geology.* Wiley, New York.

Flint, R. F. and Gebert, J. A. 1976. Latest Laurentide ice sheet: new evidence from southern New England. *Bull. Geol. Soc. Amer.* **87**, 182–188.

Flohn, H. 1981. Major climatic events associated with a prolonged CO_2-induced warming. *Institute of Energy Analytical Report, Oak Ridge Nat. Lab., Tennessee.*

Food and agriculture organization of the United Nations. 1972. *Catalogue of maps. Soil map of the world project* (4th edition). Food and agriculture organization, Rome.

Food and agriculture organization of the United Nations. 1974a. *Soil map of the world 1:5 000 000: Volume I Legend.* UNESCO, Paris.

Food and agriculture organization of the United Nations. 1974b. Approaches to land classification. *Soils Bull.* **22**, Food and agriculture organization, Rome.

Food and agriculture organization of the United Nations. 1976. A framework for land evaluation. *Soils Bull.* **32**. Food and agriculture organization, Rome.

Food and agriculture organization of the United Nations. 1977. *Guidelines for soil profile description* (2nd edition). Food and agriculture organization, Rome.

Food and agriculture organization of the United Nations. 1984. Guidelines: land evaluation for rainfed agriculture. *Soils Bull.* **52**. Food and agriculture organization, Rome.

Food and agriculture organization of the United Nations. 1985a. *Soil map of the world 1:5 000 000 revised legend.* Food and agriculture organization, Rome.
Food and agriculture organization of the United Nations. 1985b. Guidelines: land evaluation for irrigated agriculture. *Soils Bull.* 55. Food and agriculture organization, Rome.
Fookes, P. G. and Knill, J. L. 1969. The application of engineering geology in the regional development of northern and central Iran. *Engrg Geol.* **3**, 81–120.
Foose, R. M. 1953. Ground-water behavior in the Hershey Valley, Pennsylvania. *Bull. Geol. Soc. Amer.* **64**, 623–645.
Foster, SD. M. and Nicholson, T. H. 1980. Microbial aggregation of sand in a maritime dune succession. *Soil Biol. Biochem.* **13**, 205–208.
Francis, E. A. 1975. Glacial sediments: a selective review, pp. 43–68 in: *Ice ages: ancient and modern* (eds. A. E. Wright and F. Moseley). *Geological Journal* Special Issue **6**. Seel House Press, Liverpool.
Frechen, J. and Lippolt, H. J. 1965. Kalium–Argon-daten zum alter des Laacher Vulkanismus der Rheinterrassen und der Eiszeiten. *Eisz. Gegenw.* **16**, 5–30.
Freed, W. K. and Healy, N. 1974. Excursions of the Pleistocene geomagnetic field recorded in Gulf of Mexico sediments. *Earth Planet. Sci. Lett.* **24**, 99–104.
Freeze, R. A. and Cherry, J. A. 1979. *Groundwater.* Prentice-Hall, Englewood Cliffs.
French, H. M. 1971. Slope asymmetry of the Beaufort Plain, northwest Banks Island, N.W.T., Canada. *Canad. J. Earth Sci.* **8**, 717–731.
French, H. M. 1976. *The periglacial environment.* Longman, London.
Frenzel, B. 1964. Zur pollenanalyse von Lössen. Untersuchungen der Lössprofile von Oberfellabrunn und Stillfried (Niederösterreich). *Eisz. Gegenw.* **15**, 5–39.
Friedman, I. and Long, W. 1976. Hydration rate of obsidian. *Science* **191**, 347–352.
Friedman, I. and Trembour, F. W. 1978. Obsidian: the dating stone. *Amer. Sci.* **66**, 44–51.
Friedman, J. D., Frank, D., Kieffer, H. H. and Sawatzky, D. L. 1981. The 1980 eruptions of Mount St. Helens, Washington. Thermal infrared surveys of the 18 May crater, subsequent lava domes, and associated volcanic deposits. *U.S. Geol. Surv. Prof. Paper* **1250**, 279–293.
Fritts, H. C. 1976. *Tree rings and climate.* Academic Press, London.
Fryberger, S. G. 1980. Dune forms and wind regime, Mauritania, west Africa: implications for past climate, pp. 79–96 in: *Palaeoecology of Africa* (eds. E. M. Van Zinderen Bakker and J. A. Coetzee). Balkema, Rotterdam.
Frye, J. C., Swineford, A. and Leonard, A. B. 1947. Correlation of the Pearlette volcanic ash from the glaciated region into the southern highplains. *Bull. Geol. Soc. Amer.* **58**, 1182.
Frye, J. C., Leonard, A. B., Willman, H. B., Glass, H. D. and Follmer, L. R. 1974. The late Woodfordian Jules Soil and associated molluscan faunas. *Ill. State Geol. Surv. Circ.* **486**.
Fullen, M. A. 1985. Erosion of arable soils in Britain. *Int. J. Env. Stud.* **26**, 55–69.
Funnell, B. M., Norton, P. E. P. and West, R. G. 1979. The crag at Bramerton, near Norwich, Norfolk. *Phil. Trans. Roy. Soc. Lond.* **B287**, 489–534.
Gadd, N. R. 1986. Lithofacies of Leda Clay in the Ottawa basin of the Champlain Sea. *Geol. Surv. Can. Paper*, **85–21**.

Gale, S. J., Hunt, C. O. and Southgate, G. A. 1984. Kirkhead Cave: biostratigraphy and magnetostratigraphy. *Archaeometry* **26**, 192–198.
Garland, G. G. 1982. Mapping erosion with airphotos: panchromatic or black and white infrared. *I.T.C. Journal,* 309–312.
Garrard, R. A. and Dobson, M. R. 1974. The nature and maximum extent of glacial sediments off the west coast of Wales. *Marine Geol.* **16**, 31–44.
Gascoyne, M., Currant, A. P. and Lord, T. C. 1981. Ipswichian fauna of Victoria Cave and the marine palaeoclimatic record. *Nature* **294**, 652–654.
Gascoyne, M., Schwarz, H. P. and Ford, D. C. 1983. Uranium-series ages of speleothems from northwest England: correlation with Quaternary climate. *Phil. Trans. Roy. Soc. Lond.* **B301**, 143–164.
Gascoyne, P. 1978. Mudflow, debris-flow deposits, pp. 488–493 in: *The encyclopedia of sedimentology* (eds. R. W. Fairbridge and J. Bourgeois). Dowden, Hutchinson and Ross, Stroudsburg.
Genthon, C., Barnola, J. M., Raynaud, D., Lorius, C., Jouzel, J., Barkov, N. I., Korotkevich, Y. S. and Kotlyakov, V. M. 1987. Vostok ice core: climatic response to CO_2 and orbital forcing changes over the last climatic cycle. *Nature* **329**, 414–418.
Geological Society Engineering Group Working Party 1988. Engineering geophysics. *Quart J. Engng. Geol.* **21**, 207–271.
Geologists' Association. 1974. *A code for geological field work.* Geologists' Association, London.
George, T. N., Harland, W. B., Ager, D. V., Ball, H. W., Blow, W. H., Casey, R., Holland, C. H., Hughes, N. F., Kellaway, G. A., Kent, P. E., Ramsbottom, W. H. C., Stubblefield, J. and Woodland, A. W. 1969. Recommendations on stratigraphical usage. *Proc. Geol. Soc. Lond.* **1656**, 139–166.
Geyer, A. R. and Socolow, A. A. 1979. A sinkhole swallows a road before our very eyes. *Pennsylv. Geol.* **10**, 2–6.
Gibbard, P. L. 1977. Pleistocene history of the Vale of St. Albans. *Phil. Trans. Roy. Soc. Lond.* **B280**, 445–483.
Gibbs, H. S., Cowie, J. D. and Pullar, W. A. 1968. Soils of North Island, pp. 48–67 in: *Soils of New Zealand Part 1.* New Zealand Soil Bureau Bulletin **26** (1).
Gibbs, R. 1970. Mechanisms controlling world water chemistry. *Science* **170**, 1088–1090.
Gilbert, G. K. 1885. The topographic features of lake shores. *U.S. Geol. Surv. Ann. Rept* **5**, 69–123.
Gilbertson, B. and Longshaw, T. G. 1975. Multispectral aerial photography as an exploration tool. I. Concepts, techniques and instrumentation. *Remote Sensing Env.* **4**, 129–146.
Gilbertson, D. D. 1984. *Late Quaternary environments and man in Holderness.* British Archaeological Reports, British Series **134**.
Gjessing, J. 1966. Some effects of ice erosion on the development of Norwegian valleys and fjords. *Norsk. Geogr. Tidsskr.* **20**, 273–299.
Godwin, H. 1954. Recurrence-surfaces. *Danmarks Geol. Undersøg. (Afh.)* Raekke *2*, **80**, 22–30.
Göksu, H. Y. and Fremlin, J. H. 1972. Thermoluminescence from unirradiated flints: regeneration thermoluminescence. *Archaeometry* **14**, 127–132.

Good, T. R. and Bryant, I. D. 1985. Fluvio-aeolian sedimentation — an example from Banks Island, N.W.T., Canada. *Geogr. Ann.* **A67**, 33–46.

Goodchild, J. G. 1875. The glacial phenomena of the Eden Valley and the western part of the Yorkshire-Dale district. *Quart. J. Geol. Soc. Lond.* **31**, 55–99.

Goosen, D. 1967. Aerial photo interpretation in soil survey. *Soils Bull.* **6**. Food and agriculture organization, Rome.

Gordon, J. E. 1981. Glacier margin fluctuations during the 19th and 20th centuries in the Ikamiut Kangerdluarssuat area, west Greenland. *Arct. Alp. Res.* **13**, 47–62.

Goudie, A. S. 1973. *Duricrusts in tropical and sub-tropical landscapes.* Clarendon Press, Oxford.

Goudie, A. S. 1977. *Environmental change.* Clarendon Press, Oxford.

Goudie, A. S. 1978. Dust storms and their geomorphological implications. *J. Arid. Env.* **1**, 291–310.

Goudie, A. S., Cooke, R. U. and Doornkamp, J. C. 1979. The formation of silt from quartz dune sands by salt-weathering processes in deserts. *J. Arid. Env.* **2**, 105–112.

Govett, G. J. S. 1973. Geochemical exploration studies in glaciated terrain, New Brunswick, Canada, pp. 11–24 in: *Prospecting in areas of glacial terrain* (ed. M. J. Jones). Institution of Mining and Metallurgy, London.

Grainger, P., McCann, D. M. and Gallois, R. W. 1973. The application of the seismic refraction technique to the study of the Middle Chalk at Mundford, Norfolk. *Géotechnique* **23**, 219–232.

Grave, N. A. 1968. The earth's permafrost beds. *Canada Defense Research Board Translation* T499R, 1–10.

Green, C. P. and McGregor, D. F. M. 1980. Quaternary evolution of the River Thames, pp. 177–202 in: *The shaping of southern England* (ed. D. K. C. Jones). Institute of British Geographers Special Publication **11**.

Green, C. P., McGregor, D. F. M. and Evans, A. H. 1982. Development of the Thames drainage system in early and middle Pleistocene times. *Geol. Mag.* **119**, 281–290.

Greensmith, J. T. and Tucker, E. V. 1980. Evidence for differential subsidence on the Essex coast. *Proc. Geol. Assoc.* **91**, 169–175.

Gregory, K. J. and Walling, D. E. 1973. *Drainage basin form and process.* Edward Arnold, London.

Grisak, G. E. and Cherry, J. A. 1975. Hydrogeological characteristics and response of fractured till and clay confining a shallow aquifer. *Canad. Geotech. J.* **12**, 23–43.

Grisak, G. E., Cherry, J. A., Vonhof, J. A. and Bleumle, J. P. 1976. Hydrogeologic and hydrochemical properties of fractured till in the interior plains region, pp. 304–335 in: *Glacial till* (ed. R. F. Legget). Special Publication Royal Society of Canada **12**.

Grove, A. T. 1969. Landforms and climatic change in the Kalahari and Ngamiland. *Geogr. J.* **135**, 191–212.

Grove, A. T. and Warren, A. 1968. Quaternary landforms and climate on the south side of the Sahara. *Geogr. J.* **134**, 194–208.

Guillet, B. and Souchier, B. 1982. Amorphous and crystalline oxhydroxides and oxides in soils (iron, aluminium, manganese, silicon), pp. 21–42 in: *Constituents and properties of soils* (eds. M. Bonneau and B. Souchier, trans. V. C. Farmer). Academic Press, London.

Gwynne, C. S. 1950. Terraced highway side slopes in loess, southwestern Iowa. *Bull. Geol. Soc. Amer.* **61**, 1347–1354.

Hageman, B. P. 1969. Development of the western part of the Netherlands during the Holocene. *Geol. Mijnb.* **48**, 373–388.

Haldorsen, S. and Shaw, J. 1982. The problem of recognizing melt-out till. *Boreas* **11**, 261–277.

Hall, A. M. 1985. Cenozoic weathering covers in Buchan, Scotland and their significance. *Nature* **315**, 392–395.

Hall, A. M., Thomas, M. F. and Thorp, M. B. 1985. Late Quaternary alluvial placer development in the humid tropics: the case of the Birim diamond placer, Ghana. *J. Geol. Soc. Lond.* **142**, 777–787.

Hall, B. R. and Folland, C. J. 1967. Soils of the south-west Lancashire coastal plain (sheets 74 and 83). *Mem. Soil Surv. Gt. Brit.*

Hall, C. M., York, D. and Bonhommet, N. 1979. $^{40}Ar/^{39}Ar$ dating of the Laschamp event and associated volcanism in the Chaine des puys. *EOS, Trans. Amer. Geophys. Un.* **60**, 244.

Hall, D. G. M., Reeve, M. J., Thomasson, A. J. and Wright, V. F. 1977. Water retention, porosity and density of field soils. *Soil Surv. Tech. Monogr.* **9**. Soil Survey of England and Wales, Harpenden.

Hallbauer, D. K. and Utter, T. 1977. Geochemical and morphological characteristics of gold particles from recent river deposits and the fossil placers of the Witwatersrand. *Mineralium Deposita* **12**, 293–306.

Hallberg, G. R. 1986. Pre-Wisconsin glacial stratigraphy of the central plains region in Iowa, Nebraska, Kansas, and Missouri. *Quat. Sci. Rev.* **5**, 11–15.

Hammer, C. U., Clausen, H. B., Dansgaard, W., Gundestrup, N., Johnsen, S. J. and Reeh, N. 1978. Dating of Greenland ice cores by flow models, isotopes, volcanic debris, and continental dust. *J. Glaciol.* **20**, 3–26.

Hammer, M. J. and Thomson, U. B. 1966. Foundation clay shrinkage caused by large trees. *Proc. Amer. Soc. Civil Engrs* **92**, SM2, Paper 4956.

Hampton, M. A. 1975. Competence of fine-grained debris flows. *J. Sedim. Petrol.* **45**, 834–844.

Handy, R. L. 1973. Collapsible loess in Iowa. *Soil Sci. Soc. Amer. Proc.* **37**, 281–284.

Hansen, J., Johnson, D., Lacis, A., Lebedeff, S. and Lee, P. 1981. Climate impact of increasing atmospheric carbon dioxide. *Science* **213**, 957–966.

Hansen, K. 1959. Sediments from Danish lakes. *J. Sedim. Petrol.* **29**, 38–46.

Harden, J. W. 1982. A quantitative index of soil development from field descriptions: examples from a chronosequence in central California. *Geoderma* **28**, 1–28.

Hardy, R. M. 1950. Construction problems in silty soils. *Engng J. Montreal* **33**, 775–782.

Haring, A., De Vries, A. E. and De Vries, H. 1958. Radiocarbon dating up to 70 000 years by isotopic enrichment. *Science* **128**, 472–473.

Harland, W. B., Ager, D. V., Ball, H. W., Bishop, W. W., Blow, W. H., Curry, D., Deer, W. A., George, T. N., Holland, C. H., Holmes, S. C. A., Hughes, N. F.,

Kent, P. E., Pitcher, W. S., Ramsbottom, W. H. C., Stubblefield, C. J., Wallace, P. and Woodland, A. W. 1972. A concise guide to stratigraphical procedure. *J. Geol. Soc. Lond.* **128**, 295–305.

Harmer, F. W. 1914–25. The Pliocene Mollusca. *Monogr. Palaeont. Soc.*

Harmon, R. S., Land, L. S., Mitterer, R. M., Garrett, P., Schwarz, H. P. and Larson, G. J. 1981. Bermuda sea level during the last interglacial. *Nature* **289**, 481–483.

Harmon, R. S., Thompson, P., Schwarz, H. P. and Ford, D. C. 1978. Late Pleistocene paleoclimates of North America as inferred from stable isotope studies of speleothems. *Quat. Res.* **9**, 54–70.

Harris, C. 1981. Periglacial mass-wasting: a review of research. *Brit. Geomorph. Res. Group Res. Monogr.* **4**. GeoAbstracts, Norwich.

Harris, C. 1987. Solifluction and related periglacial deposits in England and Wales, pp. 209–223 in: *Periglacial processes and landforms in Britain and Ireland* (ed. J. Boardman). Cambridge University Press.

Harrison, C. G. A. and Ramirez, E. 1975. Areal coverage of spurious reversals of the earth's magnetic field. *J. Geomagn. Geoelec.* **27**, 139–151.

Hartshorne, J. H. 1958. Flowtill in southeastern Massachusetts. *Bull. Geol. Soc. Amer.* **69**, 477–481.

Hawkins, A. B. and Privett, K. D. 1981. A building site on cambered ground at Radstock, Avon. *Quart. J. Engng Geol.* **14**, 151–167.

Hay, R. L. and Jones, B. F. 1972. Weathering of basaltic tephra on the Island of Hawaii. *Bull. Geol. Soc. Amer.* **83**, 317–332.

Haynes, F. E. and Wyman, R. A. 1962. The application of heavy media separation to concrete aggregate. *Bull. Can. Inst. Min. Metall.* **55**, 489–496.

Hays, J. D., Imbrie, J. and Shackleton, N. J. 1976. Variations in the earth's orbit: pacemaker of the ice ages. *Science* **194**, 1121–1132.

Head, K. H. 1980. *Manual of soil laboratory testing. Volume* 1. *Soil classification and compaction tests.* Pentech Press, Plymouth.

Head, K. H. 1982. *Manual of soil laboratory testing. Volume* 2. *Permeability, shear strength and compressibility tests.* Pentech Press, Plymouth.

Head, K. H. 1986. *Manual of soil laboratory testing. Volume* 3. *Effective stress tests.* Pentech Press, London.

Healy, T. 1981. Submarine terraces and morphology in the Kieler Bucht, western Baltic, and their relation to Quaternary events. *Boreas* **10**, 209–217.

Hedges, R. E. M. 1981. Radiocarbon dating with an accelerator. *Archaeometry* **23**, 3–18.

Hedges, R. E. M. 1987. Radiocarbon dating by accelerator mass spectrometry: some recent results and applications. *Phil. Trans. Roy. Soc. Lond.* **A323,** 57–73.

Heer, O. 1865. *Die Urwelt der Schweiz.* Friedrich Schulthess, Zürich.

Heim, A. 1919. *Geologie der Schweiz.* Tauchnitz, Leipzig.

Heller, F. 1980. Self-reversal of natural remanent magnetization in the Olby–Laschamp lavas. *Nature* **284**, 334–335.

Heller, F. and Liu Tungsheng 1984. Magnetism of Chinese loess deposits. *Geophys. J. Roy. Astron. Soc.* **77**, 125–141.

Hennig, G. J. and Grün, R. 1983. ESR dating in Quaternary geology. *Quat. Sci. Rev.* **2**, 157–238.

Hesse, P. R. 1971. *A textbook of soil chemical analysis*. Murray, London.

Hickin, E. J. 1974. The development of meanders in natural river channels. *Amer. J. Sci.* **274**, 414–442.

Hirsch, S. N., Kruckeberg, R. F. and Madden, F. M. 1971. The bi-spectral forest fire detection system. *Proc. 7th Int. Symp. Remote Sensing Env.*, 2253–2272.

Hjort, C. 1979. Glaciation in northern East Greenland during the late Weichselian and early Flandrian. *Boreas* **8**, 281–296.

Hobbs, N. B. 1986. Mire morphology and the properties and behaviour of some British and foreign peats. *Quart. J. Engng Geol.* **19**, 7–80.

Hobbs, P. V. 1974. *Ice physics*. Clarendon Press, Oxford.

Hodder, A. P. W. 1978. Refractive index and hydration of rhyolitic glass from Holocene tephras, North Island, New Zealand. *New Zealand J. Geol. Geophys.* **21**, 155–166.

Hodgson , D. M. 1986. A study of fluted moraines in the Torridon area, NW Scotland. *J. Quat. Sci.* **1**, 109–118.

Hodgson, J. M. 1964. The low-level Pleistocene marine sands and gravels of the West Sussex coastal plain. *Proc. Geol. Assoc.* **75**, 547–562.

Hodgson, J. M. (ed.) 1976. Soil Survey field handbook. *Soil Surv. Tech. Monogr.* **5**. Soil Survey of England and Wales, Harpenden.

Hodgson, J. M., Hollis, J. M., Jones, R. J. A, and Palmer, R. C. 1976. A comparison of field estimates and laboratory analyses of the silt and clay contents of some West Midland soils. *J. Soil Sci.* **27**, 411–419.

Hoffert, M. I., Wey, Y. C., Callegari, A. J. and Broecker, W. S. 1979. Atmospheric response to deep-sea injections of fossil-fuel carbon dioxide. *Clim. Change* **2**, 53–68.

Holland, C. H., Audley-Charles, M. G., Bassett, M. G., Cowie, J. W., Curry, D., Fitch, F. J., Hancock, J. M., House, M. R., Ingham, J. K., Kent, P. E., Morton, N., Ramsbottom, W. H. C., Rawson, P. F., Smith, D. B., Stubblefield, C. J., Torrens, H. S., Wallace, P. and Woodland, A. W. 1978. A guide to stratigraphical procedure. *Geol. Soc. Lond. Spec. Rept* **11**.

Hollingworth, S. E., Taylor, J. H. and Kellaway, G. A. 1944. Large-scale superficial structures in the Northampton ironstone field. *Quart. J. Geol. Soc. Lond.* **100**, 1–44.

Hollyer, S. E. and Allender, R. 1982. The sand and gravel resources of the country around Hollesley, Suffolk: description of 1:25,000 resource sheet TM 34. *Inst. Geol. Sci. Miner. Assessm. Rept* **83**.

Holmes, C. D. 1941. Till fabric. *Bull. Geol. Soc. Amer.* **52**, 1299–1354.

Holtedahl, H. 1967. Notes on the formation of fjords and fjord-valleys. *Geogr. Ann.* **A49**, 188–203.

Holyoak, D. T. 1982. Non-marine Mollusca of the last glacial period (Devensian) in Britain. *Malacologia* **22**, 727–730.

Holyoak, D. T. 1986. Reassessment of the Grand Pile record of the last 120,000 years. *Quat. Newsl.* **50**, 35–36.

Hooghiemstra, H. 1984. Vegetational and climatic history of the High Plain of Bogotá, Colombia: a continuous record of the last 3.5 million years. *Dissert. Botan.* **79**, 1–368.

Hopkins, D. M. 1949. Thaw lakes and thaw sinks in the Imuruk Lake area, Seward Peninsula, Alaska. *J. Geol.* **57**, 119–131.

Horn, F. L. and Steinberg, M. 1982. Possible sites for disposal and environmental control of atmospheric carbon dioxide. *Rept BNL* 51597 *Brookhaven Nat. Lab., Upton, New York.*

Horner, R. W. 1984. The Thames tidal flood risk — the need for the barrier: a review of its design and construction. *Quart. J. Engng Geol.* **17**, 199–206.

Horswill, P., Horton, A. and Vaughan, P. R. 1976. Cambering and valley bulging in the Gwash Valley at Empingham, Rutland. *Phil. Trans. Roy. Soc. Lond.* **A283**, 427–462.

Horton, A., Worssam, B. C. and Whittow, J. B. 1981. The Wallingford fan gravel. *Phil. Trans. Roy. Soc. Lond.* **B293**, 215–255.

Horton, R. E. 1945. Erosional development of streams and their drainage basins: hydrophysical approach to quantitative morphology. *Bull. Geol. Soc. Amer.* **56**, 275–370.

Hudson, N. W. 1981. *Soil conservation*. Batsford, London.

Hunter, G. T. and Bird, S. J. G. 1970. Critical terrain analysis. *Photogramm. Engng* **36**, 939–952.

Hutchinson, G. E. 1957. *A treatise on limnology. Volume* 1. *Geography, physics and chemistry*. Wiley, New York.

Hutchinson, J. N., Petley, D. J. and Somerville, S. H. 1973. A landslide in periglacially disturbed Etruria Marl at Bury Hill, Staffordshire. *Quart. J. Engng Geol.* **6**, 377–404.

Hyvärinen, L., Kauranne, K. and Yletyinen, V. 1973. Modern boulder tracing in prospecting, pp. 87–95 in: *Prospecting in areas of glacial terrain* (ed. M. J. Jones). Institution of Mining and Metallurgy, London.

Ikeya, M. 1978. Electron spin resonance as a method of dating. *Archaeometry* **20**, 147–158.

Ikeya, M. 1985. Dating methods of Pleistocene deposits and their problems. IX. Electron spin resonance, pp. 73–87 in: *Dating methods of Pleistocene deposits and their problems* (ed. N. W. Rutter). Geoscience Canada Reprint Series **2**.

Imai, T., Sakayama, T. and Kanemori, T. 1987. Use of ground-probing radar and resistivity surveys for archaeological investigations. *Geophysics* **52**, 137–150.

Imbrie, J. and Kipp, N. G. 1971. A new micropaleontological method for quantitative paleoclimatology: application to a late Pleistocene Caribbean core, pp. 71–181 in: *Late Cenozoic glacial ages* (ed. K. K. Turekian). Yale University Press, New Haven.

Imbrie, J., Hays, J. D., Martinson, D. G., McIntyre, A., Mix, A. C., Morley, J. J., Pisias, N. G., Prell, W. L. and Shackleton, N. J. 1984. The orbital theory of Pleistocene climate: support from a revised chronology of the marine $\delta^{18}O$ record, pp. 269–305 in: *Milankovitch and climate. Part I.* (eds. A. Berger, J. Imbrie, J. Hays, G. Kukla and B. Saltzman). NATO ASI Series C126. Reidel, Dordrecht.

Imhuff, M. L., Petersen, G. W., Sykes, S. G. and Irons, J. R. 1982. Digital overlay of cartographic information on Landsat MSS data for soil surveys. *Photogramm. Engng Remote Sensing* **48**, 1337–1342.

Institution of Geologists 1985. *Code of practice for geological visits to quarries, mines and caves*. Institution of Geologists, London.

International Society of Soil Science 1967. Proposal for a uniform system of soil horizon designations. *Bull. Int. Soc. Soil Sci.* **31**, 4–7.
International Subcommission on Stratigraphic Classification 1976. *International stratigraphic guide. A guide to stratigraphic classification, terminology and procedure.* Wiley, New York.
Iranpanah, A. and Esfaniari, B. 1980. Interpretation of structural lineaments using Landsat 1 images. *Photogramm. Engng Remote Sensing* **46**, 225–232.
Ivanovich, M. and Harmon, R. S. 1982. *Uranium series disequilibrium applications to environmental problems.* Clarendon Press, Oxford.
Iversen, J. D. and White, B. R. 1982. Saltation threshold on Earth, Mars and Venus. *Sedimentology* **29**, 111–119.
Izett, G. A. 1981. Volcanic ash beds: recorders of upper Cenozoic silicic pyroclastic volcanism in the western United States. *J. Geophys. Res.* **86**, 10200–10222.
Jackson, M. L. 1969. *Soil chemical analysis advanced course.* University of Wisconsin, Madison.
Jackson, P. S. and Hunt, J. C. R. 1975. Flow over a small hill. *Quart. J. Roy. Meteorol. Soc.* **101**, 929–955.
Jacobi, H. S. and Davis, R. F. 1925. *Foundations of bridges and buildings.* McGraw-Hill, New York.
Jamagne, M. 1972. Some micromorphological aspects of soils developed in loess deposits of northern France, pp. 554–582 in: *Soil micromorphology* (ed. S. Kowalinski). Panstwowe Wydawnictwo Naukowe, Warszawa.
Janacek, T. R. and Rea, D. K. 1985. Quaternary fluctuations in the northern hemisphere trade winds and westerlies. *Quat. Res.* **24**, 150–163.
Janza, F. J. 1975. Interaction mechanisms, pp. 75–179 in: *Manual of remote sensing* (ed. R. G. Reeves). American Society of Photogrammetry, Falls Church.
Jarrett, P. M. (ed.) 1983. Testing of peats and organic soils. *Amer. Soc. Testing Materials Tech. Publ.* **820**.
Jarvis, M. G. and Mackney, D. (eds.) 1979. Soil survey applications. *Soil Surv. Tech. Monogr.* **13**. Soil Survey of England and Wales, Harpenden.
Jenkins, D. G. 1987. Was the Pliocene–Pleistocene boundary placed at the wrong stratigraphic level? *Quat. Sci. Rev.* **6**, 41–42.
Jenkinson, R. D. S. 1984. *Cresswell Crags: Late Pleistocene sites in the east Midlands.* British Archaeological Reports, Oxford.
Jennings, J. N. 1985. *Karst geomorphology.* Blackwell, Oxford.
Jenny, H. 1935. The clay content of the soil as related to climatic factors, particularly temperature. *Soil. Sci.* **40**, 111–128.
Jenny, H. 1941. *Factors of soil formation. A system of quantitative pedology.* McGraw-Hill, New York.
Jenny, H. 1958. Role of the plant factor in the pedogenic functions. *Ecology* **39**, 5–16.
Jenny, H. 1961. Derivation of state factor equations of soils and ecosystems. *Soil Sci. Soc. Amer. Proc.* **25**, 385–388.
Jenny, H. 1980. *The soil resource: origin and behavior.* Springer-Verlag, New York.
Jenny, H. and Leonard, C. D. 1934. Functional relationships between soil properties and rainfall. *Soil. Sci.* **38**, 363–381.
Jenny, H., Salem, A. E. and Wallis, J. R. 1968. Interplay of soil organic matter and

soil fertility with state factors and soil properties, pp. 5–44 in: *Study week on organic matter and soil fertility. Pontif. Acad. Sci. Scripta Var.* **32**. Wiley, New York.

Jensen, J. R. and Hodgson, M. E. 1983. Remote sensing brightness maps. *Photogram. Engng Remote Sensing* **49**, 93–102.

Johnson, E. E. 1966. *Ground water and wells. A reference book for the water-well industry*. E. E. Johnson Inc., Saint Paul, Minnesota.

Johnson, R. W., Glaccum, R. and Wojtasinski, R. 1980. Application of ground penetrating radar to soil survey. *Soil Crop Sci. Soc. Fla Proc.* **39**, 68–72.

Jones, P. F. and Derbyshire, E. 1983. Late Pleistocene periglacial degradation of lowland Britain: implications for civil engineering. *Quart. J. Engng Geol.* **16**, 197–210.

Jones, R. J. 1965. Aspects of biological weathering of limestone pavement. *Proc. Geol. Assoc.* **76**, 421–433.

Jones, R. L. and Beavers, A. H. 1964a. Aspects of catenary and depth distribution of opal phytoliths in Illinois soils. *Soil Sci. Soc. Amer. Proc.* **28**, 413–416.

Jones, R. L. and Beavers, A. H. 1964b. Variation in opal phytolith content among some great soil groups of Illinois. *Soil Sci. Soc. Amer. Proc.* **28**, 711–712.

Jouzel, J., Lorius, C., Petit, J. R., Genthon, C., Barkov, N. I., Kotlyakov, V. M. and Petrov, V. M. 1987. Vostok ice core: a continuous isotope temperature record over the last climatic cycle (160,000 years). *Nature* **329**, 403–408.

Jowsey, P. C. 1966. An improved peat sampler. *New Phytol.* **65**, 245–249.

Kämpf, N. and Schwertmann, U. 1983. Goethite and haematite in a climo-sequence in southern Brazil and their application in classification of kaolinitic soils. *Geoderma* **29**, 27–39.

Karlén, W. 1973. Holocene glacier variations in Sarek National Park, northern Sweden. *Geogr. Ann.* **55A**, 29–63.

Kassif, G., Livneh, M. and Wiseman, G. 1970. *Pavements on expansive clays*. Jerusalem Academic Press, Jerusalem.

Kaufman, A., Broecker, W. S., Ku, T. L. and Thurber, D. L. 1971. The status of U-series methods of mollusk dating. *Geochim. Cosmochim. Acta* **35**, 1155–1183.

Kay, G. F. 1931. Classification and duration of the Pleistocene Period. *Bull. Geol. Soc. Amer.* **42**, 425–466.

Kayan, I. and Klemas, V. 1978. Application of Landsat imagery to studies of structural geology and geomorphology of the Mentese region of south west Turkey. *Remote Sensing Env.* **7**, 61–72.

Keef, P. A. M., Wymer, J. J. and Dimbleby, G. W. 1965. A Mesolithic site on Iping Common, Sussex, England. *Proc. Prehist. Soc.* (New Ser.) **31**, 85–92.

Keeling, C. D., Bacastow, R. B. asnd Whorf, T. P. 1982. Measurements of the concentration of carbon dioxide at Mauna Loa Observatory, Hawaii, pp. 377–385 in: *Carbon dioxide review 1982* (ed. W. C. Clark). Clarendon Press, Oxford.

Keilhack, K. 1920. Das Rätsel der Lössbildung. *Zeitschr. Deutsch Geolog. Gesellsch.* **72B**, 146–167.

Kellaway, G. A. 1972. Development of non-diastrophic Pleistocene structures in relation to climate and physical relief in Britain. *Rept 24th Int. Geol. Congr., Montreal* **12**, 120–146.

Kellaway, G. A. and Taylor, J. H. 1953. Early states in the physiographic evolution of a portion of the east Midlands. *Quart. J. Geol. Soc. Lond.* **108**, 343–375.

Kellaway, G. A., Horton, A. and Poole, E. G. 1971. The development of some Pleistocene structures in the Cotswolds and upper Thames basin. *Bull. Geol. Surv. Gt. Brit.* **37**, 1–28.

Kelling, G. 1968. Patterns of sedimentation in Rhondda Beds of south Wales. *Bull. Amer. Assoc. Petrol. Geol.* **52**, 2369–2386.

Kellogg, W. W. 1979. Influences of mankind on climate. *Ann. Rev. Earth Planet. Sci.* **7**, 63–92.

Kemp, R. 1985. The cause of redness in some buried and non-buried soils in eastern England. *J. Soil Sci.* **36**, 329–334.

Kennedy, J. M. 1968. A microwave radiometric study of buried karst topography. *Bull. Geol. Soc. Amer.* **79**, 735–742.

Kent, P. E. 1966. The transport mechanism in catastrophic rock falls. *J. Geol.* **74**, 79–83.

Kerney, M. P. 1977. British Quaternary non-marine Mollusca: a brief review, pp. 31–42 in: *British Quaternary studies recent advances* (ed. F. W. Shotton). Clarendon Press, Oxford.

Kidson, C. 1982. Sea level changes in the Holocene. *Quat. Sci. Rev.* **1**, 121–151.

King. K. 1980. Applications of amino acid biogeochemistry for marine sediments, pp. 377–391 in: *Biogeochemistry of amino acids* (eds. P. E. Hare, T. C. Hoering and K. King). Wiley, New York.

Kirkby. M. J. 1969. Infiltration, throughflow and overland flow, pp. 215–238 in: *Water, earth and man. A synthesis of hydrology* (ed. R. J. Chorley). Methuen, London.

Kleiss, H. J. 1970. Hillslope sedimentation and soil formation in northeastern Iowa. *Soil Sci. Soc. Amer. Proc.* **34**, 287–290.

Kleywegt, R. J. and Enslin, J. F. 1975. The application of the gravity method to the problem of ground settlement and sinkhole formation in dolomite on the Far West Rand, South Africa. *Proc. Hanover Symp. Sinkholes Subsidence Int. Assoc. Engng Geol.* Paper T3–0.

Klimek, K. 1974. The retreat of alluvial river banks in the Wisloka valley (south Poland). *Geogr. Polon.* **28**, 59–75.

Klingebiel, A. A. and Montgomery, P. H. 1961. Land capability classification. *Agriculture handbook* 210. U.S. Department of Agriculture, Washington.

Knill, J. L. 1968. Geotechnical significance of certain glacially-induced discontinuities in rock. *Bull. Assn Engng Geol.* **5**, 49–62.

Knill, J. L. 1971. Environmental, economic and engineering factors in the selection of reservoir sites, with particular reference to northern England, pp. 124–143 in: *Geological aspects of development and planning in northern England* (ed. P. T. Warren). Yorkshire Geological Society, Leeds.

Kocurek, G. and Fielder, G. 1982. Adhesion structures. *J. Sedim. Petrol.* **52**, 1229–1241.

Kohn, B. P. 1979. Identification and significance of a late Pleistocene tephra in Canterbury district, South Island, New Zealand. *Quat. Res.* **11**, 78–92.

Kohnke, H., Stuff, R. G. and Miller, P. A. 1968. Quantitative relations between climate and soil formation. *Zeitschr. Pflanz. Düng. Bodenk.* **119**, 24–33.

Kolla, V. P., Biscaye, P. E. and Hawley, A. F. 1979. Distribution of quartz in late Quaternary Atlantic sediments in relation to climate. *Quat. Res.* **11**, 261–277.

Konischev, V. N. 1982. Characteristics of cryogenic weathering in the permafrost zone of the European S.S.R. *Arct. Alp. Res.* **14**, 261–265.

Koopmans, B. N. 1973. Drainage analysis on radar images. *I. T. C. Journal*, 464–479.

Kraft, J. C. and John, C. J. 1979. Lateral and vertical facies relations of a transgressive barrier. *Bull. Amer. Assoc. Petrol. Geol.* **63**, 2145–2163.

Krayev, V. F. 1969. On the subsidence of loess soils of Ukraine, *Actes du Colloque de Tokyo IASH–AIHS, UNESCO* **1**, 321–322.

Krinitzsky, E. L. and Turnbull, W. J. 1967. Loess deposits of Mississippi. *Geol. Soc. Amer. Spec. Paper* **94**.

Ku, T. L. 1976. The uranium-series methods of age determination. *Ann. Rev. Earth Planet. Sci.* **4**, 347–379.

Kuenen, P. H. 1960. Experimental abrasion. 4. Eolian action. *J. Geol.* **68**, 427–449.

Kukla, G. J. 1975. Missing link between Milankovitch and climate. *Nature* **253**, 600–603.

Kukla, G. J. 1977. Pleistocene land–sea correlations. 1. Europe. *Earth Sci. Rev.* **13**, 307–374.

Kukla, G. J. 1980. End of the last interglacial: a predictive model for the future? pp. 395–408 in: *Palaeoecology of Africa and the surrounding islands* (eds. E. M. Van Zinderen Bakker and J. A. Coetzee), *Volume 12: Sahara and surrounding seas, sediments and climatic changes* (eds. M. Sarnthein, E. Seibold and P. Rognon). Balkema, Rotterdam.

Kukla, G. J. and Kocí, A. 1972. End of the last interglacial in the loess record. *Quat. Res.* **2**, 374–383.

Kurtén, B. 1968. *Pleistocene mammals of Europe*. Weidenfeld and Nicholson, London.

Lacaille, A. D. 1954. *The Stone Age in Scotland*. Wellcome Historical Medical Museum and Oxford University Press, London.

Lamb, H. H. 1977. *Climate present, past and future. Volume 2. Climatic history and the future*. Methuen, London.

Lamoreaux, P. E. and Newton, J. G. 1986. Catastrophic subsidence: an environmental hazard, Shelby County, Alabama. *Env. Geol. Water Sci.* **8**, 25–40.

Landes, K. K. 1933. Caverns in loess. *Amer. J. Sci.* **25**, 137–139.

Landmesser, C. W., Johnson, T. C. and Wold, R. J. 1982. Seismic reflection study of recessional moraines beneath Lake Superior and their relationship to regional deglaciation. *Quat. Res.* **17**, 173–190.

Langley, K. M. 1978, Dating sediments by a K–Ar method. *Nature* **276**, 56–57.

Lazarenko, A. A., Bolikhovskaya, N. S. and Semenov, V. V. 1981. An attempt at a detailed stratigraphic subdivision of the loess association of the Tashkent region. *Int. Geol. Rev.* **23**, 1335–1346.

Leamy, M. L., Milne, J. D. G., Pullar, W. A. and Bruce, J. G. 1973. Paleopedology and soil stratigraphy in the New Zealand Quaternary succession. *New Zealand J. Geol. Geophys.* **16**, 723–744.

Leberl, F. 1979. Accuracy analysis of stereo side looking radar. *Photogramm. Engng Remote Sens.* **45**, 1083–1096.

Lee, H. A. 1965. Investigation of eskers for mineral exploration. *Geol. Surv. Canada Paper* **65–140**, 1–17.

Legget, R. F. and Crawford, C. B. 1965. Trees and buildings. *Canad. Building Digest.* **62**, 1–4.

Legget, R. F. and Karrow, P. F. 1983. *Handbook of geology in civil engineering.* McGraw-Hill, New York.

Leggo, P. J. 1982. Geological applications of ground impulse radar. *Trans. Inst. Mining Metall.* **B91**, 1–5.

Lehr, H. 1967. Foundation engineering problems in loess soils, pp. 20–24 in: *Proceedings 3rd Asian Regional Conference Soil Mechanics and Foundation Engineering.* Academic Press, Jerusalem.

Leopold, L. B. and Wolman, M. G. 1957. River channel patterns: braided, meandering and straight. *U.S. Geol. Surv. Prof. Paper* **282B**, 39–85.

Leopold, L. B. and Wolman, M. G. 1960. River meanders. *Bull. Geol. Soc. Amer.* **71**, 769–794.

Leopold. L. B., Wolman, M. G. and Miller, J. P. 1964. *Fluvial processes in geomorphology.* Freeman, San Francisco.

Lewis, A. F. G. (ed.) 1969. *Sea-dredged aggregate for concrete. Proceedings of a symposium.* Sand and Gravel Association of Great Britain, London.

Lewis, A. J. and Waite, W. P. 1973. Radar shadow frequency. *Photogramm. Engng* **38**, 189–196.

Libby, W. F. 1952. *Radiocarbon dating.* University of Chicago Press.

Lidgren, R. A. and Sauer, E. K. 1982. The Gronlid crossing, Saskatchewan Provincial Highway No. 6 at the Saskatchewan River. *Canad. Geotech. J.* **19**, 360–380.

Lidmar-Bergström, K. 1982. Pre-Quaternary geomorphological evolution in southern Fennoscandia. *Sver. Geol. Unders.* C 785, Årsbok 75.

Lindsay, J. F. 1970. Clast fabric of till and its development. *J. Sedim. Petrol.* **40**, 629–641.

Linke, G., Katzenberger, O. and Grün, R. 1986. Description and ESR dating of the Holsteinian interglaciation. *Quat. Sci. Rev.* **4**, 319–331.

Liu Tungsheng, An Zhisheng and Yuan Baoyin 1982. Aeolian processes and dust mantles (loess) in China, pp. 1–17 in: *Quaternary dust mantles of China, New Zealand and Australia. Proceedings of a workshop* (ed. R. J. Wasson). Australian National University, Canberra.

Lloyd, J. W., Harker, D. and Baxendale, R. A. 1981. Recharge mechanisms and groundwater flow in the Chalk and drift deposits of southern East Anglia. *Quart. J. Engng Geol.* **14**, 87–96.

Lobdell, G. T. 1981. Hydroconsolidation potential of Palouse loess. *Amer. Soc. Civil Engrs J. Geotech. Engrg Div.* **107**, 733–742.

Lock, W. W., Andrews, J. T. and Webber, P. J. 1980. A manual for lichenometry. *Brit. Geomorph. Res. Group Tech. Bull.* **26**.

Lockwood, J. G. 1980. Milankovitch theory and ice ages. *Progr. Phys. Geogr.* **4**, 79–87.

Lodge, D. W. S. 1981. The Seasat-1 synthetic aperture radar: introduction, data reception and processing, pp. 335–356 in: *Remote sensing in meteorology, oceanography and hydrology* (ed. A. P. Cracknell). Ellis Horwood, Chichester.

Lohnes, R. A. and Handy, R. L. 1968. Slope angles in friable loess. *J. Geol.* **76**, 247–258.

Lorius, C., Jouzel, J., Ritz, C., Merlivat, L., Barkov, N. I., Korotkevich, Y. S. and Kotlyakov, V. M. 1985. A 150,000-year climatic record from Antarctic ice. *Nature* **316**, 591–596.

Loughnan, F. C. 1969. *Chemical weathering of the silicate minerals.* Elsevier, Amsterdam.

Loveland, P. J. and Bullock, P. 1976. Chemical and mineralogical properties of brown podzolic soils in comparison with soils of other groups. *J. Soil. Sci.* **27**, 523–540.

Loziński, W. 1909. Über die mechanische Verwitterung der Sandsteine im gemässigten Klima. *Bull. Int. Acad. Sci. Cracov., Sci. Math. Nat. Classe* **1**, 1–25.

Ludlam, S. D. 1976. Laminated sediments in holomictic Berkshire lakes. *Limnol. Oceanogr.* **21**, 743–746.

Lulla, K. 1983. The Landsat satellites and selected aspects of physical geography. *Progr. Phys. Geogr.* **7**, 1–45.

Lundqvist, J. 1975. Ice recession in central Sweden, and the Swedish time scale. *Boreas* **4**, 47–54.

Lundqvist, J. 1980. The deglaciation of Sweden after 10000 B.P. *Boreas* **9**, 229–238.

Lutwick, L. E. 1969. Identification of phytoliths in soils. pp. 77–82 in: *Pedology and Quaternary research* (ed. S. Pawluk). University of Alberta Printing Department, Edmonton.

Maarleveld, G. C. 1960. Wind directions and cover sands in The Netherlands. *Biul. Perygl.* **8**, 49–58.

Mabbutt, J. A. 1977. *Desert landforms.* MIT Press, Cambridge, Massachusetts.

Mackay, J. R. 1978. Contemporary pingos, a discussion. *Biul. Perygl.* **27**, 133–154.

Mackay, J. R. and Black, R. F. 1973. Origin, composition and structure of perennially frozen ground and ground ice: a review. *Proc. 2nd Int. Conf. Permafrost, Yakutsk, USSR, July 1973, N. Amer. Contr.*, 185–192.

Mackin, J. H. 1941. A geologic interpretation of the failure of the Cedar Reservoir, Washington. *Univ. Washington Seattle Engng Exptl Stn Bull.* **107**.

Mackney, D. (ed.) 1974. Soil type and land capability. *Soil Surv. Tech. Monogr.* **4**. Soil Survey of England and Wales, Harpenden.

Madgett, P. A. and Catt, J. A. 1978. Petrography, stratigraphy and weathering of late Pleistocene tills in east Yorkshire, Lincolnshire and north Norfolk. *Proc. Yorks. Geol. Soc.* **42**, 55–108.

Maignien, R. 1969. *Manuel de prospection pédologique.* Office recherche scientifique technique outre-mer, Paris.

Manecki, A., Muszynski, M. and Wrzak, J. 1980. Fine-grained deposits from the bottom of Broggi Glacier and its foreland. *Polska Akad. Nauk Oddz. Krakowie Kom. Nauk Mineral. Prace Mineral.* **64**, 27–46.

Mangerud, J. 1972. Radiocarbon dating of marine shells, including a discussion of apparent age of recent shells from Norway. *Boreas* **1**, 143–172.

Mangerud, J., Sønstegaard, E., Sejrup, H. P. and Haldorsen, S. 1981. A continuous Eemian–early Weichselian sequence containing pollen and marine fossils at Fjøsanger, western Norway. *Boreas* **10**, 137–208.

Mankinen, E. A. and Dalrymple, G. B. 1979. Revised geomagnetic polarity time-scale for the interval 0–5 my B.P. *J. Geophys. Res.* **B84**, 615–626.

Manley, G. 1957. Climatic fluctuations and fuel requirements. *Scot. Geogr. Mag.* **73**, 19–28.

Mann, W. B. 1983. An international reference material for radiocarbon dating. *Radiocarbon* **25**, 519–527.

Manz, P. A. 1978. Bedforms produced by fine cohesionless granular and flaky sediments under subcritical water flows. *Sedimentology* **25**, 83–103.

Marchand, D. E. and Allwardt, A. 1981. Late Cenozoic stratigraphic units in northeastern San Joaquin Valley, California. *U.S. Geol. Surv. Bull.* **1470**.

Marchetti, C. 1977. On geoengineering the CO_2 problem. *Climatic Change* **1**, 59–68.

Marrs, R. W. and Paylor, E. D. 1987. Investigation of a surface spectral anomaly at Table Rock gas field, Wyoming. *Geophysics* **52**, 841–857.

Marshall, C. E. 1977. *The physical chemistry and mineralogy of soils. Volume II. Soils in place. Wiley*, New York.

Marsland, A. 1977. The evaluation of the engineering design parameters for glacial clays. *Quart. J. Engng Geol.* **10**, 1–26.

Masson Smith, D. 1968. An assessment of the usefulness of geophysical methods in prospecting for sand and gravel deposits in the Maldon and Terling areas of Essex. *Appl. Geophys. Unit Inst. Geol. Sci. Rept* GP/16/64A.

Mathers, S. J. and Zalasiewicz, J. A. 1985a. Producing a comprehensive geological map. A case study — the Aldeburgh–Orford area of East Anglia. *Modern Geol.* **9**, 207–220.

Mathers, S. J. and Zalasiewicz, J. A. 1985b. Defining waste and overburden associated with sand and gravel — a geophysical technique. *Quarry Managem.* January 1985, 27–29.

Mayo, L. R., Meier, M. F. and Tangborn, W. V. 1972. A system to combine stratigraphic and annual mass-balance systems: a contribution to the international hydrological decade. *J. Glaciol.* **11**, 3–14.

McCann, D. M., Jackson, P. D. and Culshaw, M. G. 1987. The use of geophysical surveying methods in the detection of natural cavities and mineshafts. *Quart. J. Engng Geol.* **20**, 59–73.

McCoy, R. M. and Lewis, A. J. 1976. Use of radar in hydrology and geomorphology. *Remote Sensing Electromag. Spectrum* **3**, 105–122.

McCrea, W. H. 1975. Ice ages and the galaxy. *Nature* **255**, 607–609.

McDowell, P. 1975. Detection of clay-filled sink holes in the Chalk by geophysical methods. *Quart. J. Engng Geol.* **8**, 303–310.

McFarlane, M. J. 1976. *Laterite and landscape.* Academic Press, London.

McGary, L. M. and Lambert, T. W. 1962. Reconnaissance of ground-water resources of the Jackson Purchase region, Kentucky. *U.S. Geol. Surv. Hydrol. Atlas* **13**.

McGown, A. and Derbyshire, E. 1977. Genetic influences on the properties of tills. *Quart. J. Engng Geol.* **10**, 389–410.

McIldowie, G. 1936. The construction of Silent Valley Reservoir, Belfast water supply. *Min. Proc. Inst. Civil Engnrs* **239**, 465.

McKay, E. D. 1979. Wisconsinan loess stratigraphy of Illinois. pp. 95–108 in: *Wisconsinan, Sargamonian and Illinoian stratigraphy in central Ilinois.* Illin. State Geol. Surv. Guidebook **13**.

McKeague, J. A. 1983. Clay skins and argillic horizons, pp. 367–387 in: *Soil micromorphology, Volume 1.* (eds. P. Bullock and C. P. Murphy). AB Academic Publishers, Berkhamsted.

McKeague, J. A., MacDougall, J. I. and Miles, N. M. 1973. Micromorphological, physical, chemical and mineralogical properties of a catena of soils from Prince Edward Island in relation to their classification and genesis. *Canad. J. Soil. Sci.* **53**, 281–295.

McRae, S. G. 1988. *Practical pedology.* Ellis Horwood, Chichester.

Meier, M. F. 1962. Proposed definitions for glacier mass budget terms. *J. Glaciol.* **4**, 252–265.

Meier, M. F. and Post, A. 1969. What are glacier surges? *Canad. J. Earth Sci.* **6**, 807–817.

Meneley, W. A. 1970. Groundwater resources, pp. 39–50 in: *Physical Environment of Saskatoon Canada* (ed. E. A. Christiansen). Saskatchewan Research Council and National Research Council of Canada, Ottawa.

Mercer, J. H. 1978. West Antarctic ice sheet and CO_2 greenhouse effect: a threat of disaster. *Nature* **271**, 321–325.

Mercer, J. H. 1983. Cenozoic glaciation in the southern hemisphere. *Ann. Rev. Earth Planet. Sci.* **11**, 99–132.

Meyer, A. 1926. Über einige Zusammanhänge zwischen Klima und Boden in Europa. *Chemie Erde* **2**, 209–247.

Miall, A. D. 1977. A review of the braided river depositional environment. *Earth Sci. Rev.* **13**, 1–62.

Miall, A. D. 1978. Lithofacies types and vertical profile models in braided rivers: a summary, pp. 597–604 in: *Fluvial sedimentology* (ed. A. D. Miall). *Canad. Soc. Petrol. Geol. Mem.* **5**.

Milankovitch, M. 1920. *Théorie mathématique des phénomènes thermiques produits par la radiation solaire.* Gauthier–Villars, Paris.

Milankovitch, M. 1930. Mathematische Klimalehre und astronomische Theorie der Klimaschwankungen, pp. 1–176 in: *Handbuch der Klimatologie 1(A)* (eds. W. Köppen and R. Geiger). Gebrüder Borntraeger, Berlin.

Miller, G. H. 1973. Late Quaternary glacial and climatic history of northern Cumberland Peninsula, Baffin Island, N.W.T., Canada. *Quat. Res.* **3**, 561–583.

Miller, G. H. and Mangerud, J. 1985. Aminostratigraphy of European marine interglacial deposits. *Quat. Sci. Rev.* **4**, 215–278.

Miller, J. A. 1972. Dating Pliocene and Pleistocene strata using the potassium–argon and argon 40/argon 39 methods, pp. 63–76 in: *Calibration of hominoid evolution* (eds. W. W. Bishop anbd J. A. Miller). Scottish Academic Press, Edinburgh.

Miller, J. K. 1984. Model for clastic indicator trains in till, pp. 69–77 in: *Prospecting in areas of glaciated terrain 1984.* Institution of Mining and Metallurgy, London.

Miller, V. C. 1961. *Photogeology.* McGraw-Hill, New York.

Milliman, J. D. and Meade, R. H. 1983. World-wide delivery of river sediment to the oceans. *J. Geol.* **91**, 1–21.

Millot, G. 1970. *The geology of clays* (trans. W. R. Farrand and H. Paquet). Chapman and Hall, London.

Milne, G. 1935. Some suggested units of classification and mapping, particularly for East African soils. *Soil Res. (I.S.S.S.)* **4**, 183–198.

Milton, L. E. 1965. Quantitative expression of drainage net patterns. *Austral. J. Sci.* **27**, 238–240.

Ministry of agriculture, fisheries and food 1982. Techniques for measuring soil physical properties. *M.A.F.F. Ref. Book* **441** (2nd edition). H.M.S.O., London.

Ministry of agriculture, fisheries and food 1986. The analysis of agricultural materials. *M.A.F.F. Ref. Book* **427** (3rd edition). H.M.S.O., London.

Missallati, A., Prelat, A. E. and Lyon, R. J. P. 1979. Simultaneous use of geological, geophysical and Landsat digital data in uranium exploration. *Remote Sensing Env.* **8**, 189–210.

Mitchell, C. W. and Howard, J. A. 1978. Land system classification. A case history: Jordan. *AGLT Bull.* **2/78**. Food and agriculture organization, Rome.

Mitchell, G. F., Penny, L. F., Shotton, F. W. and West, R. G. 1973. A corrrelation of Quaternary deposits in the British Isles. *Geol. Soc. Lond. Spec. Rept* 4.

Moffat, A. J., Catt, J. A., Webster, R. and Brown, E. H. 1986. A re-examination of the evidence for a Plio–Pleistocene marine transgression on the Chiltern Hills. 1. Structures and surfaces, *Earth Surf. Processes Landf.* **11**, 95–106.

Moffit, F. H. 1959. *Photogrammetry*. International Textbook Co, Scranton.

Mohr, H. A. 1937. Exploration of soil conditions and sampling operations. *Harvard Univ. Grad. School Engng Bull.* **208**.

Mollard, J. D. and Dishaw, H. E. 1958. Locating and mapping granular construction materials from aerial photographs. *Bull. Highw. Res. Bd* **180**, 20–32.

Moller, K. and Stablein, G. 1986. Die geomorphologische Karte 1:25 000, Blatt 17, 4725 Bad Sooden–Allendorf. Erkenntnisse und Anwendungen. *Berlin. Geogr. Abhandl.* **41**, 227–255.

Monroe, W. H. 1964. The zanjon, a solution feature of karst topography in Puerto Rico. *U.S. Geol. Surv. Prof. Paper* **501B**, 126B–129B.

Moore, P. D. and Webb, J. A. 1978. *An illustrated guide to pollen analysis*. Hodder and Stoughton, London.

Morgan, A. V. 1971. Engineering problems caused by fossil permafrost features in the English midlands. *Quart. J. Engng Geol.* **4**, 111–114.

Morgan, R. P. C. 1986. *Soil erosion and conservation*. Longman, Harlow.

Morgan, V. I. and Budd, W. F. 1975. Radio-echo sounding of the Lambert glacier basin. *J. Glaciol.* **15**, 103–111.

Morin, J., Benyamini, Y. and Michaeli, A. 1981. The effect of raindrop impact on the dynamics of soil surface crusting and water movement in the profile. *J. Hydrol.* **52**, 321–336.

Morlot, A. 1855. Notice sur le Quaternaire en Suisse. *Bull. Séanc. Soc. Vaudoise Sci. Nat. Lausanne* **4**, 41–45.

Mörner, N. A. 1972. Time scale and ice accumulation during the last 125 000 years as indicated by the Greenland O^{18} curve. *Geol. Mag.* **109**, 17–24.

Mörner, N. A. 1974. The Greenland O^{18} curve: time scale and ice accumulation. *Geol. Mag.* **111**, 431–433.

Mörner, N. A. 1976a. Eustasy and geoid changes. *J. Geol.* **84**, 123–151.

Mörner, N. A. 1976b. Paleomagnetism in deep-sea core A179–15: a reply. *Earth Planet. Sci. Lett.* **29**, 240–241.

Mörner, N. A. 1977. The Gothenburg magnetic excursion. *Quat. Res.* **7**, 413–427.

Mörner, N. A. 1979. The deglaciation of southern Sweden: a multi-parameter consideration. *Boreas* **8**, 189–198.

Mörner, N. A. and Lanser, J. P. 1974. Gothenburg magnetic 'flip'. *Nature* **251**, 408–409.

Mörner, N. A., Lanser, J. P. and Hospers, J. 1971. Late Weichselian paleomagnetic reversal. *Nature Phys. Sci.* **234**, 173–174.

Morrison, R. B. 1967. Principles of Quaternary soil stratigraphy, pp. 1–69 in: *Quaternary soils* (eds. R. B. Morrison and H. E. Wright Jr). Proc. VIIth INQUA Congr. 1965, Volume **9**.

Morrison, R. B. 1978. Quaternary soil stratigraphy — concepts, methods, and problems, pp. 77–108 in: *Quaternary soils* (ed. W. C. Mahaney). GeoAbstracts, Norwich.

Mościcki, W. J. 1987. Temperature anomalies over underground cavities. *Geophys. Prosp.* **35**, 393–423.

Mosley, M. P. 1982. The effect of a New Zealand beech forest canopy on the kinetic energy of water drops and on surface erosion. *Earth Surf. Processes Landf.* **7**, 103–107.

Mosley, M. P. and Schumm, S. A. 1977. Stream junctions: a probable location for bedrock placers. *Econ. Geol.* **72**, 691–697.

Moss, A. J., Green, P. and Hutka, J. 1981. Static breakage of granitic detritus by ice and water in comparison with breakage by flowing water. *Sedimentology* **28**, 261–272.

Moss, A. J., Green, P. and Hutka, J. 1982. Small channels: their experimental formation, nature and significance. *Earth Surf. Processes Landf.* **7**, 401–415.

Moss, R. P. 1965. Slope development and soil morphology in a part of south-west Nigeria. *J. Soil Sci.* **16**, 192–209.

Mott. R. J. and Foster, J. H. 1973. Preliminary paleomagnetic studies of freshwater lake sediment cores of late Pleistocene time. *Geol. Surv. Canada Paper* **73–1**, Part B, 149–153.

Mottershead, D. N. 1980. Lichenometry — some recent applications, pp. 95–108 in: *Timescales in geomorphology* (eds. R. A. Cullingford, D. A. Davidson and J. Lewin). Wiley, Chichester.

Mottershead, D. N. and White, I. D. 1972. The lichenometric dating of glacier recession, Tunsbergdal southern Norway. *Geogr. Ann.* **A54**, 47–52.

Mountain, M. J. 1967. The location of pedogenic materials, using aerial photographs, with some examples from South Africa. *Proc. 4th Reg. Conf. Africa Soil Mech. Found. Engng, Cape Town* **1**, 35–40.

Mücher, H. J. and De Ploey, J. 1977. Experimental and micromorphological investigation of erosion and redeposition of loess by water. *Earth Surf. Processes* **2**, 117–124.

Mücher, H. J. and Morozova, T. D. 1983. The application of soil micromorphology in Quaternary geology and geomorphology, pp. 151–194 in: *Soil micromorphology Volume 1* (eds. P. Bullock and C. P. Murphy). AB Academic Publishers, Berkhamsted.

Mücher, H. J., De Ploey, J. and Savat, J. 1981. Response of loess materials to simulated translocation by water: micromorphological observations. *Earth Surf. Processes Landf.* **6**, 331–336.

Mückenhausen, E. 1977. *Entstehung, Eigenschaften und Systematik der Böden der Bundesrepublik Deutschland.* D.L.G. Verlag, Frankfurt.

Muhs, D. R. 1982. A soil chronosequence on Quaternary marine terraces, San Clemente Island, California. *Geoderma* **28**, 257–283.

Mullineaux, D. R. 1974. Pumice and other pyroclastic deposits in Mount Rainier National Park, Washington. *U.S. Geol. Surv. Bull.* **1326**.

Murphy, C. P. 1986. *Thin section preparation of soils and sediments.* AB Academic Publishers, Berkhamsted.

Nahon, D. and Trompette, R. 1982. Origin of siltstones: glacial grinding versus weathering. *Sedimentology* **29**, 25–35.

Nakajima, T. K., Yaskawa, K., Natsuhara, N., Kawai, N. and Horie, S. 1973. Very short geomagnetic excursion 18,000 yrs b.p. *Nature Phys. Sci.* **244**, 8–10.

Neumann, A. C. and Moore, W. S. 1975. Sea level events and Pleistocene coral ages in the northern Bahamas. *Quat. Res.* **5**, 215–224.

Nickling, W. G. 1984. The stabilizing role of bonding agents on the entrainment of sediment by wind. *Sedimentology* **31**, 111–117.

Norman, J. W. 1969. Photo-interpretation of boulder clay areas as an aid to engineering geological studies. *Quart. J. Engng Geol.* **2**, 149–157.

North American Commission on Stratigraphic Nomenclature 1983. North American stratigraphic code. *Bull. Amer. Assoc. Petrol. Geol.* **67**, 841–875.

Norton, P. E. P. 1977. Marine Mollusca in the East Anglian preglacial Pleistocene, pp. 43–53 in: *British Quaternary studies recent advances* (ed. F. W. Shotton). Clarendon Press, Oxford.

Noy-Meir, I. 1974. Multivariate analysis of the semiarid vegetation in south-eastern Australia. II. Vegetation catenae and environmental gradients. *Austral. J. Bot.* **22**, 115–140.

Nye, J. F. 1976. Water flow in glaciers: jökulhlaups, tunnels and veins. *J. Glaciol.* **17**, 181–207.

Oeschger, H., Beer, J. and Andrée, M. 1987. ^{10}Be and ^{14}C in the earth system. *Phil. Trans. Roy. Soc. Lond.* **A323**, 45–56.

Oldfield, F., Dearing, J., Thompson, R. and Garrett-Jones, S. E. 1978. Some magnetic properties of lake sediments and their links with erosion rates. *Pol. Arch. Hydrobiol.* **25**, 321–333.

Ollier, C. D. 1976. Catenas in different climates, pp. 137—169 in: *Geomorphology and climate* (ed. E. Derbyshire). Wiley, New York.

Ollier, C. D. and Thomasson, A. J. 1957. Asymmetric valleys of the Chiltern Hills. *Geogr. J.* **123**, 71–80.

Olsen, P. E. 1984. Periodicity of lake-level cycles in the late Triassic Lockatong Formation of the Newark Basin (Newark Subgroup, New Jersey and Pennsylvania), pp. 129–146 in: *Milankovitch and Climate Part 1* (eds. A Berger, J. Imbrie, J. Hays, G. Kukla and B. Saltzman). NATO ASI (Ser. C) **126**. Reidel, Dordrecht.

Olson, C. G. and Doolittle, J. A. 1985. Geophysical techniques for reconnaissance investigations of soils and surficial deposits in mountainous terrain. *Soil. Sci. Soc. Amer. J.* **49**, 1490–1498.

Olsson, I. U. (ed.) 1970. *Radiocarbon variations and absolute chronology.* Almqvist and Wiksell, Stockholm.

Olsson, I. U. 1986. Radiometric dating, pp. 273–312 in: *Handbook of HolocenePalaeoecology and Palaeohydrology* (ed. B. E. Berglund). Wiley, Chichester.

Opdyke, N. D. 1972. Paleomagnetism of deep-sea cores. *Rev. Geophys. Space Phys.* **10**, 213–249.

Orvedal, A. C. 1975–81. *Bibliography of the soils of the tropics.* Office of Agriculture, Washington.

Ostry, R. C. and Deane, R. E. 1963. Microfabric analyses of till. *Bull. Geol. Soc. Amer.* **74**, 165–168.

Ovington, J. D. 1958a. Studies of the development of woodland conditions under different trees. VI. Soil sodium, potassium and phosphorus. *J. Ecol.* **46**, 127–142.

Ovington, J. D. 1958b. Studies of the development of woodland conditions under different trees. VII. Soil calcium and magnesium. *J. Ecol.* **46**, 391–406.

Paepe, R. and Vanhoorne, R. 1967. The stratigraphy and palaeobotany of the late Pleistocene in Belgium. *Mém. Exp. Cartes Géol. Min. Belg.* **8**.

Paquet, H. and Millot, G. 1973. Geochemical evolution of clay minerals in the weathered products of soils of Mediterranean climates. *Proc. Int. Clay Conf. Madrid 1972* **1**, 255–261.

Parry, J. T., Wright, R. K. and Thomson, K. P. B. 1980. Drainage on multiband radar imagery in the Laurentian area, Quebec, Canada. *Photogrammetria* **35**, 179–198.

Parsons, J. D. 1976. New York's glacial lake formation of varved clay and silt. *Proc. Amer. Soc. Civ. Engrs* **GT6**, Paper 12218.

Pastor, J. and Bockheim, J. G. 1980. Soil development on moraines of Taylor Glacier, lower Taylor Valley, Antarctica. *Soil Sci. Soc. Amer. J.* **44**, 341–348.

Pastouret, L., Chamley, H., Delibrias, G., Duplessis, J. and Thiede, J. 1978. Late Quaternary climatic changes in west tropical Africa deduced from deep sea ocean sedimentation off the Niger delta. *Oceanolog. Acta* **1**, 217–232.

Paterson, W. S. B. 1981. *The physics of glaciers* (2nd edition). Pergamon, Oxford.

Paterson, W. S. B., Koerner, R. M., Fisher, D., Johnsen, S. J., Clausen, H. B., Dansgaard, W., Bucher, P. and Oeschger, H. 1977. An oxygen-isotope climatic record from the Devon Island ice cap, Arctic Canada. *Nature* **266**, 508–511.

Pavich, M. J., Brown, L., Harden, J., Klein, J. and Middleton, R. 1986. ^{10}Be distribution in soils from Merced River terraces, California. *Geochim. Cosmochim. Acta* **50**, 1727–1735.

Pearson, G. W. and Baillie, M. G. L. 1983. High-precision ^{14}C measurement of Irish oaks to show natural atmospheric ^{14}C variations of the AD time period. *Radiocarbon* **25**, 187–196.

Pearson, G. W. and Stuiver, M. 1986. High-precision calibration of the radiocarbon time scale, 500–2500 B.C. *Radiocarbon* **28**, 2B, 839–862.

Pearson, G. W., Pilcher, J. R. and Baillie, M. G. L. 1983. High-precision ^{14}C measurement of Irish oaks to show the natural ^{14}C variations of 200 BC to 4000 BC. *Radiocarbon* **25**, 179–186.

Pécsi, M. 1984. Is typical loess older than one million years? pp. 213–224 in: *Lithology and stratigraphy of loess and paleosols* (ed. M. Pécsi). Proceedings of symposium organized by INQUA Commission on loess and paleopedology, XIth INQUA Congress, Moscow. Geographical Research Institute, Hungarian Academy of Sciences, Budapest.

Peglar, S., Fritz, S. C., Alapieti, T., Saarnisto, M. and Birks, H. J. B. 1984. The composition and formation of laminated lake sediments in Diss Mere, Norfolk, England. *Boreas* **13**, 13–28.

Penck, A. 1908. Das Alter des Menschengeschlechtes. *Zeitschr. Ethnol.* **40**, 390–407.

Penck, A. and Brückner, E. 1909. *Die Alpen im Eiszeitalter.* Tauchnitz, Leipzig.

Penck, W., 1953. *Morphological analysis of land forms: a contribution to physical geology* (trans. H. Czech and K. C. Boswell). St. Martin's Press, New York.

Penner, E. and Burn, K. N. 1978. Review of engineering behaviour of marine clays of eastern Canada. *Canad. Geotech. J.* **15**, 269–282.

Pennington, K. L. and Lewis, G. C. 1979. A comparison of electronic and pipette methods for mechanical analysis of soils. *Soil Sci.* **128**, 280–284.

Penny, L. F. and Catt, J. A. 1967. Stone orientation and other structural features of tills in East Yorkshire. *Geol. Mag.* **104**, 344–360.

Pentecost, A. 1981. The tufa deposits of the Malham district, North Yorkshire. *Field Stud.* **5**, 365–387.

Perrin, R. M. S., Davies, H. and Fysh, M. D. 1974. Distribution of late Pleistocene aeolian deposits in eastern and southern England. *Nature* **248**, 320–324.

Petersen, F. 1979. Sedimentary and tectonic controls of uranium mineralization in Morrison Formation (upper Jurassic) of south-central Utah. *Bull. Amer. Assoc. Petrol. Geol.* **63**, 837.

Peterson, F. F. 1980. Holocene desert soil formation under sodium salt influence in a playa-margin environment. *Quat. Res.* **13**, 172–186.

Petts, G. E. 1984. *Impounded rivers.* Wiley, Chichester.

Péwé, T. L. 1951. An observation on wind-blown silt. *J. Geol.* **59**, 399–401.

Péwé, T. L. 1959. Sand-wedge polygons (tesselations) in the McMurdo Sound region, Antarctica — a progress report. *Amer. J. Sci.* **257**, 545–552.

Péwé, T. L. (ed.) 1969. *The periglacial environment past and present.* McGill–Queens University Press, Montreal.

Philbrick, S. 1976. Kinzua Dam and the glacial foreground, pp. 175–197 in: *Geomorphology and engineering* (ed. D. R. Coates). Dowden, Hutchinson and Ross, Stroudsburg.

Phillips, W. J., Andrews, M. J., Lewis, T. P., Fromberg, A. F. and Packenham, T. J. R. 1984. Use of complex resistivity methods for location of disseminated mineralization beneath glacial overburden, pp. 93–102 in: *Prospecting in areas of glaciated terrain 1984.* Institution of Mining and Metallurgy, London.

Pilcher, J. R. 1973. Tree-ring research in Ireland. *Tree-ring Bull.* **33**, 1–5.

Pilcher, J. R., Hillam, J., Baillie, M. G. L. and Pearson, G. W. 1977. A long sub-fossil oak tree-ring chronology from the north of Ireland. *New Phytol.* **79**, 713–729.

Pinot, J. P. 1979. Les indicateurs deceles par des méthodes oceanographiques, geophysiques ou geochimiques. *Oceanis* **5**, 335–355.

Pitts, J. 1979. Morphological mapping in the Axmouth–Lyme Regis undercliffs, Devon. *Quart. J. Engng Geol.* **12**, 205–217.

Porsild, A. E. 1938. Earth mounds in unglaciated arctic northwestern America. *Geogr. Rev.* **28**, 46–58.

Porter, S. C. 1975. Weathering rinds as a relative-age criterion: application to subdivision of glacial deposits in the Cascade Range. *Geology* **3**, 101–104.

Pounder, E. J. and Macklin, M. G. 1985. The alluvial fan at Burrington Coombe, Mendip: a study of its morphology and development. *Proc. Bristol Nat. Soc.* **45**, 29–38.

Prescott, J. A. 1931. The soils of Australia in relation to vegetation and climate. *C.S.I.R.O. Bull.* **52**.

Prestwich, J. 1888. *Geology. Volume 2. Stratigraphical and physical.* Clarendon Press, Oxford.

Price, L. W. 1971. Vegetation, microtopography and depth of active layer on different exposures in subarctic alpine tundra. *Ecology* **52**, 638–647.

Price, R. J. 1973. *Glacial and fluvioglacial landforms.* Oliver and Boyd, Edinburgh.

Price, W. A. 1968. Oriented lakes, pp. 784–796 in: *The encyclopedia of geomorphology* (ed. R. W. Fairbridge). Reinhold, New York.

Puranen, R. 1977. Magnetic susceptibility and its anisotropy in the study of glacial transport in northern Finland, pp. 111–119 in: *Prospecting in areas of glaciated terrain 1977.* Institution of Mining and Metallurgy, London.

Pye, K. 1984. Loess. *Progr. Phys. Geogr.* **8**, 176–217.

Pye, K. 1987. *Aeolian dust and dust deposits.* Academic Press, London.

Pye, K. and Paine, A. D. M. 1984. Nature and source of aeolian deposits near the summit of Ben Arkle, northwest Scotland. *Geol. Mijnb.* **63**, 13–18.

Quinn, J. H. 1957. Paired river terraces and Pleistocene glaciation. *J. Geol.* **65**, 149–166.

Ramsay, A. C. 1852. On the superficial accumulations and surface markings of north Wales. *Quart. J. Geol. Soc. Lond.* **8**, 371–376.

Rapp. A. 1959. Avalanche boulder tongues in Lappland. Descriptions of little-known forms of periglacial debris accumulations. *Geogr. Ann.* **41**, 34–48.

Ray, R. G. 1960. Aerial photographs in geologic interpretation and mapping. *U.S. Geol. Surv. Prof. Paper* **373**.

Reedman, J. H. 1979. *Techniques in mineral exploration.* Applied Science Publishers, London.

Reger, R. D. and Péwé, T. L. 1976. Cryoplanation terraces: indicators of a permafrost environment. *Quat. Res.* **6**, 99–106.

Reid, I. and Frostick, L. E. 1985. Role of settling, entrainment and dispersive equivalence and of interstice trapping in placer formation. *J. Geol. Soc. Lond.* **142**, 739–746.

Revelle, R. 1982. Carbon dioxide and world climate. *Sci. Amer.* **247**, 35–43.

Richards, K. 1986. Fluvial environments, pp. 166–179 in: *A handbook of engineering geomorphology* (eds. P. G. Fookes and P. R. Vaughan). Surrey University Press, Guildford.

Richmond, G. M. 1962. Quaternary stratigraphy of the La Sal Mountains, Utah. *U.S. Geol. Surv. Prof. Paper* **324**.

Richmond, G. M. 1975. A partial Quaternary chronology from Yellowstone National Park, pp. 144–147 in: *IUGS–UNESCO International Geological Correlation Programme, Project 73/1/24. Quaternary glaciations in the northern hemisphere, Report 2* (ed. V. Sibrava). Geological Survey, Prague.

Richter, G. and Negendank, J. F. W. 1977. Soil erosion processes and their measurement in the German area of the Moselle river. *Earth Surf. Processes* **2**, 261–278.

Robin, G. de Q., Drewry, D. J. and Meldrum, D. T. 1977. International studies of ice sheet and bedrock. *Phil. Trans. Roy. Soc. Lond.* **B279**, 185–196.

Robinove, C. J., Chavez, P. S., Gehring, D. and Holmgren, R. 1981. Arid land monitoring using Landsat albedo difference images. *Remote Sensing Env.* **11**, 133–156.

Robinson, W. O. and Holmes, R. S. 1924. The chemical composition of soil colloids. *U.S. Dept Agric. Bull.* **1311**.

Rodine, J. D. and Johnson, A. M. 1976. The ability of debris, heavily freighted with coarse clastic material, to flow on gentle slopes. *Sedimentology* **23**, 213–234.

Rogers, J. J. W., Krueger, W. C. and Krog, M. 1963. Sizes of naturally abraded materials. *J. Sedim. Petrol.* **33**, 628–632.

Rose, J., Boardman, J., Kemp, R. A. and Whiteman, C. A. 1985. Palaeosols and the interpretation of the British Quaternary stratigraphy, pp. 348–375 in: *Geomorphology and soils* (eds. K. S. Richards, R. R. Arnett and S. Ellis). George Allen and Unwin, London.

Rosenqvist, I. T. 1977. A general theory for quick clay properties, pp. 215–228 in: *Proceedings IIIrd European Clay Conference, Oslo June 1977* (ed. I. T. Rosenqvist). Nordic Society for Clay Research.

Rossiter, J. R. 1972. Sea level observations and their secular variation. *Phil. Trans. Roy. Soc. Lond.* **A272**, 131–139.

Rovner, I. 1971. Potential of opal phytoliths for use in paleoecological reconstruction. *Quat. Res.* **1**, 343–359.

Rowan, L. C., Goetz, A. F. H. and Abbott, E. 1987. Analysis of Shuttle Multispectral Infrared Radiometer measurements of the western Saudi Arabian Shield. *Geophysics* **52**, 907–923.

Ruhe, R. V. and Walker, P. H. 1968. Hillslope models and soil formation. I. Open systems. *Trans 9th Int. Congr. Soil Sci. Adelaide* **4**, 551–560.

Russell, E. W. 1973. *Soil conditions and plant growth* (10th edition). Longman, London.

Russell, R. J. 1944. Lower Mississippi Valley loess. *Bull. Geol. Soc. Amer.* **55**, 1–40.

Rust, B. R. 1972a. Structure and process in a braided river. *Sedimentology* **18**, 221–246.

Rust, B. R. 1972b. Pebble orientation in fluvial sediments. *J. Sedim. Petrol.* **42**, 384–388.

Rust, B. R. 1978. Depositional models for braided alluvium, pp. 605–625 in: *Fluvial sedimentology* (ed. A. D. Miall). *Canadian Society of Petroleum Geologists Memoir* **5**.

Rust, B. R. 1981. Sedimentation in an arid-zone anastomosing fluvial system. *J. Sedim. Petrol.* **51**, 745–755.

Rutter, N. W. and Crawford, R. J. 1984. Utilizing wood in amino acid dating, pp. 195–209 in: *Quaternary dating methods* (ed. W. C. Mahaney). Elsevier, Amsterdam.

Rutter, N. W., Crawford, R. J. and Hamilton, R. D. 1985. Dating methods of Pleistocene deposits and their problems: IV. Amino acid racemization dating, pp. 23–30 in: *Dating methods of Pleistocene deposits and their problems* (ed. N. W. Rutter). Geoscience Canada Reprint Series **2**.

Ruttner, F. 1963. *Fundamentals of limnology* (3rd edition) (trans. D. G. Frey and F. E. G. Fry). University of Toronto Press.

Saarnisto, M. 1986. Annually laminated lake sediments, pp. 343–370 in: *Handbook of Holocene palaeoecology and palaeohydrology* (ed. B. E. Berglund). Wiley, Chichester.

Sauchyn, D. J. and Trench, N. R. 1978. Landsat applied to landslide mapping. *Photogramm. Engng Remote Sens.* **44**, 735–741.

Sauer, E. K. and Beckie, V. G. 1975. Groundwater exploration in Plesitocene deposits at Landis, Saskatchewan, Canada. *Canad. Geotech. J.* **12**, 464–481.

Saunderson, H. C. 1975. Sedimentology of the Brampton esker and its associated deposits: an empirical test of theory, pp. 155–176 in: *Glaciofluvial and glaciolacustrine sedimentation* (eds. A. V. Jopling and B. C. McDonald). Society of Economic Palaeontologists and Mineralogists Special Publication **23**.

Savat, J. 1982. Common and uncommon selectivity in the process of fluid transportation: field observations and laboratory experiments on bare surfaces. *Catena Suppl.* **1**, 139–160.

Sawyer, C. D. and Pawluk, S. 1963. Characteristics of organic matter in degrading chernozemic surface soils. *Canad. J. Soil Sci.* **43**, 275–286.

Schaefer, I. 1953. Die donaueiszeitlichen Ablagerungen an Lech und Wertach. *Geol. Bavarica* **19**, 13–64.

Schick, A. P. 1965. The effects of lineative factors on stream courses in homogeneous bedrock. *Int. Assoc. Sci. Hydr. Bull.* **10**, 5–11.

Schlesinger, M. E. 1983. Simulating CO_2-induced climatic change with mathematical climate models: capabilities, limitations and prospects, pp. III.3–III.139 in: *Proc. Carbon Dioxide Res. Conf. Berkeley Springs 1982.*

Schumm, S. A. 1956. Evolution of drainage systems and slopes in badlands at Perth Amboy, New Jersey. *Bull. Geol. Soc. Amer.* **67**, 597–646.

Schumm, S. A. 1977. *The fluvial system.* Wiley, New York.

Schweingruber, F. H., Fritts, H. C., Bräker, O. U., Drew, L. G. and Schär, E. 1978. The X-ray technique as applied to dendroclimatology. *Tree-ring Bull.* **38**, 61–91.

Schwertmann, U., Murad, E. and Schulze, D. G. 1982. Is there Holocene reddening (haematite formation) in soils of axeric temperate areas? *Geoderma* **27**, 209–223.

Scott, W. J., Sellmann, P. V. and Hunter, J. A. 1979. A review of applications of geophysics in permafrost regions. *Proc. 3rd Int. Conf. Permafrost, Edmonton 1978* **2**, Canada National Research Council.

Seale, R. S. 1975. Soils of the Chatteris district of Cambridgeshire (Sheet TL 38). *Soil Surv. Spec. Surv.* **9**. Soil Survey of England and Wales, Harpenden.

Seidel, S. and Keyes, D. 1983. Can we delay a greenhouse warming? The effectiveness and feasibility of options to slow a build-up of carbon dioxide in the atmosphere. *Office Policy Resource Management Report.* Environmental Protection Agency, Washington.

Shackleton, N. J. 1967. Oxygen isotope analyses and Pleistocene temperatures reassessed. *Nature* **215**, 15–17.

Shackleton, N. J. 1977. The oxygen isotope stratigraphic record of the late Pleistocene. *Phil. Trans. Roy. Soc. Lond.* **B280**, 169–182.

Shackleton, N. J. 1987. Oxygen isotopes, ice volume and sea level. *Quat. Sci. Rev.* **6**, 183–190.

Shackleton, N. J. and Opdyke, N. D. 1973. Oxygen isotope and paleomagnetic stratigraphy of equatorial Pacific core V28–238: oxygen isotope temperatures and ice volumes on a 10^5 year and 10^6 year scale. *Quat. Res.* **3**, 39–55.

Shackleton, N. J. and Opdyke, N. D. 1976. Oxygen-isotope and paleomagnetic stratigraphy of Pacific core V28-239 late Pliocene to latest Pleistocene, pp. 449–464 in: *Investigation of late Quaternary paleoceanography and paleoclimatology* (eds. R. M. Cline and J. D. Hays). Geological Society of America Memoir **145**.

Shackleton, N. J. and Opdyke, N. D. 1977. Oxygen isotope and palaeomagnetic evidence for early northern hemisphere glaciation. *Nature* **270**, 216–219.

Shackleton, N. J., Backman, J., Zimmerman, H., Kent, D. V., Hall, M. A., Baldauf, J. G., Desprairies, A., Homrighausen, R., Huddlestun, P., Keene, J. B., Kaltenback, A. J., Krumsiek, K. O., Morton, A. C., Murray, J. W. and Westberg-Smith, J. 1984. Oxygen isotope calibration of the onset of ice-rafting and history of glaciation in the north Atlantic region. *Nature* **307**, 620–623.

Shackley, M. L. 1980. *Neanderthal man*. Duckworth, London.

Sharp, R. P. 1942. Periglacial involutions in northeastern Illinois. *J. Geol.* **50**, 113–133.

Sharp, R. P. 1969. Semi-quantitative differentiation of glacial moraines near Convict Lake, Sierra Nevada, California. *J. Geol.* **77**, 68–91.

Shaw, J. 1987. Glacial sedimentary processes and environmental reconstruction based on lithofacies. *Sedimentology* **34**, 103–116.

Sheeler, J. B. 1968. Summarization and comparison of engineering properties of loess in the United States. *Highway Res. Rec.* **212**, 1–9.

Shennan, I. 1982. Interpretation of Flandrian sea-level data from the Fenland, England. *Proc. Geol. Assoc.* **93**, 53–63.

Shennan, I. 1986. Flandrian sea-level changes in the Fenland. II. Tendencies of sea-level movement, altitudinal changes, and local and regional factors. *J. Quat. Sci.* **1**, 155–179.

Shilts, W. W. 1976. Glacial till and mineral exploration, pp. 205–224 in: *Glacial till* (ed. R. F. Legget). Royal Society Canada Special Publication **12**.

Shreve, R. L. 1966. Sherman landslide, Alaska, *Science* **154**, 1639–1643.

Shumilov, Y. V. and Shumovskiy, A. G. 1975. Experimental data on the hydraulic size of some placer minerals in the northeast U.S.S.R. *Dokl. Akad. Nauk. S.S.S.R.* **225**, 1174–1176.

Sieveking, A. 1987. *Catalogue of Palaeolithic art in the British Museum*. British Museum Publications, London.

Sieveking, G. de G., Longworth, I. H., Hughes, M. J., Clark, A. J. and Millett, A. 1973. A new survey of Grime's Graves, Norfolk — first report. *Proc. Prehist. Soc.* **39**, 182–218.

Simakova, M. S. 1964. *Soil mapping by color aerial photography*. U.S.S.R. Academy of Sciences, Moscow and Israel Program for Scientific Translations, Jerusalem.

Simola, H. 1977. Diatom succession in the formation of annually laminated sediment in Lovojärvi, a small eutrophicated lake. *Ann. Bot. Fenn.* **14**, 143–148.

Simola, H. and Tolonen, K. 1981. Diurnal laminations in the varved sediment of Lake Lovojärvi, south Finland. *Boreas* **10**, 19–26.

Simola, H. and Uimonen-Simola, P. 1983. Recent stratigraphy and accumulation of sediment in an oligotrophic deep lake in south Finland. *Hydrobiol.* **103**, 287–293.

Simonett, D. S. 1960. Soil genesis on basalt in north Queensland. *Trans. 7th Int. Congr. Soil Sci. Madison* **4**, 238–243.

Simonson, R. W. 1978. A multiple process model of soil genesis, pp. 1–25 in: *Quaternary soils* (ed. W. C. Mahaney). GeoAbstracts, Norwich.

Singer, A. 1966. The mineralogy of the clay fraction from basaltic soils in the Galilee, Israel. *J. Soil Sci.* **17**, 136–147.

Singer, A. and Norrish, K. 1974. Pedogenic palygorskite occurrences in Australia. *Amer. Mineral.* **59**, 508–517.

Sissons, J. B. and Sutherland, D. G. 1976. Climatic inferences from former glaciers in the south-east Grampian Highlands, Scotland. *J. Glaciol.* **17**, 325–346.

Sitler, R. F. and Chapman, C. A. 1955. Microfabrics of till from Ohio and Pennsylvania. *J. Sedim. Petrol.* **25**, 262–269.

Sjögren, B. 1984. *Shallow refraction seismics.* Chapman and Hall, London.

Skempton, A. W. 1954. A foundation failure due to clay shrinkage caused by poplar trees. *Proc. Inst. Civ. Engrs* **3**, Part II, 66–86.

Skempton, A. W. and Weeks, A. G. 1976. The Quaternary history of the Lower Greensand escarpment and Weald Clay vale near Sevenoaks, Kent. *Phil. Trans. Roy. Soc. Lond.* **A283**, 493–526.

Smalley, I. J. 1966. The properties of glacial loess and the formation of loess deposits. *J. Sedim. Petrol.* **36**, 669–676.

Smalley, I. J. 1971. "In-situ" theories of loess formation and the significance of the calcium carbonate content of loess. *Earth Sci. Rev.* **7**, 67–85.

Smalley, I. J. and Krinsley, D. H. 1978. Loess deposits associated with deserts. *Catena* **5**, 53–66.

Smalley, I. J. and Vita-Finzi, C. 1968. The formation of fine particles in sandy deserts and the nature of 'desert' loess. *J. Sedim. Petrol.* **38**, 766–774.

Smith, D. G. 1983. Anastomosed fluvial deposits: modern examples from western Canada, pp. 155–168 in: *Modern and ancient fluvial systems* (eds. J. D. Collinson and J. Lewin). International Association Sedimentologists Special Publication. **6**.

Smith, D. L. and Randazzo, A. F. 1975. Detection of subsurface solution cavities in Florida using electrical resistivity measurements. *Southeastern Geol.* **16**, 227–240.

Smith, D. L. and Randazzo, A. F. 1986. Evaluation of electrical resistivity methods in the investigation of karstic features, El Cajon dam site, Honduras. *Engng Geol.* **22**, 217–230.

Smith, D. T. 1987. Geotechnical studies in Tremadog Bay. *Proc. Geol. Assoc.* **98**, 385–396.

Smith, H. T. U. 1965. Dune morphology and chronology in central and western Nebraska. *J. Geol.* **73**, 557–578.

Smith, J. D. and Foster, J. H. 1969. Geomagnetic reversal in Brunhes normal polarity epoch. *Science* **163**, 565–567.

Smith, K. G. 1950. Standards for grading texture of erosional topography. *Amer. J. Sci.* **248**, 655–668.

Smith, K. G. 1958. Erosional processes and landforms in Badlands National Monument, South Dakota. *Bull. Geol. Soc. Amer.* **69**, 975–1007.

Smith, N. D. and Beukes, N. J. 1983. Bar to bank flow convergence zones: a contribution to the origin of alluvial placers. *Econ. Geol.* **78**, 1342–1349.

Snowden, J. O. and Priddy, R. 1968. Geology of Mississippi loess. *Miss. Geol. Surv. Bull.* **111**, 13–203.

Soil Conservation Service 1972. Soil survey laboratory methods and procedures for collecting soil samples. *U.S. Dept. Agric. Soil Surv. Inv. Rept.* **1**.

Soil Survey of England and Wales 1983. *Soil map of England and Wales, Scale 1:250,000.* Soil Survey of England and Wales, Harpenden.

Soil Survey Staff 1951. Soil survey manual. *Agriculture Handbook* **18**. Department of agriculture, Washington.

Soil Survey Staff 1966. Aerial-photo interpretation in classifying and mapping soils. *Agriculture Handbook* **294**. Department of agriculture, Washington.

Soil Survey Staff 1975. Soil taxonomy, a basic system of soil classification for making and interpreting soil surveys. *U.S. Dept Agriculture Handbook* **436**. U.S. Government Printing Office.

Soil Survey Staff 1981. Soil survey manual. *Soil Conservation Service Directive* **430**. Department of agriculture, Washington.

Soiltest Inc. 1977. Geophysics in construction and construction materials exploration, pp. 652–656 in: *Subsurface geology petroleum mining construction* (eds. L. W. Le Roy, D. O. Le Roy and J. W. Raese). Colorado School of Mines, Golden.

Sorensen, C. J., Mandel, R. D. and Wallis, J. C. 1976. Changes in bioclimate inferred from paleosols and paleohydrologic evidence in east-central Texas. *J. Biogeogr.* **3**, 141–149.

Spaink, G. 1975. Zonering van het mariene Onder-Pleistoceen en Plioceen op grond van mollusken-fauna's, pp. 118–122 in: *Toelichting bij geologische overzichtskaarten van Nederland* (eds. W. H. Zagwijn and C. J. Van Staalduinen). Rijks Geol. Dienst, Haarlem.

Spears, D. A. and Reeves, M. J. 1975. The influence of superficial deposits on groundwater quality in the Vale of York. *Quart. J. Engng Geol.* **8**, 255–269.

Speight, J. G. 1965. Meander spectra of the Angabunga River. *J. Hydr.* **3**, 1–15.

Stephens, P. R., Daigle, J. L. and Cihlar, J. 1982. Use of sequential aerial photographs to detect and monitor soil management changes affecting cropland erosion. *J. Soil Water Conserv.* **37**, 101–105.

Stephens, P. R., Hicks, D. L. and Trustrum, N. A. 1981. Aerial photographic techniques for soil conservation research. *Photogramm. Engng Remote Sensing* **45**, 79–87.

Steward, W. F., Carter, V. and Brooks, R. D. 1980. Inland (non-tidal) wetland mapping. *Photogramm. Engng Remote Sensing* **46**, 617–628.

Stobbs, A. R. 1970. Soil survey procedures for development purposes, pp. 41–64 in: *New possibilities and techniques for land use and related surveys* (ed. I. H. Cox). Geographical Publications, Berkhamsted.

Stoddart, D. R. 1969. World erosion and sedimentation, pp. 43–64 in: *Water, earth and man: a synthesis of hydrology* (ed. R. J. Chorley). Methuen, London.

Stoner, E. R. and Baumgardner, M. E. 1981. Characteristic variations in the reflectance of surface soils. *Soil Sci. Soc. Amer. J.* **45**, 1161–1165.

Storzer, D. and Wagner, G. A. 1969. Correction of thermally lowered fission track ages of tektites. *Earth Planet. Sci. Lett.* **5**, 463–468.

Strahler, A. N. 1952. Hypsometric (area–altitude) analysis of erosional topography. *Bull. Geol. Soc. Amer.* **63**, 1117–1141.

Strahler, A. N. 1957. Quantitative analysis of watershed geomorphology. *Trans. Amer. Geophys, Union* **38**, 913–920.

Strahler, A. N. 1958. Dimensional analysis applied to fluvially eroded landforms. *Bull. Geol. Soc. Amer.* **69**, 279–299.

Strakhov, N. M. 1967. *Principles of lithogenesis Volume 1* (trans. J. P. FitzSimmons, S. I. Tomkieff and J. E. Hemingway). Plenum, New York.

Strandberg, C. H. 1967. Photoarchaeology. *Photogramm. Engng* **33**, 1152–1157.

Street, F. A. and Grove, A. T. 1976. Environmental and climatic implications of late Quaternary lake-level fluctuations in Africa. *Nature* **261**, 385–390.

Street, F. A. and Grove, A. T. 1979. Global maps of lake-level fluctuations since 30 000 yr BP. *Quat. Res.* **12**, 83–118.

Stuart, A. J. 1977. British Quaternary vertebrates, pp. 69–81 in: *British Quaternary studies recent advances* (ed. F. W. Shotton). Clarendon Press, Oxford.

Stuart, A. 1982. *Pleistocene vertebrates of the British Isles*. Longman, London.

Stuiver, M. 1982. A high-precision calibration of the AD radiocarbon time scale. *Radiocarbon* **24**, 1–26.

Stuiver, M. and Pearson, G. W. 1986. High-precision calibration of the radiocarbon time scale AD 1950–500 BC. *Radiocarbon* **28**, 2B, 805–838.

Stuiver, M. and Quay, P. D. 1980. Changes in atmospheric carbon-14 attributed to a variable sun. *Science* **207**, 11–19.

Stuiver, M., Kromer, B., Becker, B. and Ferguson, C. W. 1986. Radiocarbon age calibration back to 13,300 years BP and the ^{14}C age matching of the German oak and US bristlecone pine chronologies. *Radiocarbon* **28**, 2B, 969–979.

Stupavsky, M., Gravenor, C. P. and Symons, D. T. A. 1979. Paleomagnetic stratigraphy of the Meadowcliffe Till, Scarborough Bluffs, Ontario: a late Pleistocene excursion? *Geophys. Res. Lett.* **6**, 269–272.

Sugden, D. E. 1977. Reconstruction of the morphology, dynamics, and thermal characteristics of the Laurentide ice sheet at its maximum. *Arct. Alp. Res.* **9**, 21–47.

Sundborg, A. 1956. The river Klarälven, a study of fluvial processes. *Geogr. Ann.* **38**, 127–316.

Sutcliffe, A. J. 1985. *On the track of ice age mammals*. British Museum (Natural History), London.

Sutcliffe, A. J. and Kowalski, K. 1976. Pleistocene rodents of the British Isles. *Bull. Brit. Mus. (Nat. Hist.) Geol.* **27**(2), 33–147.

Sutherland, D. G. 1985. Geomorphological controls on the distribution of placer deposits. *J. Geol Soc. Lond.* **142**, 727–737.

Sutherland, R. A., Hannah, H. E., Cook, A. F. and Martsolf, J. D. 1981. Remote sensing of thermal radiation from an aircraft — an analysis and evaluation of crop-freeze protection methods. *J. Appl. Meteorol.* **20**, 813–820.

Sutinen, R. 1985. Application of impulse radar profiling to structural studies in morainic landforms in northern Finland, pp. 31–37 in: *Glacial tills 1985* (ed. M. C. Forde). Proceedings of international conference on construction in glacial tills and boulder clays. Engineering Technics Press.

Suttill, R. J. 1980. Post-depositional remanent magnetisation in recent tidal-flat sediments. *Earth Planet. Sci. Lett.* **49**, 132–140.

Sweeting, M. M. 1965. Introduction, pp. 34–37 in: Denudation in limestone regions: a symposium. *Geogr. J.* **131**, 34–56.

Szabo, B. J. 1980. Results and assessment of uranium-series dating of vertebrate fossils from Quaternary alluviums in Colorado. *Arct. Alpine Res.* **12**, 95–100.

Talbot, M. R. 1981. Holocene changes in tropical wind intensity and rainfall: evidence from south east Ghana. *Quat. Res.* **16**, 201–220.

Tanada, T. 1951. Certain properties of the inorganic colloidal fraction of Hawaiian soils. *J. Soil Sci.* **2**, 83–96.

Tanner, W. F. 1971. The river profile. *J. Geol.* **79**, 482–492.

Tardy, Y., Bocquier, G., Paquet, H. and Millot, G. 1973. Formation of clay from granite and its distribution in relation to climate and topography. *Geoderma* **10**, 271–284.

Tavenas, F., Chagnon, J. Y. and La Rochelle, P. 1971. The Saint-Jean-Vianney landslide: observations and eyewitnesses accounts. *Canad. Geotech. J.* **8**, 463–478.

Taylor N. H. and Pohlen, I. J. 1970. Soil survey method. A New Zealand handbook for the field study of soils. *New Zealand Soil Bureau Bull.* **25**. New Zealand Department of Scientific and Industrial Research.

Theinemann, A. 1928. Die Sauerstoff im eutrophen und oligotrophen Seen. *Die Binnengewasser* **4**. Schweizerbartsche, Stuttgart.

Thomas, G. S. P. and Dackombe, R. V. 1985. Comment on "Glaciomarine sediments of the Isle of Man as a key to late Pleistocene stratigraphic investigations in the Irish Sea Basin". *Geology* **13**, 445–446.

Thomas, M. F. 1974. *Tropical geomorphology*. Macmillan, London.

Thomas, M. F. 1986. Savanna, pp. 125–136 in: *A handbook of engineering geomorphology* (eds. P. G. Fookes and P. R. Vaughan). Surrey University Press, Guildford.

Thompson, L. L. 1979. Remote sensing using solid-state linear array technology. *Photogramm. Engng Remote Sensing.* **45**, 47–55.

Thompson, R. 1977. Stratigraphic consequences of palaeomagnetic studies of Pleistocene and Recent sediments. *J. Geol. Soc. Lond.* **133**, 51–59.

Thompson, R. and Kelts, K. 1975. Holocene sediments and magnetic stratigraphy of Lakes Zug and Zurich, Switzerland. *Sedimentology* **21**, 577–596.

Thompson, R. and Turner, G. M. 1979. British geomagnetic master curve 10,000–0 yr B.P. for dating European sediments. *Geophys. Res. Lett.* **6**, 249–252.

Thorez, J., Bourguignon, P. and Paepe, R. 1970. Étude preliminaire des associations de minéraux argileux des loess Pleistocènes en Belgique. *Ann. Soc. Géol. Belg.* **593**, 265–285.

Thornes, J. B. 1980. Erosional processes of running water and their spatial and temporal controls: a theoretical viewpoint, pp. 129–182 in: *Soil erosion* (eds. M. J. Kirkby and R. P. C. Morgan). Wiley, Chichester.

Thomthwaite, C. R. 1948. Am approach toward a rational classification of climate. *Geogr. Rev.* **38**, 55–94.

Tinsley, H. M. and Smith, R. T. 1974. Surface pollen studies across a woodland/heath transition and their application to the interpretation of pollen diagrams. *New Phytol.* **73**, 549–567.

Tooley, M. J. 1978. *Sea-level changes. North-west England during the Flandrian Stage.* Clarendon Press, Oxford.

Tooley, M. J. 1982. Sea-level changes in northern England. *Proc. Geol. Assoc.* **93**, 43–51.

Tooley, M. J. 1985. Sea levels. *Progr. Phys. Geogr.* **9**, 113–120.

Trewzecki, S. 1972. Model research into the speed and height of capillary infiltration in some soils with two levels of moisture, pp. 582–592 in: *Proc. 2nd Symp. Fundamentals Transp. Phen. Porous Media* **2**. International Association for Hydraulic Research.

Tricart, J. 1975. Influence des oscillations climatiques récentes sur le modelé en Amazonie orientale (Région de Santarem) d'après les images de radar latéral. *Zeitschr, Geomorph.* **19**, 140–163.

Troels-Smith, J. 1955. Characterisation of unconsolidated sediments. *Danmarks Geol. Undersøg. (Afh.)* Raekke 4, **3**(10), 38–73.

Turner, C. 1970. The Middle Pleistocene deposits at Marks Tey, Essex. *Phil. Trans. Roy. Soc. Lond.* **B257**, 373–437.

Turner, C. and West, R. G. 1968. The subdivision and zonation of interglacial periods. *Eisz. Gegenw.* **19**, 93–101.

Turner, G. M. and Thompson, R. 1979. Behaviour of the earth's magnetic field as recorded in the sediment of Loch Lomond. *Earth Planet. Sci. Lett.* **42**, 412–426.

Twomey, S. 1977. *Atmospheric aerosols.* Elsevier, Amsterdam.

Ugolini, F. C., Reanier, R. E., Rau, G. H. and Hedges, J. I. 1981. Pedological, isotopic and geochemical investigations of the soils at the boreal forest and alpine tundra transition in northern Alaska. *Soil Sci.* **131**, 359–374.

Ulaby, F. T., Bradley, G. A. and Dobson, M. C. 1979. Microwave backscatter dependence on surface roughness, soil moisture and soil texture. Part II. Vegetation covered soil. *Inst. Electr. Electron. Engrs Trans. Geosci. Electron.* **17**, 33–40.

Ulaby, F. T., Batlivala, P. P. and Bare, J. E. 1980. Crop identification with L band radar. *Photogramm. Engng Remote Sensing* **46**, 101–105.

Ulaby, F. T., Moore, R. K. and Fung, A. K. 1981. *Microwave remote sensing, active and passive. Volume I. Fundamentals and radiometry*. Addison-Wesley, Reading, Massachusetts.

Ulaby, F. T., Moore, R. K. and Fung, A. K. 1982. *Microwave remote sensing, active and passive. Volume II. Radar remote sensing and surface scattering and emission theory*. Addison-Wesley, Reading, Massachusetts.

Van der Hammen, T. 1978. Stratigraphy and environments of the Upper Quaternary of the El Abra corridor and rock shelter (Colombia). *Palaeogeogr. Palaeoclimat. Palaeoecol.* **25**, 111–162.

Van der Hammen, T. and González, E. 1960. Holocene and Late Glacial climate and vegetation of Páramo de Palacio (Eastern Cordillera, Colombia, South America). *Geol. Mijnb.* **39**, 737–746.

Van der Hammen, T., Wijmstra, T. A. and Zagwijn, W. H. 1971. The floral record of the late Cenozoic in Europe, pp. 391–424 in: *The late Cenozoic glacial ages* (ed. K. K. Turekian). Yale University Press, New Haven.

Van Dijk, D. C., Riddler, A. M. H. and Rowe, R. K. 1968. Criteria and problems in groundsurface correlations with reference to a regional correlation in south-eastern Australia. *Proc. 9th Int. Congr. Soil Sci. Adelaide* **4**, 131–138.

Van Donk, J. 1976. O^{18} record of the Atlantic Ocean for the entire Pleistocene epoch, pp. 147–163 in: *Investigation of late Quaternary paleoceanography and paleoclimatology* (eds. R. M. Cline and J. D. Hays). Geological Society of America Memoir **145**.

Vane, G., Goetz, A. F. H. and Willman, J. B. 1983. Airborne imaging spectrometer: a new tool for remote sensing. *Inst. Electr. Electron. Engrs Int. Geosci. Remote Sensing Symposium,* I-1–I-5.

Van Vliet-Lanoë, B. 1985. Frost effects in soils, pp. 117–158 in: *Soils and Quaternary landscape evolution* (ed. J. Boardman). Wiley, Chichester.

Varnes, D. J. 1958. Landslide types and processes. *Highw. Res. Board. Spec. Rept* **29**., 20–47.

Vernekar, A. D. 1972. Long-period global variations of incoming solar radiation. *Meteorol. Monogr.* **12**.

Verosub, K. L. 1979. Paleomagnetic evidence for the occurrence of rapid shifts in the position of the geomagnetic pole. *EOS, Trans. Amer. Geophys. Union* **60**, 244.

Verstappen, H. T. 1977. *Remote sensing in geomorphology*. Elsevier, Amsterdam.

Vincent, P. L. and Cavelier, C. 1968. *Carte Géologique des formations superficielles: Creil XXIII–12, 1:50,000.* Bureau de Recherches Géologiques et Minières, Paris.

Vincent, R. K. 1973. An ERTS multispectral scanner experiment for mapping iron compounds. *Proc. 8th Int. Symp. Remote Sensing Env.,* 1239–1247. University of Michigan, Ann Arbor.

Vitorello, I. and Van der Voo, R. 1977. Magnetic stratigraphy of Lake Michigan sediments obtained from cores of lacustrine clay. *Quat. Res.* **7**, 398–412.

Von Post, L. 1924. Das genetische System der organogenen Bildungen Schwedens, pp. 287–304 in: *Memoires sur la nomenclature et la classification des sols.* International Committee of Soil Science, Helsingfors.

Vreeken, W. J. 1973. Soil variability in small loess watersheds: clay and organic matter content. *Catena* **1**, 181–196.

Vreeken, W. J. 1975. Principal kinds of chronosequences and their significance in soil history. *J. Soil Sci.* **26**, 378–394.

Waitland, D. 1953. The application of geophysical methods to problems in civil engineering. *Bull. Canad. Inst. Mining Metall.* **46**, 288–296.

Walker, P. H. 1966. Postglacial environments in relation to landscape and soils on the Cary drift, Iowa. *Iowa State Univ. Exptl Stn Res. Bull.* **549**, 838–875.

Walker, P. H., Hall, G. F. and Protz, R. 1968a. Soil trends and variability across selected landscapes in Iowa. *Soil Sci. Soc. Amer. Proc.* **32**, 97–101.

Walker, P. H., Hall, G. F. and Protz, R. 1968b. Relation between landform parameters and soil properties. *Soil Sci. Soc. Amer. Proc.* **32**, 101–104.

Walker, T. W. and Syers, J. K. 1976. The fate of phosphorus during pedogenesis. *Geoderma* **15**, 1–19.

Wallace, D. E. 1981. A report on the use of remote sensing techniques for the supervision of New England coastal marshes. *Remote Sensing Quart.* **3**, 45–53.

Wallace, G. A. 1973. Remote sensing for detecting feedlot runoff. *Photogramm. Engng* **39**, 949–957.

Washburn, A. L. 1956. Classification of patterned ground and review of suggested origins. *Bull. Geol. Soc. Amer.* **67**, 823–865.

Washburn, A. L. 1979. *Geocryology. A survey of periglacial processes and environments.* Edward Arnold, London.

Watson, E. 1972. Pingos of Cardiganshire and the latest ice limit. *Nature* **236**, 343–344.

Watson, E. 1977. The periglacial environment of Great Britain during the Devensian. *Phil. Trans. Roy. Soc. Lond.* **B280**, 183–198.

Watson, J. P. 1960. Soil catenas. *Soils Fert.* **28**, 307–310.

Weeks, A. G. 1969. The stability of natural slopes in south-east England as affected by periglacial activity. *Quart. J. Engng Geol.* **2**, 49–61.

Wehmiller, J. F. 1982. A review of amino acid racemization studies in Quaternary mollusks: stratigraphic and chronologic applications in coastal and interglacial sites, Pacific and Atlantic coasts, United States, United Kingdom, Baffin Island, and tropical islands. *Quat. Sci. Rev.* **1**, 83–120.

Wehmiller, J. F., Hare, P. E. and Kujala, G. A. 1976. Amino acids in fossil corals: racemization (epimerization) reactions and their implications for diagenetic models and geochronological studies. *Geochim. Cosmochim. Acta* **40**, 763–776.

Weir, A. H., Catt, J. A. and Madgett, P. A. 1971. Postglacial soil formation in the loess of Pegwell Bay, Kent (England). *Geoderma* **5**, 131–149.

Weir, A. H., Rayner, J. H., Catt, J. A., Shipley, D. G. and Hollies, J. D. 1984. Soil factors affecting the yield of winter wheat: analysis of results from I.C.I. surveys 1979–80. *J. Agric. Sci. Camb.* **103**, 639–649.

Welch, N. H., Allen, P. B. and Galindo, D. J. 1979. Particle size analysis by pipette and Sedigraph. *J. Env. Qual.* **8**, 544–546.

Welch, R. and Howarth, P. J. 1968. Photogrammetric measurement of glacial landforms. *Photogramm. Rec.* **6**, 75–96.

Welsted, J. 1979. Air photo interpretation in coastal studies. Examples from the Bay of Fundy, Canada. *Photogrammetria* **35**, 1–28.

West, R. G. 1963. Problems of the British Quaternary. *Proc. Geol. Assoc.* **74**, 147–186.

West, R. G. 1977. *Pleistocene geology and biology with especial reference to the British Isles.* Longman, London.

West, R. G. 1980. Pleistocene forest history in East Anglia. *New Phytol.* **85**, 571–622.

Western, S. 1978. *Soil survey contracts and quality control.* Clarendon Press, Oxford.

Westgate, J. A. and Naeser, N. D. 1985. Dating methods of Pleistocene deposits and their problems. V. Tephrochronology and fission-track dating, pp. 31–38 in: *Dating methods of Pleistocene deposits and their problems* (ed. N. W. Rutter). Geoscience Canada Reprint Series **2**.

Westin, F. C. and Frazee, C. J. 1976. Landsat data, its use in a soil survey program. *Soil Sci. Soc. Amer. Proc.* **49**, 81–89.

Whalley, W. B. 1979. Quartz silt production and sand grain surface textures from fluvial and glacial environments. *Scanning Electron Microscopy* **1**, 547–554.

Whalley, W. B., Marshall, J. R. and Smith, B. J. 1982. Origin of desert loess from some experimental observations. *Nature* **300**, 433–435.

Whillans, I. N. 1976. Radio-echo layers and the recent stability of the west Antarctic ice sheet. *Nature* **264**, 152–155.

White, E. M. and Riecken, F. F. 1955. Brunizem–gray brown podsolic soil biosequences, *Soil Sci. Soc. Amer. Proc.* **19**, 504–509.

White, L. P. 1977. *Aerial photography and remote sensing for soil survey.* Clarendon Press, Oxford.

White, S. E. 1976. Rock glaciers and block fields: review and new data. *Quat. Res.* **6**, 77–97.

Wiersum, K. F. 1985. Effects of various vegetation layers of an *Acacia auriculiformis* forest plantation on surface erosion in Java, Indonesia, pp. 79–89 in: *Soil erosion and conservation* (eds. S. A. El-Swaify, W. C. Moldenhauer and A. Lo). Soil Science Society of America.

Wilding, L. P. and Drees, L. R. 1969. Biogenetic opal in soils as an index of vegetative history in the Prairie Peninsula, pp. 96–103 in: *The Quaternary of Illinois* (ed. R. E. Bergstrom). University of Illinois College of Agriculture Special Publication **14**.

Williams, J. R. 1970. Ground water in the permafrost regions of Alaska. *U.S. Geol. Surv. Prof. Paper* **696**.

Williams, R. B. G. 1975. The British climate during the last glaciation: an interpretation based on periglacial phenomena, pp. 95–120 in: *Ice ages: ancient and modern* (eds. A. E. Wright and F. Moseley). *Geological Journal* Special Issue 6. Seel House Press, Liverpool.

Williams, R. B. G. 1980. The weathering and erosion of chalk under periglacial conditions, pp. 225–248 in: *The shaping of southern England* (ed. D. K. C. Jones). Institute of British Geographers Special Publication **11**. *Academic Press, London.*

Williams, R. B. G. 1987. Frost weathered mantles on the Chalk, pp. 127–133 in: *Periglacial processes and landforms in Britain and Ireland* (ed. J. Boardman). Cambridge University Press.

Williams, R. E. and Farvolden, R. N. 1969. The influence of joints on the movement of groundwater through glacial till. *J. Hydrol.* **5**, 163–170.

Willman, H. B. and Frye, J. C. 1970. Pleistocene stratigraphy of Illinois. *Illin. State Geol. Surv. Bull.* **94**.

Wilson, L. 1969. Les relations entre les processus géomorphologiques et le climat moderne comme méthode de paléoclimatologie. *Rev. Géogr. Phys. Géol. Dynam.* (Ser. 2) **11**, 303–314.

Wilson, P., Bateman, R. M. and Catt, J. A. 1981. Petrography, origin and environment of deposition of the Shirdley Hill Sand of southwest Lancashire, England. *Proc. Geol. Assoc.* **92**, 211–229.

Wingfield, R. T. R. 1987. Giant sand waves and relict periglacial features on the sea bed west of Anglesey. *Proc. Geol. Assoc.* **98**, 400–404.

Wintle, A. G. 1981. Thermoluminescence dating of late Devensian loesses in southern England. *Nature* **289**, 479–480.

Wintle, A. G. 1987. Thermoluminescence dating of loess. *Catena Suppl.* **9**, 103–115.

Wintle, A. G. and Catt, J. A. 1985a. Thermoluminescence dating of soils developed in late Devensian loess at Pegwell Bay, Kent. *J. Soil. Sci.* **36**, 293–298.

Wintle, A. G. and Catt, J. A. 1985b. Thermoluminescence dating of Dimlington Stadial deposits in eastern England. *Boreas* **14**, 231–234.

Wintle, A. G. and Huntley, D. J. 1980. Thermoluminescence dating of ocean sediments. *Canad. J. Earth Sci.* **17**, 348–360.

Wintle, A. G. and Huntley, D. J. 1982. Thermoluminescence dating of sediments. *Quat. Sci. Rev.* **1**. 31–53.

Wintle, A. G. and Prózyńska, H. 1983. TL dating of loess in Germany and Poland. *PACT (Journal of the European study group on physical, chemical and mathematical techniques applied to archaeology)* **9**, 547–554.

Wischmeier, W. H., Johnson, C. B. and Cross, B. V. 1971. A soil erodibility nomograph for farmland and construction sites. *J. Soil Water Cons.* **26**, 189–193.

Wischmeier, W. H. and Smith, D. D. 1978. Predicting rainfall erosion losses. *Agriculture handbook* **537**. U.S. Dept Agriculture Research Service, Washington.

Woillard, G., 1979. Abrupt end of last interglacial s.s. in north-east France. *Nature* **281**, 558–562.

Wood, S. V. 1882. On the origin of the loess. *Geol. Mag.* (Decade II) **9**, 339–343.

Woodland. A. W. 1970. The buried tunnel-valleys of East Anglia. *Proc. Yorks. Geol. Soc.* **37**, 521–578.

Wooldridge, S. W. and Linton, D. L. 1955. Structure, surface and drainage in south-east England (2nd edition). G. Philip, London.

Worssam, B. C. 1981. Pleistocene deposits and superficial structures, Allington Quarry, Maidstone, Kent, pp. 20–31 in: *The Quaternary in Britain* (eds. J. Neale and J. Flenley). Pergamon, Oxford.

Wright, H. E. 1980. Cores of soft lake sediments. *Boreas* **9**, 107–114.

Wymer, J. J. 1982. *The Palaeolithic age.* Croom Helm, London.

Yaalon, D. H. 1975. Conceptual models in pedogenesis: can soil-forming functions be solved? *Geoderma* **14**, 189–205.

Yaalon, D. H. and Ganor, E. 1975. Rate of aeolian dust accretion in the Mediterranean and desert fringe environments of Israel. *19th Int. Congr. Sedimentology Theme 2*, 169–174.

Yaalon, D. H. and Ginzbourg, D. 1966. Sedimentary characteristics and climatic analysis of easterly dust storms in the Negev (Israel). *Sedimentology* **6**, 315–332.

Yaskawa, K., Nakajima, T., Kawai, N., Torii, M., Natsuhara, N. and Horie, S. 1973. Paleomagnetism of a core from Lake Biwa 1. *J. Geomagn. Geoelectr.* **25**, 447–474.

Young, A. 1973. Soil survey procedures in land development planning. *Geogr. J.* **139**, 53–64.

Young, A. 1976. *Tropical soils and soil survey*. Cambridge University Press.

Zagwijn, W. H. 1975a. Variations in climate as shown by pollen analysis, especially in the lower Pleistocene of Europe, pp. 137–152 in: *Ice ages: ancient and modern* (eds. A. E. Wright and F. Moseley). *Geological Journal* Special Issue 6. Seel House Press, Liverpool.

Zagwijn, W. H. 1975b. Indeling van het Kwartair op grond van veranderingen in vegetatie en klimat, pp. 109–114 in: *Toelichting bij geologische overzichtskaar-*

ten van Nederland (eds. W. H. Zagwijn and C. J. Van Staalduinen). Rijks Geol. Dienst, Haarlem.

Zalasiewicz, J. A. and Mathers, S. J. 1985. A new approach to mapping tills, pp. 55–59 in: *Glacial tills 1985* (ed. M. C. Forde). Proceedings of international conference on construction in glacial tills and boulder clays. Engineering Technics Press.

Zalasiewicz, J. A., Mathers, S. J. and Cornwell, J. D. 1985. The application of ground conductivity measurements to geological mapping. *Quart. J. Engng Geol.* **18**, 139–148.

Zeuner, F. E. 1946. *Dating the past: an introduction to geochronology*. Methuen, London.

Zeuner, F. E. 1949. Frost soils on Mount Kenya, and the relation of frost soils to aeolian deposits. *J. Soil. Sci.* **1**, 20–30.

Zingg, A. W. 1940. Degree and length of land slope as it affects soil loss in runoff. *Agric. Engng* **21**, 59–64.

Index